BIOLOGICAL PROTOTYPES
and
SYNTHETIC SYSTEMS

Volume 1

BIOLOGICAL PROTOTYPES
and
SYNTHETIC SYSTEMS

Volume 1

Proceedings of the Second Annual Bionics Symposium
sponsored by Cornell University and the
General Electric Company, Advanced Electronics Center,
held at Cornell University, August 30-September 1, 1961

edited by

Eugene E. Bernard
and
Morley R. Kare

PLENUM PRESS
NEW YORK
1962

Library of Congress Catalog Card Number 62-9964

Printed in the United States of America

INTRODUCTION

When the present symposium was first conceived, it was decided that more emphasis be given to contributions from biological laboratories than has typically appeared in previous bionics meetings. Accordingly, most of the invited speakers are biologists, in the broad sense of representing some area of the life sciences. Likewise, many of the submitted papers eventually chosen by the technical committee were from the life sciences, rather than the physical sciences or mathematics. In this way, it was hoped that a greater direct interest in the technological problems of bionics might be stimulated among biologists, upon whose work much of the success of bionics necessarily lies.

Because of the wide interdisciplinary span of the papers, it was necessary to impose some artificial organization upon them, specifically for continuity in the transactions. We elected to put the biological papers first, followed by those which deal with reasonably specific models, and reserve to the last those papers reporting models which are more general in nature.

The editorial function was kept to a minimum, with no major alterations of content and few of style being exercised. Several of the papers delivered at the symposium required a longer format for clarity and are included here in expanded versions. Assitance in the preparation of this volume was received from the National Institute of Neurologic Diseases and Blindness, Grant number B-3896.

E.E.B.*
M.R.K.*

*Dr. Bernard and Dr. Kare are both currently affiliated with the Consolidated University of North Carolina at Raleigh, North Carolina

ACKNOWLEDGMENTS

We wish to express our gratitude to our colleagues on the Technical and Arrangements Committees, upon whose efforts so much of the success of the symposium depended:

Chairman of the Technical Committee: Professor C. L. Comar, Department of Physical Biology, Cornell University.

Professor R.D. O'Brien, Department of Entomology, Cornell University.

Mr. W.A. Porter, Advanced Engineering Physics, General Electric Advanced Electronics Center at Cornell University.

Mr. R.D. Turner, Consultant, General Electric Advanced Electronics Center at Cornell University.

Chairman of the Arrangements Committee: Dr. S.W. Davis, Bionics, General Electric Advanced Electronics Center at Cornell University.

Mr. N. Morse, Bionics, General Electric Advanced Electronics Center at Cornell University.

Very special acknowledgments are due to Mrs. Sylvia Switzer for her assistance in organizing the symposium, and to Dr. Millicent Ficken, who aided us greatly in editing the transactions. Assistance in the preparation of this volume was received from the National Institute of Neurological Diseases and Blindness, Grant number B-3896.

E.E.B.
M.R.K.

CONTENTS

Heinz Von Foerster
Bio-Logic 1

Donald I. Tepas, John C. Armington, and Walter J. Kropfl
Evoked Potentials in the Human Visual System 13

Bruce P. Halpern
Neural-Behavioral Interrelationships in Taste 22

Joseph J. Peters and Charles J. Cusick
Bioelectric Patterns as Indicators of Behavioral Development in the Chick Embryo 29

Robert O. Becker
Some Observations Indicating the Possibility of Longitudinal Charge-Carrier Flow in the Peripheral Nerves 31

James B. Preston
Spontaneous Neural Activity* 38

J. H. Whitlock
Bionics and Experimental Epidemiology 39

J. M. Hartshorne
The Development of the Eastern Bluebird's Vocal Repertoire* 49

R. S. Payne
Prey Location in Owls* 50

Richard L. Gregory
The Logic of the Localization of Function in the Central Nervous System 51

K. D. Roeder
Ultrasonic Interaction of Bats and Moths 54

V. Braitenberg and F. Lauria
What is a Synapse?* 58

E. E. Loebner and T. Henneberger
Modeling Visual Organs and Perceptions* 59

*Asterisks indicate that only an abstract of the paper is presented in this volume.

F. Heinmets and A. Herschman
Theoretical Analysis of Models for Enzyme Synthesis 60

Alan Hein and Richard Held
A Neural Model for Labile Sensorimotor Coordinations 71

Louis L. Sutro
A Model of Visual Space 75

Frank N. Marzocco and Philip R. Bartram
Statistical Learning Models for Behavior of an Artificial Organism . 88

W. F. Caldwell, E. Glaesser, and J. L. Stewart
Design of an Analog Ear 97

D. Hildebrand
An Electronic Model of the Limulus Eye 104

Harry F. Olson and Herbert Belar
Recognition of the Spoken Word by Machine 110

Roy M. Pritchard
Stabilized Retinal Images and Visual Perception 119

Huseyin Yilmaz
Color Vision and a New Approach to General Perception 126

E. B. Johnston
Neuromime Modeling of Sensory Pathways 142

D. R. Smith and C. H. Davidson
Activity Levels and Oscillation Modes in Neural Nets 148

Bernard Widrow and Marcian E. Hoff
Associative Storage and Retrieval of Digital Information in Networks of Adaptive "Neurons"* 160

Roger L. Boyell
A Semantically Associative Memory 161

A. P. Sage and J. L. Melsa
Electronic Simulation of the Biological Clock 170

Howard C. Howland
Structural, Hydraulic, and "Economic" Aspects of Leaf Venation and Shape 183

P. Mueller, T. Martin, and F. Putzrath
General Principles of Operations in Neuron Nets with Application to Acoustical Pattern Recognition 192

J. L. Stewart
A Model for Hearing 213

Ming-kuei Hu
A Mathematical Model for Visual Perception. 222

James J. Gibson
The Survival Value of Sensory Perception 230

Charles Vossler and Leonard Uhr
A Computer Simulation of Pattern Perception and Concept Formation. 233

Harry Blum
An Associative Machine for Dealing with the Visual Field and Some of its Biological Implications. 244

Laveen Kanal
Evaluation of a Class of Pattern-Recognition Networks 261

K. S. Fu
A Sequential Decision Model for Optimum Recognition 270

A. J. Cote, Jr.
Machine Interpretation of Radar Displays 278

H. J. Hunt
Some Models for Pulse-Interval Modulation Systems 291

W. R. Baum
Quantitative Aspects of the Problem of Shape in Biology* 294

Kenneth H. Reid
Design Studies of Conditional Probability Computers 295

Raymond A. Wiesen and Emir H. Shuford
Bayes Strategies as Adaptive Behavior 303

E. B. Carne, E. M. Connelly, P. H. Halpern, and B. A. Logan
A Self-Organizing Binary Logical Element. 311

Robert D. Turner
First-Order Experiential Concept Formation 331

Lars Lofgren
Kinematic and Tessellation Models of Self-Repair 342

R. M. Stewart
Theory of Structurally Homogeneous Logic Nets 370

M. C. Goodall
Induction and Logical Types 381

C. Levy and M. J. Schuller
Microwatt Transistor Circuits-A Solution to the Heat Problem in Ultralarge Computers 387

Warren S. McCulloch
The Imitation of One Form of Life by Another-Biomimesis 393

BIO-LOGIC

Heinz Von Foerster

University of Illinois, Urbana, Illinois

If in the past somebody had asked about the fundamental difference between the animate and inanimate world, the most likely answer would have been: living organisms possess that unique feature of reproduction, the capacity of self-replication, while dead matter obviously does not have this power. Today, however, I would be hesitant to give this answer. We know by now of several schemes, even very simple schemes, which display the features of self-replication (Von Neumann, 1951; Lofgren, 1958) and in the course of this symposium you will be exposed to some interesting ideas on error correction (Lofgren, 1962) which is, in a sense, a more general case of self-reproduction. But I doubt whether we would classify systems displaying these features as "living organisms." I certainly would not do so, because I believe that this capacity of self-replication is only a particular manifestation of a much more general principle which is the basis for all life. I shall come to it in a moment, after I have shown in a "Gedanken Experiment" that self-replication is not fundamental to life. Assume that I have a gadget which, by the flick of a switch, inhibits all meioses on this globe. As you may remember, meiosis is the chromosome-pair-splitting cell division which initiates oogenesis or spermatogenesis; hence, without meiosis, no sexual reproduction. Imagine that I turn on this switch. Certainly no drastic change will occur. We may happily live on as before, although after a while we may observe fewer and fewer people around us. This side effect, however, could be counteracted by another gadget which would secure immortality. Since this gadget is not yet on the market, let me turn off the switch again, and let us look for a moment on this peculiar fertility—mortality interdependence, which is a consequence of one of the neat tricks of life, namely, to live on life. Since the so-called "higher forms" live on "lower forms," they must be able to break up the lower forms into those constituents out of which the higher forms are built. If these lower forms were so stable that they could not be decomposed, higher forms could not develop. In other words, the ultimate in stability—immortality—leads to stagnation and sets the end point in evolution. Since for each level of stability there always developed a higher level which could crack up the lower ones, fertility is the way out of this problem. It seems to me, however, that those who have their fingers on the bomb triggers have a different solution for this problem in mind.

As we have seen, the capacity of self-reproduction, although omnipresent in the animate world, is tied up with a host of other characteristics of living organisms and cannot claim to be a fundamental principle.

I propose to consider as a fundamental principle of living things their capacity to form coalitions. Thus, sexual reproduction appears to be only a particular manifestation of this capacity. What I call a "coalition" is an aggregate of elements which jointly can do things which all of them separately could never achieve. In more precise terms this means that a coalition is characterized by a superadditive nonlinear composition rule where some measure Φ of the whole is more than the sum of the measure of the parts:

$$\Phi(x, y) > \Phi(x) + \Phi(y)$$

It is noteworthy that as an example of such a measure negentropy ($-H$) can be cited, because we have with Shannon (1949)

$$H(x, y) \leq H(x) + H(y)$$

with equality only if x and y are completely independent. This suggests that information plays an important part in the formation of coalitions and that information reduction is one of the desired outcomes.

Let me show two examples that aggregations in the inanimate world increase the instability of the aggregate and thus exemplify a subadditive nonlinear composition rule, while aggregates of living elements secure higher survival values (stability) for the individual elements and thus are capable of forming true coalitions.

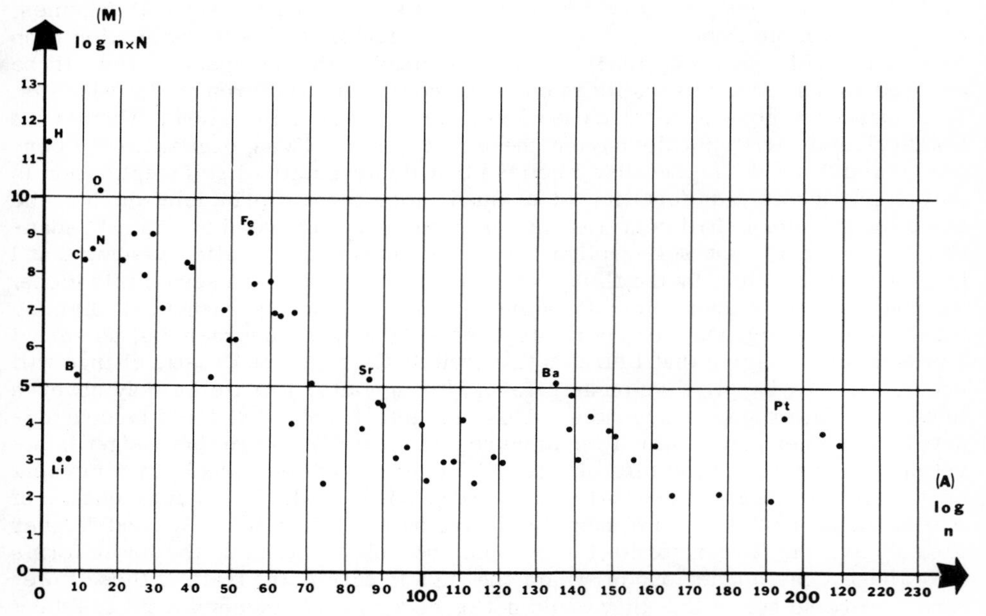

Fig. 1. Relative abundance of elementary particles forming the various chemical elements.

Figure 1 is a representation of some measure of the relative abundance of the chemical elements (adapted from Grotrian, 1934) in the universe ordered according to their atomic weights, which represent a fair measure of the number, n, of fundamental particles aggregated in the atomic nuclei of the various elements. Note that the abscissa does not represent just N, the number of atoms of a certain kind found in an arbitrarily large unit of cosmical volume,* but the number of fundamental particles $n \cdot N$ which constitute the various elements. In other words, Fig. 1 gives an indication of the probability of finding an elementary particle as a member of a nucleus of one of the various elements. From this figure it is easily seen that if a cosmonaut were to make a random collection of elementary particles, he would find with overwhelming probability particles forming the nucleus of hydrogen, i.e., single particles. Five percent of his catch would be particles found in nuclear aggregates of 16 particles (oxygen) and 0.5% in aggregates of 56 (iron), the third most probable aggregate. The probability

*This volume has been chosen to give the number of fundamental particles which constitute oxygen, a value of about 10^{10}.

of finding elementary particles in higher aggregates becomes extremely small, being always less than 10^{-7} for aggregates of more than 150 particles. Clearly, the "stability per elementary constituent" is decreased in larger and larger aggregates, which suggests a subadditive composition rule.

Applying similar reasoning to living organisms, our first guess might be that the situation is about the same, because small cellular aggregates, e.g., mosquitoes, are by far more abundant than large ones, e.g., elephants. True, but this doesn't say anything about the stability per elementary constituent. In order to give a rough estimate of this stability, in exact analogy to our previous example, I have compiled in Fig. 2 the global abundance of cells forming the various species ordered according to the number, n, of cells aggregated in typical specimen of the various species. Note again that the abscissa does not represent just N, the number of specimens, i.e., the global population of a certain species, but the number of cells $n \cdot N$ which constitute the various species. In other words, Fig. 2 gives an indication of the probability of finding a cell as a member of cellular aggregates of various sizes. From this figure it is easily seen that if a statistical cytologist were to make a random collection of cells, he would find with overwhelming probability mammalian cells, and amongst these, human cells in greatest abundance. It may come as a surprise, but the number of cells belonging to the participants of this symposium outnumber by a few orders of magnitude all the unicellular organisms on this globe. This sug-

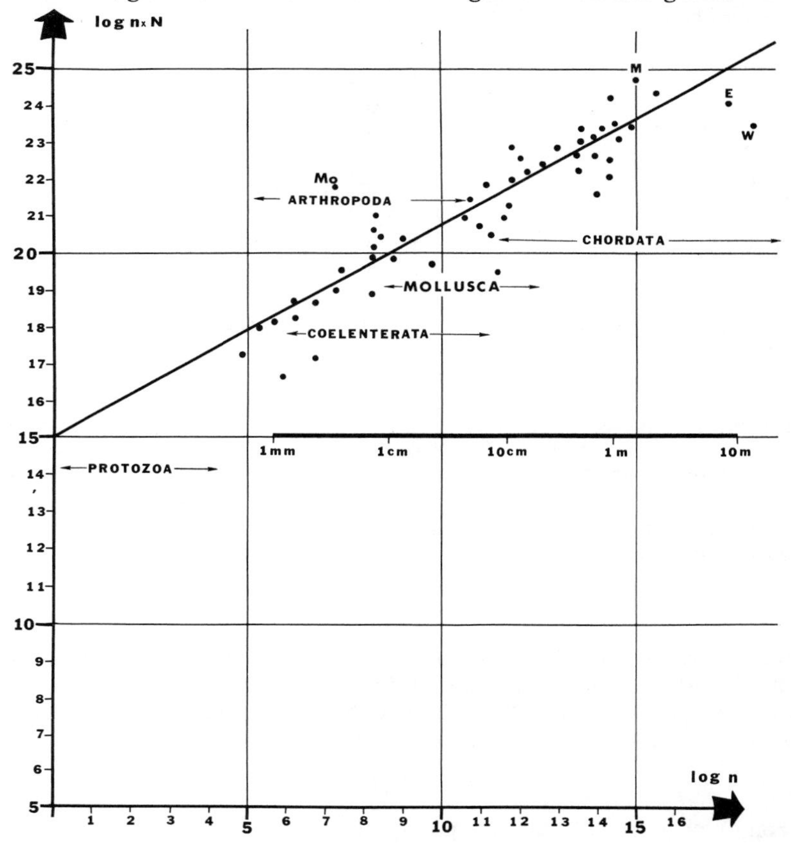

Fig. 2. Global abundance of cells forming the various species (E, elephant; M, man; Mo, mosquito; W, whale).

gests that the stability of elementary constituents of living organisms is very much increased if these constituents form aggregates of higher and higher complexity. Here we have a case of a superadditive composition rule—a true coalition—where the pay-off comes in the form of an increased survival value for the elementary constituents, the cells, whenever they aggregate to form systems of higher organization.

I hope that these introductory examples have made it sufficiently clear that if I am to elaborate my theme, "bio-logic," I have to concern myself with the logic of coalitions.

We may now ask, what is indeed this logic of coalition which makes an aggregation superadditive? Let me illustrate this situation first with a simple example which I shall generalize in a moment. Assume that there is a highly specialized zoologist, Z, whose only knowledge is the truth of the proposition x_1:

$$x_1 = \text{"elephants are gray"}$$

Assume, furthermore, that there is a highly specialized physicist, P, whose only knowledge is the truth of the proposition x_2:

$$x_2 = \text{"electrons are negative"}$$

The "truth table" of the two scientists Z, P with respect to the two propositions x_1, x_2 is clearly

x_1	x_2	Z	P
0	0	0	0
0	1	0	1
1	0	1	0
1	1	1	1

0 = false
1 = true

because the zoologist describes his universe with the logical function

$$x_1 \cdot (x_2 \vee \bar{x}_2)$$

or, in words,

"elephants are gray, and electrons are negative or electrons are not negative"

while the physicist does not care about the color of elephants and describes his universe by the logical function

$$x_2 \cdot (x_1 \vee \bar{x}_1)$$

Following Carnap, Bar-Hillel (1955), and others, I shall introduce the "strength," S, of a logical statement, which is defined by the number of ways in which such a statement can be false, $N(0)$, divided by the number of ways it can be either true or false, $N(1,0)$. Since with m propositions we must have

$$N(1,0) = 2^m$$

the strength of a logical statement is given by

$$S = N(0) \cdot 2^{-m}$$

with the two extreme values

$$S = 0 \text{ for tautology}$$

and

$$S = 1 \text{ for contradiction}$$

Although it appears at first absurd to call a statement stronger than another one if it is false in more instances, on second thought the definition given above follows our intuition insofar as we would consider a statement very weak if it is almost always true, independent of whether the propositions it contains are true or false. Such a statement would tell us very little about the universe, as is seen in the case of the tautology which is always true but says nothing ($S = 0$). Let us apply this measure of logical strength to the wisdom of our two scientists. We find that in both cases the strength of their statements is $^1/_2$. However, if the two scientists form a coalition by establishing, say, a Biophysical Society, the society is ambivalent with respect to neither the color of elephants nor the charge of electrons and its truth table would read:

x_1	x_2	$Z\,\&\,P$
0	0	0
0	1	0
1	0	0
1	1	1

with the logical strength of the wisdom of the society being $^3/_4$, which indeed represents an appreciable gain over the previous situation, where the two scientists were sitting isolated in their ivory towers.

The mechanics of computing truth tables of coalitions from the truth tables of individual partners is quite obvious: the product of the truth values in each row represents the truth value of the coalition in this row. Thus, the presence of a zero in such a row will convert all ones into zeros and the resulting number of ways in which false statements can be made has increased.

It is easy to generalize this process for an arbitrary number of k elements $E_1, E_2, \ldots, E_k$, dealing with an arbitrary number of m propositions $x_1, x_2, \ldots, x_m$, each of these elements E_i describing its knowledge in form of a logical function $F_i(x_1, x_2, \ldots, x_m)$ with strength S_i. Let two of these elements, say E_1, E_2, form a coalition. We may ask the following question: What is the most probable resulting strength $S_{1,2}$ of this coalition? I shall forego cumbersome arithmetic and give you immediately an approximate result. It turns out that with overwhelming probability the resulting strength will be

$$S_{1,2} = S_1 + S_2 - S_1 S_2$$

or, even simpler, if $W = 1 - S$ defines the "logical weakness" of a statement, the resulting weakness will be

$$W_{1,2} = W_1 W_2$$

In other words, the logical weakness of a coalition is with overwhelming probability the product of the logical weaknesses of its components. If, for simplicity, we assume all elements equally ignorant

$$W_1 = W_2 = W_3 = \ldots = W_0 < 1$$

the coalition weakness of k elements decreases with the kth power of the weakness of the individual element:

$$W_k = W_0^k$$

and thus the coalition strength increases according to

$$S_k = 1 - e^{-\alpha k}$$

where

$$\alpha = \ln \frac{1}{(1 - S_0)} > 0$$

This expression for S_k, which indicates an asymptotic increase of the measure of knowledge for a coalition which keeps growing by absorbing more and more members, allows many different interpretations. In the middle of the last century it would have been interpreted as our hopeless strife for absolute truth, which we may never reach, however close we may come. The second half of the last century would have observed that, since there is only a finite number of propositions, m, in order to be in possession of the perfect truth it is only necessary that

$$S_k = 1 - 2^{-m}$$

This would insure that the final truth table contains only a single "true" precisely for that combination of the truth values of the propositions which represents a unique and unambiguous description of the universe. Indeed, some of the great physicists of that period believed that all essential problems had been solved and what was left for the epigones was only to clean up a few side issues. However, the Curies, Planck, and Einstein, discovered not only that some of the "side issues" were the main issues, but also that there are plenty of new issues. Thus, the beginning of our century saw the fallacy of our progenitors in their trust in a fixed number of m propositions. This number constantly grows with new discoveries which add new variables to our system of knowledge. In this connection it may amuse you that in order just to keep the logical strength of our wisdom from slipping, the ratio of the rate of coalescing, $\dot{k}$, to the rate of discovery, $\dot{m}$, must obey the inequality

$$\frac{\dot{k}}{\dot{m}} \geq k \cdot \ln 2$$

I have the feeling that today, with our tremendous increase in experimental techniques, $\dot{m}$ is occasionally so large that the above inequality is not fulfilled, and we are left with more riddles than before.

To this frustration to reach perfect truth we, children of the second half of the twentieth century, have added another doubt. This is the suspicion that noise may enter the most effective coalition, flipping an established "false" into a deceptive "true" or, what might be even worse, flipping an irrelevant "true" into an unwarranted "false."

The occurrence of such spontaneous errors is far from an uncommon event. Conservative estimates suggest about 10^{14} elementary operations per second in a single human brain. If we can believe the recent work of Hyden (1960) and Pauling (1961), these operations are performed on about 10^{21} molecules. From stability considerations (Von Foerster, 1948) we may estimate that per second from 10^9 to 10^{11} molecules will spontaneously change their quantum state as a result of the tunnel effect. This suggests that from 10^{-3} to 10^{-1}% of all operations in the brain are afflicted with an intrinsic noise figure which has to be taken care of in one way or another. I am happy to see that later on in this symposium issue will be taken with this intriguing problem (Lofgren, 1962).

I shall now leave this short historical interlude and turn to possible realizations of superadditive composition rules on the most elementary level of our information processing network, namely, on the neurons themselves.

In Fig. 3 I have collected a few examples of neurons to which the endbulbs of preceding neurons A, B, C, . . . are attached (column I). We know from the work by McCulloch (1958) and others (Blum, 1960; Verbeek, 1960) that if the

	I	II	III	IV
	SCHEME	ϕ	F	S
1	A	0	$\mathcal{T}$	0.
		1	A	0.5
		2	$\mathcal{C}$	1.0
2	A B	0	$\mathcal{T}$	0.
		1	A v B	0.25
		2	B	0.50
		3	A · B	0.75
		4	$\mathcal{C}$	1.00
3	A B C	0	$\mathcal{T}$	0.
		1	A v B v C	0.125
		2	B v C	0.250
		3	A · B v C	0.375
		4	A · C v B · C	0.625
		5	B · C	0.750
		6	A · B · C	0.875
		7	$\mathcal{C}$	1.000
4	A B C	0	$\mathcal{T}$	0.
		1	A v B v C	0.125
		2	A v B v C	0.125
		3	A · B v A · C v B · C	0.500
		4	A · B v A · C v B · C	0.500
		5	A · B · C	0.875
		6	A · B · C	0.875
		7	$\mathcal{C}$	1.000
5	X_1 X_2 ···· X_n; x_i; N_i		$p(N_i) = \frac{N!\,Z^{-N}}{\prod N_i!}$	
			$\Sigma N_i = N \cdots\cdots N_i = N/n$	$p = \max$
			$\Sigma y_i N_i = \Phi \cdots\cdots N_i = Ae^{-\beta y_i}$	$p = \max$

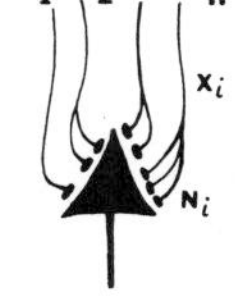

Fig. 3. Neural functionals defined by various synaptic distributions.

threshold Θ of these neurons increases in unit steps, in most cases the neuron will compute a different logical function with the input neurons A, B, C, . . . as variables. For each of the different connection schemes, 3.1 to 3.4 in column I, the logical function computed is given in column III if Θ assumes values as listed in column II. $\mathcal{T}$ stands for tautology, $\mathcal{C}$ for contradiction. Column IV gives the logical strength s for the functions computed. There are three points which I would like to make in connection with this figure, points which I believe are pertinent to my theme.

First, I would like to draw your attention to the important observation made by McCulloch and Ashby (1945) that a given synaptic pattern in connection with a variable threshold represents a functional in the sense that the synaptic pattern defines a set Σ of functions F_i in such a manner that to each F_i in Σ corresponds an F_j in Σ, namely, the one with the next higher logical strength, the correspondence being established by the unit shift of the operator Θ.

Second, it is worthwhile to note that for the same number of input neurons a variety of sets of logical functions may be computed, depending upon the distribution of endbulbs over the input neurons. This is exemplified in schemes 3.3 and 3.4, which both have three input neurons and six endbulbs, with the endbulbs distributed (1,2,3) in the first case and (2,2,2) in the second case. In general, it is easy to see that N endbulbs distributed over n input neurons will permit the formation of $p(N, n)$ different functionals, where $p(N, n)$ gives the number of partitions of N elements into precisely n parts. At this point it may also be interesting to note that while the endbulb distribution (1,2,3) produces—omitting tautology and contradiction—a functional of six "useful" logical functions with great sensitivity to changes in threshold, the endbulb distribution (2,2,2) produces only three useful functions, yet with reasonable stability to threshold variations. More sophisticated logical stable networks have been extensively studied by McCulloch and his school (McCulloch, 1958; Blum, 1960, 1961; Verbeek, 1960, 1961; Cowan, 1961). Nevertheless, it is tempting to pursue the relationship between the endbulb distribution and the generated set of logical functions a bit further on a statistical basis. Since we know of several neuron types with synaptic connections going into the thousands and tens of thousands, such an approach seems to be not completely unwarranted. Take n input neurons $x_1, x_2, \ldots, x_i, \ldots, x_n$, each having $N_1, N_2, \ldots, N_i, \ldots, N_n$ endbulbs connected to our neurons of interest as indicated in Fig. 3 (5). The total number of endbulbs

$$N = \sum_1^n N_i$$

is assumed to be fixed. Since each input neuron is distinguishable from any other, the number of ways in which a particular distribution of endbulbs may be obtained is

$$\frac{N!}{\Pi N_i!}$$

and the number of possible distributions is

$$Z^N$$

Thus, the probability of a particular distribution is

$$p(N_i) = \frac{N!\,Z^{-N}}{\Pi N_i!}$$

with

$$\sum_1^n N_i = N$$

This is nothing else but Boltzmann's way of counting distinguishable states for the molecules of a diluted, nondegenerate gas. Hence, the answer for the distribution which has greatest probability can just be copied from introductory textbooks in statistical thermodynamics. One obtains:

$$p(N_i) = \max \qquad \text{for } N_i = N_0 = N/n$$

that is, a uniform distribution. The set of logical functions generated by this connection pattern is minimum and contains n useful logical functions with a maximum threshold safety margin of N_0 unit steps. This is also intuitively quite plausible considering the great redundancy of this connection pattern provided by the multitude of like connectivities. However, it may be argued that each input neuron may transmit, on the average, a different amount of information, which would require the ith neuron to have ϕ_i units of energy available per unit time.

Under these circumstances it may be impossible to maintain the distribution suggested above, because the energy produced per unit time on the surface of a perikaryon is limited to, say, Φ. Hence, we have to consider an additional restriction, namely, that the total energy released per unit time should be constant

$$\Sigma \phi_i N_i = \Phi$$

The problem of finding the most probable distribution for our endbulbs, observing the restriction mentioned above, leads, as you may recall, to Boltzmann's energy distribution:

$$N_i = A_e^{-\beta \phi_i}$$

where A and β are constants, depending upon Φ and N in a somewhat involved manner. Here the most vigorous neuron develops the least number of endbulbs, while the slowpoke is endowed with the loudest voice. The generated set of logical functions is maximum and contains of the order of N useful logical functions with a minimum threshold safety margin of the order of a single unit step.

After this little excursion into thermodynamics, I shall now turn to my third point in reference to Fig. 3, and this point may be the most pertinent one regarding the topic of my presentation. It involves column IV of Fig. 3, which lists S, the logical strength, of the functions generated by a certain connection pattern and determined by the various threshold levels.

A brief inspection of this column shows that the logical strength increases monotonously with increasing threshold. Translated into our coalition language this means that for low threshold values the n input neurons are still acting as if they were almost independent. However, with increasing threshold values, stronger and stronger coalitions between the n input neurons are formed. In other words, the output of the neuron which collects the wisdom of its n input neurons reports the wisdom of their coalition with the threshold as coalescing agent. Of course, an increasing threshold can be replaced by afferent inhibitory fibers which may be stimulated by some neurons watching the output of our coalition neuron. Increasing inhibition will thus produce two effects. First, the logical functions computed will approach closer and closer the one function which represents most closely that "what is the case," as we have seen earlier; second, the output activity of our coalition neuron will be further and further diminished until it fires only if "what is the case" is indeed the case. In other words, formation of coalitions by inhibition, and adaptation by inhibition in connection with diminished activity are two processes which go hand in hand. The only missing link in this equivalence is: What regulates the inhibition?

The following example may suggest an answer. Assume two layers of neurons where each neuron in the upper layer grows its axons toward its corresponding neuron in the lower layer. However, the intermediate tissue will cause random-walk deviations, and with the two different target sizes for excitation and inhibition, i.e., perikarya and dendritic ramifications, respectively, the response of the lower layer as a result of the random connectivity will be

$$R(r_2) = A_1 \int_0^\infty S(r_1) e^{-(r_1 - r_2)^2/\sigma_1^2} da - A_2 \int_0^\infty S(r_1) e^{-(r_1 - r_2)^2/\sigma_2^2} da$$

where r_1 and r_2 are the vector loci on the upper and lower layers, respectively; $S(r_1)$, $R(r_2)$ are stimulus and response; and A_1, σ_1 and A_2, σ_2 are amplitude and variance of excitation and inhibition, respectively. It is well known (Inselberg, et al., 1960) that such a connectivity would produce an adequate computer for second derivatives of the stimulus pattern—or a "contour detector," if you wish—if the following condition is fulfilled:

$$A_1\sigma_1^2 = A_2\sigma_2^2$$

The necessity of this condition is easy to see, because only under this condition does a uniform stimulus, $S(r_1) = \text{const}$, elicit no response in the lower layer, i.e., $R = 0$; and indeed, a uniform stimulus does not have a contour. The question arises, how can this randomly growing net accomplish the trick of obeying the above-mentioned condition? A genetic preprogramming of the growth of the fibers according to our condition can be dismissed as absurd. In addition, this suggestion would spoil our simple assumption of random growth. Here, our principle of adaptation by inhibition will come in handy. Assume that initially the connections between our layers are such that a uniform stimulus will elicit a response in the second layer, that is, the left-hand side of our condition will predominate (Fig. 4a). If this response stimulates growth in the descending axons and activates further dendritic ramifications in the target neurons in the interface between our two layers (Fig. 4b), it is the right-hand side which gains, because A_1 and A_2 will increase in proportionate amounts, σ_1, the facilitatory variance, will remain the same, but σ_2 will increase due to the increase of the inhibitory target size (Fig. 4c). This stimulus for growth will last until inhibitions precisely counterbalance excitations, at which instant the zero-response condition is fulfilled, the growth stimulus ceases, and the net is ready for contour extraction. We may also say that the net is now "adapted" for a uniform stimulus distribution. Uniformity is not to be registered; it is the perturbation of uniformity which is to be recognized. In passing, I may mention that during the

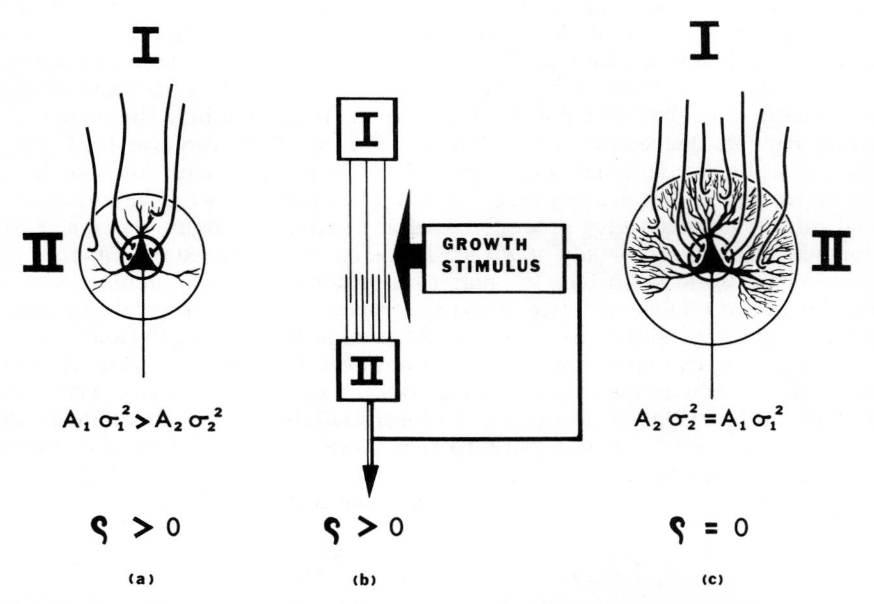

Fig. 4. Adaptation by inhibition: (a) Initial state; (b) axonal and dendritic growth; (c) final state of adaptation.

process of increasing inhibition the logical strength of each neuron in the lower layer has moved up from an initial value ϵ to a final value of $0.5 + \epsilon$, where ϵ depends inversely on the number of coalescing neurons.

Up to this point I have only spoken of the blessings of coalitions. However, I cannot conclude my remarks on the logic of coalitions without a warning. This warning refers to a peculiar instability which seems to be inherent in aggregates of reproducing, coalition-forming elements. Consider N elements and their rate of reproduction $\dot{N}$. At any instant of time, this rate will be proportional to the number of elements:

$$\dot{N} = a(N) \cdot N$$

where the proportionality $a(N)$ will depend on the number of elements and the energy supply available for each element in such a manner that for elements competing for these commodities, $a(N)$ will decrease as the number of competitors increases, while if the elements are capable of forming ever-stronger coalitions, $a(N)$ will increase with the number of elements. If, as representatives of these two kinds of elements, we chose fruit flies living in a container in the first case, and human beings inhabiting this globe in the second case, the following expressions for $a(N)$

$$\text{(I)} \quad a(N) = a - bN$$

$$\text{(II)} \quad a(N) = cN^{1/k}$$

where a, b, c, and k are constants, give very good agreement with observations (Vance, 1959; Von Foerster et al., 1960). Solving our differential equation in $\dot{N}$ for N, while observing the different suggestions for $a(N)$, one obtains for the two cases:

$$\text{(I)} \quad N = \frac{ae^{at}}{b(e^{at} - 1) + a/N_0}$$

$$\text{(II)} \quad N = \frac{K}{(t_0 - t)^k}$$

While a competitive population will asymptotically reach an equilibrium when the number of elements is $N_\infty = a/b$, a coalescing population exhibits an instability at $t = t_0$, at which instant the number of elements approaches infinity. In case you would like to know the date at which for the human race this instability occurs: it will be on Friday, November 13, 2026. It is up to the bionicists to improve the bio-logic of our human coalition, which has failed us in a decisive point: it has not given us an inhibitory mechanism, a "peoplostat," so to say, which would keep our presently ever-faster-growing population on a constant level. If we go on as we do now, we shall end like lemmings. Let us not give in so easily. Should we, who have wrung such decided advantages from many a shortcoming, be defeated by our own nature? We must do at least as well as fruit flies!

We have strong support. When we leave this conference we shall do so with greatly increased knowledge and wisdom, thanks to our enlightened organizers, who enabled us to participate in a most promising coalition, the Second Symposium on Bionics.

REFERENCES

Ashby, R. W. 1945. The physical origin of adaptation by trial and error. J. Gen. Psych. 32, 13-25.
Bar-Hillel, Y. 1955. Semantic information and its measure, p. 33-48. In: H. Von Foerster et al. [ed.], Cybernetics. Tr. Xth Conf. Josiah Macy, Jr. Found., New York.

Blum, M. 1960. Property of a neuron with many inputs, p. 55-83. Bionics Symp. WADD, TR 60-600. Dayton, Ohio.

Blum, M. 1961. Properties of a neuron with many inputs, p. 95-119. In: Von Foerster, H. and Zopf, G. W. [ed.], Principles of self-organization. Pergamon, London.

Cowan, J.D. 1961. Many-valued logics and reliable automata, p. 135-179. In: Von Foerster, H. and Zopf, G.W. [ed.], Principles of self-organization. Pergamon, London.

Grotrian, W. 1934. Die Sonne, p. 134. In: ten Bruggencate [ed.], Zur Erforschung des Weltalls. Julius Springer, Berlin.

Hyden, H. 1960. The neuron, p. 305. In: The cell, Vol. 4,1. Academic Press, New York.

Inselberg, A., Lofgren, L., and Von Foerster, H. 1960. Property detector nets and fields. Some principles of preorganization in self-organizing systems, p. 1-37. TR2, Contract Nonr 1834(21). Elec. Eng. Res. Lab., Eng. Exper. Sta., Univ. Ill., Urbana, Ill.

Lofgren, L. 1958. Automata of high complexity and methods of increasing their reliability by redundancy. Information and Control 1, p. 127-147.

Lofgren, L. 1962. Tesselation and kinematic models of self-repair. This volume, p. 342.

McCulloch, W.S. 1958. Stability of biological systems, p. 207-216. In: Homeostatic Mechanisms. Brookhaven Symp. No. 10, Brookhaven, N.Y.

Pauling, L. 1961. A molecular theory of general anesthesia. Science 134, 15-22.

Shannon, C.E. 1949. The mathematical theory of communication, p. 21. Univ. Ill. Press, Urbana, Ill.

Vance, R.B. 1959. The development and status of American demography, p. 297. In: Hauser, R.M. and Duncan, O.D. [ed.], The study of population. Univ. Chicago Press, Chicago.

Verbeck, L.A.M. 1960. Reliable computation with unreliable circuitry, p. 83-93. Bionics Symp. WADD, TR 60-600. Dayton, Ohio.

Verbeck, L.A.M. 1961. On error-minimizing neural nets, p. 121-133. In: Von Foerster, H. and Zopf, G.W. [ed.], Principles of self-organization. Pergamon, London.

Von Foerster, H. 1948. Das Gedächtnis, p. 21. Deuticke, Vienna.

Von Foerster, H., Mora, P.M., and Amiot, W. 1960. Doomsday: Friday, 13 November, A.D. 2026. Science 132, 1291-1295.

Von Neumann, J. 1951. The general and logical theory of automata, p. 1-52. In: Jeffress, L.A. [ed.], Cerebral mechanisms in behavior. John Wiley and Sons, New York.

EVOKED POTENTIALS IN THE HUMAN VISUAL SYSTEM

Donald I. Tepas, John C. Armington, and Walter J. Kropfl

Walter Reed Army Institute of Research, Washington, D.C.

For several decades the sciences have studied extensively the bioelectrical activity which can be recorded from living organisms. These potentials may be clustered roughly into two groupings or classes: those potentials which are clearly and specifically related to the organisms' exposure to a stimulus, and those in which the potentials are related to the environmental status of the organisms in a more general sense. Potential changes falling into the former category are usually termed "evoked" responses.

In the normal man, activity of the general, less specific class can be easily recorded in several ways. The electroencephalogram (EEG), obtained from electrodes pasted on the scalp, might be identified as a good example of activity falling into this classification. Evoked potentials, however, are more difficult to detect. In the visual system, evoked responses are only observed in normal man within a relatively narrow range of quite well-defined conditions. The electroretinogram (ERG) has proved to be one such evoked potential which may be both detected and measured in the intact human visual system.

The ERG is recorded from an electrode held in contact with the surface of the eye with the aid of a contact lens. The presentation of a high-luminance stimulus to the subject under these conditions usually evokes a measurable potential change. An evoked response is not observed, however, in the EEG activity recorded under the same conditions. The evoked response in this case is masked in the ongoing bioelectrical potentials. If the stimulus magnitude is sufficiently decreased, the ERG will also become so small that it too is difficult to discern from bioelectric potentials produced by other variables.

Applications of computer technology have demonstrated that it is possible to separate evoked potentials from masking activity by the averaging of the electrical activity following a repetitive stimulus. Electronic averaging has been successfully used to detect responses of the human nervous system to photic (Cobb and Dawson, 1956; Brazier, 1958), auditory (Geisler et al., 1958), and somatosensory (Rosner et al., 1960) stimulation.

In experiments recently reported by this laboratory, the averaging technique has been applied to the study of the electroretinogram (ERG) under conditions where this evoked response cannot be seen in conventional recordings (Armington et al., 1961b). Several properties of these low-amplitude ERGs have been ascertained. The ERG becomes smaller as test flash luminance is reduced. It has been found that the sensitivity of the electroretinogram is related in a regular way to the area of the stimulus producing it. The photopic electroretinogram has been shown to vary in amplitude depending upon the position of the stimulus on the retina; the largest responses are obtained when the stimulus is centered on the fovea.

In clinical application (Armington et al., 1961a) responses have been recorded from subjects with impaired retinas. The greatest attention has been paid to patients with retinitis pigmentosa. All of the patients examined had been previously tested and had failed to produce detectable responses when conventional recording procedures were used. The averaging technique has demonstrated that such patients do have a small response which is buried in various kinds of interference. In most of the patients the response is in the same waveform, but smaller than that seen in the normal subjects. The sensitivity of the ERG in retinitis pigmentosa was directly related to the field size of the retina which remains perceptually active.

The data reported in this paper present an additional demonstration that the averaging technique provides a powerful tool for the study of the human visual system. An analysis of summed scalp potentials, obtained from intermittent photic stimulation of the intact human retina, was made. Stimulus parameters were varied to detect some of the significant characteristics of summed potentials obtained from occipital EEG records.

METHOD

Electrical activity occurring while the eye was stimulated with flickering light was recorded simultaneously from two sets of electrodes. The electrical activity from these two sources, together with a signal marker, was amplified and recorded on a multichannel FM magnetic tape recorder. The tape recordings thus obtained were played through a special-purpose analog computer system for averaging physiological potentials (Kropfl et al., 1960), and through an automatic scoring system for measuring alpha activity (Armington et al., 1958).

Stimulator

The stimulation apparatus was identical to that described in a previous study (Armington et al., 1961). Flickering light was presented to the subject in Maxwellian view. A motor-driven rotating sectored disc determined the stimulus repetition rate. Five stimulation rates were used in this study: 1, 2, 5, 10, and 20 flashes per second. Interchangeable stops and filters prior to the final lens in the visual stimulator enabled the experimenter to control the stimulus diameter, luminance, and spectral composition. The cross section of the circular stimulus beam was 1.2 mm in diameter when it passed through the pupil. The stimulus field was also circular and could be set to subtend the following visual angles: 16°, 8°, 3°12', 1°4', or 24'. The relative luminances of the stimuli used were determined according to a previously described procedure (Armington and Thiede, 1954). The maximum available luminance matched a white surface of 0.23 ft-L when 5 log units of neutral density filtering were placed in the beam.

The Computer

The special-purpose analog computer device (Kropfl et al., 1960) adds the electrophysiological activity which follows the signal marker as a function of time. With repetitive summation, potentials which are synchronous with the repetitive stimulus cumulate, while nonsynchronous bioelectrical noise present in the record tends to average out. Thus, the signal-to-noise ratio is improved by averaging. In the present study, an average-response computer system was used which sums activity at 19 preset time intervals or segments following the stimulus marker. With each repetition of the signal marker, the integrated activity of each of the 19 segments was presented on an oscilloscope and on an inkwriter in such a manner that an image of the average-response waveform could be seen. In addition, the signal marker triggered an electronic counter, giving the experimenter a precise count of the number of responses summed.

Alpha Scoring System

EEG potentials recorded were also analyzed for alpha activity by an automatic scoring system (Armington et al., 1958). This device filters the recorded EEG activity, permitting only activity in the alpha frequency range to pass. The alpha activity is directed to a sensitive scoring circuit which is triggered only when activity above a calibrated amplitude is present. Triggering of the scoring circuit closed the contacts of a relay which in turn activated the clutch of a standard electric timer. Thus, one could determine the percent of alpha activity, above a set amplitude, present in a given EEG sample.

PROCEDURE

For all of the experiments conducted, one set of standard EEG electrodes was placed on the midline of the occipital area, approximately 1 in. on either side of the inion. The other set of electrodes used consisted of either EEG electrodes, in a bipolar frontal placement, or ERG electrodes of the standard contact-lens type. To facilitate an analysis of day-to-day variations in the summed activity, merthiolate was used to mark the placement of electrodes.

Three subjects with normal vision were used. All of the subjects had normal EEGs.

RESULTS

Properties of the Response

An occipital response was detected in each of the three subjects with each of the five stimulation rates used. In each case this response was readily detectable over a range of luminances and, with the introduction of considerable neutral density filtering, the response eventually disappeared into the baseline. In general, the occipital-response waveform appeared more complex with increases in the stimulation rate, the stimulus luminance, and the size of the retinal area stimulated.

With 1-per-second white-light stimulation, changes in waveform latency and amplitude were apparent. In Fig. 1, tracings of the inkwriter display under these

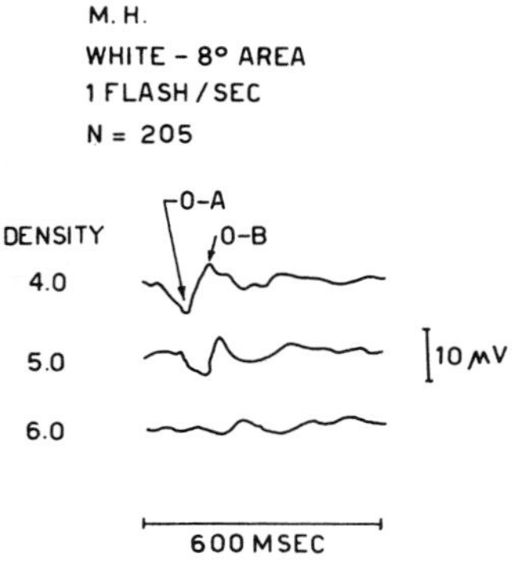

M. H.
WHITE - 8° AREA
1 FLASH / SEC
N = 205

O-A
O-B
DENSITY
4.0
5.0
6.0
10 μV
600 MSEC

Fig. 1. Tracings of the 1-per-second evoked occipital response. The average responses to three luminances of white light obtained from one subject are shown. The drawings were made from inkwriter records.

conditions give us a relatively accurate picture of the changes which occurred when luminance was decreased. All three of the responses presented in this figure contain the prominent biphasic complex which was characteristically observed with 1-per-second white-light stimulation. The initial deflection in this response pattern has been labeled O-A. This response-pattern deflection is negative with respect to the top electrode of our bipolar occipital placement. The second phase of this response is positive with respect to the top electrode and has been labeled O-B.

This biphasic response complex of the 1-per-second activity was quite prominent and easily measured at most of the luminance levels used in this study. At high luminance levels, however, the waveform became more complex, and at low luminance levels the amplitude of the waveform was considerably reduced.

These two factors made the identification of this waveform complex more difficult with relatively strong and weak stimuli.

Figure 2 shows the changes in peak latency which accompanied changes in luminance over a range of 8 log units with the 1-per-second rate. The peak latency of both O-A and O-B increased as the stimulus luminance was decreased. The response latency appeared to approach a minimum with the strongest stimuli.

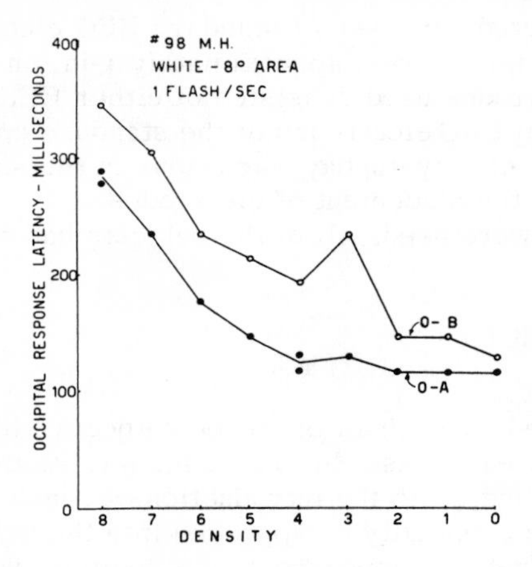

Fig. 2. Changes in the peak latency of the 1-per-second evoked occipital response which accompany changes in luminance. O-A and O-B refer to the response pattern identified in Fig. 1.

Changes in peak-to-peak amplitude of the occipital response which accompany luminance change are shown in Fig. 3. In this case, blue stimuli were presented at the 5-per-second rate and both luminance and size of the retinal area stimulated were varied. When a relatively small area of the retina was stimulated,

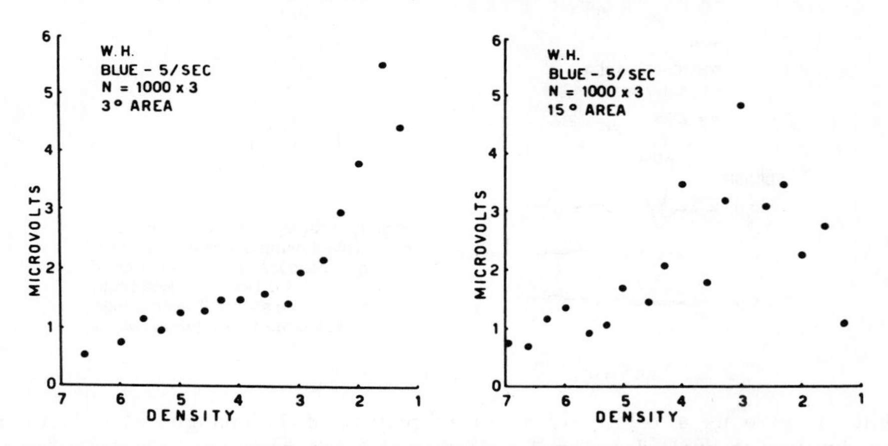

Fig. 3. Changes in the peak-to-peak amplitude of the 5-per-second evoked occipital response to blue stimulation which accompany changes in luminance. Data obtained with two different-size stimulus fields are presented.

with, for example, a 3° stimulus field, the amplitude of the response increased with an increase in the intensity of the light over a range of 7 log units. If, however, a larger retinal area was stimulated, with, for example, a 15° stimulus field, the relationship between stimulus luminance and occipital-response amplitude was not such a simple one. Under these conditions, the variability of the data increased, and the maximum responses were no longer obtained with the strongest stimuli.

Electrode Placement

The characteristics of the summed potentials were clearly dependent upon electrode placement. In Fig. 4, the inkwriter display during integration of 1-per-second activity is reproduced to demonstrate this. For each data channel shown in this figure, both the raw record and the integral growth are reproduced. The upper half of the figure represents the integration of simultaneously recorded ERG and occipital scalp activity. Both of these placements yielded a relatively

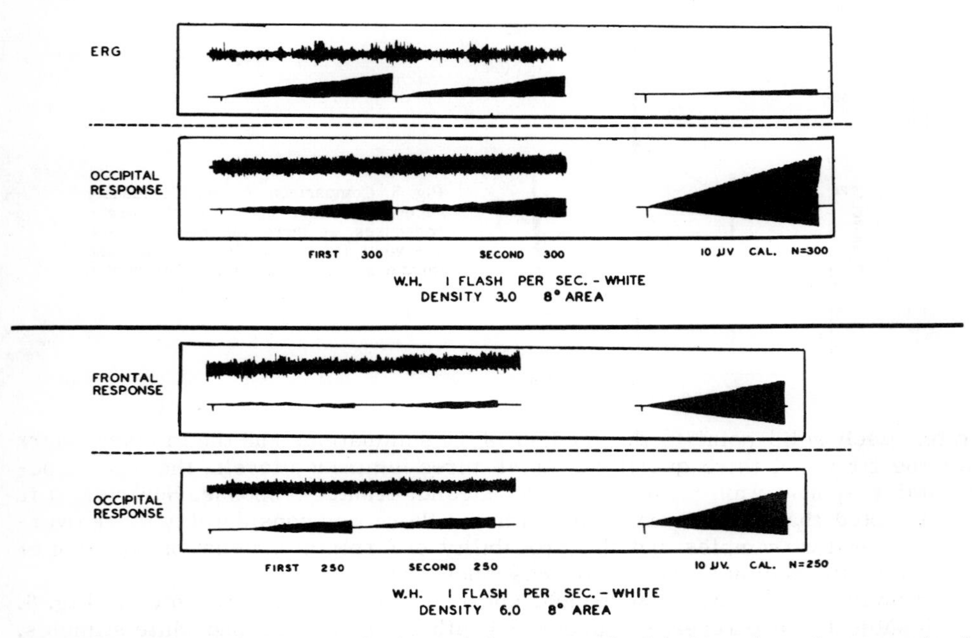

Fig. 4. Photographs of the inkwriter display. Both the raw record and the integral growth are reproduced for each data channel. The ERG and occipital-response activity presented in the upper half of the figure were recorded simultaneously. The frontal-response and the occipital-response activity presented in the lower half of the figure were also recorded simultaneously.

large response with the summation of the potentials following 300 stimulus presentations. Both placements also yielded quite similar response summations if the averaging was repeated. Given the stated stimulus conditions, however, the integrations appeared to differ along at least two dimensions. First, the rate of integral growth was quite regular for the potentials recorded from the eye (ERG), and relatively irregular for the potentials obtained from the occipital scalp placement. In the second place, there was, under these conditions, a considerable difference in average size of the two responses. The upper right-hand corner of Fig. 4 contains the summation of a 10-μv calibration pulse sent through both recording channels. This indicates a relatively large difference in the gain of the two channels. Thus the amplitude of the average responses obtained from electrodes pasted on the scalp was smaller than the amplitude of those simultaneously recorded from the ERG electrodes.

In the lower half of Fig. 4, the integration of simultaneously recorded potentials obtained from frontal and occipital scalp electrodes is presented. Under these conditions, both channels had approximately the same gain. The average response obtained with the integration of potentials recorded from electrodes placed in the frontal areas is considerably smaller than the average response obtained from the occipital placement used. Both placements yielded potentials with a rate of integral growth which is irregular in relation to the integration of ERG potentials. Of these two scalp positions, the frontal potentials were smaller and more irregular than the occipital potentials.

Figure 5 compares simultaneously recorded frontal and occipital summed scalp potentials obtained with three luminances and the 20-per-second flicker

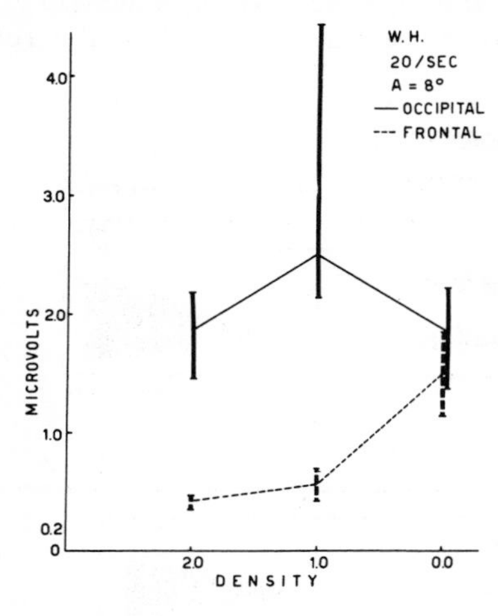

Fig. 5. Comparison of simultaneously recorded frontal and occipital average responses at three luminance levels. The vertical brackets mark the first and third quartiles of the sample. The median points are connected.

rate. Each solid point is the median of 20 summations and the brackets mark off the first and third quartiles. At all three luminance levels, the median occipital response was greater than the median frontal response. However, it is to be noted that with a very high luminance there was considerably more overlap in the two samples and the probability of a frontal summation equaling or exceeding the occipital summation was much higher.

Stimulus parameters were held constant for the data presented in Fig. 6. Both subjects were repeatedly presented with the 10-per-second white stimulus. Twenty summations of simultaneously recorded occipital and frontal potentials were obtained from each subject every day for three consecutive days. Again,

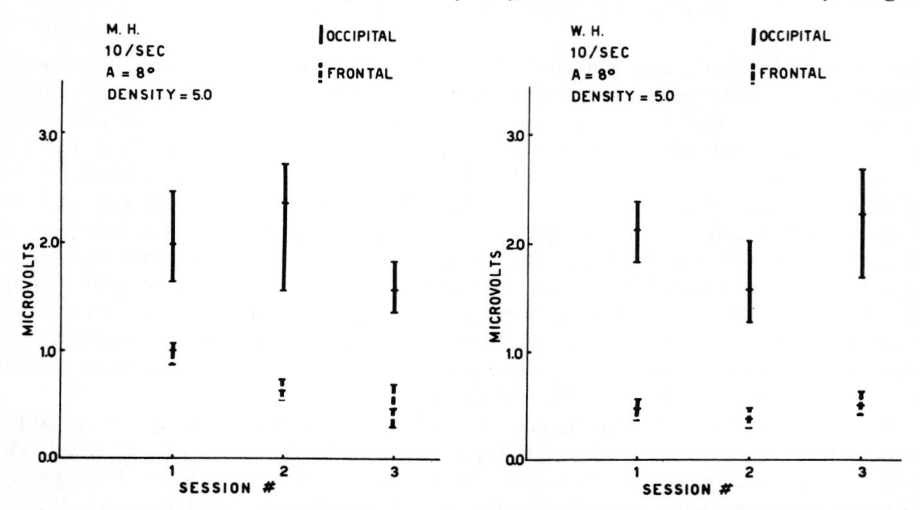

Fig. 6. Analysis of the day-to-day and subject-to-subject variability in average-response amplitude. Stimulus parameters were held constant for all of the data used in this analysis. Each solid point is the median of 20 summations and the brackets mark the first and third quartiles.

the median and quartile deviations are presented. As would be expected from Fig. 5, there was a significant difference in the amplitude of the occipital and frontal summations obtained with this relatively low-luminance stimulation. Day-to-day and subject-to-subject variability in the amplitude of the summations obtained from either set of electrodes was considerable, but the amplitude differences associated with electrode placement differences were consistent. The average waveforms, although differing in amplitude, were consistent from session to session and from subject to subject.

Occipital Scalp Summations and the ERG

The peak-to-peak amplitudes obtained from simultaneously recorded, summed occipital and ERG potentials over a range of 8 log units of neutral density filtering is presented in Fig. 7. The stimulus was a 1-per-second white light. Each point in the figure was the result of only one summation, but with each subject all of the average responses were obtained during one experimental session. Data from two of the subjects are presented. At relatively high luminance, the ERG average response was many times greater than the average occipital response. As the luminance of the stimulus was decreased, the difference in amplitude between the ERG and the occipital response decreased. With a further decrease in the luminance, under these conditions, the ERG became even smaller and eventually could no longer be detected with a high degree of certainty. The summed occipital response, however, retained a recognizable and measurable amplitude and form at these lower luminance levels. Thus, at low luminances, the summed occipital response was detected with greater ease than the summed ERG. This relationship was demonstrated in all three subjects with the 1-per-second flicker rate.

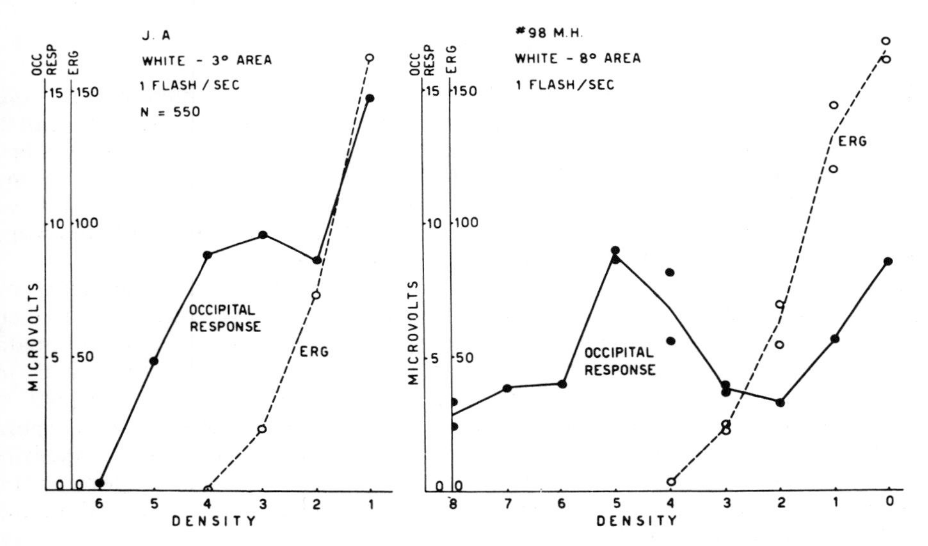

Fig. 7. A comparison of the peak-to-peak amplitude of the ERG and the evoked occipital response. ERG and occipital EEG were recorded simultaneously. Note the scale differences on the vertical axis.

Occipital Scalp Summations and Alpha Rhythm

An alpha index, defined by the percent of time in which an alpha rhythm greater than 25 μv was present during the summation of the occipital responses, was determined with the aid of the automatic scoring device (Armington et al., 1958). The degree of alpha activity was related to the amplitude of the occipital scalp potential. This analysis was made with the data collected at each of the five stimulation rates used in the study.

Figure 8 is a scattergram showing the result of one such analysis. In this case the Pearson product-moment correlation between the amplitude of the average scalp response, peak to peak, and the alpha index was +0.128. This low correlation is quite representative of the data analyzed. No strong relationship between these two measures was observed under any of the conditions.

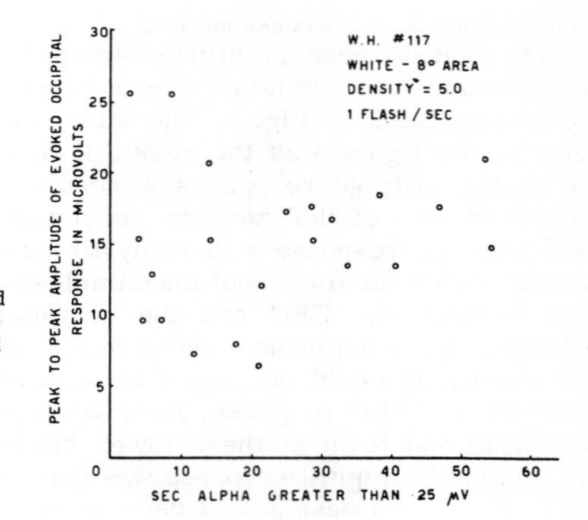

Fig. 8. Scattergram: amplitude of the evoked occipital response vs. amount of alpha in the raw EEG record. Flash rate, luminance, and stimulus field size are constant for all points.

DISCUSSION

The data demonstrate that, when appropriate stimulus conditions are chosen, summed scalp potentials possess qualities supporting the hypothesis that they are evoked potentials of the classical type. Changes in the amplitude and latency of summed scalp potentials which are systematically related to changes in stimulus parameters were demonstrated. Electrode placement appeared to have significant effects under certain conditions. All of these relationships were repeatedly demonstrated with each of the subjects tested.

It is noted that photic stimulation of the retina which is characterized by high luminance and/or large retinal area resulted in relatively complex summed scalp responses. The stimulus levels, however, which appeared to yield data which could be easily analyzed were considerably different from those used in electrophysiological studies where the more conventional recording techniques are used. In the conventional study, it is usually necessary to expose the receptor to relatively strong or intense stimuli if an analyzable response is to be discerned. The summation techniques used in the present data permitted the experimenter to identify and measure stimulus-related responses at levels approaching the subject's absolute threshold.

The data appear to indicate that relatively reliable information can be obtained from the summed scalp potentials despite their variable properties. The failure to demonstrate a strong relationship between occipital alpha activity and the summed occipital potentials would appear to support the hypothesis that these responses are not merely a summation of alpha activity.

The findings suggest that a detailed parametric study of summed scalp potentials over an unusually wide range of stimulus conditions is necessary for an accurate analysis of stimulus-response relationships.

REFERENCES

Armington, J.C., Biersdorf, W.R., and Mailloux, L.D. 1958. An apparatus for scoring electroencephalograms. Am. J. Psychol. 71, 594-599.

Armington, J.C., Gouras, P., Tepas, D.I., and Gunkel, R.D. 1961a. Detection of the electroretinogram in retinitis pigmentosa. Exp. Eye Research 1, 74-80.

Armington, J.C., Tepas, D.I., Kropfl, W.J., and Hengst, W.H. 1961b. Summation of retinal potentials. J. Opt. Soc. Am. 51, 877-886.

Armington, J.C. and Thiede, F.C. 1954. Selective adaptation of components of the human electroretinogram. J. Opt. Soc. Am. 44, 779-786.

Brazier, M.A.B. 1958. Studies of evoked responses by flash in man and cat, pp. 151-160. In: Reticular formation of the brain. Little, Brown and Co., Boston.

Cobb, W. and Dawson, G.D. 1956. The form and latency in man of the occipital potentials evoked by bright flashes. Intern. Physiol. Congr. 20th Congr. Abstr. Commun. p. 182.

Geisler, C.D., Frishkopf, L.S., and Rosenblith, W.A. 1958. Extracranial responses to acoustic clicks in man. Science 128, 1210-1211.

Kropfl, W.J., Robinson, R.E., Armington, J.C., and Tepas, D.I. 1960. An analogue computer for separating evoked physiological potentials from background noise. Conf. Proc. 4th Natl. Conven. Military Electronics. pp. 57-60.

Rosner, B.S., Allison, T., Swanson, E., and Goff, W.R. 1960. A new instrument for the summation of evoked responses from the nervous system. EEG Clin. Neurophysiol. 12, 745-747.

NEURAL-BEHAVIORAL INTERRELATIONSHIPS IN TASTE

Bruce P. Halpern*

Department of Physiology, State University of New York
Upstate Medical Center, Syracuse, New York

Direct relations between the nervous system and behavior have long been assumed. When careful anatomical dissection was permitted, the accumulated data on "normal specimens" were compared to the anatomical lesions of humans who exhibited aberrant behavior. The advent of electrical recording provided a powerful additional tool. It became possible to measure the electrical signs of neural activity while observing or controlling the stimulating conditions. The same stimuli could then be presented to an intact, unanesthetized subject, and the subject's behavior observed.

Unfortunately, the second part of this sequence, the quantitative measurement of behavior under controlled conditions, has too often been ignored. Limited behavioral data, of questionable generality and reliability, have been correlated with masses of carefully gathered neurophysiological information. In other instances, no actual measurements of behavior were made. Such failure to verify the hypothesized behavioral aspects of neural activity may lead to serious problems. An example can be found in experiments on the neurophysiological basis of learning. Twenty years ago, it was learned that the alpha rhythm of the human electroencephalogram could be used as the unconditioned response in classical, or Pavlovian, conditioning (Jasper and Shagars, 1941). Similar "cortical conditioning" has been demonstrated in the unanesthetized monkey (Morrell and Jasper, 1956). The general assumption has been that the observed changes in central nervous system responses were directly related to parallel changes in behavioral responses. However, the hypothesized correlation was not tested. Recently, Chow and his coworkers proceeded to test this particular, assumed, neurophysiological-behavioral relationship (Chow et al., 1957). They found that the establishment of the conditioned cortical response could be unrelated to changes in behavioral responses.

In taste, one must be particularly careful in order to avoid such problems. Attempts to combine gustatory neural responses from various species and human taste experience are tempting. The marked interspecies differences in taste preference behavior (Kare, 1961) suggest that an assumption of human—nonhuman gustatory interchangeability is unwarranted. If one attempts an alternative approach, deducing behavioral responses to chemicals from the neural responses to tongue taste stimulation, many difficulties develop. The present level of understanding of the gustatory systems of vertebrates does not permit prediction of behavioral selection, acceptance, or rejection of a compound from neural data. However, estimates of more limited relationships can be made and checked.

For example, the absence of recordable neural responses to both high and low concentrations of a chemical suggests that behavioral selection or rejection of that chemical is relatively unlikely. In contrast, sizeable neural responses are usually related to a differential response in a preference situation. With individual chemicals, the slope of the stimulus-concentration neural-response-magnitude function may show a relatively abrupt change. It would then be ap-

*National Institutes of Health—NIMH Postdoctoral Fellow at Cornell University while these experiments were conducted.

propriate to look for a related change in preference behavior. A more complex gustatory neurophysiological event is prolonged depression of responses to a class of chemicals following stimulation with a compound from the same or a different group. Such an observation would suggest that preference depression or modification might follow presentation of the same chemicals. Neural and behavioral responses to various substances can be used to illustrate these points.

A schematic representation of the electronic apparatus used for recording gustatory nerve responses is illustrated in Fig. 1. The broken line represents

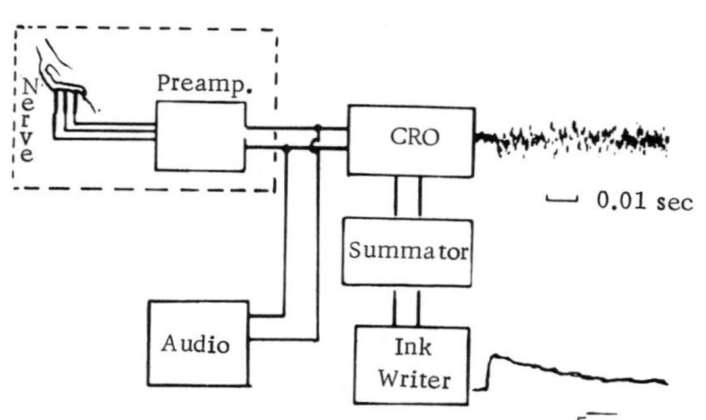

Fig. 1. Electronic apparatus for recording gustatory nerve responses.

a shielded enclosure. The shielded enclosure reduces external electrical interference and permits the small-magnitude neural activity to be recorded. The nerve discharges are led off the intact nerve, amplified, and then displayed on a cathode-ray oscilloscope. The direct neural response might look like the upper record. This type of display is difficult to quantify. Consequently, the neural activity is led through a summator. The summator, basically an RC circuit, gives an output proportional to the total energy of the neural spike input. The summator output, as displayed on a recording milliammeter, would look like the bottom record. Note that the time scales are quite different.

We can now turn to gustatory nerve response data. Figure 2 shows summated neural-response magnitudes recorded from the lingual nerve of one group of chickens. The ordinate is relative response magnitude, with the response to

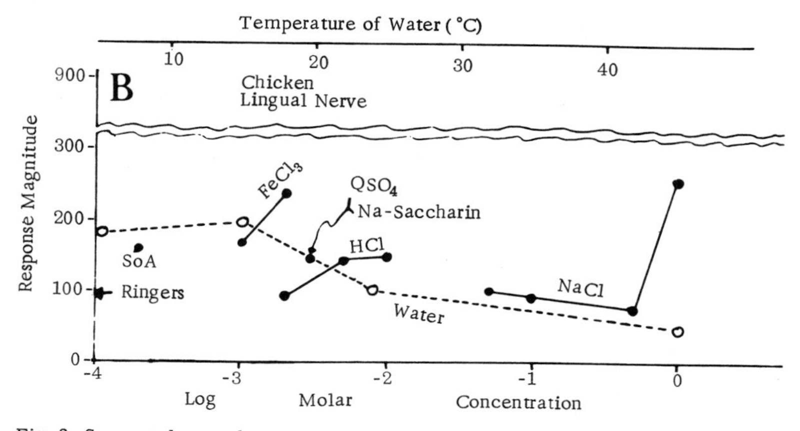

Fig. 2. Summated neural-response magnitudes recorded from the lingual nerve of the chicken.

distilled water at 24° C taken as 100. All solutions are made up in distilled water and used at 24° C. The abscissae are log molar concentration for the solutions, and temperature for the water. Sodium chloride, at concentrations ranging from 0.01 M through 0.1 M, gives response magnitudes equal to room-temperature water. Since 0.1 M NaCl is a reasonably concentrated solution, one might go no higher in concentration and thus be inclined to predict that a NaCl—water choice for chickens would show no differential preference behavior. However, still higher concentrations of NaCl do give neural responses (Halpern and Kare, 1961, Halpern, 1962). We then modify our prediction to read that there may be relatively little differential preference below 0.1 M, but somewhere above 0.1 M selection or rejection is likely to appear. Behavioral tests indicate that chickens accept low concentrations of sodium chloride and reject high concentrations. (Kare et al., 1957; Kare, unpublished data.) Thus, a chemical can be called "not a stimulus" only after a wide range of concentrations is used. Other interesting data on this figure are the responses to low concentrations of SOA (sucrose-octa-acetate) and ferric chloride ($FeCl_3$).

Figure 3 illustrates summated response magnitude recorded from another group of chickens. The ordinate is relative response magnitude, with the re-

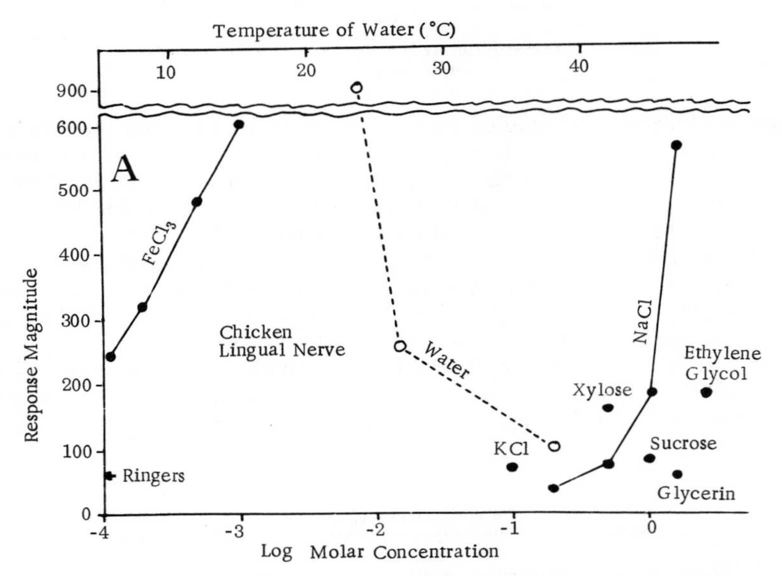

Fig. 3. Summated neural-response magnitudes recorded from the lingual nerve of the chicken.

sponse to distilled water at 38° C taken as 100. All solutions are made up in Ringer's solution and are used at 38° C.* Responses to $FeCl_3$ over a wider concentration range are shown. Such relatively sizeable response magnitudes suggest that differential preference behavior toward SOA and $FeCl_3$ is likely to be found at low solution concentrations. The prediction is half correct. Chickens strongly reject low concentrations of $FeCl_3$, with the rejection threshold lying between 0.001 M and 0.0001 M. In contrast, 0.0002 M SOA, which is also a good gustatory-

*Approximately one-half of the chickens studied gave the response pattern shown in Fig. 2: relatively small responses to room-temperature water, and responses to Ringer's solution equal in magnitude to responses to water. The other 50% of the chickens studied (Fig. 3) showed large-magnitude responses to room-temperature water. Also, the magnitude of responses to Ringer's solution at 38°C was 6/10 of the response magnitude to water at 38°C. The second response pattern, i.e., "water" and temperature responses, has previously been reported (Kitchell et al., 1959).

neural-response stimulus, is accepted equally with water in a two-choice situation (Kare, unpublished data). Behavioral tests must be done to verify or reject electrophysiologically based hypotheses.

Gustatory nerve discharges to amino acids, recorded from the rat, demonstrate other interesting points. Figure 4 illustrates summated neural-response

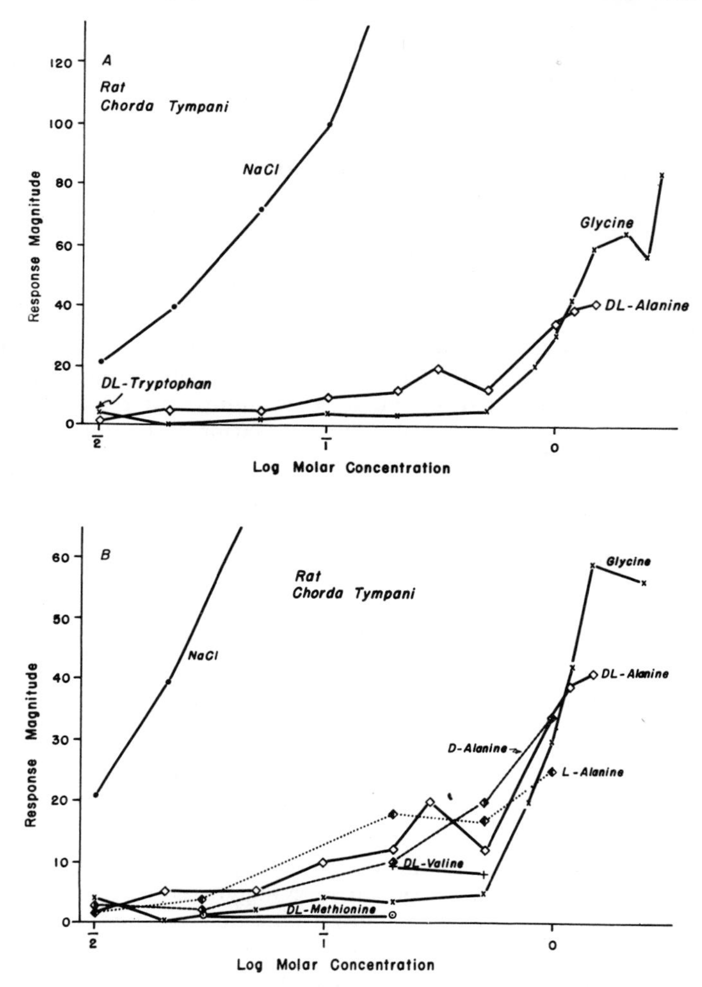

Fig. 4. Summated neural-response magnitudes recorded from the chorda tympani nerve of the rat.

magnitudes recorded from the chorda tympani nerve of the rat. The ordinates are relative response magnitude, with the response to 0.1 M NaCl taken as 100. The ordinate scale on the lower graph is expanded to twice that on the upper graph. The abscissae are log molar concentration. All the stimuli are amino acids except sodium chloride. Between 0.5 M and 1.0 M, glycine and DL-alanine show sharp increases in response magnitude. Figure 5 shows that above 0.5 M, glycine and DL-alanine also require considerably more time to reach maximum response magnitude than they do at or below 0.5 M. These neural response changes led us to look for changes in behavioral responses toward alanine and glycine in this solution-concentration region.

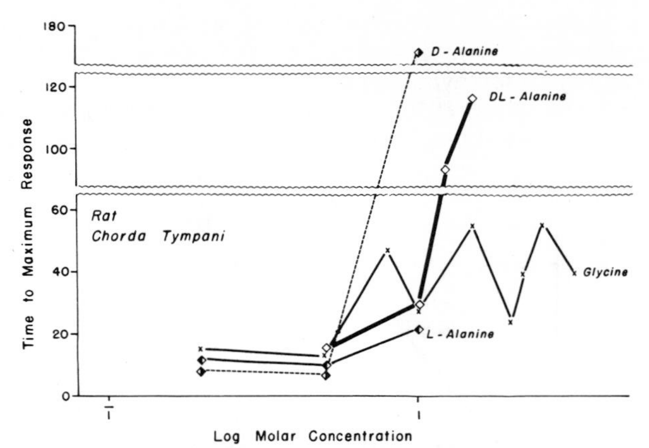

Fig. 5. Summated neural-response magnitudes recorded from the chorda tympani of the rat.

Figure 6 indicates that we were not disappointed. The ordinate on this figure and on Fig. 7 is percent preference, calculated as cubic centimeters of amino acid solution ingested divided by cubic centimeters of total fluid consumed, times 100. The abscissa is log molar concentration. DL-alanine was selected between 0.01 M and 0.4 M, and rejected at higher concentrations. The descending group, represented by the broken line, received high concentrations first and

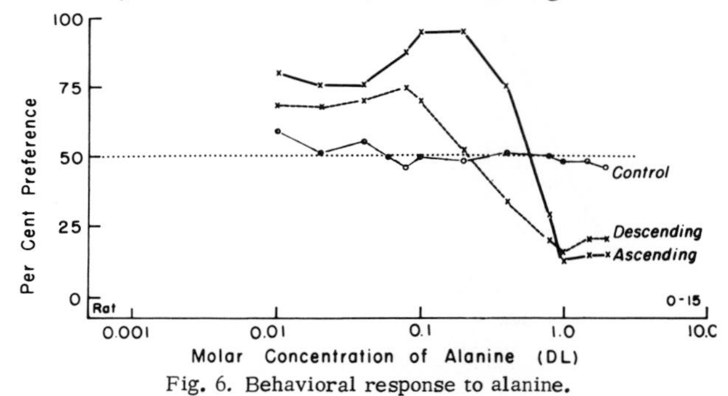

Fig. 6. Behavioral response to alanine.

showed delay and depression in the development of selection. The results for glycine are illustrated in Fig. 7. As had been suggested by the neural-response pattern, a change in preference behavior, selection replaced by rejection, developed between 0.5 M and 1.0 M. However, this applies only to the ascending group. Glycine selection in the descending group was not observed. Presumably, this is due to the prior exposure to high concentrations. Since a similar effect

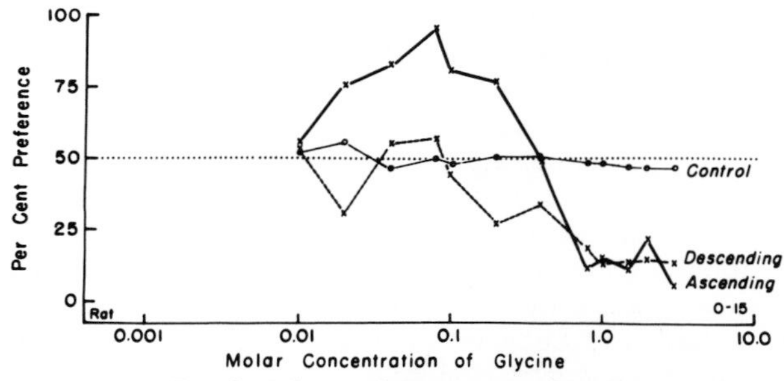

Fig. 7. Behavioral response to glycine.

was observed with DL-alanine, the neurophysiological data should now be consulted.

Figure 8 shows that tongue stimulation with glycine and DL-alanine depresses subsequent neural responses to NaCl. The ordinate is absolute response magnitude, as recorded on the milliammeter. The upper curve is the sodium chloride

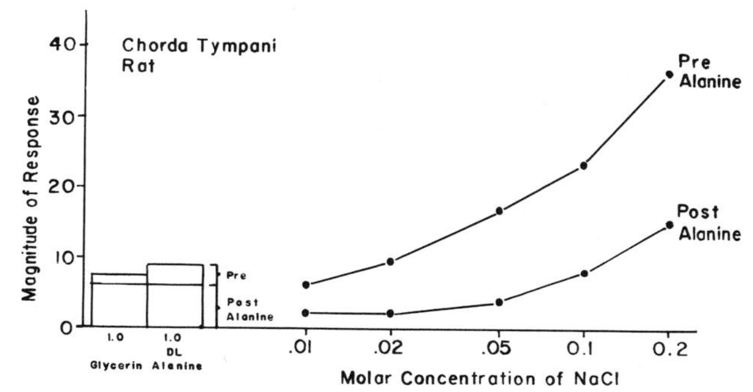

Fig. 8. Neural responses to sodium chloride before and after stimulation with glycine and DL-alanine.

response-magnitude function obtained prior to the application of high concentrations of DL-alanine and glycine to the tongue. DL-alanine, 1.0 M, was then passed over the tongue several times. The "pre-alanine" response magnitudes to most of the sodium chloride concentrations exceeded the responses to alanine. Following this, the tongue was stimulated repeatedly with high concentrations of glycine and DL-alanine. Twenty hours later, the lower NaCl curve ("post-alanine") was secured. The smallest NaCl reduction was a 60% fall in response height. Thus, almost all the NaCl responses are now smaller than the response to alanine. The correlation between depression of neural responses and depression of preference behavior was interesting. Perhaps electrophysiological experiments can be used to screen chemicals for such effects? Then, only those chemicals which show neural-response depression would be tested behaviorally. Figure 9 indicates

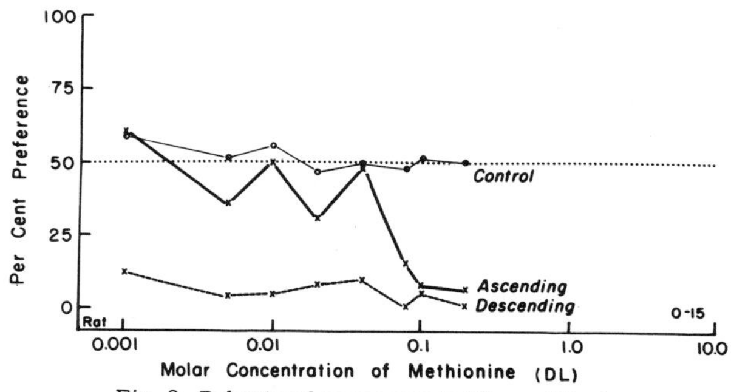

Fig. 9. Behavioral responses to DL-methionine.

that such a screening procedure would provide a distorted picture. This figure illustrates the behavioral responses for DL-methionine. The neural responses to methionine were of very low magnitude, showed no clear changes in magnitude with concentration, and had no discernible depressing effect. One might expect DL-methionine to be uninteresting behaviorally, perhaps not worth testing. Since it is an essential amino acid, and thus of inherent interest, we used it. Rats on an ascending concentration sequence accepted DL-methionine equally with water over a wide concentration range, and abruptly began to show strong rejection at high concentrations. Rats on a descending concentration sequence rejected methionine at all concentrations used. The electrophysiologically based prediction missed on all counts. All the behavioral phenomena found with the other chemicals were observed here, but none was forecast by the neural data (Halpern et al., 1961, 1962).

Where does all this take us? In vertebrate taste, neurophysiological data seem to be, at the present time, a useful but not always reliable guide to behavioral responses. The neural responses do not yet predict the type of behavior which will occur. Rather, changes in behavior, and the presence or absence of differential response, are suggested. Conversely, behavioral experiments frequently indicate that neural responses to certain chemicals should be more carefully studied, under a greater range of conditions. Thus, these two types of experiments have valuable interactions. At the risk of violating the previously stated suggestion against generalizing upon limited evidence, the above statement might be broadened to propose that simultaneous or successive neurophysiological and behavioral investigations are not only necessary for sound progress, but actually speed research and point to pathways which might otherwise be missed.

REFERENCES

Chow, K. L., Dement, W. C., and John, E. R. 1957. Conditioned electrocorticographic potentials and behavioral avoidance responses in the cat. J. Neurophysiol. 20, 482.

Halpern, B. P., Bernard, R. A., and Kare, M. R. 1961. Gustatory nerve responses and preference behavior for amino acids in the rat. Fed. Proc. 20, I. 338 (abstr.).

Halpern, B. P., Bernard, R. A., and Kare, M. R. 1962. Amino acids as gustatory stimuli in the rat. J. Gen. Physiol. 45, No. 4.

Halpern, B. P. and Kare, M. R. 1961. Neural responses to tongue stimulation in the domestic fowl. Poultry Sci. 40, 1412.

Halpern, B. P. 1962. Gustatory nerve responses in the chicken. (Submitted for publication.)

Jasper, H. H. and Shagars, C. 1941. Conditioning the occipital alpha rhythm in man. J. Exp. Psychol. 26, 373.

Kare, M. R. 1961. Comparative aspects of the sense of taste. In: Kare, M. R. and Halpern, B. P., eds., Physiological and behavioral aspects of taste. Univ. of Chicago Press, Chicago.

Kare, M. R., Black, R., and Allison, E. G. 1957. The sense of taste in the fowl. Poultry Sci. 36, 129.

Kitchell, R. L., Ström, L., and Zotterman, Y. 1959. Electrophysiological studies of thermal and taste reception in chickens and pigeons. Acta Physiol. Scand. 46, 133.

Morrell, F. and Jasper, H. H. 1956. Electrographic studies of the formation of temporary connections in the brain. EEG Clin. Neurophysiol. 8, 201.

BIOELECTRIC PATTERNS AS INDICATORS OF BEHAVIORAL DEVELOPMENT IN THE CHICK EMBRYO

Joseph J. Peters and Charles J. Cusick

Department of Biology, Xavier University, Cincinnati, Ohio

A study of transitional stages in the embryological development of living organisms provides a clearer understanding of anatomical assembly and the interdependence of parts, and a technique for distinguishing between essential and nonessential components for achieving integrated function. Some studies from this point of view are presented here. They deal with the beginning of and subsequent changes in the bioelectric patterns of heart, muscle, brain, and eye, as this electrical activity appears in association with behavioral movements in the developing chick embryo. In this report, behavior is regarded as an output of energy in the form of muscular contraction which is usually initiated by motor neurons in the adult organism and integrated by the central nervous system, often as an adaptive response to a sensory input.

For recordings, electrodes were so placed that they spanned the heart, muscles of the shank, the cerebral lobes, and the eyeball of chicks from the embryonic age of 3 days until 7 days after hatching. A model III-D 4-channel Grass electroencephalograph was used for electrical recordings and a Grass photic stimulator for providing light flashes at frequencies of 10 to 60 per second.

Within 48 hr after incubation, electrodes spanning the heart pick up rhythmic electrical activity characteristic of the electrocardiogram. On about the fourth or fifth day of incubation the embryo exhibits gross writhing movements along the vertebral column. Later it uses the limbs as stiff paddles, and with progressive maturation delicate movements gradually appear in the terminal portions of the extremities. This orderly and sequential acquisition of behavior, from early gross movements to later movements which are delicate and refined, reminds the observer of the development of behavior in the salamander as described by Coghill (1926, 1930) and Herrick (1950). Associated with the contraction of skeletal muscles employed in these movements are volleys of spike-like electrical discharges whose amplitude and complexity grow as the age of the embryo advances (Peters et al., 1956).

On about the thirteenth day of incubation, electrodes from the cerebral lobes begin to pick up spontaneous electrical activity of very small amplitude and low frequency (Peters et al., 1960). With the increasing age of the embryo, the amplitude of these electrical discharges also increases, so that at the time of hatching the electrical activity of the cerebral lobes is characterized by waves of large amplitude with a frequency of 1 to 5 waves per second on which are superimposed waves of smaller amplitude and a frequency of 18 to 24 per second. When the hatched chick appears to be asleep or under anaesthesia caused by barbiturate drugs, these faster waves of small amplitude tend to disappear from the record; when the chick shows external signs of arousal, the slow waves tend to become less prominent. Some explanation for the appearance and changes in electrical patterns of the cerebral lobes may be sought in the differentiation and migration of neurons as described by Jones and Levi-Montalcini (1958), or in the embryological development of neurons and glia cells as suggested by Galambos (1961).

On approximately the seventeenth day of incubation the eyes of the chick manifest electrical activity associated with changes in the intensity of light directed toward the eye (Peters et al., 1958). At the onset of photic stimulation the eye shows an electrical "on" response; at the cessation of light flashes it shows an electrical "off" response. In addition, during photic stimulation the electrical records from the eye show separate electrical waves for each flash of light at frequencies above 60 per second. Such responses are obtained during photic stimulation even though the chick has closed eyelids and is under the anesthetic effects of a barbiturate (Seconal).

In summary, it may be noted that the electrical activity of the chick embryo nicely parallels the chronological age and developmental stages. At very early stages electrical activity is absent, or of small amplitude and simple pattern. As the tissues mature and new functions are acquired, the amplitude of electrical activity increases and the patterns of both behavior and electrical activity become more complex. Further studies of these bioelectric patterns and the highly integrated anatomical components in the chick embryo may be useful in the construction of mechanical models serving the functions of input—output integration.

REFERENCES

Coghill, G. E. 1926. The growth of functional neurones and its relation to the development of behavior. Proc. Amer. Phil. Soc. 65, 51-55.

Coghill, G. E. 1930. The structural basis of the integration of behavior. Proc. Nat. Acad. Sci., Wash. 16, 637-643.

Galambos, R. 1961. A glia-neural theory of brain function. Proc. Nat. Acad. Sci., Wash. 47, 129-136.

Herrick, C. J. 1950. The brain of the tiger salamander. Univ. Chicago Press, Chicago.

Jones, A. W. and Levi-Montalcini, R. 1958. Patterns of differentiation of the nerve centers and fiber tracts in the avian cerebral hemispheres. Arch. Ital. Biol. 96, 231-284.

Peters, J. J., Vonderahe, A. R., and Huesman, A. A. 1960. Chronological development of electrical activity in the optic lobes, cerebellum, and cerebrum of the chick embryo. Physiol. Zool. 33, 225-231.

Peters, J. J., Vonderahe, A. R., and Powers, T. H. 1956. The functional chronology in developing chick nervous system. J. Exp. Zool. 133, 505-518.

Peters, J. J., Vonderahe, A. R., and Powers, T. H. 1958. Electrical studies of the functional development of the eye and optic lobes in the chick embryo. J. Exp. Zool. 139, 459-468.

SOME OBSERVATIONS INDICATING THE POSSIBILITY OF LONGITUDINAL CHARGE-CARRIER FLOW IN THE PERIPHERAL NERVES

Robert O. Becker

State University of New York, Upstate Medical Center, Syracuse, New York
and
Veterans Administration Hospital, Syracuse, New York

The direct-current potentials measurable on the surface of amphibians have been shown to be organized into a complex dc "field" pattern, with a remarkable relationship to the underlying neural structures (Fig. 1). Further observations

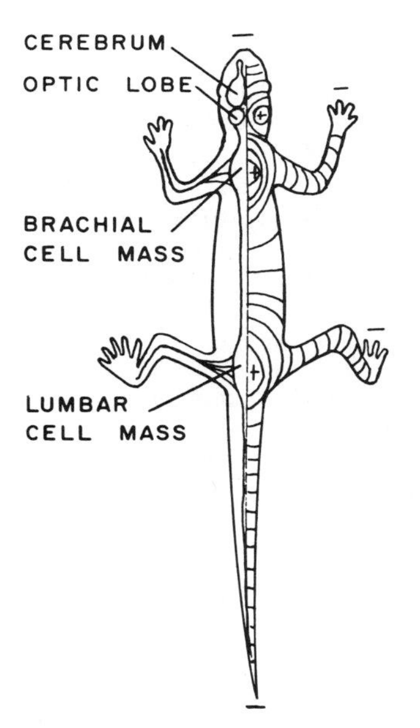

Fig. 1. Schematic view of salamander's central nervous system (left) and surface dc field (right). The lines of the dc field are equipotential and continue across the left side of the body. Note the congruity between the cellular enlargements of the CNS (cranial, brachial, and lumbar) with the positive sink areas. The nerve-outflow terminations are negative.

have led to the thesis that this dc field is generated within and distributed by elements of the central nervous system and that it constitutes a primitive type of data transmission and control system (Becker, 1960; Becker and Bachman, 1961a). The surface dc potentials of the human have been found to be similarly organized (Fig. 2) and to have similar control-system characteristics (Becker and Bachman, 1961b). Input parameters of the system have been found to be trauma and external electromagnetic force fields. System outputs are some measure of control over the propagated action potential activity of the neurons and some control over postembryonic growth processes.

The possibility of actual longitudinal charge-carrier flow as an element of this dc field was considered. To obviate the technical difficulties inherent in direct measurements of current flow, the Hall effect phenomenon was utilized on intact animals. Definite transverse or Hall voltages were obtained in the presence of a steady-state magnetic field indicating the existence of some type of charge-carrier flow in a longitudinal direction (Becker, 1961). This phenomenon was shown to be dependent upon an intact central nervous system, although the

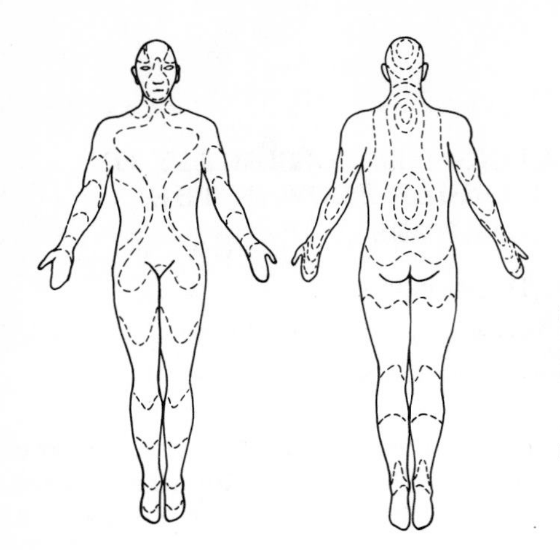

Fig. 2. Equipotential line plot of the surface dc field in the human. The central nervous system is not shown but the positive sinks again overlie areas of cellular aggregation in the neural axis. (The spinal cord becomes progressively shorter compared to body length as one ascends the evolutionary scale. This accounts for the apparent cephalad shift of the brachial and lumbar sink areas.)

relationship demonstrated was an indirect one. A consideration of the results obtained under the experimental circumstances strongly indicated that the charge carriers possessed a high mobility and were, therefore, probably electrons or similar units rather than ions.

The present report concerns observations made directly upon the sciatic nerves of the bullfrog (Rana catesbeiana), utilizing different techniques. Evidence has been obtained to substantiate the charge-carrier hypothesis and to further delineate the operating parameters of the dc field control system.

METHODS

Animals were anesthetized by titration with Tricaine® (Sandoz).

The sciatic nerves were atraumatically dissected free from their surrounding tissues in the thigh, lifted from their bed, and a 7-10 cm length was isolated by inserting a thin polyethylene plastic sheet beneath it. The nerves were not sectioned and were left attached to both the spinal cord and their peripheral terminations. Electrodes were Ag-AgCl, saline agar with flexible terminal wicks. Electrode potentials were under 100 μv and remained stable. Nerve potentials were amplified by either a Hewlett Packard 425A microvoltmeter or a Kiethley 600A electrometer. Input impedances from 10^6 to 10^{14} ohms were used and no system loading was noted above 10^7 ohms. The recorder was a Varian Type G 11A servo potentiometer.

RESULTS

The dc potential gradients along 1-cm segments of the main trunk and the two main branches of the sciatic nerve were measured in 24 specimens. In very deep anesthesia, the 1-cm gradients of all areas were either zero or slightly positive (in all cases the polarity is expressed as that of the distal electrode referred to the proximal electrode). This phase of very deep anesthesia was generally brief—less than 5 min—and was followed by a 30-min period of moderate anesthesia during which the animal did not respond to painful stimuli of any type and no other reflexes were elicitable. All measurements were taken during this phase to insure compatibility of results. The main sciatic trunk revealed 1-cm potential gradients ranging from 2 to 8 mv, roughly inversely proportional in amplitude to the depth of anesthesia. Invariably these potentials showed a negative distal polarity. One main branch (posterior tibial serving the calf area of the lower leg) was also negative distal in polarity but gradient amplitudes were always higher than those of the main trunk, averaging 6 to 15 mv. The other main branch of the sciatic (the peroneal serving the anterior portion of the lower extremity) always displayed a positive distal polarity that was invariably less than that of the posterior tibial in amplitude (Fig. 3). In some instances the algebraic sum of the potentials of the two branches was equal in amplitude and polarity to that of the main trunk. Generally, however, the posterior tibial negativity was too high for such a manipulation and an excess negativity resulted.

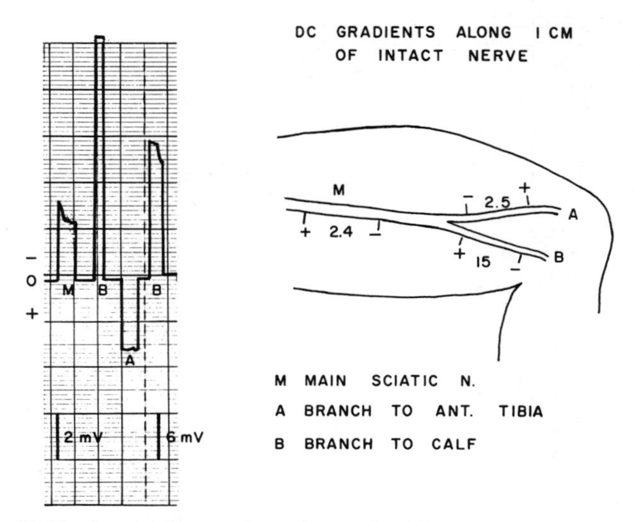

Fig. 3. One-centimeter dc gradients along the sciatic nerve and its main branches. On the left are actually recorded potentials in a representative experiment during moderate anesthesia. The main sciatic (M) and the posterior tibial branch (B) are negative in polarity while the peroneal branch (A) is positive. A recording from the posterior tibial at a lower level of amplification is shown in the right-hand portion of the chart record. The results are schematically represented on the right, showing the relationship of the main nerve and its two branches.

The effect of quick-freezing a 4-mm segment centered between two electrodes 1 cm apart on the main trunk was noted. Freezing was accomplished by liquid nitrogen which was enclosed in a 6-mm-diameter round-bottom test tube and was kept in a Dewar until used. The rounded tip of the tube was lightly approximated to that portion of the nerve equidistant between the two electrodes. Freezing the two electrodes in a similar manner produced no potential variation. Chemical and electrical contact was avoided; the temperature of the tube end was not measured but was assumed to be close to that of the liquid nitrogen (−320° F). Quick-freezing in this fashion produced a prompt increase in the distal negative potential of 1-2 mv with each application. Visual observations indicated thorough, quick-freezing of the 4-mm segment and correlated thawing of the area with a return to the original baseline potential (Fig. 4, upper). This phenomenon could be repeatedly obtained from a good preparation up to a maximum of ten times before potentials abruptly fell off and evidence of injury currents from the frozen area could be noticed.

It had been previously noted (Becker, 1960, 1961) that sectioning of the spinal cord at the level of the base of the brain produced a prompt drop in all surface dc potentials below the level of the section. Sorokhtin and Temper (1959) correlated this phase with that of "spinal shock," during which all neural activity distal to the area of section is completely depressed and no reflexes can be

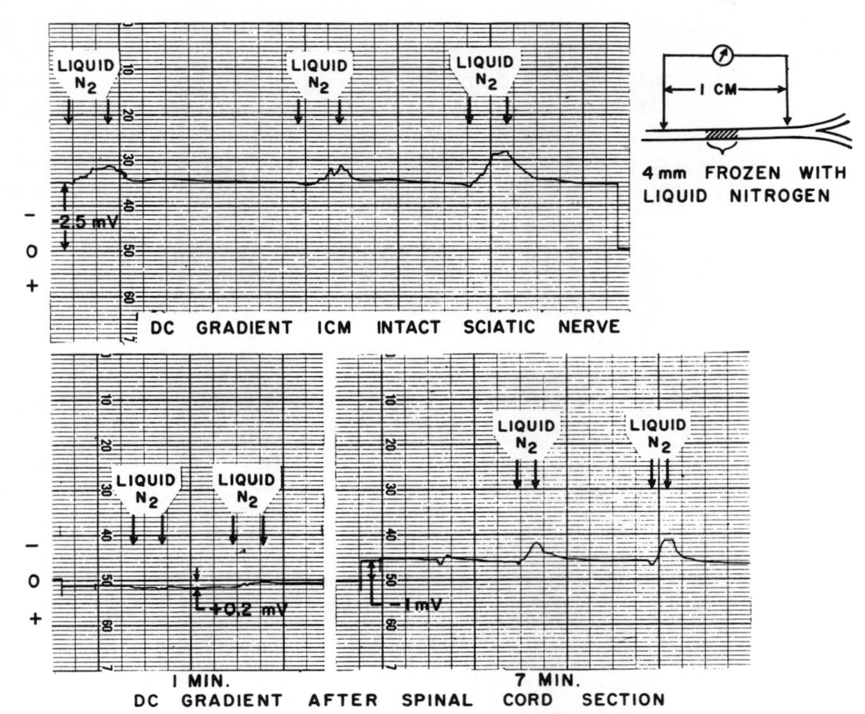

Fig. 4. Effect of quick-freezing on the 1-cm dc gradient of the main sciatic nerve. Upper trace: The 1-cm dc gradient of the main sciatic of the moderately anesthetized frog—in this case 2.5 mv. Application of the liquid nitrogen as indicated for 7-8 sec produced increase in the dc gradient of from 0.5 mv to 1.25 mv. Lower left trace: The dc gradient and effect of liquid nitrogen during the phase of spinal shock. There was a slight distal-positive potential noted but negligible potential variation from the freezing process. Lower right trace: The dc gradient and effect of liquid nitrogen during the phase of recovery from spinal shock. There is a return to a distal-negative gradient and freezing again produces an increase in the amplitude of the gradient. The same nerve was used for all three traces. The chart speed was 5 sec between vertical lines. The experimental setup is shown schematically at the right top.

obtained. Recovery from spinal shock is characterized by hyperreflexia and a return of the dc potentials to original levels. In the frog, the phase of spinal shock lasts approximately 5 min and during this time the 1-cm gradient along the sciatic nerve was found to be essentially zero. Additionally, during this phase the application of liquid nitrogen did not alter the dc gradient in any manner (Fig. 4, lower left). With recovery from the depressed spinal-shock state, the dc gradient returned, again negative distal in polarity. The application of the liquid nitrogen at this time produced an increase in the negative gradient similar to that noted prior to the spinal cord sectioning.

Observations were made upon the dc injury potentials generated by a 2-cm length of previously undamaged main sciatic nerve. The nerve segment was placed on a thin glass microscope cover slip and was kept slightly moistened with isotonic saline. Injury potentials, negative in polarity and equal in amplitude, could be measured at each cut surface with reference to the undamaged center of the 2-cm segment. These potentials generally averaged 8-12 mv in amplitude. Quick-freezing the entire fiber (by immersing it in a beaker into liquid nitrogen in a Dewar) invariably produced a polarity reversal of the injury potential with an amplitude less than that of the original prefreezing potential. Thawing produced a return to a normal negative gradient which was less in amplitude than either the prefreezing-negative or the frozen-positive potentials. It was found that a good preparation could be cycled in this fashion, up to a maximum of 8 cycles, with little change in either the unfrozen-negative or the frozen-positive potentials (Fig. 5).

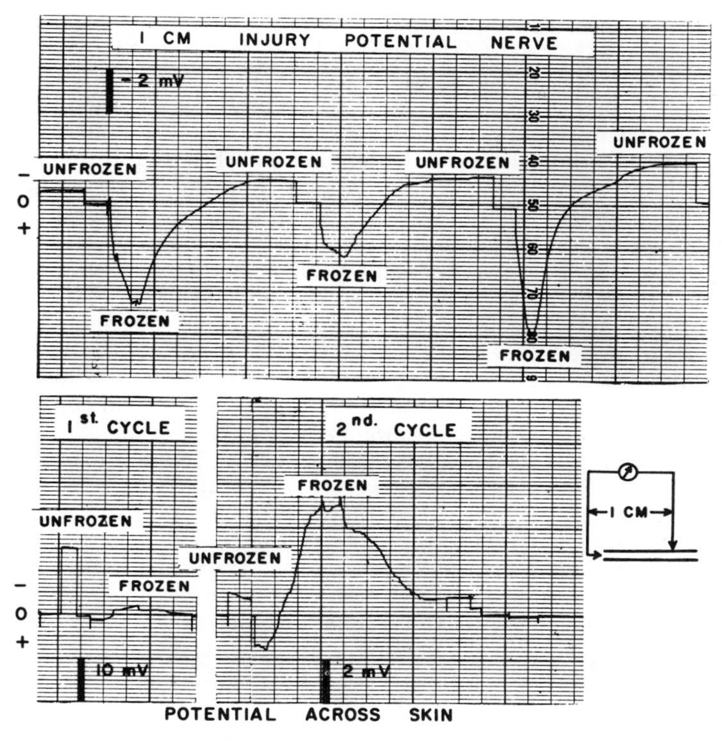

Fig. 5. Upper trace: The effect of quick-freezing on the dc injury potentials of nerve. The tracing shows 3 cycles of alternate freezing and thawing with unfrozen injury potentials running between 1 and 2 mv negative. (The original injury potential—before any freezing—was 6 mv negative.) The frozen potentials are reversed in polarity and average 2 to 6 mv in amplitude. Lower trace: The first and second cycle of freezing-thawing in skin potentials. The prefrozen potential was 15 mv negative-exterior. The first frozen potential was approximately 2 mv of the same polarity as the unfrozen. Thawing produced a very low 1-mv negative-exterior potential which could be increased to 5 mv at the same polarity. However, following the second freezing, potentials fell to zero and remained at this level.

The effect of quick-freezing on the transverse (inside to outside) potentials of frog skin was determined. The normal potential was found to average 15 to 20 mv across the unfrozen skin with the exterior surface negative. Freezing (by the same technique as above) produced a potential of the same polarity but of only a few millivolts amplitude. This potential declined with thawing to about 1 mv with still the same polarity. Refreezing then would produce an increase in amplitude of approximately 4-5 mv but thawing at this time was accompanied by a fall to zero potential. In all instances two cycles of freezing—thawing resulted in an inert preparation with zero potentials under both circumstances.

COMMENTS

One of the difficulties encountered in elaborating the control system thesis for the dc field system was the return path of the current. Early analog devices (Becker, 1960) had assumed a return path through the tissue fluid but this was disproved by the observation that the muscles making up the bulk of the extremity were polarized in a distal-negative fashion also. The observation that the two branches of the sciatic nerve are oppositely polarized appeared to furnish a solution to this return-path problem. Libet and Gerard (1941), working with the isolated cerebral hemisphere of the frog, postulated that these neurons were polarized in an axonic-dendritic fashion and suggested the possibility of current flow within the neuron. If this concept is extended to include the peripheral spinal neurons as well, then there should be a differential polarization between motor and sensory fibers in the peripheral nerves (the motor fibers are axons while the sensory fibers are, anatomically, dendrites). While definite identification of the proportions of motor to sensory fibers in a nerve can be made only by degeneration experiments, some indication of the composition can be made on the basis of the fiber-size spectrum. Preliminary determinations made by this method show that the positive peroneal branch is composed of a much greater proportion of small fibers compared to the negative posterior tibial branch. The latter branch also contains a group of very large myelinated fibers which are not seen in the peroneal branch. In accordance with these observations, we now propose the extension of axonic-dendritic polarization to include all neurons of the central nervous system. Since the peroneal branch appears to have a higher percentage of sensory fibers, we postulate that the dendrites in the peripheral nerves display a distal-positive dc gradient. The posterior tibial branch would therefore indicate that the axons have a distal-negative dc gradient. The circuit completion would therefore be via opposite polarization and current flow in the motor fibers, contrasted to the sensory fibers.

The increase in the 1-cm dc gradient along the intact sciatic nerve when a central segment was frozen appears to be a genuine phenomenon, dependent upon some active mechanism in the central nervous system. This is illustrated by the lack of response to the freezing process during the neural-depressed phase of spinal shock. Such an increase in potential could be produced by increasing either the resistance or the current flow and preliminary measurements have shown that the freezing process does produce an increase in the dc resistance. However, if one allows the assumption that the current of injury is based on a similar charge-carrier system, the polarity reversal with freezing cannot be explained on the basis of a resistance increase alone. In any event, the observations are best explained on the basis of some charge-carrier flow in the neural structures. It seems highly unlikely that the charge carriers could be ions since ionic mobility at $-320°F$ would be negligible. However, electron-transfer mechanisms have been found to be operative at this temperature (Chance and Nishimura, 1960) and the suggestion has been made that such circumstances might actually favor such a mechanism (Szent-Gyorgyi, 1960).

SUMMARY

Observations are reported indicating that the thesis of axonic-dendritic polarization of cerebral neurons can be extended to include mixed spinal nerves as well. This permits the return path necessary to complete the circuit of the dc fields. Potential changes at low temperatures in both dc gradients of intact nerves and nerve-injury potentials further indicate the possibility of charge-carrier flow involving units of high mobility.

REFERENCES

Becker, R.O. 1960. The bio-electric field of the salamander and its simulation by an electronic analogue. IRE Trans. Med. Electronics ME-7, 202-207.

Becker, R.O. 1961. Search for evidence of axial current flow in peripheral nerves of salamander. Science 134, 101-102.

Becker, R.O. and Bachman, C.H. 1961a. The dc field, a new data transmission and control system for living organisms. 4th Internat. Conf. on Med. Electronics. New York, N.Y., July, 1961.

Becker, R.O. and Bachman, C.H. 1961b. The dc field of the human, a new control system. Proc. 1st Multidisciplinary Res. Conf., Am. Med. Assoc.

Chance, B. and Nishimura, M. 1960. On the mechanism of chlorophyll-cytochrome interaction: The temperature insensitivity of light-induced cytochrome oxidation in chromatium. Proc. Nat. Acad. Sci. (USA) 46, 19-24.

Libet, B. and Gerard, R.W. 1941. Steady potentials and neuron activity. J. Neurophysiol. 4, 438-455.

Sorokhtin, G.N. and Temper, Y.B. 1959. The state of hyperpolarization in spinal shock. Bull. Exp. Biol. Med. (Russ) 47, 27-31.

Szent-Gyorgyi, A. 1960. Introduction to submolecular biology. Academic Press, New York.

SPONTANEOUS NEURAL ACTIVITY

James B. Preston *

Department of Physiology, College of Medicine
State University of New York, Syracuse, N.Y.

ABSTRACT

Single units which discharged with regular spontaneous rhythms without intentional stimulation were isolated from the ventral nerve cord of the crayfish by intracellular recording methods in the proximity of the sixth abdominal ganglion. These units were divided into two groups: group A units in which interspike intervals varied less than 10 msec; group B units in which interspike intervals varied within a ringe of 10-30 msec. Group A units maintained "constant" interspike intervals and could not be discharged by sensory inputs, while the group B units could be discharged by appropriate sensory-nerve stimulation. Both group A and B units discharged to direct stimulation of the impaled unit, and the evoked direct single-spike activity reset the spontaneous activity. In Group B units presynaptic volleys reset the spontaneous rhythm of some units and in other units synaptically evoked spikes were interpolated within the spontaneous rhythm without resetting the rhythms. In a few units it was possible to initiate ongoing spontaneous activity by direct stimulation of the impaled unit. Spontaneously active units demonstrated the property of enhancement when driven by repetitive direct stimulation. It is concluded that endogenous pacemaker activity is responsible for much of the ongoing regular spontaneous rhythms of the crayfish central neurons and that interaction of evoked responses with endogenous pacemaker sites is responsible for the observed results.

*This study was done in collaboration with Dr. Donald Kennedy, Department of Biological Sciences, Stanford University.

BIONICS AND EXPERIMENTAL EPIDEMIOLOGY

J. H. Whitlock

Cornell University, Ithaca, New York

The organizers of this conference invited papers that dealt with biological systems which might contain models of interest to engineers and mathematicians. It is the purpose of the present report to bring to your attention a case where the biological model is sufficiently simple that ordinary biostatistics can separate the error component from main effects, but where the essential complexity is such that the best available description comes from probability models applied to engineering.

It has been apparent to many biologists that within those self-organizing living systems which create natural fields of study (the cells, the tissues, the organs, and so forth, right up to the community and the ecosystem), the machinery which creates and maintains each natural field may be sufficiently homologous that we may some day be able to characterize it mathematically. Ecologists have been circling this problem for some time. The most lucid biological definition is in Odum's textbook of ecology (Odum and Odum, 1959). This is essentially the phenomenon that Quastler (1956) refers to as unitization. While at the present time unitization is purely empirical, it is important to consider because its existence means that the appropriate field of study of biological prototypes has to be sought experimentally. Living systems may be considered as levels of organization equivalent to Odum's (cells, tissues, organs, . . . , communities, ecosystem, biosphere) and each of these may be subdivided into sublevels. Consider that we dub an ordered set of levels A, B, C, D, . . ., N. A is characterized by certain interactions (a_1, a_2, a_3, . . . , a_n), B by certain interactions (b_1, b_2, b_3, . . . , b_n), and so forth, and that interactions characteristic of one set may appear in any higher set but not in a lower since their components are nonadditive even under a transformation. In general, an interaction which is distinctive in many sets is important, while one which is limited is relatively unimportant.

Unitization acts to amalgamate many of the a interactions in B, a few more in C, and thus relatively few reach N in a recognizable form. Tradition dictates that an a interaction should be studied at A level, but if it also appears in B, C, and D, tradition may be wrong. The homeostatic mechanisms that maintain each distinctive set or subset may clear away confusing extraneous reactions at the higher levels. If one is interested in a biologically significant interaction there is no a priori method of selecting the appropriate field of study. It has to be located empirically by examining the effect of various levels of organization on the variance components (Whitlock, 1961). One may not end up with homogeneous variance components, but one will, at least, see a useful effect. Another way of looking at this is that relatively big, slowly moving, natural biological systems may present apparently simple phenomena which may mirror the forms of underlying complex reactions of living structures. It might be fruitful, therefore, to test newer mathematical models on the apparently simpler but more massive biological reactions. If, as seems possible, biological unitization is fundamentally homologous at each level, it might be profitable to work from the top down.

As a parasitologist my special interest is the epidemiology of helminthic disease. I have the temerity to address you chiefly because a recent article by Drenick (1960) in "Science" on random processes in control and communications contained the best model of an experimental epidemic I have found to date. Time does not permit us to explore in detail the analogies to the Drenick article, but we believe some of them may be of interest to you.

The particular host-parasite relationship we have chosen to study is the occurrence of natural helminthic disease in sheep due to a blood-sucking nematode or worm dubbed Haemonchus contortus. The interrelations of the biomass of host and parasite are in terms of oscillating components, some of which are certainly, and many of which are likely or possibly, under genetic control of host or parasite. This host-parasite relationship is almost universal wherever sheep are found; furthermore, it unquestionably has a remote past. If one visualizes the individual host-parasite reaction as a point in multiply dimensional signal space, one can accept the idea of sets of such reactions; one can accept the idea of receding layers of similar past reactions in sets maintained by the total ecosystem channel, including the germ plasm of host and parasite. One of the most intriguing possibilities of the analogy is that the residual Borel field may contain an indication of the essential components (Drenick, 1960).

We started our study of experimental epidemiology of helminthic disease about 14 years ago simply because we could not reproduce in the laboratory the same disease which occurred in the field. At the current writing our best hypothesis for this failure is that we have not been able to duplicate in the laboratory the channel provided by the extrahost environment.

We have concrete evidence for not less than three different components in the ecosystem which influence the reaction. The first is the rate at which the hosts are infected; the second is the rate at which the parasites exsheath to the parasitic form, which is a function of salt and carbon dioxide concentrations in the rumen. This in turn depends on the diet. The parasite "recognizes" the correct host by a relatively simple probabilistic model based on a simple biochemical interaction. The third is an apparent hemopoietic (blood-forming) stimulus in the natural ecosystem which is not present in the laboratory.

The biological system is very simple. The parasite, which is a 1-in.-long worm, lives in the sheep stomach chiefly on blood of the host; so the essential lesion of the disease is anemia. It is a prodigious egg layer; therefore, the eggs in the feces assay the worm population. The eggs pass out with the feces, develop, and hatch out larvae which, after undergoing two molts, become infective. These infective larvae winter-kill; thus the whole system is started in motion as soon as we put the carrier ewes and lambs out to pasture in May. The first lambs become sick at the end of June or first of July and by the middle of August the vast proportion of the animals have either recovered or have become so seriously ill that they have had to be treated. We regard it as especially interesting that our epidemic goes off at the maximum rate predicted possible for the worm by Crofton (1957) on the basis of extending certain of Cole's (1954) general postulates about the outcome of restrictions of the life cycle.

In creating our epidemic all we do is turn 80 to 100 ewes and their offspring loose in a relatively natural environment which is about as optimum as we can make it for both host and parasite. Nature constructs a big black box for us, with a remarkably predictable outcome out of some remarkably unreliable elements.

When we open the big black box composing the whole ecosystem, we find there are ordered sets of smaller black boxes (the hosts) within the big one, and each smaller black box has in turn still smaller boxes within it (the worms). The order of the hosts is predetermined by the restrictions of the breeding pen. In addition, within the blood lines it is important to note the configuration: whether the smaller sets are in doublets or triplets, that is, whether each ewe has twins or only a single. These units are not independent. Thus, twins may react differently from singles (Whitlock, 1951). Furthermore, the lamb's response is influenced by the presence of the ewe.

We can, however, do quite a bit of tinkering within the big box without affecting the output in an appreciable fashion. We can both add and subtract elements. As a matter of fact, Crofton (1958) has submitted data to indicate that even if the worm population is cleaned out of the hosts by treatment one merely shifts the time scale but not the ultimate outcome.

The problem of exploring the relevance of control and communications theory to experimental epidemiology is not easily solved. The first steps consist in amassing sufficient data to separate random effects from main components by orthodox techniques. We have done fairly well with this since we can run about 100 adults and lambs in a single year.

As a parasitologist, most of my experience has been with disturbed host homeostatic systems—the result of disease, and disturbed parasite homeostatic systems—the result of treatment. It is remarkable how many cases we have found over the years where the means and variances of disease and treatment processes are grossly related. Furthermore, those cases which we have examined more closely have often shown evidence of some type of genetic mechanism.

If one is interested in measuring a signal from a disturbed system, it is obvious that the best measurement of the disturbance is the deviation of the individual components in the disturbed from the undisturbed state.

The total mass of the host itself shifts under challenge from a parasitic disease. The disease with which we work is easily cured, so the data presented in Fig. 1 are the deviations of rates of gain observed under disease challenge from the expected, predicted from rate of gain before illness and after the disease was cured. Each histogram represents the reaction of the progeny of the listed ram.

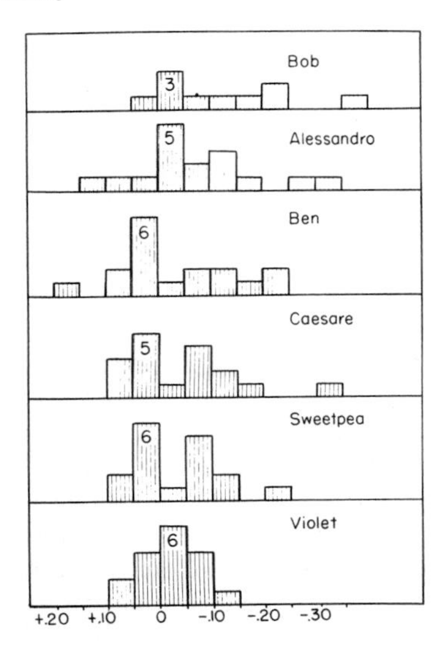

Fig. 1. Deviations of rates of gain during illness from predictions based on normal for each animal. Histogram is of progeny of each listed ram. An example of variance being more sensitive than mean as a measure of effect. From Whitlock (1955).

The ram dubbed Violet produced progeny which demonstrated a minimum reaction on all scales. Several of the other rams produced progeny which not only become seriously ill on the anemia scale but during the period of illnesses gained more rapidly than one could reasonably predict from their performance in the nondiseased state. This is a nice example of abnormal variance. It is likely that this reaction has a genetic background, possible that it is influenced by heterosis, and there is a chance that it is an overshoot. The analogy of this reaction to various reports of bimodal distribution of response to radiation exposure (Yockey, 1956a) is thought-provoking. Since these gross shifts in host weight are several steps removed from the primary disease problem, our biological model is probably not a good one for the study of this overcompensation reaction. Furthermore, adequate hardware is not available.

On the other hand, the hematocrit (packed erythrocyte volume) and worm-egg counting data are sufficiently involved in the primary reactions of the disease that they provide an excellent lever to take it apart.

Since the time scale of the output of the ecosystem black box is very consistent, we initially expected that the time scale of the measurements of the host anemia would be similar. This was not the case.

When we initially plotted the net hematocrit loss against the square root of the fecal egg count we got a funnel-shaped distribution along a 1-for-1 regression line (Fig. 2). This corrected after a fashion with a log transformation for co-

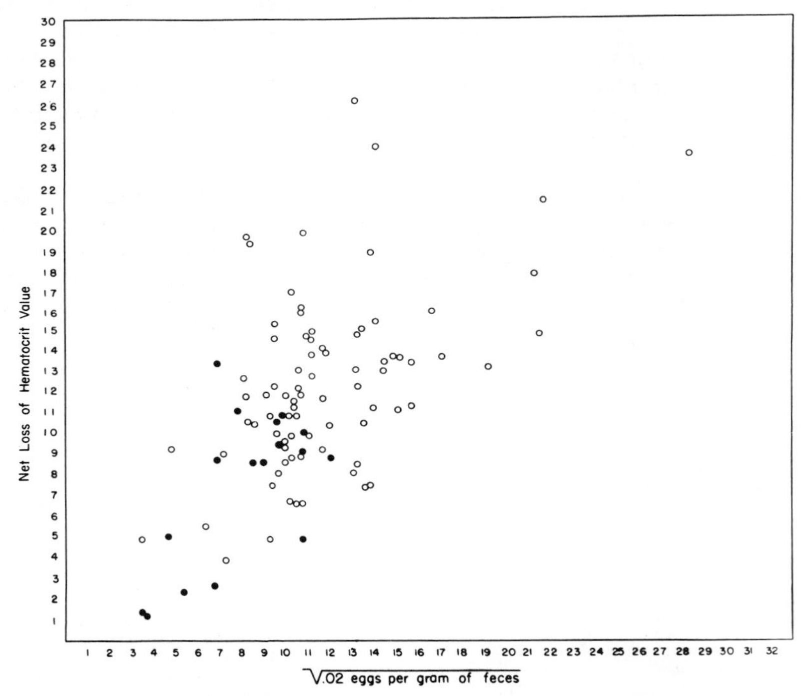

Fig. 2. ● = Violet progeny, ○ = progeny of other rams. From Whitlock (1955).

variance analysis (Fig. 3), but fortunately we did not stop there since the log transformation did not divide the sample space equally. We ultimately discovered that: (1) the hematocrit values oscillated; (2) the oscillations were not in phase; and (3) the amplitude of the hematocrits was under genetic control.

When we used the best estimate of hematocrit peak (HP) instead of the hematocrit at a single time as a base to measure the anemia, we cut off the lower part of the funnel and essentially created an empty set below two standard deviations under the 1-for-1 regression line.

Furthermore, it became quite apparent that the fecal egg counts were becoming more uniform as we bred for high and low counts. Other workers (Northam and Rocha, 1958) demonstrated that in a radically different helminthic infection, highly inbred chickens carried Poisson distributions of parasites, but

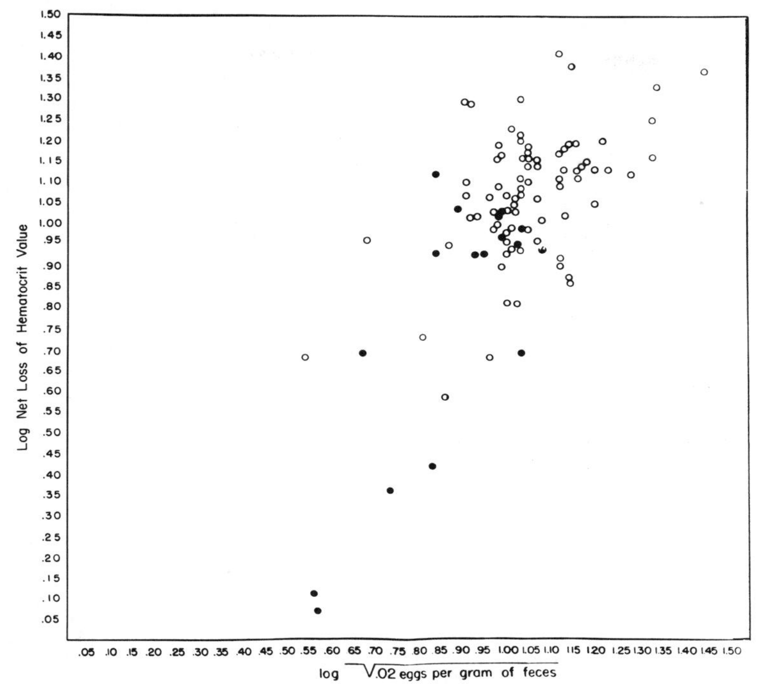

Fig. 3. Note relative increase in size of sample space occupied by Violet data. From Whitlock (1955).

miscellaneous strains of chickens carried negative binomial distributions of the same worm. For reasons which we have discussed elsewhere (Whitlock, 1961) this seems to fit our worm population problem. However, the point of this is that here is the third case of genetically mediated alteration of a variance as a real effect with relatively minor shifts in mean values.

Figure 4 represents data from Violet offspring superimposed on a standard grid to illustrate the formula $HL = V \pm 5$.* Figure 5 illustrates the offspring of another ram, 57-55, to demonstrate the existence of a reaction characterized by a higher position in the grid channel. The × represents lambs that had to be

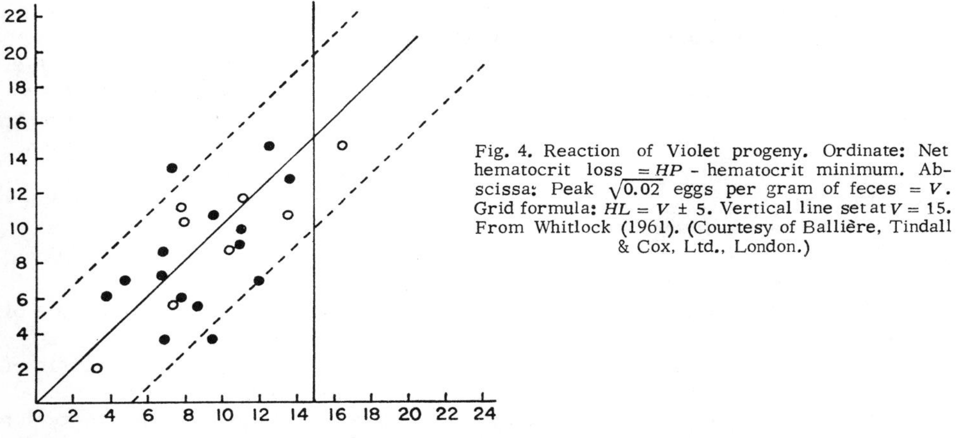

Fig. 4. Reaction of Violet progeny. Ordinate: Net hematocrit loss $= HP$ - hematocrit minimum. Abscissa: Peak $\sqrt{0.02}$ eggs per gram of feces $= V$. Grid formula: $HL = V \pm 5$. Vertical line set at $V = 15$. From Whitlock (1961). (Courtesy of Ballière, Tindall & Cox, Ltd., London.)

*Where hematocrit loss $= HL = HP$ - hematocrit minimum and $V = \sqrt{0.02}$ eggs per gram of feces.

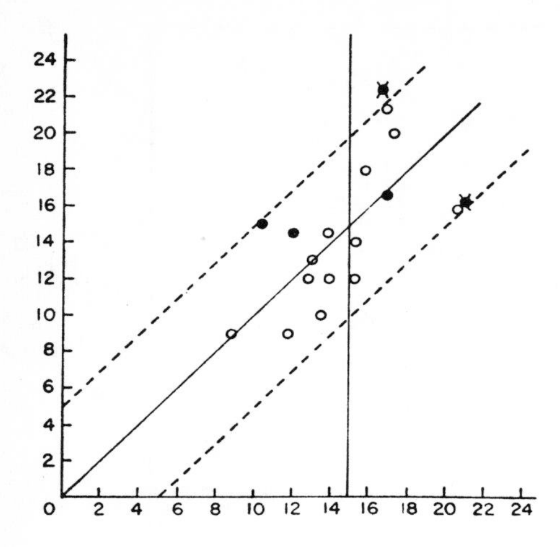

Fig. 5. Reaction of progeny of 57-55. ● = 1958 offspring, ○ = 1959 offspring. Ordinate: = *HL* = *HP* - hematocrit minimum. Abscissa: = $V = \sqrt{0.02}$ eggs per gram of feces. × = Treated animals. From Whitlock (1961). (Courtesy of Ballière, Tindall & Cox, Ltd., London.)

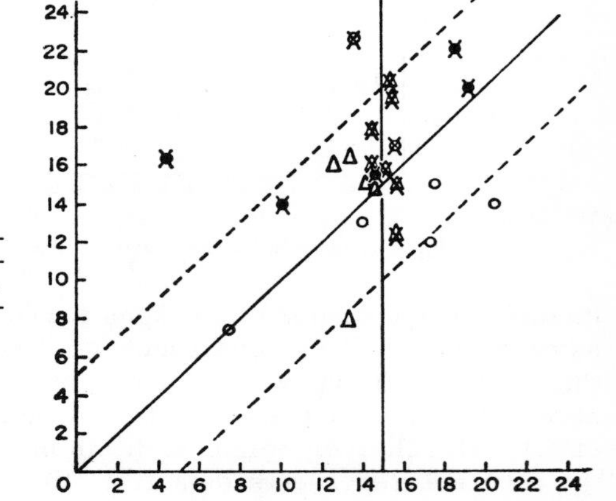

Fig. 6. Reaction of progeny of 615. Δ = 1957 offspring, ● = 1958 offspring, ○ = 1959 offspring. Ordinate = *HL*, Abscissa = *V*. × = treated animals. From Whitlock (1961). (Courtesy of Ballière, Tindall & Cox, Ltd., London.)

treated to save their lives. Figure 6 represents the offspring of ram 615. There is little difference in reaction between 57-55 and 615, but the assembly of × indicates that the progeny of the latter got into serious straits during the epidemic.

Figure 7 represents the regression of ewe *HP* on lamb *HP* for the progeny of the two rams. Obviously the "erythrostat" setting is so low in the 615 progeny that they succumb to a challenge that the 57-55 progeny can successfully manage.

The analysis is clear, reasonable, and since we can produce different erythrostat settings in the breeding pen, we have a new lever to determine their mechanism. What, then, is the problem? In the first place, most medical people would say the parasite eggs are a direct function of the cause of the disease, so this is the independent variable. The ecologist would say that the *HL* was a function of input and *V* a function of output and reverse the two.

As a parasitologist I think they are both right, with a better than even chance that the two variables are connected by feedback loops.

Orthodox statistical procedures are sufficiently powerful that the role of chance in these data can be reasonably assayed. However, it is not a very satisfying intellectual exercise to think in terms of an additive model (e.g., analysis of variance and covariance) when the data violate the assumptions of that model.

Earlier in this paper we reported that we were able to develop an empty set once we caught on to the fact that it was partially filled in our older data by the

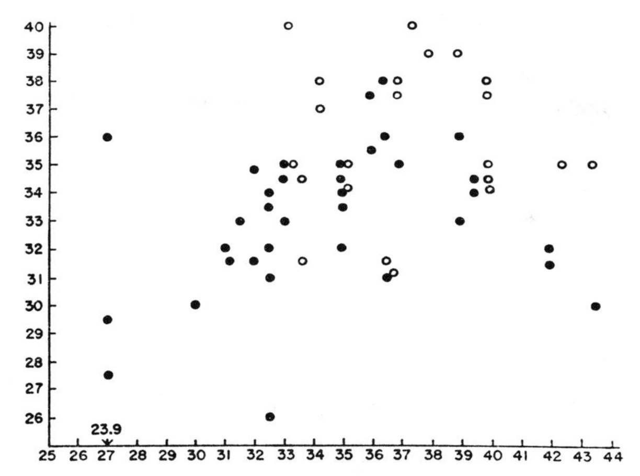

Fig. 7. Scatter diagram of ewe peak hematocrits (abscissa) vs. lamb peak hematocrits (ordinate) for offspring of 615 (•) and 57-55 (∘). From Whitlock (1961). (Courtesy of Ballière, Tindall & Cox, Ltd., London.)

error associated with sectioning the process at an instant of time. Another way of looking at the development of the empty set was an extension of the principle that at the level of organization that we are studying, association of means and variances (beyond what can be taken care of by a transformation) is often a sign of a genetic mechanism. This seems to be equally true of the signals more than two standard deviations above the 1-for-1 regression line.

First consider the case of the progeny of 602. 602 was an inbred son of Violet. He also produced a disproportionate number of runt offspring. If we display these reactions (Fig. 8) on the standard grid, it is easily seen that the normal and

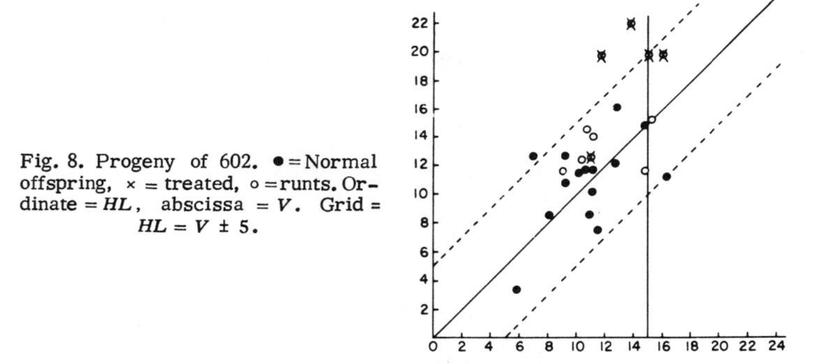

Fig. 8. Progeny of 602. • = Normal offspring, × = treated, ∘ = runts. Ordinate = *HL*, abscissa = *V*. Grid = $HL = V \pm 5$.

stunted offspring of this ram differed significantly in their reactions. Biologically we can say that there is a disproportionate degree of anemia per unit of parasite biomass in the runt lambs.

The progeny of 57-22 gave us the biggest shock (Fig. 9). We had selected him to produce progeny with a minimum disease reaction. There are no stunted offspring on this grid. Still we observe a disproportionate degree of anemia per unit of parasite biomass. It might be instructive to look at the progeny of 57-22 compared with that of two sons each selected from the extremes of the distribution and bred to ewes probably in a similar set.

Suppose we abandon the grid with its assumptions of causality and regression at this point and think in terms of ellipses of concentration (Cramer, 1946). If we forget between-year variance components for a minute and superimpose the

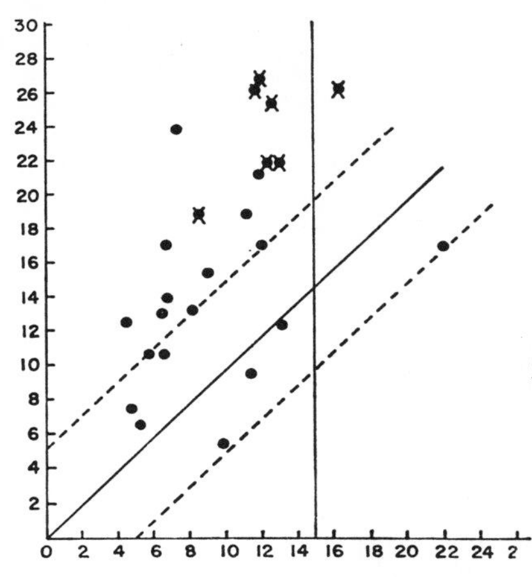

Fig. 9. Progeny of 57-22. Ordinate = *HL*, abscissa = *V*. × = Treated. Grid = *HL* = *V* ± 5. From Whitlock (1961). (Courtesy of Baillière, Tindall & Cox, Ltd., London.)

58-91 and 58-37 ellipses on the 57-22 ellipse (Fig. 10), the suggestion is strong that we are sectioning a signal space in another dimension which is fundamentally much like that of the histograms of deviations from expected weight gains due to disease. These are surely forms of Drenick's lumpy probability blanket.

At this juncture I would emphasize that we are not convinced that the ellipse of concentration is the ultimate answer to definition of a set of continuous variables, but it seems reasonable. On the basis of our current analysis, it looks as though we divide up the sample space nicely and relatively evenly by the scale of parameters on the old grid. Relative heterozygosis is signaled by enlargement of the ellipse, relative homozygosis by a contraction down to a segment of the heterozygous ellipse. The idea of the total signal space being an expression

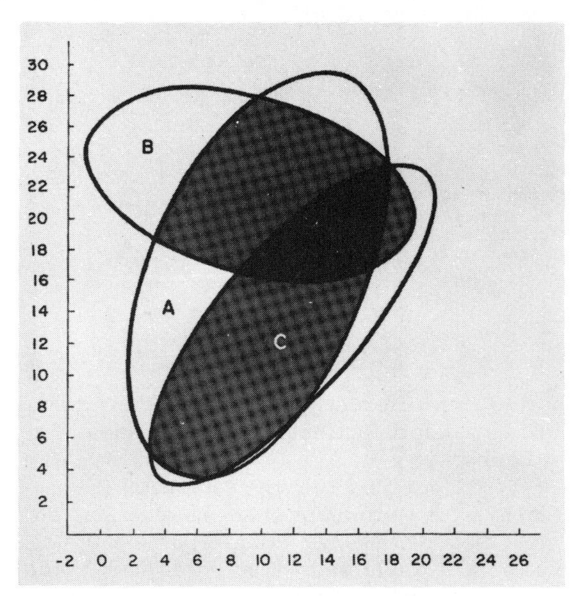

Fig. 10. Ellipses of concentration for progeny of 57-22 (A) and sons, 58-91 (B), and 58-37 (C) where each son was selected from the extremes of A and bred to ewes likely to be in a similar set. Between-year variance components (although important) are ignored in this comparison. Ordinate = *HL*, abscissa = *V*.

of heterozygosis with relative homozygosis providing sub- and sub-subsets is an intellectually satisfying picture under stipulations of circular causality. Assuming that the ellipses of concentration for relative homozygosis are an expression of noise, the peculiar fact is that the pattern of the points within some of the sets may be a log distribution.

This is comparable to the 93% ceiling placed on mouse genetic resistance to salmonellosis as reported by Gowen (1954). Yockey (1956b) uses this as an illustration of noise in a genetic channel. One of the fascinating asides is that this skewed distribution may also be a function of genetic heterogeneity since Schneider (1956) has demonstrated that genetic resistance to mouse salmonellosis will only appear if due provision has been made for genetic heterogeneity of the pathogen.

Finally, it seems important to emphasize that the genetic effects are not the only ones in the epidemic. Within the ecosystem black box, between-year variance components are easily found, and important environmental effects are easily demonstrated experimentally. However, the genetic effects seem closest to the bionics field because one is examining inputs and outputs with a minimum of manipulation of the machine.

In summarizing this talk, my first point is that if a unifying mathematical theory for all systems in biology is possible, it needs to include the reactions of natural disease within an ecosystem. Such a theory must include circular causality relation between means and variances as a measure of effect, and multidimensional multimodal sample spaces. In a search for biological prototypes one should consider that slowly moving, massive biological systems may display certain types of energy transformations in a simpler, more accessible form than can be found in the faster systems.

My second point is that we started out to determine why some animals died and some recovered from a natural epidemic of disease. When we assembled the (as we thought) minimum components we got nowhere. When we allowed the disease to reproduce itself naturally, we uncovered a whole spectrum of important reactions which are essentially interactions extending up from considerably lower levels of organization. If there is a model in this for the electrical engineer, it is confirmation that the most effectively analyzed system may not be the simplest system. Our guess is that the natural epidemic provided additional and different channels and feedback loops as well as replicate assemblies of the components. Since the engineer cannot go to nature to assemble his components, I would guess, if bionics is a valid field, that he might watch the effects of assembly at macrolevels on the variance components to find the appropriate field of study for the phenomena of interest.

My third point is that many biologists using statistics think in terms of relatively constant variances and shifts of means as the only valid model. I would present the idea that there exist intriguing cases where the variance shifts excessively without much shift in mean as a mark of a real effect. I have a hunch that at least some of these are really cases where the range is stable, at least in time, and the modes shift.

My final point is that redefinition of the problems of experimental epidemiology in terms analogous to those relevant to electrical engineering gives the first probability models that seem geometrically related to the biological problem. The epidemiologist is really interested in sets and predictions made from the sets. While information theory has been applied to mortality data, these are essentially all-or-none reactions. We presently offer a way of getting epidemiological data involving continuous variables into a form where they seem to be relevant to information theory.

The author wishes to acknowledge the support given for these researches by the Division of Biological and Medical Sciences of the National Science Foundation (G-18757 Disease Within An Ecosystem) and the Division of General Medical Sciences of the National Institutes of Health (RG 5900 Biometry of Disease). He is further indebted to Professors Walter Federer and Charles R. Henderson for statistical advice, and is especially indebted to Prof. D. A. Robson for the suggestion of the ellipse of concentration as a transformation.

REFERENCES

Cole, L.C. 1954. The population consequences of life history phenomena. Quart. Rev. Biol. 29, 103-137.

Cramer, Harold. 1946. Mathematical methods of statistics. Princeton Univ. Press.

Crofton, H.D. 1957. Nematode parasite populations in sheep on lowland farms. III. The seasonal incidence of species. Parasitology 47, 304-318.

Crofton, H.D. 1958. Nematode parasite populations in sheep on lowland farms. IV. The effects of anti-helminthic treatment. Parasitology 48, 235-242.

Drenick, R.F. 1960. Random processes in control and communication. Science 132, 865-870.

Gowen, J.W. 1954. Significance and utilization of animal individuality in disease research. J. Nat. Cancer Inst. 15, 555-570.

Northam, J.I. and Rocha, U.F. 1958. On the statistical analysis of worm counts in chickens. Exp. Parasitol. 7, 428-438.

Odum, E.P. and Odum, H.T. 1959. Fundamentals of ecology. 2nd ed. W.B. Saunders Co., Philadelphia.

Quastler, Henry. 1956. A primer on information theory. Symposium on information theory in biology. Pergamon Press, N.Y.

Schneider, H.A. 1956. Nutritional and genetic factors in natural resistance of mice to Salmonella infections. Ann. N.Y. Acad. Sci. 66, 337-347.

Whitlock, John H. 1951. The relationship of the available natural milk supply to the production of the trichostrongylidoses in sheep. Cornell Vet. 41, 299-311.

Whitlock, John H. 1955. The evaluation of pathological growth and parasitic disease. Cornell Vet. 45, 411-422.

Whitlock, John H. 1961. Parasitology, ecology and biometry. Brit. Vet. J. 117, 337-348.

Yockey, H.P. 1956a. Aging and radiation damage. Symposium on information theory in biology. Pergamon Press, N.Y.

Yockey, H.P. 1956b. Some introductory ideas concerning the application of information theory in biology. Symposium on information theory in biology. Pergamon Press, N.Y.

THE DEVELOPMENT OF THE EASTERN BLUEBIRD'S VOCAL REPERTOIRE

J. M. Hartshorne

Laboratory of Ornithology, Cornell University
Ithaca, New York

ABSTRACT

The experimental bluebirds (Siala sialis) used in this study were taken from the wild at three main stages of development: the egg stage, the nestling stage, and the post-nestling juvenile stage. Thus, birds constituting the egg-stage category were placed in sound isolation as eggs soon after they were laid in the wild, those constituting the nestling stage were isolated as nestlings, and those comprising the post-nestling juvenile stage were removed from the wild and isolated as juveniles at approximately two months of age. The development of vocalizations and resulting vocal repertoires of the birds in each category were then compared.

Isolation, as used here, means that a bird could not hear any other bird outside of its own group. To accomplish this, the birds were housed (usually in pairs consisting of male and female) in specially designed sound-isolation chambers, each consisting of a double-shelled structure with an animal cage at the interior, containing their own lighting and ventilation systems, microphone, speaker, and one-way-glass viewing window.

It was found that learning plays but a small part in the bluebird's acquisition of call notes; all of the common calls such as those of alarm, distress, location, etc., appeared in all age classes sampled. Primary song, on the other hand, appeared only in the oldest age class sampled; that is, only the post-nestling juveniles taken from the wild at about two months of age have produced these vocalizations.

PREY LOCATION IN OWLS

R. S. Payne

Department of Ornithology, Cornell University
Ithaca, New York

ABSTRACT

Barn owls (Tyto alba) can locate prey in total darkness, using hearing alone, with an accuracy of about one degree in both the vertical and horizontal planes. Differences between the behavior of barn owls flying at prey in complete darkness (analyzed from films taken under infrared illumination) and their behavior in the light are correlated with the problems they must face in acoustical orientation. Experiments with owls trained to strike a concealed loudspeaker show that they depend on frequencies of sound above 9000 cps. Measurements of sound pressure in the region of the owl's eardrum, made with a probe-tube microphone while moving a loudspeaker around the owl's head, reveal that the ear is highly directional for frequencies above 9000 cps. At such frequencies, regions of high and low sensitivity are directed along different paths for the two ears. These are correlated with the asymmetry of the barn owl's external ears. Movements of a flap of skin in front of the ear opening change the over-all pattern of sensitivity by redirecting regions of maximum and minimum sensitivity. A theory is presented to explain how a barn owl might localize the position of a sound source by moving its head and ear flaps until the intensity of all frequencies comprising a complex sound is maximal in both ears. When it hears this maximum frequency spectrum with both ears, it will automatically be facing the sound.

THE LOGIC OF THE LOCALIZATION OF FUNCTION IN THE CENTRAL NERVOUS SYSTEM

Richard L. Gregory

Psychological Laboratory, Downing Street
University of Cambridge, England

The attempt to discover the functions of various parts of the body, especially the clearly distinguishable organs, has a long history. Children very soon learn that their eyes are necessary for seeing, and a little later that their ears provide hearing, by performing such simple experiments as shutting the eyes and blocking the ears, and noting the effects. In the case of organs such as the heart, the matter is not quite so simple, which may account for some of the bizarre ideas associated with primitive medicine. At various times the heart, stomach, and liver have been regarded as the seat of the soul and of thought, while the brain was given the cryogenic function, by Aristotle, of cooling the blood.

Consider the child's discovery that the eye is necessary for vision. If he closes his eyes or finds a person without eyes, he discovers that vision is absent. He thus discovers that intact and open eyes are necessary, though not sufficient, for vision. They are not sufficient, for it is also necessary for the individual at least to be living and to have a partly functional brain. We thus think of the eye as an organ of sight. Consider the various parts of the eye—the cornea, lens, iris, retina, the internal humors, and the network of interconnected nerve cells placed oddly in front of the retina. How do we discover the function of these parts? We might try many methods; in particular, we might remove a part at a time and find the effect upon vision, or we might compare the eye with other systems, such as cameras, which seem similar and whose function we already understand. Both these methods are used in the study of organisms and they both have their uses and dangers. The dangers of analogical models are rather obvious, the principal danger being that of becoming enchanted with a too-beautiful model. The dangers in using ablation techniques to discover the function of parts are less obvious, but very real. It is my belief that the experience of engineers could be put to better use by neurologists who hope to discover the function of parts of the nervous system by techniques of stimulation and ablation.

When a part is removed from any interrelated device, very odd things may happen. Consider removing a spark plug from a car engine; we get vibration, spitting, coughing, and loss of power. Now if a neurologist removes part of the brain he may get loss of motor control, or memory, or some defects in vision or hearing. He may get changes in personality, or in motor control—a host of possible changes may take place. He then tends to say that the *function of a part of the brain is shown by a corresponding loss in behavior when that part is removed.* But how does this work out for our test case of the spark plug removed from an engine? Is the function of the plug to suppress or inhibit vibration, spitting, and coughing? Did the plug contain part of the power of the engine? This may sound silly, but it is very much the way areas of the brain have from time to time been described and imagined through ablation studies, and this is hardly surprising, for in the absence of a working model, what other type of description is available?

Suppose we did not have any idea of how a car engine works: how could we assign a function to a part, such as a plug, except by noting the changes which take place when it is removed? As soon as we know something about engines we can say that its function is, e.g., to ignite the mixture which produces power by releasing gas at high pressure. We can also say why the bizarre symptoms arose upon its removal; coughing and spitting occurred because the unburned mixture reached the hot exhaust manifold, for example.

To engineers, a wealth of such examples will occur in electronic systems. Remove a part, or bundle of parts, from a television set; you may get flashes of light, a horizontal line across the screen, screams, a puff of smoke, or an acrid smell, "death." To the engineer each of these is explicable, and given the symptom he may spot the cause at a glance. If, however, he does not know how the system is organized he is in a very different position, and identifying the cause of a fault becomes extremely difficult.

The neurologist is in a worse case than the engineer localizing a fault in the absence of detailed knowledge of how the system works, for the neurologist is trying to discover how it *works* by the results of ablation. Now it is fair to ask: would it be possible to discover the manner of working of a comparatively simple system, such as an engine or a television set, using the neurologist's techniques and manner of argument? What would happen if a group of non-engineer neurologists were given a chassis and asked to discover its manner of working by pulling bits out and noting the effects upon the output? This would be an interesting experiment. I would think that their only hope would be to use the results to test between possible models of how it might work. If they ascribed a function to each part by the output changes resulting from removal or stimulation, they could become extremely confused.

Consider removing the oscillator valve or coil from a heterodyne receiver; the results might be various kinds of whistles, but the output of this stage never reaches the output of the set at all, and so could not be observed directly, but would have to be inferred from a model involving the idea of producing an intermediate frequency by beating the carrier with a local oscillator. This is a sophisticated idea, and would have to be recognized or discovered by the investigators of this system if an appropriate function were to be assigned to the parts. It might be very useful to know what happens when parts become damaged or are removed, either for fault finding or brain surgery, but to ascribe functions to parts without knowing what functions are involved in the system is strictly impossible, and the attempt can lead to misleading language. This is not to say that ablation studies could not give theoretically important results, but it does indicate that the results should be described with great caution, and not intepreted as indicating function except in terms of some explicitly described model.

The analogy with removing parts of devices suggests, however, that some things could be determined with reasonable confidence for the brain in the absence of a model. It is not difficult to discover by "ablation" which parts of a television receiver are responsible for the sound and which for the vision, though there may be difficulties if, say, a power pack or a radio-frequency amplifier is shared. In general, where there are parallel independent systems, ablation techniques should work well. Consider a piano; each string could be removed and a single note would be lost in the output corresponding to each string. A pipe organ is not quite so simple; a derangement of the air supply might affect only the low notes, which require more air, and we might be badly misled if we ascribed functions to parts removed by noting changes in the output. In general, the input and output terminals and channels of a system can be identified without much risk of error, being parallel systems. The trouble occurs with systems in which the parts interact. In such systems any disturbance produces a different system, the parts taking on new roles. If a component is removed from a circuit, the other components will, in general, function differently. If the bias is changed on a valve, this stage may no longer amplify, but may oscillate or produce high-energy harmonics. We then have a different circuit with new properties which can be explained only by knowing the parameters and sufficient general principles.

If part of the brain is removed and the patient loses his anxieties, or his speech, or the ability to make sensible decisions, what can we infer as to the function of the part lost? Can we say, as the phrenologists said, that the various abilities and characteristics of the individual are to be found located in specific parts of the brain? An elementary knowledge of engineering would suggest that this is an inappropriate way of looking at the matter. The results can be understood only by knowing what the new circuit is like. In general, a system which has been designed—either by man or by selection—is likely to be reasonably efficient, and should be easier to understand than a mutilated or arbitrarily designed system.

It is found that large amounts of brain may be lost with very little change in output, at any rate until great demands are made. This is just what would be expected of a system involving a lot of stabilizing feedback. If parts are removed from a servo-stabilized system, the rest of the system will tend to compensate for the changes just as though these were in the environment. To an engineer, K. S. Lashley's principles (Lashley, 1929, 1950) of Mass Action and Equipotentiality may look unnecessary. His important results suggest that the brain is rich in stabilizing loops, and this is a discovery based on ablation studies. The point is not that ablation is of no theoretical interest, but rather that the results should be interpreted according to what should happen when recognized parts of a similar system are removed. This involves the neurologist in bionic ways of thinking.

REFERENCES

Gregory, R. L. 1959. Models and localisation of function in the central nervous system. In: Mechanisation of thought processes. N.P.L. Symposium 10, H. M. Stationery Office, London.

Gregory, R. L. 1961. The brain as an engineering problem. In: Thorpe, W. H. and Zangwill, O. L. (ed.), Current problems in animal behaviour. Cambridge Univ. Press, Cambridge.

Lashley, K. S. 1929. Brain mechanisms and intelligence. Chicago Univ. Press, Chicago.

Lashley, K. S. 1950. In search of the engram. In: Physiological mechanisms in animal behaviour. SEB Symposium IV, Cambridge Univ. Press, Cambridge.

ULTRASONIC INTERACTION OF BATS AND MOTHS*

K. D. Roeder

Tufts University, Medford, Massachusetts

Much of the work described in this paper has been recently reviewed and discussed (Roeder and Treat, 1961b). Details of the experiments and a review of the earlier literature on hearing in moths are to be found in earlier papers (Roeder and Treat, 1957, 1961a, 1961c). Therefore, only a short statement of the general objectives of the work and a summary of the findings will be presented here.

Attempts to describe animal behavior in terms of neural events must be carried on at many levels and with many animals. The nerve impulse is the primary neural event in the transmission of short-term information over any considerable distance within the body. The manner in which a single nerve cell encodes external changes into a time sequence of transmitted nerve impulses is fairly well known. Most of the behavior shown by higher animals involves tens or hundreds of thousands of nerve cells in both series and parallel arrays. This makes it difficult, or more often impossible, to relate the activity of individual nerve cells to the behavior of the neural system.

The obvious and naive approach to this problem is to choose for study an animal containing fewer nerve cells and, hence, fewer possible combinations. With practically all animals the situation is still too complex, but it can be further simplified if the simplest type of behavior of such an animal is selected.

In the present study the simple-minded animals are insects. One adult generation of insects rarely encounters the next, and in many cases the adult stage concerned with distribution and reproduction of the species survives for only a few days or hours. Under these circumstances behavior must be perfectly adapted to conditions the first time it is manifest, and individually acquired or learned behavior must play only a negligible and specialized role (e.g., as in food source indication and nest location in bees and wasps). Thus, most of the behavior patterns of insects are built into their nervous systems, and have been acquired during species evolution through the trial-and-error method of natural selection.

The simple behavior is escape from a predator. When a lion pounces there is no time for cerebration or computer programming. A few milliseconds distinguish the quick from the dead. The signaling and the neural machinery involved must be simple and unambiguous.

Bats and Moths

The predator and the prey are bats and moths. Griffin and his many students (Griffin, 1958) have shown that bats emit a series of ultrasonic cries or pulses and detect their echoes in a highly sophisticated manner. The ultrasonic pulses are complex, but for present purposes they may be said to consist of amplitude- and frequency-modulated sound bursts 1 to 15 msec long and containing frequencies ranging from 20 to 100 kcps. They are vocally generated in trains of from 10 to over 100 pulses/sec. The echoes from these cries enable bats to locate with great speed and precision objects ranging in size from the ground below to flying insects smaller than mosquitoes.

*The experiments described in this paper were made possible by a grant from the National Institutes of Health to Tufts University.

Bats feed on a wide range of insects which they capture on the wing. Most of their prey are apparently deaf, but as long as 100 years ago it was suspected that several families of night-flying moths could detect and avoid the onslaught of bats through a sense of hearing.

Knowledge of the structure of the moth ear, and the first scientific consideration of its function, was provided by the German zoologist, Eggers, working during the twenties. Soon after the Second World War several workers recorded reactions of moths to pure ultrasonic tones, and the first nerve impulses were registered from the tympanic nerve.

Dr. Asher Treat was among the first to demonstrate behavioral responses of moths to ultrasound (Treat, 1955). In 1955 we were able to register nerve impulses in the nerve fibers of the tympanic receptors during ultrasonic stimulation. The work described below is a result of continued collaboration between Treat and myself.

Before summarizing the experimental results, I wish to point out those aspects of the bat-moth interaction which seem to be most relevant and auspicious to the problem of relating neural events to behavior.

1. The behavioral situation is natural and not man-made or restricted to laboratory conditions. Attack and escape have obvious significance in the survival and evolution of both participants. We have tried to recognize this throughout our experiments by letting the participants set the stage wherever possible, perhaps often at the expense of quantitative precision.

2. The signal that couples the participants appears to be limited to the ultrasonic pulse sequence emitted by the bat. This is a relatively simple and reproducible physical event when compared with the complex Gestalten involved in many interactions between animals.

3. The channel that conveys the impulse-coded version of this signal to the central nervous system of the moth comprises only two nerve fibers from each ear, in comparison with the many thousands of nerve fibers in the auditory nerve of higher animals.

4. The evasive behavior released in the moth by this signal depends principally upon speed and unpredictability for its effectiveness in protecting the prey. This implies simple and unequivocal central connections with the effector mechanisms—a situation which should simplify the task of unraveling central nervous connections.

The Tympanic Nerve Response

In Noctuid moths each tympanic organ contains two acoustic receptor cells (A cells), and one sense cell (B cell) that probably functions as a proprioceptor (Treat and Roeder, 1959). The impulse discharge from the A cells, when stimulated by pure tones and by pulsed ultrasound, reveals the following characteristics:

1. The tympanic organ responds to sounds ranging from 3 to over 150 kcps.

2. The sensitivity is such that a natural bat cry is detected as an impulse discharge in the A nerve fibers when the bat is at a distance of more than 100 ft.

3. Sensory adaptation to a continuous pure tone is very rapid (50% decrease in impulse frequency in 0.1 sec), indicating that the ear is primarily a pulse detector.

4. There is no evidence that the ear can discriminate different sound frequencies.

The tympanic organ is especially adapted to discriminate small differences in sound intensity. There are at least four ways in which this is accomplished by the receptor mechanism. Ultrasonic pulses having gradual rise and fall times and increasing intensity have the following effects:

1. First one A cell responds and then the other when the intensity is about 20 db above the threshold of the first. This provides the ear with a two-step system.

2. Proportional increases in the spike frequency (up to about 1000 impulses per sec) occur in both A cells as the intensity is increased.

3. Both A cells may continue to discharge impulses for several milliseconds after the sound has ceased. This after-discharge is roughly proportional to the sound intensity.

4. There is a proportional decrease in the time interval between arrival of the sound pulse and the appearance of impulses in the A nerve fibers. The response time may vary with sound intensity up to 1.5 msec.

Tympanic Response to Bat Cries

Monaural recording of the A-fiber response in the presence of bats flying under natural conditions shows that the first three forms of intensity coding would provide the moth with information about the distance and approach of its predator.

Binaural recording from right and left tympanic organs under the same conditions gives a differential response which would provide the moth with a rough indication of the horizontal direction of the approaching predator relative to its own flight path.

Preliminary experiments show that the tympanic organ is directional, detecting a click at about twice the distance on the near side compared with the far side. It has also been established that the ear saturates (gives a maximal response) at sound intensities about 40 db above threshold. Hence the differential response between right and left would be present only between threshold intensity and 40 db above.

From this it can be estimated that if a bat is detected by a moth at a distance of 100 ft and subsequently approaches at 90° to the moth's course while making cries of constant intensity, the moth would continue to receive information on the bat's direction relative to its own flight path until the contestants were 15 to 20 ft apart. At shorter range the tympanic organs would saturate and the moth would cease to receive directional information. This estimate contains many assumptions and the figures must not be taken very seriously. Bats do not appear to react to the average-sized Noctuid at distances greater than 12 ft.

The Evasive Behavior of Moths

Even if the quantitative estimates in this conclusion are disregarded, the sensory data suggest that there are two ways in which a moth could react to an approaching bat. First, when the bat is still at some distance, the moth could turn and fly directly away from the bat's feeding area. Second, when the bat is at close quarters, the moth would be capable only of nondirectional evasive behavior.

The flight paths of moths flying under natural conditions in the field were photographed as continuous tracks against the night sky both before and after exposure to a train of simulated bat cries. The latter were generated on demand by means of a stationary multidirectional ultrasonic transmitter mounted 16 ft above the ground.

Moths turned away from the sound source when they were at some distance or the sound intensity was low. Flight on a relatively straight path was noted in an upward, lateral, or downward direction, depending upon the position of the moth relative to the sound source when the ultrasonic pulse train was initiated.

When the moths were close to the source, or when the intensity was high, a wide variety of nondirectional maneuvers was observed. These included a passive fall with folded wings, a power dive, an alternation of passive fall and power dive, sharp turns and loops followed by passive fall or power dive, a continuous series of tight turns, and other complex maneuvers. The reaction times of these nondirectional maneuvers ranged from 0.2 to 1.0 sec. They were accomplished by an increased or decreased wingbeat frequency, or by a complete cessation of wing movement. The difficulty experienced in classifying these nondirectional evasive movements is probably significant in the biological situation, since it may be expected to tax the predictive powers of the predatory bats as well as those of the experimenter.

The Ultrasonic Echoes Cast by Flying Moths

Another aspect of this interaction between prey and predator is the nature of the echo returning to the ears of a bat when it encounters a flying moth. There is some evidence (Griffin, 1958) that bats can discriminate flying insects from inert objects such as tossed pebbles. This could be due to detection by the bat of (a) the nonballistic flight path of the insect, (b) its wingbeat tone, or (c) fluctuations in the returning echo due to changes in the wing attitude of the prey.

Moths were mounted on a wire and allowed to fly while they were exposed to a sequence of ultrasonic pulses (60 to 100 kcps, 0.6 msec in duration). Echoes were detected by a Granath microphone. The moth was illuminated by a 10-μsec flash at the instant each sound pulse reached it. The echo (displayed on an oscilloscope) and the flight attitude of the moth were brought together by means of a prism and photographed on single frames.

The plane surface of the wing cast the greatest echo, which was 20 db or more above that returning from the body of the moth. During flight the wing assumes an attitude capable of casting an echo in the direction of the sound source for only a brief period during each wing cycle, and then only when the moth is flying at certain angles with respect to the sound path. When the moth is in horizontal flight with its axis at 90° to the sound path, the maximum echo occurs only when the wings are at the top of their stroke. The maximum echo is less frequent or entirely absent when the moth is in horizontal flight with its axis at other angles to the sound path. Other angles between the horizontal plane of the moth and the sound path have not been studied, but it is clear that this maximally fluctuating echo recurring at wingbeat frequency would be detected by the bat only during certain spatial relations between the flight paths of prey and predator.

From this it may be concluded that (1) an echo that fluctuates at wingbeat frequency could provide the bat with information about the nature of its prey, and (2) when both bat and moth are flying horizontally and at about the same altitude, the most disadvantageous maneuver for a moth is to cross the flight path of the bat at 90°. In this relation the maximum echo would occur and the moth could be detected by the bat at the greatest distance. This supports the evidence presented earlier that moths turn and fly directly away from a source of relatively faint ultrasonic pulses.

REFERENCES

Griffin, D.R. 1958. Listening in the dark. Yale Univ. Press.

Roeder, K.D. and Treat, A.E. 1957. Ultrasonic reception by the tympanic organ of Noctuid moths. J. Exp. Zool. 134, 127-158.

Roeder, K.D. and Treat, A.E. 1961a. The acoustic detection of bats by moths. Proc. XI Intern. Ent. Congr. (in press).

Roeder, K.D. and Treat, A.E. 1961b. The detection and evasion of bats by moths. Am. Scientist 49, 135-148.

Roeder, K.D. and Treat, A.E. 1961c. The detection of bat cries by moths. In: Rosenblith, W. (ed.), Sensory communication. MIT Technology Press, Cambridge.

Treat, A.E. 1955. The response to sound of certain Lepidoptera. Ann. Ent. Soc. Am. 48, 272-284.

Treat, A.E. and Roeder, K.D. 1959. A nervous element of unknown function in the tympanic organs of moths. J. Insect Physiol. 3, 262-270.

WHAT IS A SYNAPSE ?

V. Braitenberg and F. Lauria

Istituto di Fisica Teorica e Nucleare
Mostra d'Oltremare, Naples

ABSTRACT

Suppose we want to translate a nerve net into some sort of mathematical formalism. Suppose we recognize the neurons according to the classical histological definition, as the appropriate functional constituents (not portions of neurons or collections of neurons). We may record the states of some of them directly, using microelectrodes, or perhaps even control one while we observe another which is connected to it, thus testing the properties of individual synapses. But if (a) the number of incoming and outgoing fibers is of the order of 10^6 or 10^{10}, (b) every part of the input is relevant for every part of the output, as "Gestalt" implies, and (c) memory changes continually distort the pattern of the connections, then direct observation of significant events in central nerve nets, in terms of constellations of active neurons, will, for some time, be beyond our technical means.

However, we know that propositions about the histology must be somehow translatable into propositions about the function. The picture, neuron—axonal branching—endfeet—other neurons, suggests combinatorial schemes but leads to defeatism because of the sheer complexity of the histology analyzed this way. A more useful type of synapse which results in numerical coupling coefficients between any two neurons of the net can be obtained if trees of axonal and dendritic ramifications are replaced by plots of axonal and dendritic density, or even by regions of constant density whose intersection represents the amount of coupling. A concrete example (undifferentiated cerebral cortex of man) is given.

MODELING VISUAL ORGANS AND PERCEPTIONS

E. E. Loebner and T. Henneberger

RCA Laboratories, Princeton, New Jersey

ABSTRACT

A synthetic retina design, consisting of three layers of active parallel-processing optoelectronic elements which are coupled by two synaptic fields, has been described.* This system attempted to duplicate functionally the four-image feature-extracting processes found by Lettvin and coworkers in the frog retina.† Since then we have significantly expanded and improved the model. The new model is more general. It is based on majority logic, attempts to provide realistic receptive fields and provides for duplication of all the time dependences reported in a later paper by Maturana and coworkers.‡ We have also extrapolated image-processing functions to include those which might have biological counterparts in subcortical and cortical activity. A crude eight-stage model for visual pathways in the human brain has been worked out.

Furthermore, we have considered generalized Boolean neighborhood operations of several kinds. Among others we have studied arrays containing up to several dozen image elements. We have shown the existence of image transformations which break up the message space of all inputs into disjoint subsets called constellations. These are isomorphic with isolated clusters in flow graphs denoting changes of internal states of an image configuration produced by sequential transformations. The analogy between these manipulations and the image-processing manipulations in humans during classifying and categorizing responses will be discussed. An analogy between aural and visual perceptions will be developed.

*Loebner, E. E. 1960. WADD Symposium on Bionics (WADD TR 60-600). Dayton, Ohio, Sept., 1960.
†Lettvin, J., Maturana, H., McCulloch, W., and Pitts, W. 1940 (1959). Proc. IRE 47.
‡Maturana, H., Lettvin, J., McCulloch, W., and Pitts, W. 1960. J. Gen. Physiol. 43, 6, Part 2, 129.

THEORETICAL ANALYSIS OF MODELS FOR ENZYME SYNTHESIS

F. Heinmets

Quartermaster Research and Engineering Command
U.S. Army, Natick, Massachusetts

and

A. Herschman*

Department of Physics, Worcester Polytechnic Institute
Worcester, Massachusetts

Biological processes at the molecular level are extremely complex and descriptive analysis alone is completely inadequate for evaluation of the relationships between individual functional units. Therefore, it is essential that formalized relationships be established between the operational elements of the system and that the problem be solved in a quantitative manner. In order to facilitate the analysis, it is often useful to set up a functional model of the system. The validity of such models depends essentially on the available experimental data and the ingenuity of the model builder. Since the performance of a realistic model will be compared with that of the normal system, its success depends essentially on the soundness of the model. We assume, of course, that adequate mathematical procedures are used. In contrast, highly sophisticated mathematical treatment does not produce any significant results when applied to a poor model.

At the current level of information, the models representing biological processes are, of necessity, simplified and simulate the system in terms of some general parameters. This way, only the cross-behaviors of the system will be presented, but when more detailed experimental data become available, a more refined model system, leading to a more detailed description of the system, can be developed. Complex metabolic processes can be analyzed on such premises. In the current work we will consider the formation of enzymes on a model-system basis. Previous work in this area (Heinmets, 1960; Heinmets and Herschman, 1960, 1961a, 1961b) revealed that the conventional mathematical approach was not adequate for treatment of systems composed of an aggregate of operational parameters. Computer analysis seems to be suggested. However, in order to analyze complex biological processes, it is essential that methods should be developed for treatment of such systems. The purpose of this paper is to demonstrate the enzyme synthesis in systems where regulatory and feedback mechanisms are operative. In mathematical terms, the output of such a system is nonlinear and accurate solutions are unobtainable. These difficulties can be overcome by use of a suitable computer. An analysis will be carried out with the aid of an analog computer and models will be presented in sequence of increasing complexity. At the current phase, the main objective is to develop methods of treating the complex synthetic processes. In addition, it serves to demonstrate for the experimental biologist that metabolic schemes can be analyzed in terms of transient-state end products and intermediates.

It is our opinion that such a quantitative approach to synthetic and other cellular processes is necessary, since only by understanding of normal cellular processes can one gain insight into abnormal processes, such as malignancy

*Present address: Brookhaven National Laboratory, Long Island, New York.

and alteration of cellular characteristics during the aging of species, etc. Furthermore, the action of agents (drugs, antibiotics, antimetabolites, etc.) which interfere with the normal metabolic process and synthesis can be understood wholly when metabolic systems are presented in terms of quantitative relations and interactions. This, of course, is a prerequisite for rational therapy.

Scheme I-1 demonstrates the notation and the use of operational elements (in systems involving multiple elements, subscripts are used):

$$T + S \leftrightarrow (TS) \qquad \dot{T} = k_1 ST + \bar{k}_1 B$$

$$(TS) + P \rightarrow (TSP) \qquad \dot{B} = k_1 ST - \bar{k}_1 B - k_2 BP = k_3 C$$

$$(TSP) \rightarrow (TS) + E \qquad \dot{E} = k_3 C$$

where:

T = Template concentration
S = Inducer concentration
B = Specific template concentration (TS)
C = Complex concentration (TSP)
E = Enzyme concentration
P = Pool

This notation is used throughout the paper. When new symbols are added, they will be mentioned specifically. A systematic study of various schemes for synthesis will be carried out. Special emphasis will be placed on variations of various parameters and their effect on the end product of the system.

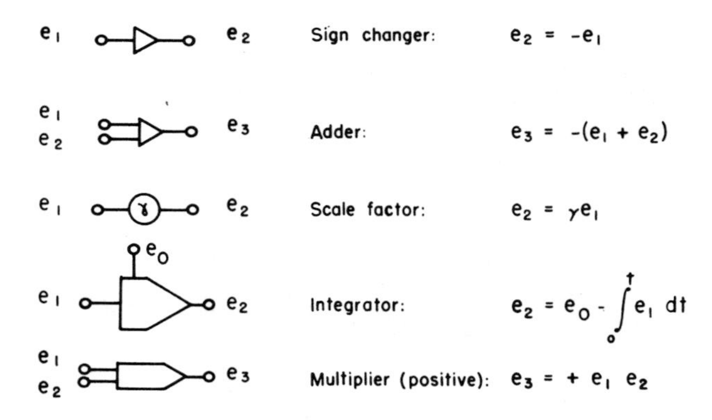

Fig. 1. Symbols for analog computer circuit. (From: Jackson, A. S. 1960. Analog computers. McGraw-Hill, New York.)

The first system considered was II-1 (see Fig. 2):

$$S_1 + E \rightarrow S_2 + E \qquad \dot{S}_1 = \dot{P} = O$$

$$T_1 + P \rightarrow T_1 + E \qquad \dot{S}_2 = k_1 S_1 E = k_1 S_2 T_1$$

$$S_2 + T_1 \rightarrow T_2 \qquad \dot{T}_1 = k_4 S_1 T_2 - k_3 S_2 T_1 = -\dot{T}_2$$

$$S_1 + T_2 \rightarrow T_1 \qquad \dot{E} = k_2 P T_1$$

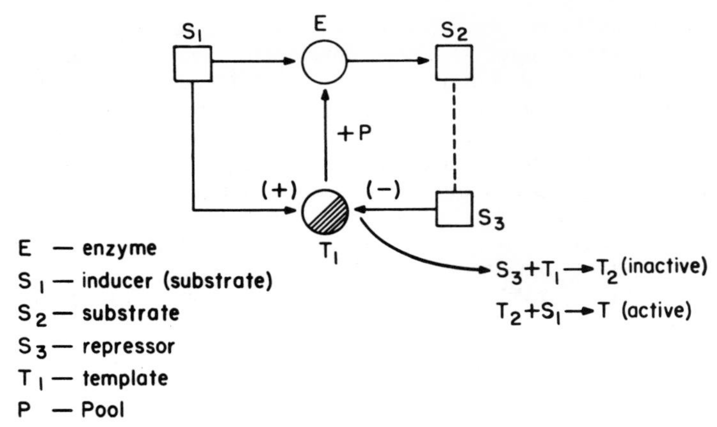

Fig. 2. Single-step enzyme synthesis with repression by the end product (S_2) on template level.

Since an obvious first integral is $T_1 + T_2 = T_0 =$ const, and one may choose the rate of the first reaction as a time unit, viz., assume $k_1S_1 = k_4S_1 = 1$, giving only the intermediate and final reaction times as parameters,

$$k_2P = \beta \quad \text{and} \quad k_3 = \gamma$$

one obtains the following simplified form of the equations,

$$\dot{T}_1 = T_0 - T_1 - \gamma S_2 T_1$$

$$\dot{S}_2 = E - \gamma S_2 T_1$$

$$\dot{E} = \beta T_1$$

which set may be readily coded for the computer as in Fig. 3. In the computer circuit, we have dropped the subscripts on T_1 and S_2, since in the final equations these are the only quantities of this form involved. This convention is also adhered to in the output curves shown in Figs. 4a and 4b.

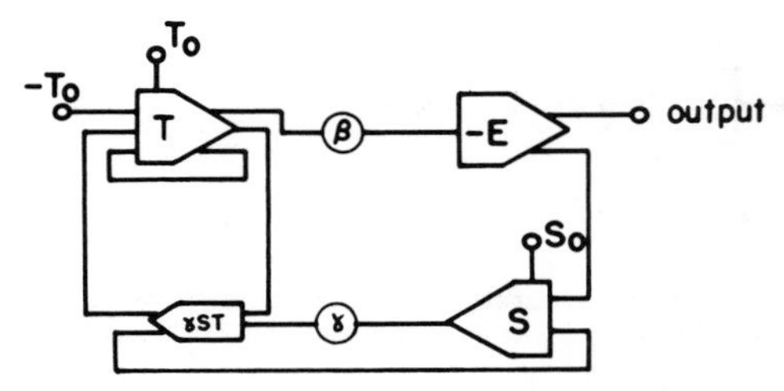

Fig. 3. Schematic computer diagram for system II-1 (see Fig. 1 for symbols).

In Fig. 4a, the machine computation for E is plotted for values of S_0 (the initial value of S_2) of 0, 4, 10, and 20 v. In this scheme T_0 was arbitrarily taken as 10 v and β was fixed at 0.1, whereas γ was taken as 1.0. In Fig. 4b, T is plotted for the same conditions. Also indicated on this plot, as dotted lines, are two representative S curves. We first note that since E is essentially the integral of T, the extreme fluctuations in T for small times give rise only to a slight displacement of the various E curves, one from another. What is more signif-

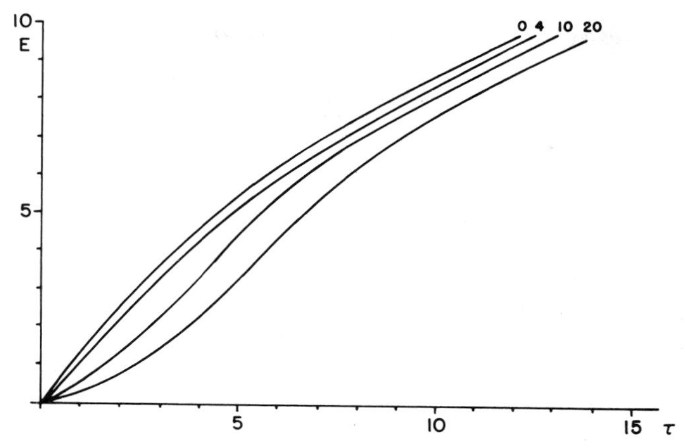

Fig. 4a. Enzyme curves for system II-1, for various values of S_0 as indicated.

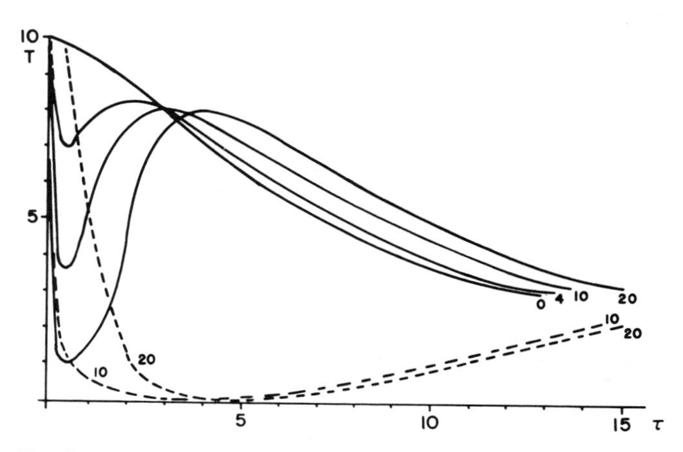

Fig. 4b. Template curves for system II-1, for various values of S_0 as indicated. The dotted curves give the inducer (S) for two representative values of S_0.

icant, however, is that the various T curves, which begin in such a widely different manner, all approach the same general form, except for a slight relative displacement. This, one of the most important properties of the nonlinear system, will show itself in all the future variations as well. Briefly, it can be stated as follows: even though the initial conditions play a large role in the initial behavior of the systems, ultimately the behavior becomes substantially independent of them, being a function, primarily, of the form of the equations. Mathematically this can be seen from the following formal integral of the equations

$$S = \exp\left(\frac{-\gamma E}{\beta}\right)\left[S_0 + \int_0^t E \exp\left(\frac{+\gamma E}{\beta}\right) dt\right]$$

Thus, since E is an apparently increasing function of the time, the first term in the brackets ultimately damps out to zero, leaving the asymptotic behavior independent of the initial condition in S_0.

Attempts to solve the equations by successive approximation, starting from an asymptotic series for this integral, are not wholly consistent since the series has almost no radius of convergence. For example, one may obtain the following formal series for S:

$$S = \frac{\beta E}{\gamma \dot{E}} - \frac{\beta^2 (E/\dot{E})}{\gamma^2 \dot{E}} + \cdots$$

so that

$$\gamma S T = E - \frac{\beta (E/\dot{E})}{\gamma} + \cdots$$

implying that S ultimately saturates, as does E (to the value T_0/β, in this case, about 100 v). The difficulty of this line of approach, however, is that the perturbation term in the series is not really small, and, in fact, diverges (the presence of a time derivative of a constant in the denominator).

The saturation properties in the solution become much more accentuated when intermediates are placed into the circuit. This becomes apparent in Scheme II-2, in which an additional S is placed in an intermediate position (see Fig. 5):

$S_1 + E \rightarrow S_2 + E \qquad \dot{S}_2 = k_1 S_1 E - k_2 S_2$

$S_2 \rightarrow S_3 \qquad \dot{S}_3 = k_2 S_2 - k_3 S_3 T_1$

$S_3 + T_1 \rightarrow T_2 \qquad \dot{T}_1 = k_4 S_1 T_2 - k_3 S_3 T_1 = -\dot{T}_2$

$S_1 + T_2 \rightarrow T_1 \qquad \dot{E} = k_5 P T_1$

$T_1 + P \rightarrow T_1 + E$

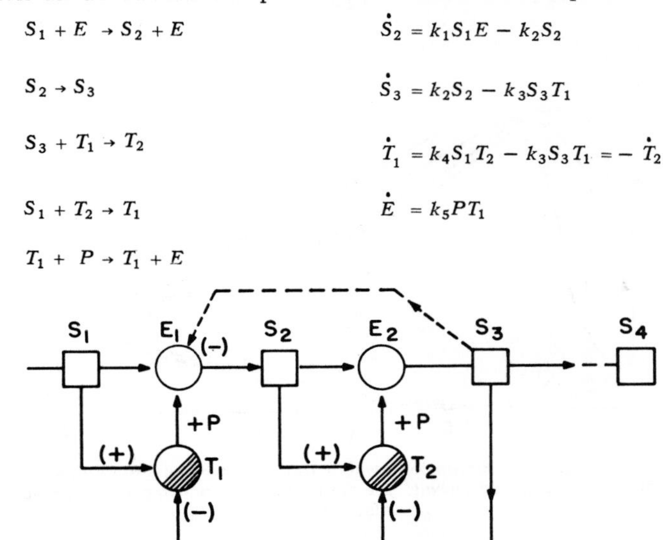

Fig. 5. Single-step enzyme synthesis with repression by the converted end product (S_3) on template level.

$S_3 + T_1 \rightarrow T_2$ (inactive)

$T_2 + S_1 \rightarrow T_1$ (active)

Again we choose as our time unit the time of the first process and set $k_1 S_1 = k_4 S_1 = 1$, taking for the other rate constants $k_2 = \alpha$, $k_5 P = \beta$, and $k_3 = \gamma$, so that with the first integral $T_1 + T_2 = T_0$, we have the simplified set

$$\dot{S}_2 = E - \alpha S_2$$

$$\dot{S}_3 = \alpha S_2 - \gamma S_3 T_1$$

$$\dot{T}_1 = T_0 - T_1 - \gamma S_3 T_1$$

$$\dot{E} = \beta T_1$$

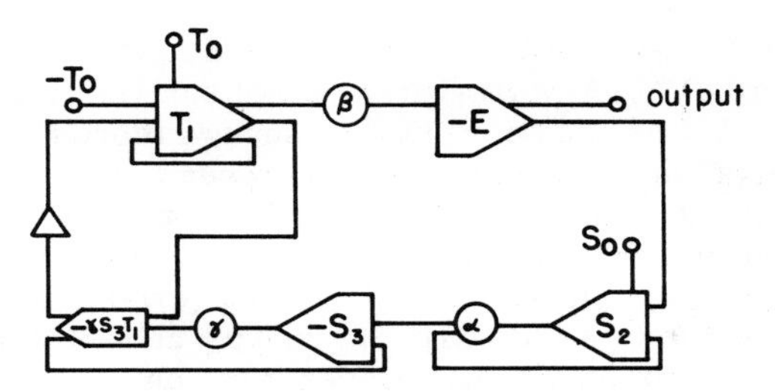

Fig. 6. Schematic computer circuit for system II-2.

The computer circuit for this set of equations is indicated in Fig. 6. Figure 7a gives the resultant value of E for the choice $\alpha = \gamma = 1.0$, $\beta = 0.1$, $T_0 = 10$, $S_0 = 0$, 5, 10, 16 (the initial value of S_2). Figure 7b gives T_1 for the same parameters, and S_3 and S_2 are given by Figs. 8a and 8b, respectively.

One readily sees that the presence of the additional intermediate step merely modifies the sharpness of the initial T_1 response and has little effect on the long-time behavior; however, in this case one does see a much more pronounced

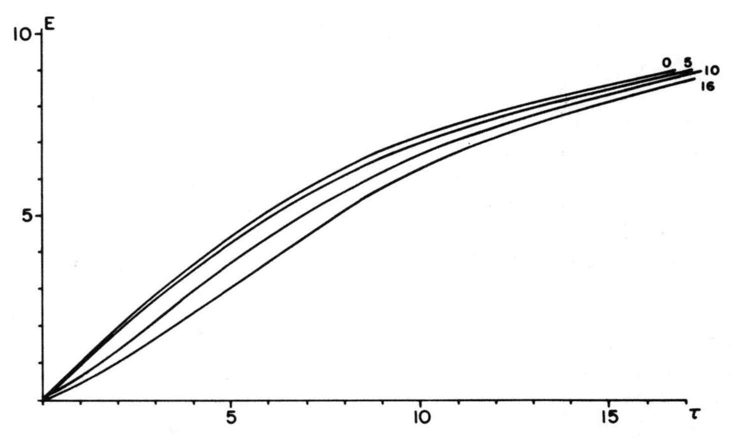

Fig. 7a. Enzyme curves for system II-2, for various S_0 values as indicated.

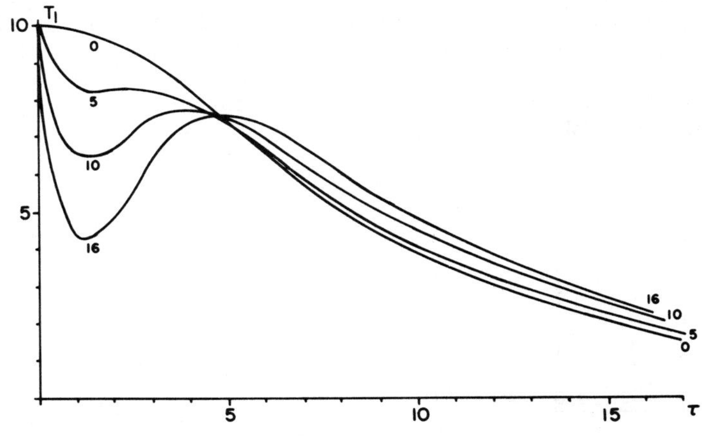

Fig. 7b. Template curves for system II-2, for various S_0 values as indicated.

saturation effect in E than in the first case considered. Both E and S_2 apparently saturate to the value T_0. A perturbation expansion similar to II-1 can also be made in this case, but would be on just as shaky grounds. Another conspicuous point of structure in these results is the sharpness of the focus of the T_1 and S_2 families of curves. In Scheme II-1, the diffuse region in which the T curves apparently crossed has given way, in II-2, to a very sharp crossing point at $t = 4.8$ sec and $T_1 = 7.5$ v. Also, the S_2 curves exhibit a similar structure at $t = 3.0$ sec and $S_2 = 1.9$ v, as do the S_3 curves at $t = 4.0$ sec, $S_3 = 0.3$ v. This "focusing" property is not an unusual property of nonlinear systems.

In the final version of this scheme, II-3, we make the final step in the enzyme synthesis nonsoluble, so that the amount of active template available, T_1, is steadily depleted by the production of enzyme. This scheme has the form

$$S_1 + E \rightarrow S_2 + E \qquad \dot{S}_2 = k_1 S_1 E - k_2 S_2$$

$$S_2 \rightarrow S_3 \qquad \dot{S}_3 = k_2 S_2 - k_3 S_3 T_1$$

$$S_3 + T_1 \rightarrow T_2 \qquad \dot{T}_1 = k_4 S_1 T_2 - k_3 S_1 T_1 - k_5 T_1 P$$

$$S_1 + T_2 \rightarrow T_1 \qquad \dot{T}_2 = k_3 S_3 T_1 - k_4 S_2 T_2$$

$$T_1 + P = E \qquad \dot{E} = k_5 T_1 P$$

And again we choose $k_1 \dot{S}_1 = k_4 S_1 = 1$ and define α, β, and γ as before. In this case, however, there are no simple first integrals, but the computer circuit is straightforward and will be found in Fig. 9. We expect the results of Scheme II-3 to be essentially the same as those for II-2, except for a tendency of T_1 to fall off to zero more rapidly and, therefore, for E to saturate more rapidly (since it is essentially the integral of T_1). This is borne out by Figs. 10a and 10b, which give the values of E and T_1, respectively, for the same parameters used in II-2. In Figs. 11a and 11b are plotted the values of S_3 and S_2, respectively, for the same conditions. Investigation of these curves shows that the same points are maintained, except that the crossover point in T_1 of II-2 has given way to a region declining in a manner similar to T_1 itself. We see that our qualitative conclusion, arrived at earlier, of the asymptotic weak dependence on parameters appears to be upheld in this case as well.

As a final investigation of this conclusion, we have obtained results for the case $S_0 = T_0 = 10$ v, in which α and γ were varied independently, keeping β fixed at 0.1. In Fig. 12a, we see that the effect on E is completely unimportant, i.e., the final output is virtually unaffected by the intermediate rate constants. We also see that the asymptotic values of T_1 (Fig. 12b) are also unaffected and that there are only some short-time fluctuations from the standard value. In the case

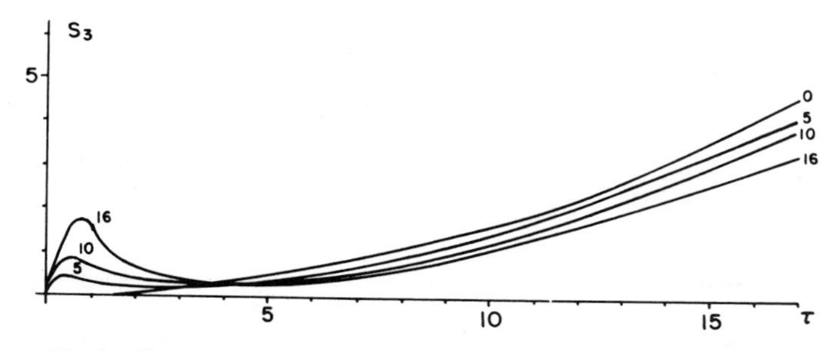

Fig. 8a. The inducer, S_3, in system II-2, for various S_0 values as indicated.

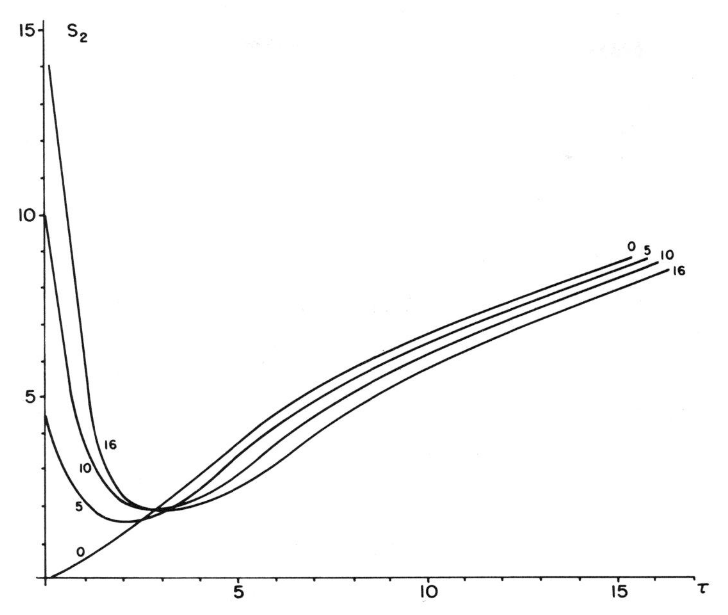

Fig. 8b. The inducer, S_2, in system II-2, for various S_0 values as indicated.

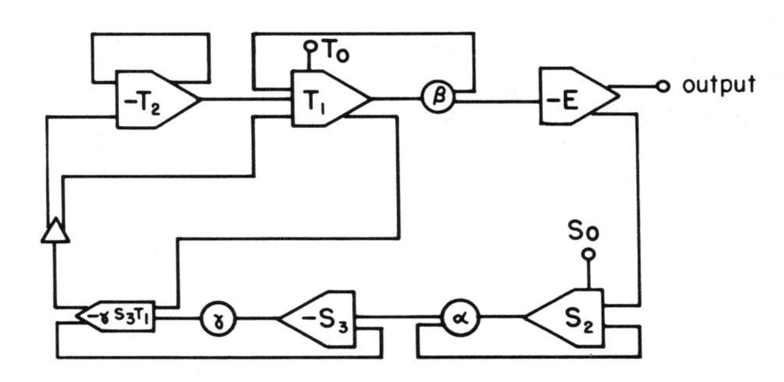

Fig. 9. Schematic computer circuit for system II-3.

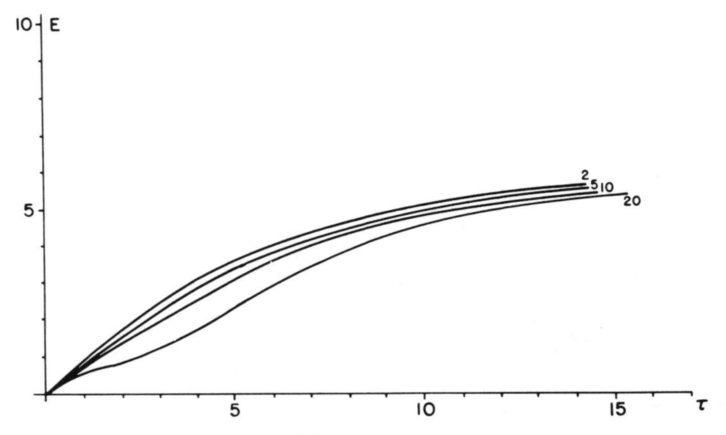

Fig. 10a. Enzyme curves for system II-3, for various S_0 values as indicated.

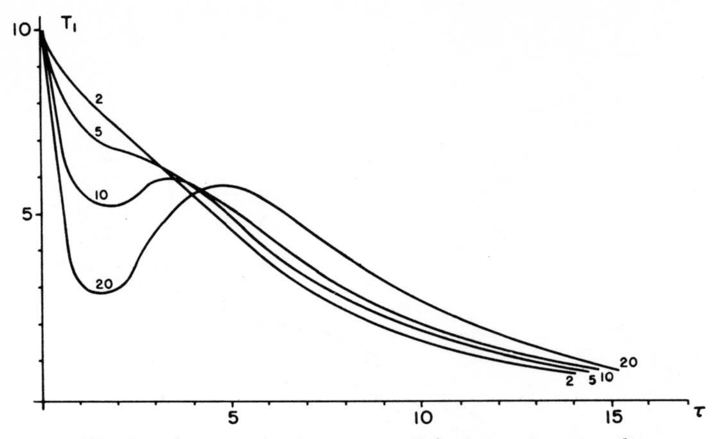

Fig. 10b. Template curves for system II-3, for various S_0 values as indicated.

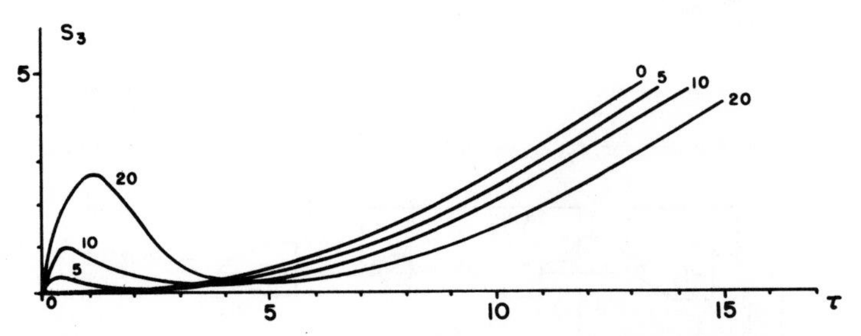

Fig. 11a. The inducer, S_3, in system II-3, for various values of S_0 as indicated.

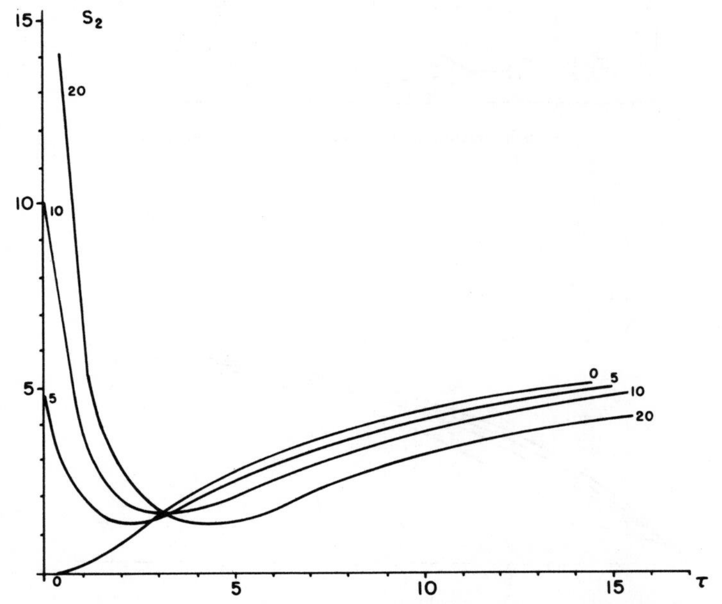

Fig. 11b. The inducer, S_2, in system II-3, for various values of S_0 as. indicated.

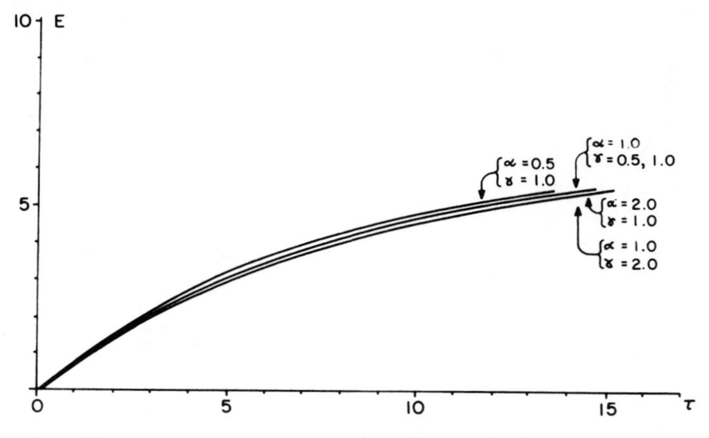

Fig. 12a. Enzyme curves for system II-3, with $S_0 = T_0 = 10$ v, $\beta = 0.1$, and α and γ varied as indicated.

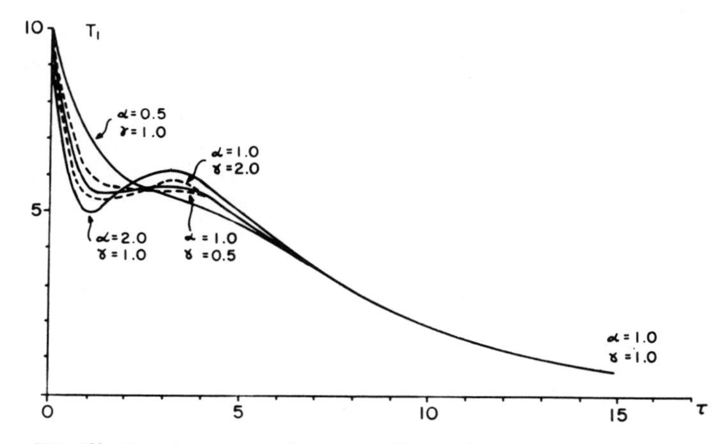

Fig. 12b. Template curves for system II-3, with $S_0 = T_0 = 10$ v, $\beta = 0.1$, and α and γ varied as indicated.

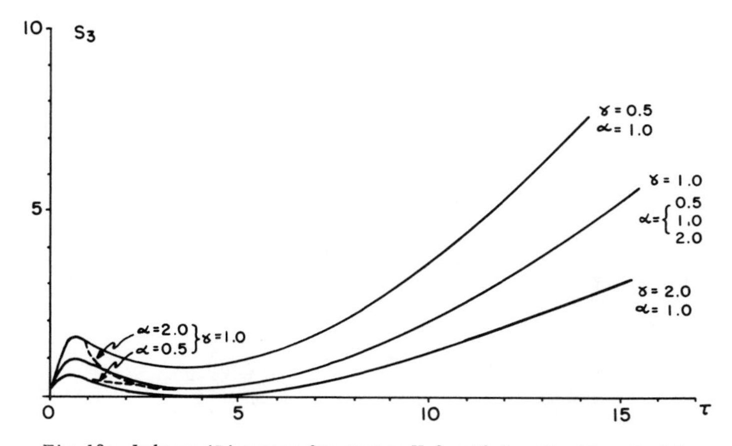

Fig. 13a. Inducer (S_3) curves for system II-3, with $S_0 = T_0 = 10$ v, $\beta = 0.1$, and α and γ varied as indicated.

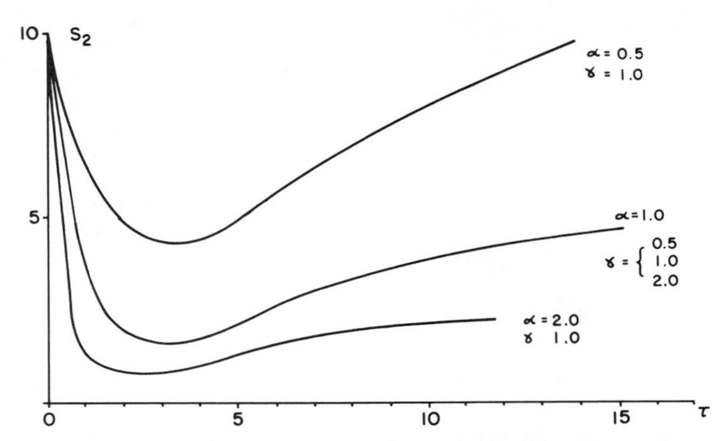

Fig. 13b. Inducer (S_2) curves for system II-3, with $S_0 = T_0 = 10$ v, $\beta = 0.1$, and α and γ varied as indicated.

of the inducers, however, there is a rather pronounced effect. Variation of the rate constant which governs the feedback to a specific inducer (see Fig. 9) has a large and inverse effect on that inducer, as can be seen from Figs. 13a and 13b, but variation of the other rate constant has substantially no effect. Thus we see that the output of the circuit is substantially stable against variation in its parameters, at least as far as its asymptotic behavior is concerned.

REFERENCES

Heinmets, F. 1960. An analysis of the concept of cellular injury and death. Int. J. Rad. Biol. 2, 341-352.

Heinmets, F. and Herschman, A. 1960. Quantitative analysis of metabolic processes. Phys. Med. Biol. 4, 238-253.

Heinmets, F. and Herschman, A. 1961a. A model-system for enzyme synthesis by sequential induction and mathematical formulation of the process. Bull. Mat. Biophys. 23, 69-89.

Heinmets, F. and Herschman, A. 1961b. A model-system for the synthesis of dissociable enzyme and mathematical formulation of the process. Bull. Math. Phys. (in press).

A NEURAL MODEL FOR LABILE SENSORIMOTOR COORDINATIONS*

Alan Hein and Richard Held

Brandeis University, Waltham, Massachusetts

Recent studies of the effects of exposure to unusual or atypical environments have revealed a surprising lability in the sensorimotor coordinations of humans and higher mammals. The surprise is occasioned by the contrast of this lability with the high order of stability normally shown by the coordinations of these higher animals. Evidence has come from three principal sources: rearrangement experiments, studies of neonatal development, and observation of the effects of sensory deprivation. Despite the challenge of the new findings, little progress has been made toward an understanding of the underlying processes. Our work has been directed toward the development of a theory of these plastic systems of coordination.

ADAPTATION TO REARRANGEMENT

A simple wedge prism, when placed in front of the eye, produces a shift in the retinal image and an apparent displacement of objects in the visual field. Immediate consequences of the induced change include a number of sensorimotor discoordinations which become readjusted during prolonged exposure. In our laboratory we have analyzed the conditions of exposure required for sensorimotor adjustments to rearrangements of the type induced by prisms (Held and Bossom, 1961; Held and Hein, 1958) and by mirrors (Held and Schlank, 1959).

One hypothesis tested in several studies is that re-afference (Held and Hein, 1958)—fedback stimulation correlated with the self-produced movements of the stimulated organism—is essential for readjustment of visual-motor coordination during rearrangement. In one experimental test of this hypothesis, subjects who wore wedge-prisms which were oriented to displace their visual field laterally either actively walked about while viewing the environment, thus receiving re-afferent stimulation, or viewed the same environment as they were moved passively in a wheelchair (Held and Bossom, 1961). The measuring procedure required the subject to orient himself to a slit of light in an otherwise dark room. Measurements taken before and after 1 hr of wearing the prisms demonstrated that the initial errors of localization induced by the prism were substantially reduced during walking. In contrast, the wheelchair subjects never achieved a significant readjustment of localization. Similar results were obtained in an experiment involving hand-eye coordination (Held and Hein, 1958). Compensatory changes of coordination occurred only when prism wearers received visual feedback from self-produced motions of their hands. When hand movements were passively produced by fixing the subject's relaxed arm to an oscillating lever, no adjustment to the prisms was noted. The congruent results of these and other experiments [Cohen and Held, 1960; Held (in press); Mikaelian and Held, 1961] have confirmed our hypothesis that re-afference is essential for adjustment to rearrangement.

*This investigation was supported by the National Science Foundation and by research grant M-3657 from the National Institute of Mental Health, United States Public Health Service.

THE DEVELOPMENT OF VISUALLY GUIDED BEHAVIOR

The relevance of these findings to the development of spatial coordination in the neonate is strongly suggested by the work of Riesen (1958) and Riesen and Aarons (1959). In these experiments a newborn chimpanzee was exposed to patterned light for 90 min per day, and kittens, reared in total darkness for eight weeks, were similarly exposed during several subsequent weeks for 1 hr per day in a normally lighted laboratory. During this daily exposure period the animals were kept in holders that prevented gross movements. The visual deficits found in their behavior—inability to make form or motion discriminations—suggested that patterned visual stimulation alone is not sufficient for the development of space perception and perceptual-motor coordination. Movement of the animal appears to be essential. The experimental procedure used in this research permitted neither active nor passive gross bodily movements and consequently did not provide a stringent test of our re-afference hypothesis. The essential factor unavailable to the holder-animals might have been either the variation in stimulation that occurs with motion, irrespective of the source of the motion, or the correlation of stimulus variation with self-produced movement found necessary for adaptation to rearrangement. We are performing an experiment to decide between these two alternatives.

Duplicating Riesen's procedure, kittens raised in the dark are given their first experience in light at 8 to 12 weeks of age. This experience consists of a short daily period of controlled visual stimulation in a patterned environment. The remainder of the day is spent in the dark. The kittens are exposed to light in the apparatus shown in Fig. 1. The apparatus permits motion around three

Fig. 1. Apparatus for equating motion and consequent visual feedback for an actively moving and a passively moved animal. (Photograph by T. Polumbaum.)

axes to be transferred from the actively moving to the passively moved kitten. Visual inputs to the animals are controlled by surrounding the apparatus with a vertically striped field. In this manner, equivalence of input to the visual system is approximated for the active and passive members of the pair of animals. However, for the active kitten, gross changes in stimulation are correlated with self-produced locomotion. No such correlation exists for the passively moved animal. Tests of visual-motor coordination are made following each daily exposure. Although this experiment is not yet completed, our early results show that kittens of our active group behave as do normal kittens, whereas the passive kittens show deficits similar to those found by Riesen et al. If the final results are consistent with these early findings, they will strongly reinforce our claim of the importance of re-afference in perceptual development and of the relevance of the findings of rearrangement studies to neonatal development.

A NEURAL MODEL

We have proposed a provisional model to account for the results of these experiments and, more generally, for the prolonged effects of sensorimotor experience in development and in adaptation to rearrangement (Held, 1961). The model is derived from one proposed by the German physiologist Erich von Holst (1954). Holst's model indicates how the fedback sensory inputs resulting from an animal's own movements may be discriminated from sensory inputs not so dependent. For example, when a movement of the eye is produced by efferent impulse to an extraocular muscle, it is assumed that a corollary discharge carries a neural copy of the impulse to a brain center. The fedback or re-afferent visual input is then supposed to summate with the corollary discharge in this center. For the simple case in which the scene viewed is stationary, the resultant signal is interpreted by higher brain centers as indicating no objective movement in the environment, despite the movement of the retinal image. When there is no efferent impulse, hence, no corollary discharge, movements of an image across the retina are interpreted as movements in the environment.

Holst's model describes a process that is completed within a fraction of a second and does not attempt to account for the prolonged modifications of perception we have been studying. The results of both the rearrangement and developmental studies indicate that the combinations of monitored efferent and re-afferent signals have long-term consequences, that is, they must not merely be summed, as Holst has indicated, but correlated and stored as well. In other words, a more adequate model must have a memory component. The diagram of Fig. 2 (Held, 1961) presents our extension of the Holstian model, previously described by Held (1961) as follows:

"The model is not restricted to eye movements; the skeletal muscle at the origin of the External Loop represents any motor system that can be a source of re-afferent visual stimulation. Instead of assuming a summation between monitored efferent and re-afferent signals, we assume that the re-afferent signal is compared (in the Comparator) with a signal selected from the Correlation Storage by the monitored efferent signal. The Correlation Storage acts as a kind of memory which retains traces of previous combinations of concurrent efferent and re-afferent signals. The currently monitored efferent signal is presumed to select the trace combination containing the identical efferent part and to activate the re-afferent trace combined with it. The resulting revived re-afferent signal is sent to the Comparator for comparison with the current re-afferent signal. The outcome of this comparison determines further performance.

Evidence for progressive adaptation to rearrangement implies that the selection from storage by the currently monitored efferent signal must be weighted by recency of trace combinations when alternatives are available. Thus, for example, if the conditions that make for typical combinations of signals are systematically changed, as they are by rearrangement, then new combinations will be stored. The same monitored efferent signal may now revive either an old or a new re-afferent trace or both. If, however, conditions are such that an efferent signal becomes concurrently combined with more than one re-afferent signal, the selection from storage must be made from among many trace combinations of roughly equal weight. Consequently, a number of revived re-afferent signals may with roughly equal likelihood be sent to the Comparator, whose response will become correspondingly ambiguous. We may expect that the precision of the response of the Comparator will reflect the range of alternative combinations available in storage. The progressive degradation of coordination produced by disarrangement would be the outcome of an increasing number of stored alternatives. The same consequences could be produced by exposure to an unstable environment (external loop) which rendered the re-afferent signals fed back as a consequence of a repeated efferent signal now one value and now another."

To test the prediction of the model concerning ambiguous feedback, a disarrangement study was performed in which controlled disorder was experimentally introduced into the normally orderly feedback circuit between hand and eye (Cohen and Held, 1960). Each subject was required to view his hand through an

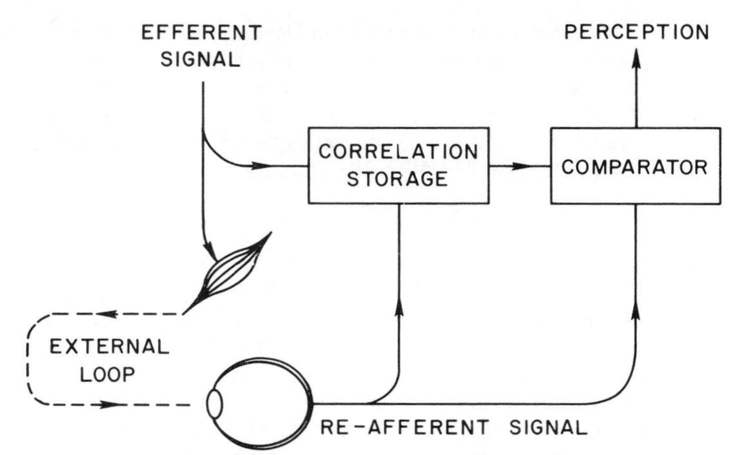

Fig. 2. Schematized process assumed to underlie the consequences of rearrangement, neonatal development, disarrangement, and deprivation.

optical device that produced a continuous variation in its apparent position from 22° right to 22° left of its veridical position. This optically induced motion was superimposed upon the movements of the subject's hand. When these movements were self-produced, measurement of accuracy of localization revealed a degradation of hand-eye coordination in the right-left dimension. When the relaxed hand was passively moved, no such degradation of coordination was observed. This result confirms still another implication of the model, which is thus seen to comprehend findings from studies of neonatal development, adult rearrangement, and disarrangement. A discussion of the relevance of the model to stimulus deprivation in adults is presented elsewhere (Held, 1961).

REFERENCES

Cohen, M. and Held, R. 1960. Degrading visual-motor coordination by exposure to disordered re-afferent stimulation. Paper read at Eastern Psychol. Assn. Convention, 1960.

Held, R. 1961. Exposure history as a factor in maintaining stability of perception and coordination. J. Nerv. Ment. Dis. 132, 26-32.

Held, R. Adaptation to rearrangement and visual-spatial aftereffects. Psychologische Beitrage (in press).

Held, R. and Bossom, J. 1961. Neonatal deprivation and adult rearrangement: complementary techniques for analyzing plastic sensory-motor coordinations. J. Comp. Physiol. Psychol. 54, 33-37.

Held, R. and Hein, A.V. 1958. Adaptation of disarranged hand-eye coordination contingent upon re-afferent stimulation. Percept. Mot. Skills 8, 87-90.

Held, R. and Schlank, M. 1959. Adaptation to disarranged eye-hand coordination in the distance dimension. Am. J. Psychol. 72, 603-605.

Holst, E. von. 1954. Relations between the central nervous system and the peripheral organs. Brit. J. Anim. Behav. 2, 89-94.

Mikaelian, H. and Held, R. 1961. Two types of adaptation to optically rotated visual field. Amer. Psychol. 16, 421 (abstr.).

Riesen, A. 1958. Plasticity of behavior: Psychological aspects. In: Harlow, H. and Woolsey, C.N. (ed.), Biological and biochemical bases of behavior. Univ. Wisconsin Press, Madison, Wis.

Riesen, A. and Aarons, L. 1959. Visual movement and intensity discrimination in cats after early deprivation of pattern vision. J. Comp. Physiol. Psychol. 52, 142-149.

A MODEL OF VISUAL SPACE*

Louis L. Sutro

Instrumentation Laboratory, Department of Aeronautics and Astronautics
Massachusetts Institute of Technology, Cambridge, Massachusetts

1. TWO NEEDS

Can we create a picture on the face of a television picture tube simply by manipulating switches on a keyboard? That was a question that I tackled 20 years ago. Working then on problems of city planning, I found that many people had suggestions on how to improve a city or region, but these suggestions were in the form of visual images. To communicate these images by words took so long that few people would listen long enough for the words to build up images in their minds. What was needed was a way of communicating the visual images to a television network which could display them to everyone interested.

Consider what this would mean. There would be no television camera scanning a scene. Instead, the video signal would be generated by a computer. The picture formed by this video signal would have many of the features of a television display. Objects would move. The shading on their surfaces would give them shape. Because of perspective, the distant objects would be smaller on the screen than the near ones.

This paper attempts to pin down what people mean by visual space. It describes this space analytically and presents a method of generating perspective projections of each object, with lighting effects, rapidly enough to give the illusion of motion. This section is concerned with the needs for such a computer or "Visualizer," as we will call it.

The first need in city and regional planning illustrates a need that exists in many fields of design. Anyone who watches people looking at TV soon discovers that their main interest is in other people. The first practical task in meeting the first need, therefore, is to generate displays of people walking, talking, sitting, eating, and playing. Proposed improvements for a city or region can then be presented by generating sequences of pictures of people using and enjoying these improvements.

Each man and woman to be pictured could be stored in the Visualizer as an assembly of objects, trunk, pelvic region, head, arms, and legs, interconnected by cartilage, tendons, and muscles. Each assembly could be made to appear to walk, sit down, eat, etc., by forces exerted between the parts and between the assembly and the ground.

Motion, it is expected, will be controlled in the first model of the Visualizer by a program which will place each object in successive positions. In a later model, it should be possible for an operator to program the forces acting on each object. The Visualizer would then compute the motion and display it. In a still later model, it should be possible to program by such a sentence as

Mr. Smith walks from *a* to *b*.

The Visualizer would compute the forces between the objects that comprise Mr. Smith, then the motion of these objects, and finally the display. This process resembles what human beings call "visualizing."

Fig. 1. View of stage, sculptured head, picture plane, and eyes.

Figure 1 shows the relations between an object at the left, a picture of it that could be erected on the plane at the center, and models of eyes at the right. The object is a sculpture whose appearance in the picture plane will be somewhat like the photograph in Fig. 2. This is the left-eye image and can be com-

Fig. 2. Sculptured head illuminated by single light source.

puted by projecting each point of the object to the picture plane, toward the left eye. A right-eye image can be computed by projecting each point to the picture plane, toward the right eye. Black lines mark the limit of visual space to be represented.

The Visualizer may be used to make TV entertainment and news programs. An assembly of objects representing a man or woman would appear as a puppet. Manipulated by programing in early models of the Visualizer and by typed or spoken commands in later models, these apparent puppets could entertain and inform as animated drawings do. Performances of the apparent puppets could be produced faster and eventually more cheaply than animated drawings. The speed of production would permit illustrating news events where no photographs had been made. A trained operator of the Visualizer could employ information about the place and participants to create motion pictures of the events.

The second need for the Visualizer is as a component in a guidance system resembling animal vision. There is reason to believe that an animal erects an image of what it expects to see in each retina (McCulloch, 1959-1961). Light from the environment forms another image. The three layers of logic known to comprise the retina (McCulloch, 1959-1961) compare the two images and report incongruities to the brain. This operation could explain both fast visual response and perception of three-dimensional objects. The Visualizer is proposed as part of a system to imitate both the fast response and three-dimensional perception of animal vision.

Consider first the imitation of fast visual response. When a cat watches a mouse it is ready to catch, the following sequence may take place. The cat erects images on its retinas of the mouse in the many positions that it may take and, for each image, gets set to dart toward the mouse. In other words, the cat's retinas receive a cycle of crude predicted images of the mouse escaping. The cat's brain and body go through a cycle of preparations to respond to these images. When the mouse does attempt to escape, one image in the cycle matches the image of the mouse escaping. No incongruity is reported to the cat's brain. The cat pounces on the mouse.

There is reason to believe that when a person reads rapidly, his brain supplies his retinas with crude predicted images of each word or group of words. A reader who knows an author's style predicts many of his words and skips to the words that convey information.

Facts about the structure of the human visual system support this hypothesis of predictive vision. In measurements on human beings, Hernandez-Peon found that he could obtain the same retinal response by suggesting what could be seen as by having a subject see it. Of the number of large, or fast, nerve fibers in the optic nerve, approximately 10% are estimated to convey signals from the brain to the retina. The three layers of logic that comprise the retina appear capable of receiving images from both the brain and the external environment and comparing them. A working model may demonstrate that such a comparison is carried out.

If, in the model of Fig. 1, model retinas sensitive to the visual space marked by the black lines were to be installed in the model eyes, they would occupy the shaded areas at the backs of these eyes. However, large numbers of high-resolution protodetectors cannot be mounted in so small a space today. They can be built into the faces of television camera tubes which can be mounted in place of these eyes.

Since a television camera tube performs no logic, working models of the layers of logic known to be included in the retina will have to be located elsewhere. Sheet computers with three layers of logic are proposed for this. The optical image picked up as a video signal by each camera tube will be encoded and mapped on one face of such a computer. An image generated by the Visualizer will be mapped on the other face. The logic will determine incongruities between the images and report these to a control computer able to command more images from the Visualizer and control action. The action could consist of motion of the cameras, motion of the vehicle supporting the cameras, and manipulation of objects seen.

Consider now the imitation of three-dimensional perception. The cameras, sheet computers, Visualizer, control computer, and other components of animal visual systems (Loebner and Henneberger, 1961, 1962) are proposed as a working model of stereoscopic vision. The proposed sequence of operations is: (1) the control computer deduces that one of a set of objects is in the field of view. (2) It commands the Visualizer to erect images of these objects in the sheet computers. (3) The television cameras turn in the direction appropriate to the images being erected (Kris, 1957, 1960, Stark, Vossius, and Young, 1961). (4) The sheet computer determines incongruities between images and reports these to the control computer. (5) The control computer determines that an object has been detected and guides the vehicle either toward it or around it, whichever is intended.

2. SPECIFICATION OF VISUAL SPACE

Professor James J. Gibson (1962) has shown that vision is concerned with objects. A description of visual space, therefore, is a description of objects, their location, and their motion. This description should be analytical to meet the needs described above.

What the eye sees is brightness or, to break this down into small parts, a mosaic of brightnesses. The illuminating engineer's concept of brightness is fairly easy to work with. In designing lighting systems, he finds that brightness is produced either by a light source or by a reflecting surface. In the latter case he computes brightness as a function of incident illumination and the reflecting properties of the surface. He measures brightness with either a foot-candle meter, a photographer's exposure meter, or a narrow-angle brightness meter.

What the illuminating engineer both computes and measures could be called absolute brightness and is known technically as luminance (I.R.E., 1961). Subjective or apparent brightness is measured in the same way but has a different scale of apparently equal steps (Bartley, 1941). This paper will be concerned with absolute brightness.

The surface of an object can be considered to be made of elements no larger than a "spot" on the display screen. A "spot" in TV terminology is the area excited by the electron beam as it sweeps the back of the TV screen. Since the electron beam traverses 525 horizontal lines and the ratio of width to height is 4:3, the total number of spots is $4/3 \times 525 \times 525$, or approximately $\frac{1}{3}$ million.

Illuminating engineers describe the reflecting properties of a surface by its diffuse, spread, and specular reflectance (I. E. S., 1959). Since spread reflectance can be defined in terms of the other two, only diffuse and specular reflectance are necessary.

To specify the reflectance of an element on the surface of a moving object, at least two systems of coordinates are needed. Consider the sculptured head photographed from above in Fig. 1 and from the front in Fig. 2. The human head pivots about the pin of the axis vertebra and rocks on the articular surfaces of the atlas vertebra. For the head of Fig. 2, assume the origin of coordinates to be a point on the pin of the axis vertebra at the height of the articular surfaces

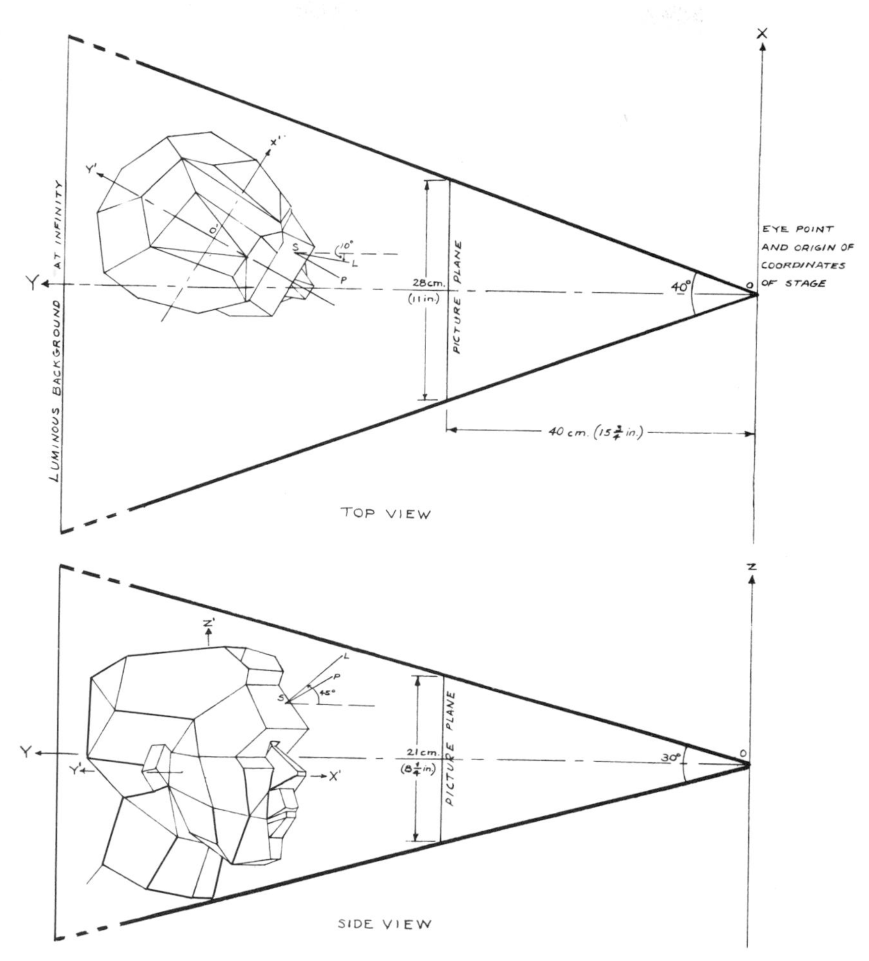

Fig. 3. Coordinate system of head (X', Y', Z') placed on coordinate system of stage (X, Y, Z).

of the atlas vertebra. Figure 3 shows this head in its coordinate system (X', Y', Z') within the coordinate system of the space that will be called the stage. A surface element S is marked on the forehead. The direction of the normal to S can be computed from the coordinates of S and a point P on the normal.

Figure 4 is a tabulation of the specifications of the head, with the coordinates of S entered as an example. Four significant figures are expected to be sufficient. These, together with the algebraic sign, require 17 bits in the computer memory. Small measurements will be given in centimeters, larger ones in meters, mass in grams and kilograms. The shift in units from small to large then requires only a shift in decimal point. Velocity and acceleration, needed to determine motion, will be computed by simple multiplication and division without the awkward conversions of units required in the English system. The advantages of the metric system have been recognized by the adoption of the MKS system in electrical engineering, and the CGS system in science.

The fourth, fifth, and sixth columns show the coordinates of a point on the normal to each surface element. The seventh and eighth columns show the diffuse and specular reflectances of the surface element to white light. The example in

Object No. = I_X =

Mass = I_Y =

I_Z =

Surface Element			Point on Normal			Reflectances	
x'	y'	z'	x'	y'	z'	r_D	r_S
+4.00	+10.00	+10.00					
17 bits	17 bits	17 bits	17 bits	17 bits	17 bits	12 bits	12 bits

126 bits

Fig. 4. Tabulation of data describing an object.

this paper considers only the generation of a black-and-white display and, therefore, requires only one diffuse and one specular reflectance. For a later model of the Visualizer in which the displays will be presented on a three-color picture tube, diffuse and specular reflectance to the three light primaries will be required. These six reflectances would be employed in calculating the brightness of noticeable areas only. In color television a combination of black-and-white detail and colored areas gives the illusion of color.

The total number of bits required to specify one surface element is seen to be 126. Add to this a parity bit and the total is 127. The number of surface elements in an object could be in the order of two million, computed by assuming that the object has six sides and each side has as many elements as the display screen has spots, $\frac{1}{3}$ million. The total number or bits to be stored is, thus, in the order of 127×2 million, or 254 million. To display the motion of several objects, any one of which may be shown in a close-up, requires the storage of several billion bits. Tape, drum, and disc memories of this size are available. High-speed memories of this size are being made possible by the development of the batch-process method of computer manufacture (Rice, 1959; Seeber, and Lindquist, 1962; Beesley, 1960, 1961).

The entries at the top of the table in Fig. 4 will be employed when motion is computed from masses and forces. Initially, however, motion will be computed as only translation and rotation. Figure 3 shows the head translated so that the origin of its coordinate system 0' is at $X = 7$ cm, $Y = 72$ cm, and $Z = -2.4$ cm. The head is rotated so that its Y' axis forms an angle of 30° with the Y axis of the stage.

Note the size and position of the picture plane. It subtends a vertical angle of 30° at the eye point and a horizontal angle of 40°, is 21 cm ($8^1/_4$ in.) high, 28 cm (11 in.) wide, and 40 cm ($15^3/_4$ in.) distant. The height was chosen first because it is the height of a human face when it has come forward into this plane. The vertical and horizontal angles were determined next. They must be in the ratio of the height to the width of a TV display. This is the aspect ratio and in TV it is 3 : 4. The angles should be as small as possible lest the scene fan out and require calculation of the brightness of a very large number of objects in the distance; yet the angles should equal those subtended by the operator at the console shown in Fig. 5. Vertical and horizontal angles of 30° and 40° appear to satisfy all of these requirements.

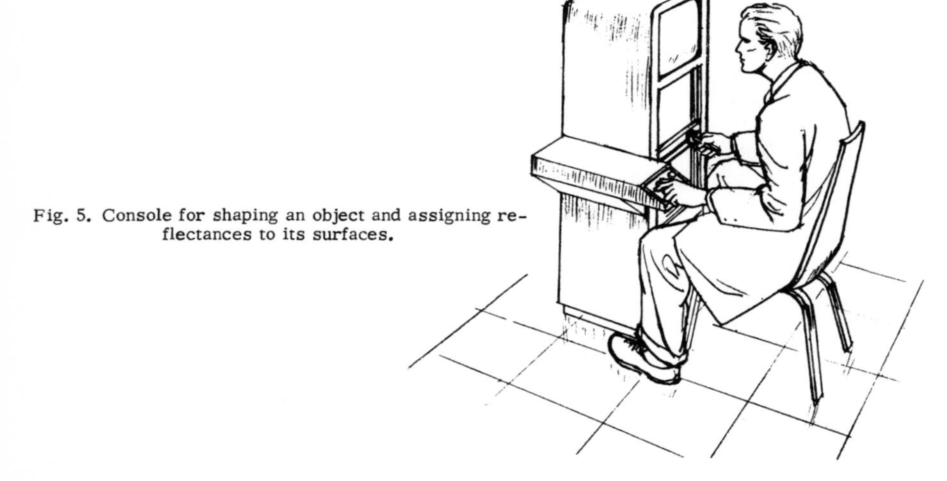

Fig. 5. Console for shaping an object and assigning reflectances to its surfaces.

Figure 5 illustrates a proposed method of imparting a static model of an object to the Visualizer. With his right hand, the operator manipulates the handle of what appears on the display screen to be a knife. He can turn the handle of the "knife," move it up or down, move it sidewards, move it in and out, and twist it to "carve" an object. Under his left hand are controls which enable him to assign reflectances to the object he is "carving." Not shown is a joy stick that will project up from the box at the operator's left to permit him to turn and tilt the object he is "carving."

He can carve planes, as in the head of Fig. 2, or he can carve smooth curved surfaces. The head in Fig. 2 was carved in about 50 planes, so that in manually computing its display, only 50 calculations of brightness were required. When the Visualizer computes this display, it will compute the brightness of every surface element. There will then be no advantage in sculpturing with planes.

In using the console illustrated in Fig. 5, judgement of the depth of a scene may be difficult. For example, to change the reflectance of a few surface elements on the cheek of the face, how far should you reach in with the knife? A stereoscopic display will largely remove this difficulty and can be obtained by the following modifications. The present display tube can be moved back and a second display tube mounted above the space thus vacated, aimed down. A half-silvered mirror, formed by sputtering silver on glass, can be placed in the vacated space. It should be tilted so that the operator sees the face of the upper tube reflected in the sputterings of silver, and the face of the moved-back tube between the sputterings. If two pieces of Polaroid oriented in the same direction are placed over both his left eye and the upper display, his left eye will see only the upper display. If two more pieces of Polaroid oriented 90° with respect to the first two are placed in front of his right eye and the display in front of him, his right eye will see only this display.

3. COMPUTING THE IMAGE OF AN OBJECT

For each of the applications described in section 1, a mosaic of brightnesses needs to be computed. To do this we will follow the practice of the illuminating engineer, who bases his methods of computation on his methods of measurement. Here we will review how he measures brightness and how he computes it for both diffuse and specular reflection. Then we will consider how to compute a TV frame, and a sequence of frames that can show motion.

An illuminating engineer in the United States measures brightness with either a foot-candle meter or a narrow-angle meter such as a Spectra Brightness Spot Meter.* For photography, he measures it with an exposure meter.

The foot-candle meter is primarily intended to be placed on a surface, aimed away. It indicates the number of lumens normally incident on each square foot of the surface (foot-candles). Multiplying the reading by 10.76 converts it to lumens per square meter (meter-candles or lux).

If the surface is a diffuse reflector, the illuminating engineer may turn the meter around, hold it far enough away that it does not cast a shadow, and read the surface's brightness in foot-lamberts. Multiplying the reading by 10.76 converts it to apostilbs.† The ratio of the foot-candle reading to the foot-lambert reading is the diffuse reflectance of the surface. In metric units it is the ratio of the lux reading to the apostilb reading. When the two readings made in either English or metric units are the same, the diffuse reflectance is 1.

Diffuse reflectance is an ideal that is approached in freshly fallen snow and the matte finish of paints and papers, particularly blotting paper. It enables the illuminating engineer to conceive of brightness as the product of diffuse reflectance r_D and the luminous flux normally incident on the surface, E_N. The equation for computing brightness due to diffuse reflectance is

$$B_D = r_D E_N \tag{1}$$

When the surface does not reflect diffusely, that is, when its brightness is different in each direction, its brightness may be determined by comparison with a surface of known diffuse reflectance and known incident flux density. Brightness meters, such as the Spectra Brightness Spot Meter and photographic exposure meters, function in this way. They are calibrated by being aimed at a surface of known diffuse reflectance and known incident flux density. They have narrow angles of acceptance which permit reading the brightness of small areas.

Note that the term "incident flux density" has been used in the above discussion. The word "illumination" is more common, but it has two meanings (Moon, 1936). It may mean the flux density normal to a surface, which we will represent

*Other narrow-angle brightness meters are the Spectra Pritchard Photometer, Luckiesh-Taylor Brightness Meter, and Macbeth Illuminometer.

†Other metric units of brightness are the lambert and the stilb. The apostilb is preferred for the Visualizer because it bears the same convenient relation to the lux that the foot-lambert bears to the foot-candle.

by a vector normal to the surface, of magnitude E_N, or it may mean the flux density in the direction of the light, which we will represent by a vector of magnitude E. The relation of the two magnitudes is shown in Fig. 6 and in the equation

$$E_N = E \cos i \tag{2}$$

where i is the angle of incidence.

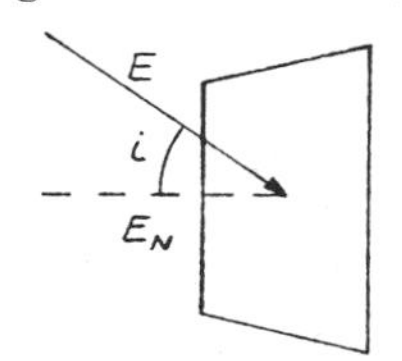

Fig. 6. Obliquely incident illumination E and its normal component E_N.

In section 2 it was stated that the reflecting properties of a surface could be described by its diffuse and specular reflectance. The word "specular" means mirror-like quality. "Reflectance" means the proportion of light reflected. Thus a clear glass mirror has a specular reflectance approaching 1, while a black glass mirror has a specular reflectance of but 0.1 since it absorbs most of the light incident upon it. Specular reflection differs from diffuse in its directionality. A perfectly diffuse reflector appears the same from every direction, i.e., its brightness is the same in every direction. A specular reflector, on the other hand, can have a different appearance from every direction.

In the example of Fig. 3 we will compute the brightness due to specular reflection, B_S, only where it causes light to enter the pupil of the eye at position 0. The calculation of the B_S of a surface element will consist of: (1) determining that the angle of incidence of light to this surface element equals the angle of reflection to the pupil of the eye; (2) determining that the two angles are in the same plane and, if these two conditions are met; (3) computing the product of the brightness of the source of light, B_{source}, and the specular reflectance r_S:

$$B_S = r_S \, B_{source} \tag{3}$$

B_{source} is the luminous flux from the source to the pupil of the eye. To determine B_{source} the illuminating engineer either holds a foot-candle or lux meter close to the source or reads it from a distance with a narrow-angle brightness meter. In effect, he compares the light source to a perfectly diffusing surface of known illumination and reflectance. In a similar manner B_{source} can be computed when the properties of the source are known. (See Appendix.)

Let us apply the above principles to computing the brightness B of surface element S in Fig. 3. The illumination on S is represented by the vector $\overrightarrow{LS}$ whose component normal to S is $\overrightarrow{PS}$. The point P was described in section 2 as any point that determines the direction of the normal to S. In Fig. 3 the location of P has been further restricted so that

$$PS = LS \cos i \tag{4}$$

This equation was formed from equation (2) by replacing E_N and E with the scalar components of the vectors $\overrightarrow{PS}$ and $\overrightarrow{LS}$. The angle i may be computed from the coordinates of P and S and from the direction of $\overrightarrow{LS}$ indicated by the angles that its projections make with the Y axis in Fig. 3 (10° in the top view and 45° in the side view). In computing the display of an object illuminated by a single light, and particularly a spotlight, the vectors representing illumination can be assumed parallel.

The check to determine if the angle of incidence $\angle LSP$ and the angle of reflection $\angle PSO$ are equal and in the same plane results, in this case, in

$$i \neq r \tag{5}$$

Brightness is computed by the formula derived above, namely,

$$B = r_D \, E \cos i + r_S \, B_{source} \tag{6}$$

In this case the second term is zero. The X and Z coordinates of B in the picture plane are the piercing point of a line drawn from S to 0 in Fig. 3.

To generate a picture like that of Fig. 2 for display on a TV screen requires computing $\frac{1}{3}$ million brightnesses. If the head is to be shown in motion, this number must be computed 30 times per second. This computation can be performed today, but not in real time. To use existing computers, one frame at a time will have to be computed and stored on tape or disc. When a sequence of frames has been computed, all of the stored brightnesses can be converted to voltage amplitudes, formed into a video signal, and stored on video tape.

Computers now under development promise to have the speed and memory capacity to permit real-time generation of the display of, first, an object that an operator "carves" at the console of Fig. 5 and, later, of a scene of objects in motion. A combination of digital and analog computing equipment is being planned for this.

4. CONCLUSION

This paper presents the principles of operation of the Visualizer. This device should (1) enable an individual to create motion pictures on a television screen and (2) provide a component in a system resembling animal vision which could be used to guide an automatic vehicle. In application 1 the Visualizer would enable individuals to picture improvements and show how these benefit people; it should provide a faster and cheaper way of making the kind of entertainment now provided by animated drawings. In application 2 the Visualizer would erect predicted images in a sheet computer for comparison with images obtained by electronic scanning of the environment. The sheet computer would determine incongruities and feed these to a control computer which would decide when recognition of an object had been achieved.

In the first model of the Visualizer, each object will be defined by shape and reflecting properties introduced by an operator at a special console; motion will be defined by a computer program. In later models each object will be further defined by its mass and its mechanical connection to other objects.

The image to be erected on television screens in application 1, or in a sheet computer in application 2, will be a mosaic of brightnesses, each of which can be computed in a few steps. The computation can be performed today, but more slowly than an operator would "carve" an object and much more slowly than the object would appear to move across the display screen. The required speed appears likely to be attained by computers now under development.

ACKNOWLEDGMENTS

The following assistance is gratefully acknowledged: Sculpture by Mrs. Ruth W. Sutro, illustration by Mr. Calvin Burnett, and photographs by Mr. William Stirling.

APPENDIX

ILLUMINATION AND BRIGHTNESS

This appendix explains how illumination determines the brightness of a surface and how this brightness determines the illumination of other surfaces. Thus "light" that enters the stage of the Visualizer can be accounted for as it is transmitted or reflected from surface to surface. The "light" finally is either attenuated or leaves the stage. Each reflecting surface is assumed to have both diffuse and specular reflectance, but only the diffuse component will be considered.

The common denominator of illumination and brightness is the lumen, represented by the unit vector in Fig. 7. A lumen is defined as the light flux from a standard candle down a unit solid angle such as that formed by a candle at 0 and the area ABCD in Fig. 7. Since there are 4π or 12.57 unit solid angles (steradians) in a sphere, a standard candle emits 12.57 lumens.

The vector in Fig. 7 can also represent unit flux density. If the radius of the sphere is 1 ft and each side of the unit area is also 1 ft, then the vector represents 1 foot-candle. If each of these dimensions is 1 m the vector represents 1 lux.

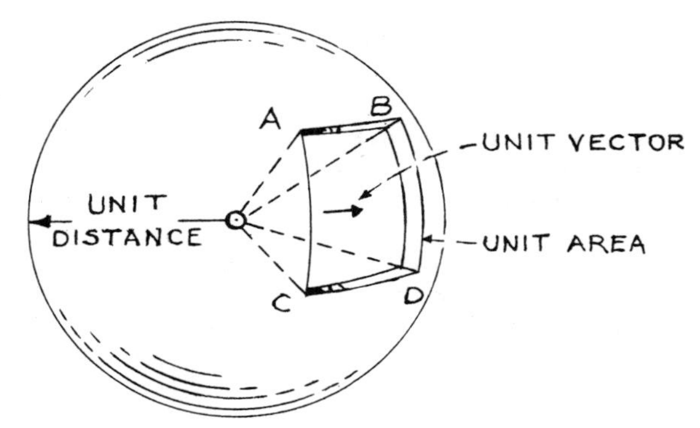

Fig. 7. Luminous flux down a unit solid angle, represented by a unit vector.

Consider the unit area of Fig. 7 to be occupied by completely diffusing material of transmittance t. Figure 8a shows such a unit area flattened out and receiving illumination E_N. The area is assumed to be surrounded by many identical areas equally illuminated. Figure 8c shows E_N transformed into the illumination on the face of a foot-candle meter or lux meter tE_N.

To follow the sequence shown in Fig. 8, consider the unit area of Fig. 8a to be divided into differential areas. The vector E_N should then be divided into differential vectors, each incident on a differential area. As the light represented by each differential vector passes through each differential area, it is diffused, that is, it spreads out in the manner represented by the clusters of vectors in Fig. 8b. The locus of the tips in each cluster is a sphere and the length of each vector equals the normal vector times the cosine of the angle between it and the normal. This relation is called the cosine law of emission (Moon, 1936).

The magnitude of each vector in Fig. 8b represents light flux per unit solid angle. If the vectors are spaced so that they represent light flux down less than a unit solid angle, their magnitudes must be appropriately smaller.

When a foot-candle or lux meter is held as in Fig. 9 to measure the light from a very large diffusely reflecting or transmitting surface, it reads the same no matter what angle its axis forms with the surface. This condition is represented by a cluster of equal-length vectors in Fig. 8c, the locus of whose tips is a hemisphere. Each vector in Fig. 8c represents the illumination on the face of the foot-candle or lux meter when the meter is pointed toward it. Note that each vector represents flux density at the meter face, as does the vector in Fig. 8a, rather than flux per unit solid angle as in Fig. 8b.

The magnitude of each vector in Fig. 8c remains constant, as the meter is moved away from the surface, only if the surface is very large. If the surface

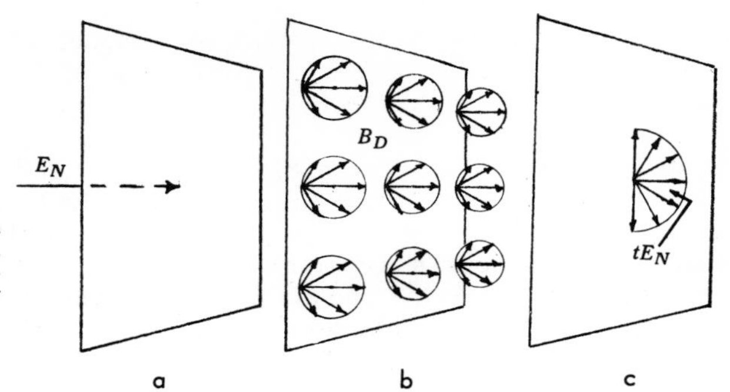

Fig. 8. Conversion or illumination to brightness, then to illumination again, when the surface has transmittance t, is very large, perfectly diffusing, and uniformly illuminated.

is small, the magnitude decreases as the meter is moved away. If the surface is very small, it decreases as the square of the distance from the meter to the surface. This inverse-square relation will not, in general, enter Visualizer computations because the Visualizer's task is to compute brightness. This remains constant with distance. In the integration performed by a foot-candle or lux meter, the brightness of a small area becomes a smaller part of the integrated sum as the meter is moved away.

The magnitude and direction of the vectors in Figs. 8 and 9 will be represented by numbers in the Visualizer and the integration performed by a foot-candle or lux meter will be performed numerically. Integration will consist of summing the normal components of the flux received at the meter from every direction.

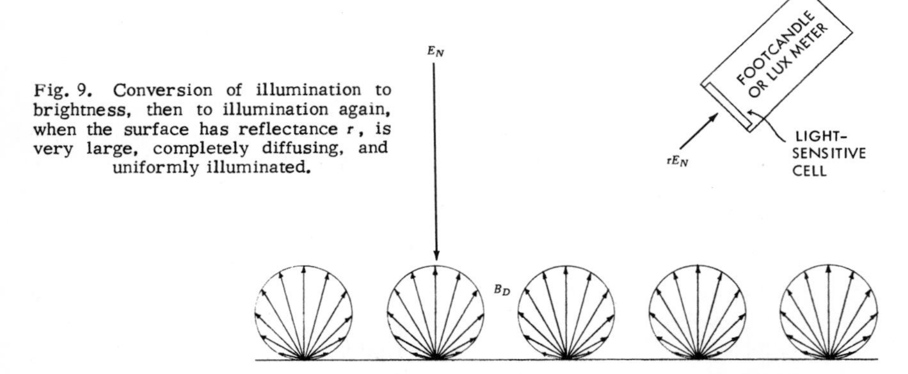

Fig. 9. Conversion of illumination to brightness, then to illumination again, when the surface has reflectance r, is very large, completely diffusing, and uniformly illuminated.

The normal component is computed in each case by multiplying the magnitude of the vector by the cosine of its angle of incidence (see Fig. 6). This is called the cosine law of illumination (Moon, 1936). The effect of the cosine law of emission exactly cancels the effect of the cosine law of illumination so that illumination of 1 foot-candle on a very large, perfectly diffusing, perfectly transmitting surface in Fig. 8a is read as 1 foot-candle by the meter in Fig. 8c. Similarly, illumination of 1 lux in Fig. 8a is read as 1 apostilb in Fig. 8c. Between the two readings (or computations) of illumination in Fig. 8a and c there is the reading (or computation) of brightness shown in Fig. 8b, which is measured in the same manner and is numerically the same as the measurement in Fig. 8c. If the meter employed is a foot-candle meter the brightness is 1 foot-lambert; if it is a lux meter, the brightness is 1 apostilb. A transmittance of less than 1 in Fig. 8, or a reflectance of less than 1 in Fig. 9, is an attenutation factor to be applied to the first illumination reading to compute both the brightness and second illumination readings.

Thus the brightness of every detail of any object can be computed. But would we want to compute it? Here we ask the artist to tell us which details to include and which to omit. The rules that he employs can be part of the program of the Visualizer.

REFERENCES

Bartley, S. H. 1941. Vision. D. Van Nostrand Co., New York, p. 33.
Beesley, J. I. B. M. Federal Products Division, Kingston, N.Y. Communications to the author, Dec. 1960 and Aug. 1961.
Gibson, J. The survival value of sensory perception. This volume, p. 230.
I. E. S. lighting handbook. 3rd ed. 1959. Illuminating Engineering Society, New York, pp. 3-7, 3-8, 4-7, 4-8, 6-6, 6-7, and appendix.
I.R.E. 1961. I.R.E. dictionary, Institute of Radio Engineers, New York, p. 86.
Kris, C. 1957. A technique for electrically recording eye position. Aero Medical Laboratory, Wright Air Development Center final technical report, printed as WADC technical report AD 209385 (Astia document No. AD 209385), Wright Patterson Air Force Base, Ohio.
Kris, C. 1960. Vision: electro-oculography. Medical Physics 3, The Year Book Publishers, Inc., Chicago.
Loebner, E. E. Image processing and functional retina synthesis. Proceedings of Bionics Symposium, Wright Air Development Division, Wright-Patterson Air Force Base, Ohio.
Loebner, E. E. and Henneberger, T. Investigation of image analysis techniques, Dec. 1, 1960 to May 31, 1961. R.C.A. Laboratories, Princeton, N.J.
Loebner, E. E. and Henneberger, T. Modeling visual organs and perceptions. This volume, p. 59.
McCulloch, W. S. Conversations with the author, 1959-1961 (unpublished).
Moon, P. 1936. The scientific basis of illuminating engineering. McGraw-Hill Book Co., New York, pp. 53, 183, 256, 304.
Rice, R. 1960. Computers of the future. Proceedings of the Eastern Joint Computer Conference, 1959. Institute of Radio Engineers, New York, pp. 11-14.
Seeber, R. R. and Lindquist, A. B. 1962. Associative memory with ordered retrieval. I.B.M. Journal of Research and Development, Vol. 6, No. 1, pp. 126-136.
Stark, L., Vossius, G., and Young, L. R. 1961. Predictive control of eye movements. Quarterly Progress Report No. 62, Research Laboratory of Electronics, pp. 271-284.

STATISTICAL LEARNING MODELS FOR BEHAVIOR OF AN ARTIFICIAL ORGANISM

Frank N. Marzocco and Philip R. Bartram

System Development Corporation
Santa Monica, California

BACKGROUND

Probabilistic formulations have been used to design both mathematical models for the behavior of living organisms and machines which display some of the properties of living organisms. Examples of the former include the statistical learning theory of Estes (1950) and the stochastic learning model of Bush and Mosteller (1951). Examples of the latter include the conditional probability machines of Uttley (1956) and the Perceptron of Rosenblatt (1958). Additional references may be found in the reviews by Estes (1959), Gilstrap and Lee (1960), and Minsky (1961). Since these uses of the probabilistic approach apply to either purpose individually, the same approach may be useful in combining purposes, using the machine to learn more about the behavior of living organisms and the principles of learning theory to extend the capabilities of the machine.

DESIGN OF THE PROGRAM

The first step has been to prepare a computer program based on the conceptual model for Estes' 1959 description of his 1950 statistical learning theory. That model was chosen for several reasons: it has demonstrated considerable power for predicting behavior; the few concepts employed are set forth clearly and unequivocally; the model deals specifically with the problems of stimulus, response, and intervening process, all of which are important in a machine which is to exhibit behavior as well as predict it; and finally, the model is completely general in the situations it deals with. Like Guthrie's (1935, 1959) theory, from which the model derives in part, there are no intrinsic limitations on the applications.

The stimulus environment is defined for the program by a vector whose components may be one or zero. The vector may be subdivided into a number of smaller vectors or fields to represent individual stimuli in the environment. Figure 1 shows an example. Each stimulus element in the speaker's environment is mapped into a unique component of the vector. Any stimulus may, of course, give rise to a number of elements. Those elements which correspond to the stimulus "light on" might be mapped into the first 1000 components of the vector, which would then be identified as the "light-on" field; elements corresponding to the stimulus "light off" might be mapped into the next 1000 components; elements corresponding to the lectern, into the next 1000; etc. It is not necessary to consider only stimuli in the organism's external environment; internal sources of stimulation can be treated in the same fashion. Since stimuli are identified by their ordinary names, a single element may belong in several stimulus fields. This situation may be handled either by allowing fields to overlap or by defining special fields to represent the intersections of stimulus classes.

Any particular stimulus situation can now be represented by a pattern of ones in the stimulus vector. An entry of one for any component indicates that the corresponding stimulus element is both present in the situation and sensed

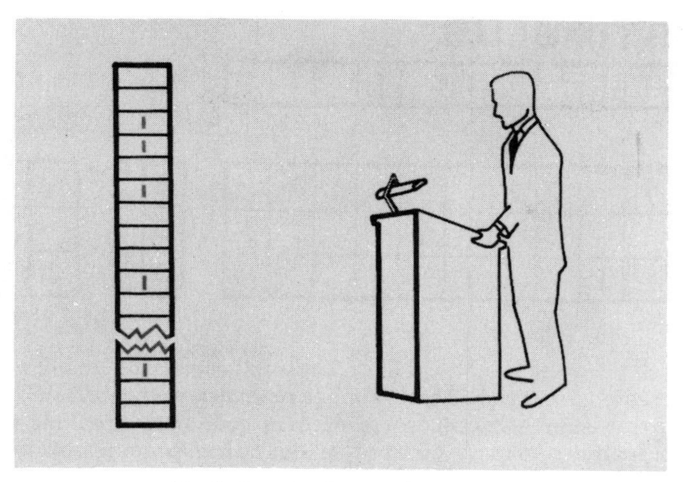

Fig. 1. Forming the stimulus vector.

by the organism. The pattern of ones for each trial or moment of time is determined by a statistical sampling process applied to the stimulus fields available at that time. Rules governing the appearance and interrelationships of stimuli may be programmed to force selection of elements from certain stimulus combinations while forbidding other combinations to occur. Thus, in the situation of Fig. 1, "light-on" and "light-off" elements would not be permitted to occur simultaneously, and "light-on" might be forced to occur after a switch-turning response in the presence of "light-off" elements.

Responses are represented within the computer by another vector whose components are one or zero. Each of the responses that can occur in a situation is mapped into a unique component of the vector. In this case, vector components correspond to whole responses rather than parts, but no limitation is placed on the specificity with which a response may be defined. Thus, in the situation of Fig. 1, "touching the nose with right index finger," "touching the nose with right middle finger," and "touching the nose with any other finger" might be mapped into three different components of the response vector if the distinction made a difference for some application. Responses may also be treated as stimuli, in which case the whole response is mapped into a component of the response vector and its elements are mapped into components of the stimulus vector. Responses may be internal as well as peripheral, and internal responses may be necessary to serve as stimuli in simulating some kinds of behavior. A limitation on the definition of responses has been inherited from the Estes model. The complete set of individual responses must exhaust all possibilities, so that at least one response will appear for any trial or moment; likewise the responses must be mutually exclusive, so that one at most will appear.

Each stimulus element is connected at any time to one, and only one, response. This feature is represented in the computer by an association matrix, as shown in Fig. 2. Columns correspond to stimulus elements; rows, to responses. An entry of one in any cell indicates that the stimulus element for that column is connected to the response for that row. A single entry appears in each column, but any number of entries may appear in a row. The response produced by a given stimulus pattern and a given state of the association matrix is that connected to the greatest number of sampled stimulus elements. A computation is represented in Fig. 2. For each row of the association matrix, the sum of products of corresponding entries in that row and the stimulus vector is formed;

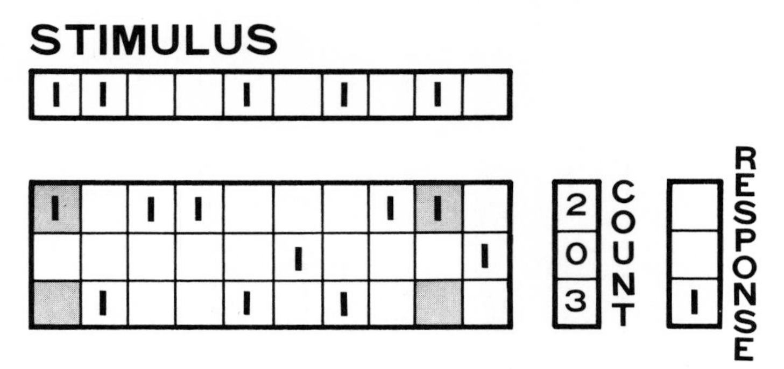

Fig. 2. The association matrix and its use.

blanks are treated as zeros. These sums are shown in the cells marked "count." Next the largest sum of products is determined; a tie-breaking rule is used if necessary. Finally, a one is entered in the corresponding row of the response vector to mark the response which occurs.

Learning is accomplished in this system by changing association-matrix connections in accordance with a reinforcement principle. All stimulus elements present in a situation and sensed by the organism become connected with the response that occurs if the response is selected for reinforcement. No change is made otherwise. In the example of Fig. 2, if (and only if) the response is to be reinforced, ones are entered in the two shaded cells in the bottom row of the association matrix. When these ones are entered, those in the two shaded cells of the top row must be removed. This procedure increases the probability that the bottom-row response will occur on the next trial; at the same time, the probability of the top-row response has decreased and that of the middle row has remained the same. Selection of responses to be reinforced may be accomplished in a number of ways. Some responses may be selected for reinforcement whenever they occur; others may be selected on the basis of complex stimulus contingencies. Selection may even be made outside the computer and decided after inspection of the response actually produced. The selection rules need not be consistent and a variety of rules may be applied simultaneously as long as the computer is not thrown into a quandary in determining whether or not to reinforce a response.

The computer program which carries out the operations described above was written in JOVIAL (Shaw, 1961)—a procedure-oriented language designed by the System Development Corporation—and compiled for the IBM 7090. Computer runs to date have been used to trace the detailed behavior of the machine in various simple situations, such as those used with animals in experimental psychology laboratories. The purpose of these runs has been to discover errors in the program and to perform empirical investigations of the effects of varying program parameters.

RESULTS AND DISCUSSION

Data from a group of artificial rats in a simulated T-maze are typical of those obtained. The situation modeled is shown in Fig. 3. Curtains or doors prevent stimuli within the arms from affecting the rat's choice-point behavior. A single source of stimulation was, therefore, considered to include all stimulus elements that the "rat" could sense in the stem of the T and at the choice point. The stimulus vector contained 1152 components, all equally likely to be sampled. The choice of elements to form any stimulus presentation was random, with a

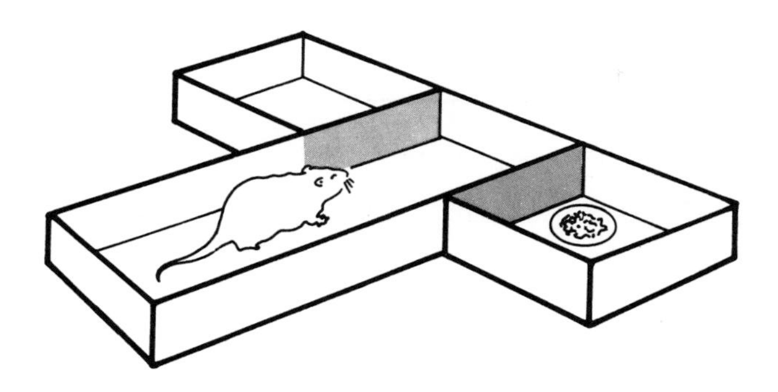

Fig. 3. Rat in a T-maze.

probability of 0.008 of selecting any given element. The artificial rats were permitted three responses. Entering the right arm of the maze was always reinforced since food appears in that arm of the model; entering the left arm was never reinforced, nor was the third response, which covered the miscellany of behavior usually considered irrelevant in the real situation and seldom recorded. The simulated rats were assumed to have no prior experience that would favor any of the responses, so that all three were considered equally likely at the beginning. Each association matrix was, therefore, set up initially by random placement of a one in each column. A correction procedure was used, each entry into the right arm of the maze terminating the current trial. Each "rat" continued performing until the criterion of nine successive error-free trials was met.

Results obtained from eight artificial rats are shown in Figs. 4-11, where the "rats" are numbered and arranged according to speed of learning. The mean number of trials required to reach the criterion of learning was 52.4; the standard deviation of that number was 21.9. The mean number of responses produced was 95.6; the standard deviation, 25.9. The mean number of errors was 40.7; the standard deviation, 18.9. Also of interest, although not reflected in the data shown, was the distribution of nonreinforced trials. The mean number of entries into the left arm of the maze was 19.1; the standard deviation, 8.9. The mean number of miscellaneous responses was 21.6; the standard deviation, 10.7.

Changes that took place in the association matrix as the artificial rats learned the maze problem are shown in Table 1. Entries indicate the proportion of stimulus elements connected at the beginning and end of each run to each of the three responses: right-stem entry, miscellaneous, and left-stem entry. The former was always reinforced; the latter two, never. If these data were reanalyzed to show the relative probabilities of the R and L responses only, probabilities in the initial matrix would center around 0.5, and those in the final matrix would show a considerably larger spread than they do when the M response is also considered. This observation points up the fact that the calculated probabilities of response in most psychological experiments primarily reflect artifacts of the observation technique. When all the responses available to an organism are considered, the absolute probability of any one is quite small—this feature may help explain both the variability of organismic behavior and its plasticity.

The question naturally arises whether the data from the artificial rats might be considered representative of the behavior displayed by live rats in a com-

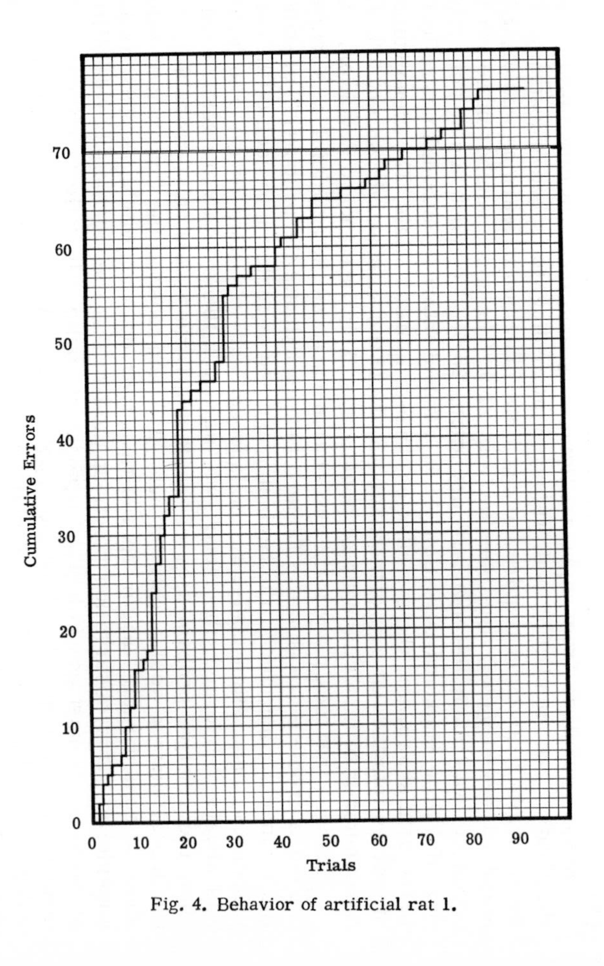

Fig. 4. Behavior of artificial rat 1.

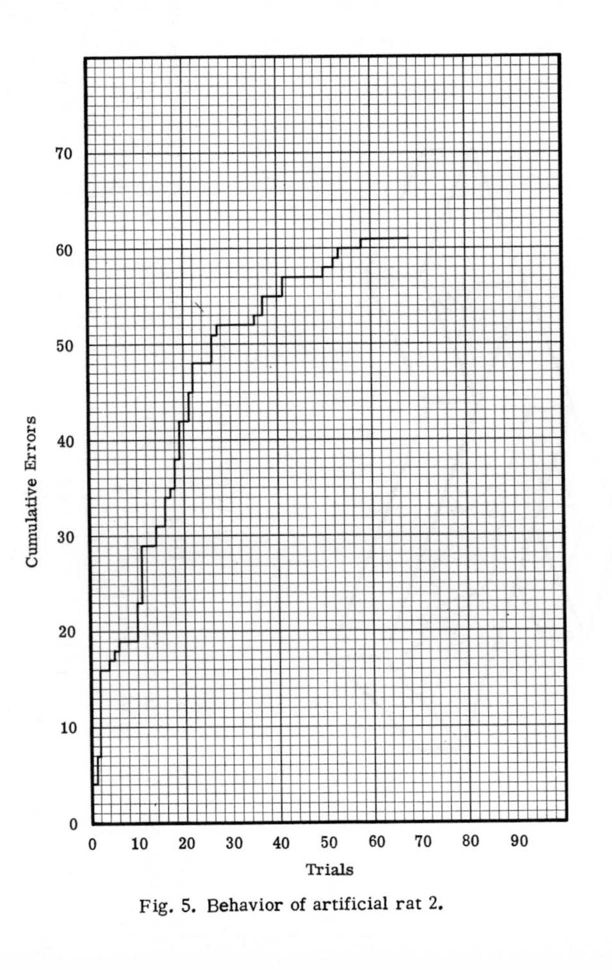

Fig. 5. Behavior of artificial rat 2.

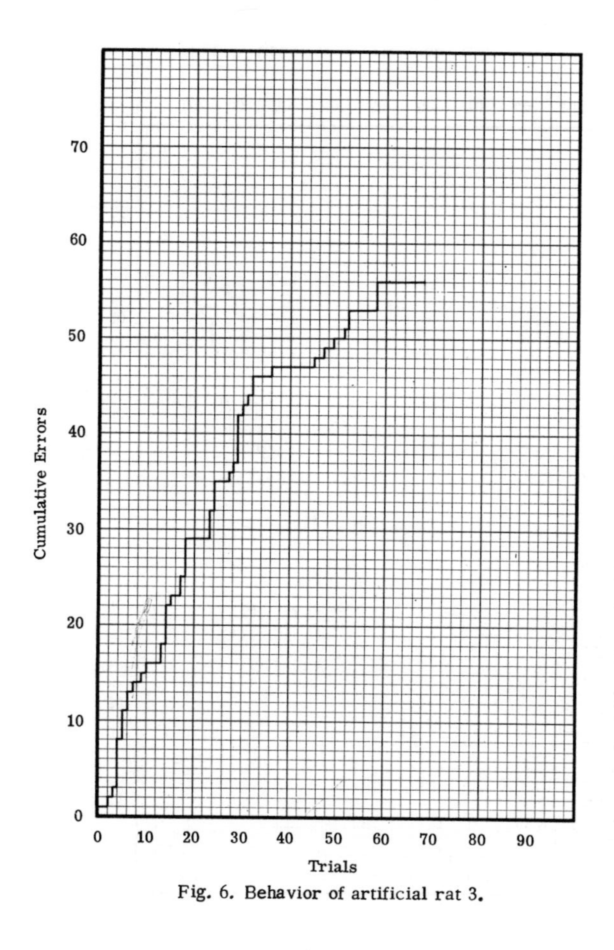

Fig. 6. Behavior of artificial rat 3.

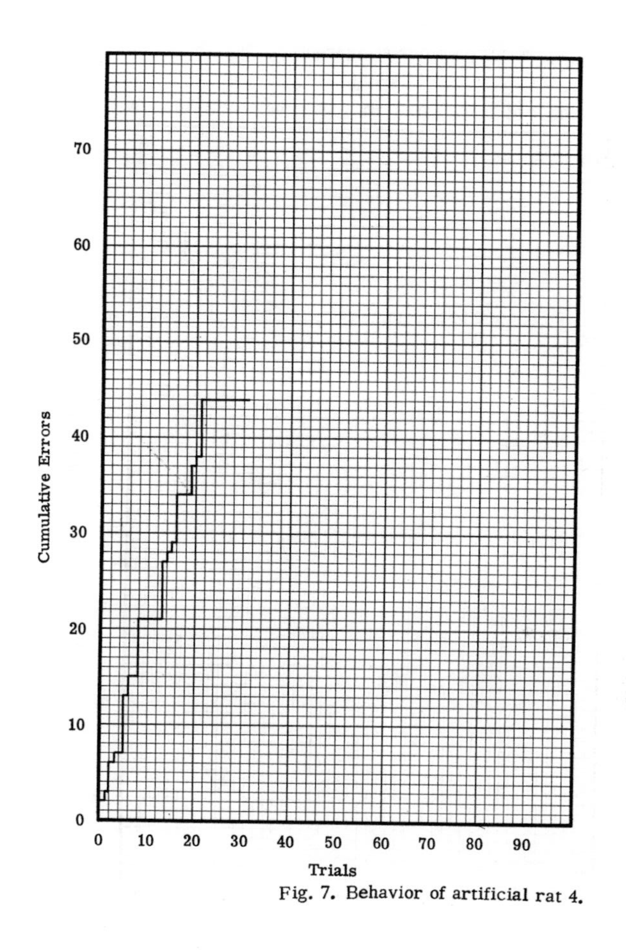

Fig. 7. Behavior of artificial rat 4.

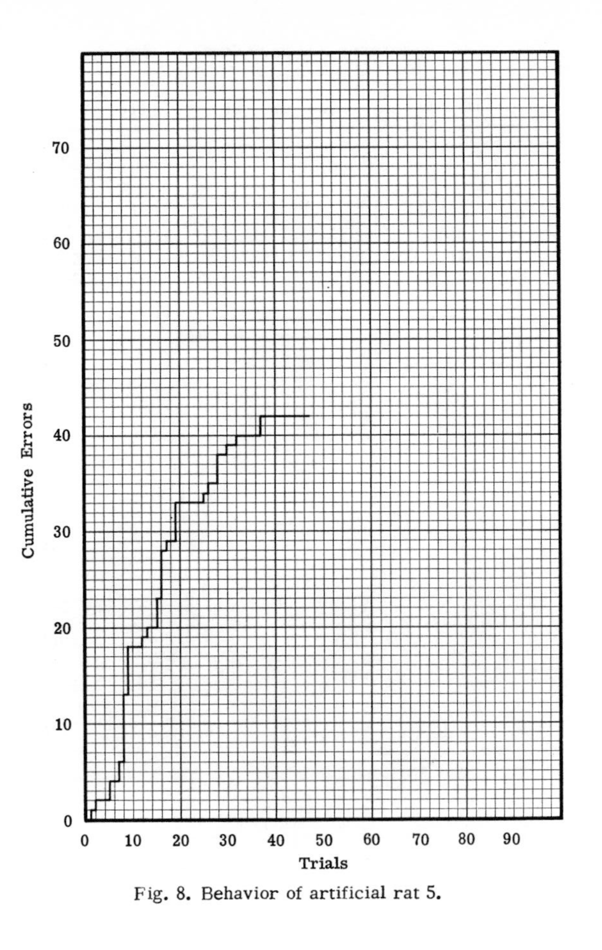

Fig. 8. Behavior of artificial rat 5.

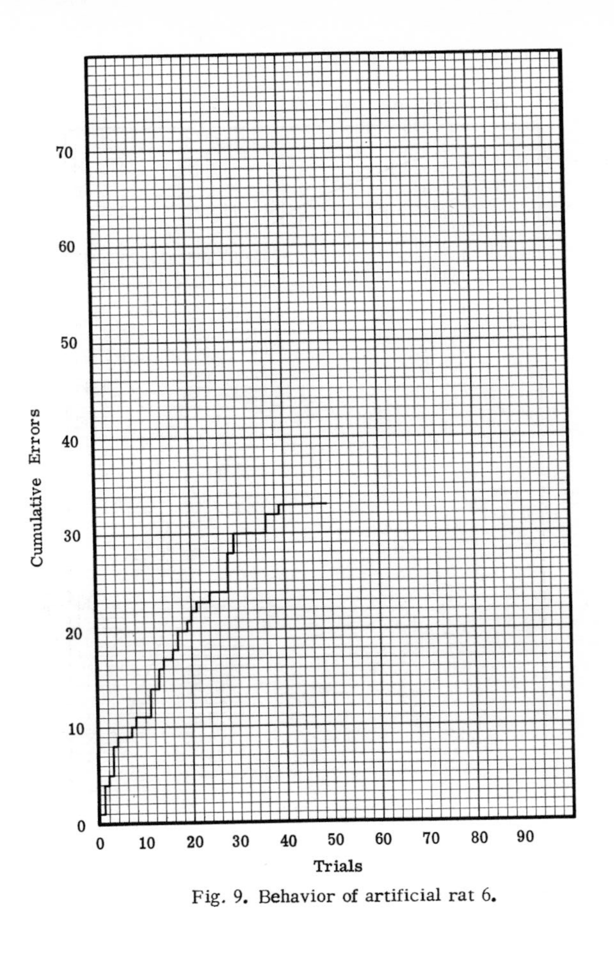

Fig. 9. Behavior of artificial rat 6.

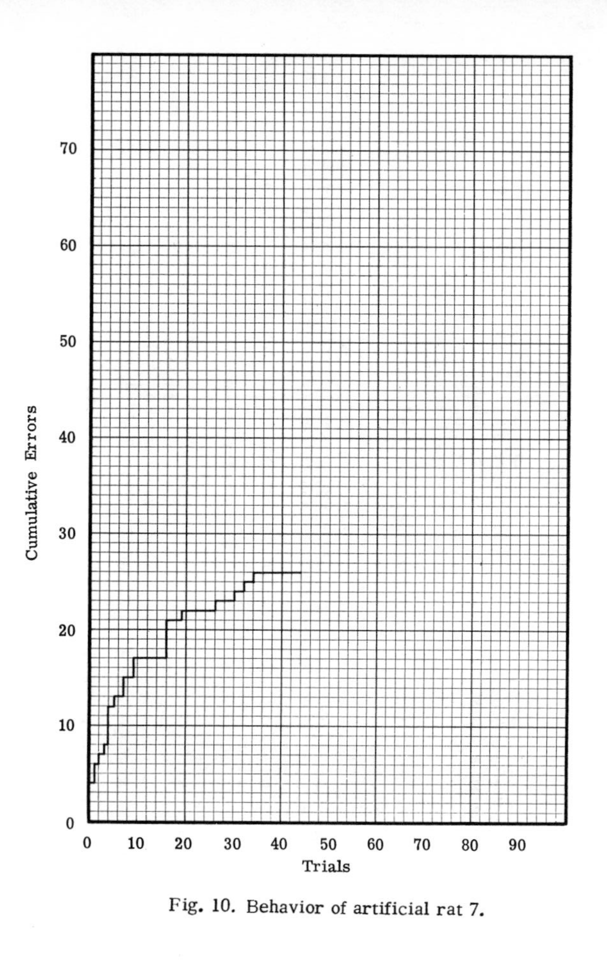

Fig. 10. Behavior of artificial rat 7.

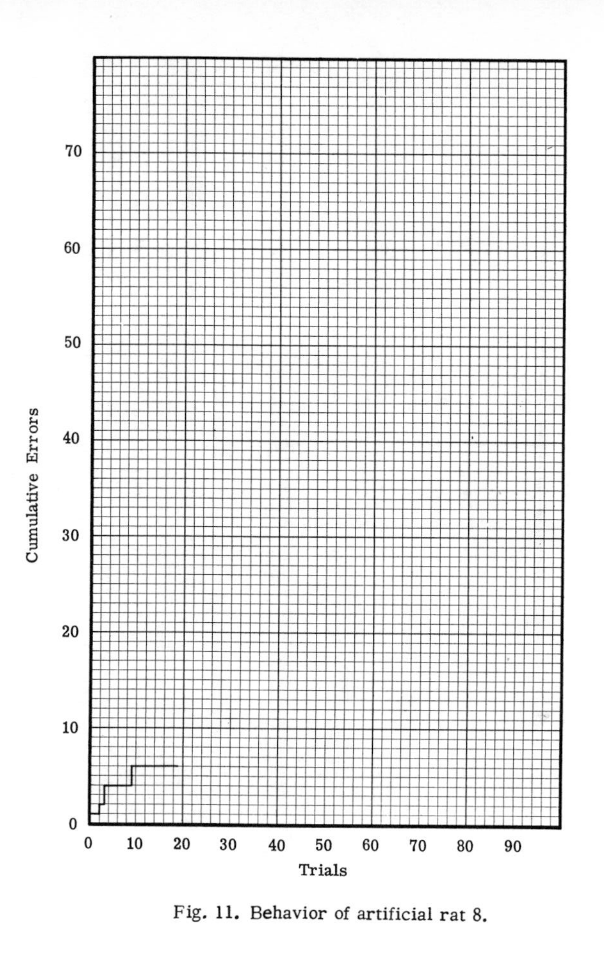

Fig. 11. Behavior of artificial rat 8.

Table I. Association Matrix Changes

"Rat"	Initial matrix			Final matrix		
	P(R)*	P(M)	P(L)	P(R)	P(M)	P(L)
1	0.33	0.35	0.32	0.65	0.18	0.17
2	0.31	0.34	0.35	0.55	0.21	0.24
3	0.35	0.32	0.33	0.59	0.21	0.20
4	0.33	0.33	0.34	0.44	0.27	0.29
5	0.35	0.32	0.33	0.53	0.23	0.24
6	0.34	0.34	0.32	0.55	0.23	0.22
7	0.32	0.34	0.34	0.50	0.25	0.25
8	0.34	0.31	0.35	0.42	0.27	0.31

*P, proportion of stimulus elements connected at the beginning and end of each run; R, right-stem entry; M, miscellaneous; L, left-stem entry.

parable situation. Three available studies (Brunswik, 1939; Hull and Spence, 1938; Stanley, 1950) used a situation nearly identical with that described as the model for the computer simulation. Unfortunately, the data in these studies are not presented in a manner than allows comparison throughout the acquisition series, but it happens that the proportion of entries into each of the maze arms can be calculated for trials 17-24 for each of the studies. Brunswik found the relative proportion of reinforced responses to be 44%; Hull and Spence, 98% for one group and 89% for another; Stanley, 71%. The comparable value for the eight artificial rats of the present experiment is 77%, a value that happens to fall close to the mean for the other four groups. This comparison, of course, proves nothing. It does, however, lend some support to the belief that an alliance between learning theory and machine technology can contribute to the advancement of both fields.

REFERENCES

Brunswik, E. 1939. Probability as a determiner of rat behavior. J. Exp. Psychol. 25, 195-197.
Bush, R.R. and Mosteller, F. 1951. A mathematical model for simple learning. Psychol. Rev. 58, 313-323.
Estes, W.K. 1950. Toward a statistical theory of learning. Psychol. Rev. 57, 95-107.
Estes, W.K. 1959. The statistical approach to learning theory, p. 380-491. In: Koch, S. (ed.), Psychology: a study of a science. Vol. 2. General systematic formulations, learning, and special processes. McGraw-Hill, New York.
Gilstrap, L.O. and Lee, R.J. 1960. Learning machines, p. 437-450. In: Bionics symposium. WADD Technical Report 60-600. Wright Air Develop. Div.
Guthrie, E.R. 1935. The psychology of learning. Harper & Brothers, New York.
Guthrie, E.R. 1959. Association by contiguity, p. 158-195. In: Koch, S. (ed.), Psychology: a study of a science. Vol. 2. General systematic formulations, learning, and special processes. McGraw-Hill, New York.
Hull, C.L. and Spence, K.W. 1938. "Correction" vs. "non-correction" method of trial-and-error learning in rats. J. Comp. Psychol. 25, 127-145.
Minsky, M. 1961. A selected descriptor-indexed bibliography to the literature on artificial intelligence. IRE Trans. on Human Factors in Electron. HFE-2, 39-55.
Rosenblatt, F. 1958. The perceptron. A theory of statistical separability in cognitive systems. Cornell Aeronaut. Lab. Rep. No. VG-1196-G-1.
Shaw, C.J. 1961. A programmer's introduction to basic JOVIAL. System Dev. Corp. Tech. Mem. TM-629.
Stanley, J.C., Jr. 1950. The differential effects of partial and continuous reward upon the acquisition and elimination of a runway response in a two-choice situation. Ed. D. Thesis, Harvard University. Cited by Bush, R.R. and Mosteller, F. 1955. Stochastic models for learning. John Wiley & Sons, Inc., New York, 291-294.
Uttley, A.M. 1956. Conditional probability machines and conditioned reflexes, p. 253-275. In: Shannon, C.E. and McCarthy, J. (ed.), Annals of mathematics studies, No. 34. Automata studies. Princeton Univ. Press, Princeton, N.J.

DESIGN OF AN ANALOG EAR

W. F. Caldwell, E. Glaesser, and J. L. Stewart

Bioacoustics Laboratory, Tucson, Arizona

Background

We subscribe to a certain philosophy for hearing. Our concept amounts to a "pattern" theory. In order to test this theory and to provide a useful real-time tool (independent of the pattern theory), we are implementing our concepts in the form of an analog ear. Insofar as is reasonable, parts of the analog bear a one-to-one relationship with parts of the ear. In this way it is hoped that the device will provide clues for the otologist as well as for the psychologist concerned with problems in recognition.

The Pattern Concept

In order to describe the pattern concept, a cross section of the human ear is shown in Fig. 1 (where the cochlea has been "unrolled" for clarity). Sound

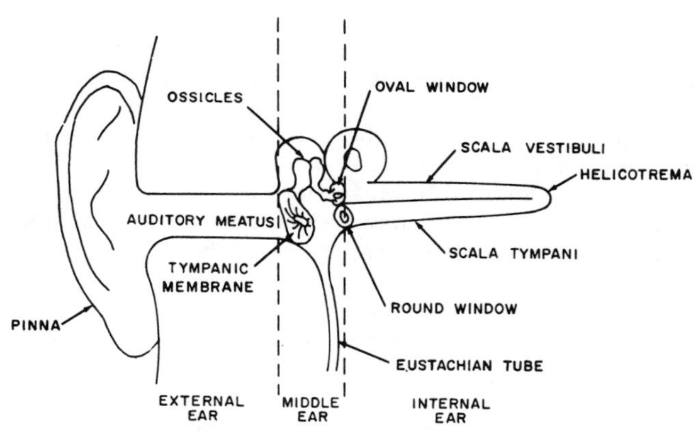

Fig. 1. Cross section of the human ear with linearized cochlea.

vibrations impinge on the ear drum and are transmitted with mechanical advantage via the middle-ear bones (ossicles) to the oval window of the cochlea. The mechanical advantage provides transformer action between air and fluid media. The pressure transfer characteristic from the pinna to the basilar end of the cochlea is typical of a capacitance-coupled low-pass filter which has a high-frequency peak. Vibrations at the oval window produce activity throughout the cochlea; this is best represented in terms of a pattern of transverse quasi-sinusoidal vibrations along the cochlear duct. The pattern of concern is like the envelope of the vibrations. Each distinct pattern corresponds to a different sustained sound. Temporal sequences of patterns represent phonemes. Such a sequence can be represented with a surface where surface height is pattern intensity, one axis is distance along the basilar membrane from the stapes, and the other is time. Recognition of phonemes is thus likened to recognition of a terrain map, as in vision. Interference between frequency components may lead to beat-frequency undulations of this "speech-cochlear surface" with time. We do not believe that regular undulations are important in (monaural) recognition (viz. whispered speech) although they are necessary for less definable naturalness and quality factors.

The Analog System

The electric analog has the form of Fig. 2, which we dare to call a "cochleograph." The oscilloscope provides a real-time sequence of patterns which

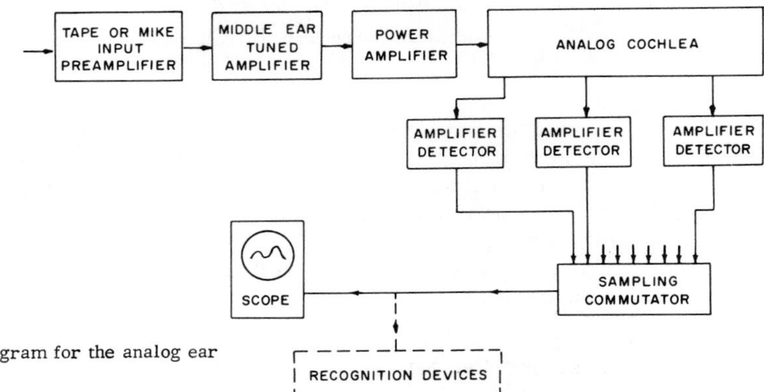

Fig. 2. Block diagram for the analog ear

can be photographed with continuously moving film; either Y-axis or Z-axis modulation may be employed, the latter giving a real-time record similar to a speech spectrograph.

The middle and external parts of the ear are modeled with a straightforward amplifier containing suitable frequency-sensitive elements. Reflex actions of middle-ear muscles are ignored because they may not be important at low speech levels. At a later date, reflexes may be included with feedback circuits which vary gain and frequency-sensitive parameters of the middle-ear amplifier.

The intensity pattern of either position or velocity along the analog cochlea (a special lumped-parameter RLC transmission line) is sampled at 36 points. The 36 signals are processed by power-law detection and post-detection averaging as explained elsewhere (Stewart, 1961). The 36 triode-diode amplifiers are straightforward, although special care has been used to insure maximum dynamic range from minimum usable levels (in excess of 60 db).

The ordered outputs from the 36 amplifiers (which may be called "loudness converters" in order to imply conversion to a subjective measure) are sampled with a high-speed mechanical (mercury jet) commutator so that 40 complete patterns per second are provided, with adequate dead time between adjacent patterns. The 40-per-second rate is consistent with high intelligibility of interrupted speech (Miller and Licklider, 1950). These patterns may be observed with a standard oscilloscope or photographed.

Patterns are also sent to a bank of correlating detectors which compare an observed pattern with memory. Each recognition filter is a reasonably simple lumped-parameter matched filter followed by a peak-level sampler (Turin, 1960). The concept of pattern recognition will not be considered further here.

Most design aspects of the analog ear should be reasonably clear. The exception is, of course, the analog cochlea itself. Hydrodynamic theories and equivalent networks have been given by Fletcher (1951), Zwislocki (1948, 1950), Bauch (1956), and Peterson and Bogert (1950). The result obtained by Fletcher is closest to the result here, although certain of the parameters differ numerically.

Before proceeding, let us summarize the various approximations and design guideposts of a general sort that have been made. First, we are interested in the "small-signal" ear. This means that reflexes, fatigue, adaptation, nonlinearities, "Tartini beats," and the like are ignored. Inasmuch as these factors may not be significant below 40 db above threshold, this approximation is a justifiable one, at least for softly spoken words. The small-signal approximation also minimizes the possibility that cross-connecting and efferent fibers in the cochlea (about which we know very little) are of major importance. It is emphasized that the model can and perhaps will eventually be equipped with various components which represent non-small-signal aspects.

Design assumptions presume a 36-section line by virtue of "engineering judgement" (and the totally irrelevant fact that the cochlea is 35 mm long, but six panels of six ear sections each are convenient). Tubes and quality components are employed in order to insure maximum accuracy and flexibility in the role of a computer. With the aid of computer studies, "second-generation" devices (not necessarily electric) may be constructed using transistors and perhaps lossy and innaccurate components such as tantalum capacitors and low-Q coils.

The Inner Ear

Assumptions relevant to the inner ear are that the perilymph is incompressible and that the walls of the cochlea are rigid. That two scalae may be represented with a single transmission-line equivalent does not appear to constitute an approximation.

Partial differential equations of continuity and of motion may be written in order to describe pressure and velocity distributions in the cochlea. An alternate but equivalent approach which aids in clarifying accuracy notions is to specify the highest derivative order of each of four applicable differential equations; in this manner, it becomes evident that artificial assumptions, such as separate ribbon-like elements for the basilar membrane, are unnecessary. Vibrations in each scala parallel with the cochlear duct are represented with first-order equations. Transverse motion of the cochlear duct is represented with a second-order equation. The relation between transverse and longitudinal motions is a first-order equation. The degree of accuracy is the same as that employed by Fletcher (1951). Accuracy is better than that obtained by Zwislocki (1948, 1950), who uses only a first-order equation for transverse motion of the cochlear duct (because he ignores the mass of the duct).

The hydrodynamic equations may be put into a form which implies a pressure difference as a measure of transverse motion. If the equations are placed in difference form, an analog consisting of a balanced ladder network is obtained. Because only differences are important, the balanced network may be unbalanced to give the final result shown in Fig. 3. (Note, however, that the unbalancing operation does not cause the common connection to become a zero-pressure reference point.) The network of Fig. 3a uses a pressure-voltage analog, and that in Fig. 3b employs a pressure-current analog. In order to have an idea of element values, we provide value ranges from basilar to apical ends, using the pressure-voltage analog: series resistance, 2-10 ohms; series inductance, 0.3-1.25 h; shunt resistance, 100 ohms to 90 kohm; shunt inductance, 0.35-1.5 h. Shunt-capacitance series resonates with shunt inductance at the appropriate place-principle resonance frequency; this capacitance varies by over five orders of magnitude along the line.

Data from many sources are employed for determining element values. Series elements presume water as the fluid. Data for shunt inductance were obtained using the estimated energy-equivalent mass of the cochlear duct in the manner given by Zwislocki (1948, 1950). An effort has been made to employ actual

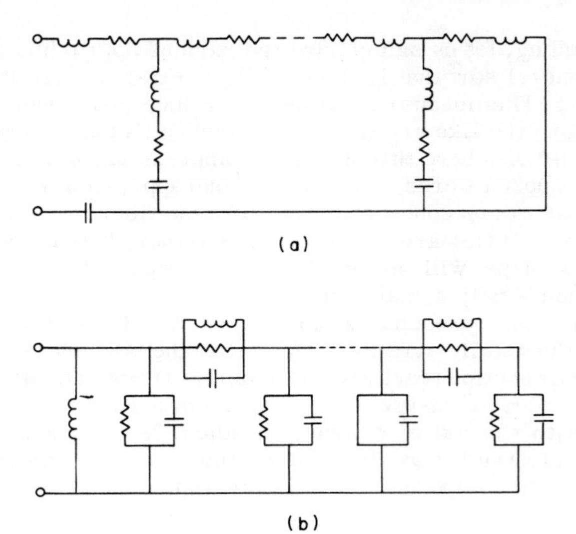

Fig. 3. Dual network representations for the inner ear: (a) pressure-voltage analog, (b) pressure-current analog.

dimensions of the human cochlear duct. Mass due to loading from fluids in the scalae has also been included; the loading effect was estimated from the change in resonant frequency that Békésy (1960) observed in going from a two-scala fluid model to a one-scala model. Shunt resistance was estimated from experimental damping characteristics (Békésy, 1960). Elasticity of the basilar membrane was not employed directly, but was inferred from total mass and place-principle resonant frequency.

The first series capacitance for the pressure-voltage analog in Fig. 3a (which can be represented as two larger capacitors in series) models the round window in series with the oval window. Increasing the stiffness of either of these windows obviously decouples the cochlea as an ordinary amplifier *RC* decoupling filter. Thus, low-frequency deafness occurs which spreads through all frequencies if elasticity is increased excessively (or if either window is immobilized). The manner in which this representation was found is interesting because it demonstrates how study from the analog may provide valuable hints for the physiologist and the otologist.

Development of the Equivalent Circuit

The artifice of push-pull excitation of the two cochlear windows is employed. That is, there is presumed an equal and opposite system of ossicles and a second tympanic membrane. Each driving system is coupled to its own scala. The ultimate parameter of interest is the pressure difference between the two scala representations. Because of the helicotrema, no pressure difference can exist at the apical end of the cochlea; the helicotrema is thus represented with a short circuit. The first-order result is shown in Fig. 4a. Zero-pressure reference is indicated with the usual ground symbol and the ideal pressure source is presumed to be applied subsequent to the middle-ear apparatus.

In addition to bone paths between ear drum and windows, there exist air-conduction paths. These are important only when bones are damaged. Air paths can be represented with ideal transformers and suitable delay networks. If each such composite device is represented as in Fig. 4b, then Fig. 4a can be shown as in Fig. 4c. A conduction path due to middle-ear bones is represented with a pair of terminals with a dashed connection; in some cases, a relatively complex

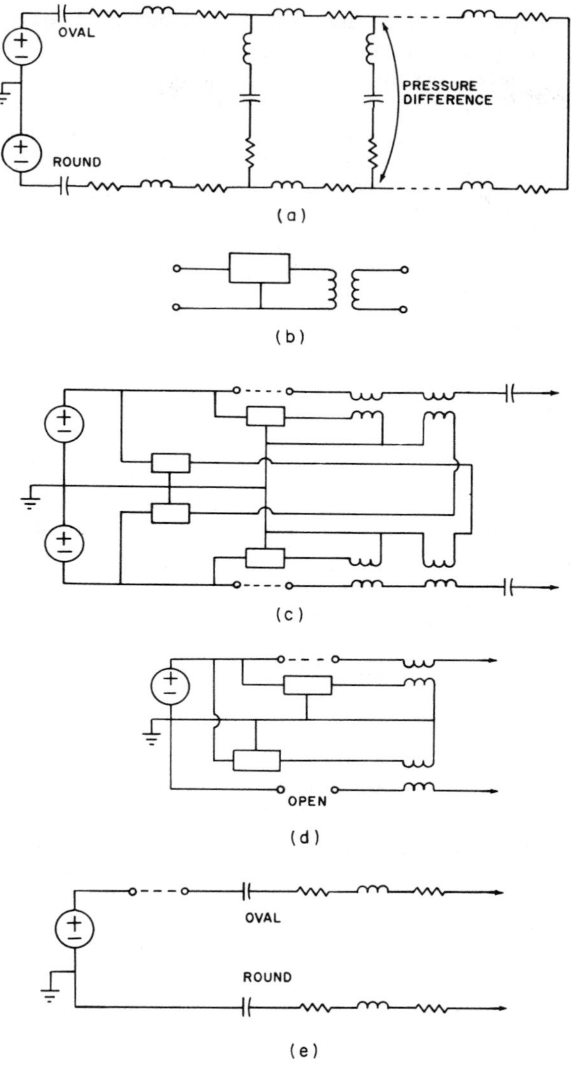

Fig. 4. Steps in the development of the equivalent circuit.

three-terminal network may be placed between these terminals as if, for example, feedback to middle-ear muscles or a pathological ear is to be represented. The roughest approximation for middle-ear bones is a direct connection; a somewhat better representation is a series RLC circuit.

In truth, the lower voltage generator in Fig. 4c does not exist; thus we set its voltage to zero, which is equivalent to replacing it with a short circuit. The two boxes which represent air conduction paths driven with the lower voltage generator may then also be ignored (which is facilitated by presuming output impedances of the boxes to be zero). Of course, the round window is not associated with middle-ear bones and, hence, the appropriate terminal pair may be opened. The result is Fig. 4d, which may be employed to infer what occurs if middle-ear bones are damaged (because then air conduction paths become relatively more important).

As an aside, it may be noted that removal of ossicles leaves only air paths. As stated before, both windows must operate; if one is immobilized, a new window must be constructed (as in fenestration). If attenuation and delay (which is not a significant factor) from the ear drum to the two windows are the same, hearing cannot exist because pressure effects along the basilar membrane cancel. In this event, it is important that one window be appreciably less susceptible (few decibels) to motion of the ear drum than the other; in fenestration, this can be achieved by suitably positioning a new window. Alternate usage of a baffle in the middle-ear cavity can also be suggested.

In the normal ear we can ignore air conduction. Since the output impedance of the equivalent in Fig. 4b is zero, and if we ignore the slight delay involved, the final result of Fig. 4e obtains.

Data pertaining to the transfer characteristics of the external ear are given by Wiener and Ross (1946). For the middle ear, Fletcher (1952) provides data inferred from experiments by Békésy.

Conclusion

In the foregoing we have tried to present certain of our ideas regarding hearing and how we are proceeding to reduce these ideas to model form. We believe that the small-signal model is as accurate as the available data allow. We further believe that eventual inclusion of second-order effects such as fatigue, reflexes, and so forth will not invalidate the model; hence, what we thus far propose may be relatively basic. We have yet a long way to go in order to provide features of automatic recognition. Nevertheless, our expected approach is even now specific to the point of suggesting the ultimate goal in bandwidth reduction in a device which apes human behavior to the point of duplicating human mistakes.

Parenthetical Note

The impedance level of the source in the equivalent-circuit representation of Fig. 4 is referred to the position of the oval window. In order to refer the source to the malleus side of the tympanic membrane, an ideal transformer may be inserted which provides a step-up ratio from source to equivalent circuit.

It should also be noted that the source in Fig. 4 is not really an ideal one. Rather, it should be replaced with a source-network combination which represents the outer and part of the middle ear; in this way, the equivalent for the entire ear system becomes a single passive bilateral network. The network so added has a transfer characteristic that is typically low pass with series capacitors, so that voltage transfer does not extend to zero frequency (except when capacitance voltage divider action is possible). It is important to observe that the transfer characteristic depends on loading by subsequent network representations, especially the inner ear.

The low-frequency cutoff characteristics in human hearing can be equated to the combined effects of series-capacitance representations for windows, ossicles, ear drum, middle-ear cavity, and the cochlea. High-frequency cutoff properties are identified with transmission characteristics of the external and middle parts of the ear. However, simple equivalent circuits are no longer adequate for representation, as is attested by the ever-increasing slope of typical threshold curves. At elevated frequencies, equivalent circuits consisting of numerous low-pass-type sections are more accurate structurally but more difficult to evaluate experimentally. Also, seemingly minor individual differences become important at high frequencies.

Acknowledgment

This research was supported by contract AF 33(616)-7800 between the University of Arizona and Aeronautical Systems Division, Air Force Systems Command. The authors are especially grateful to members of the Bio-Acoustics Branch, Aerospace Medical Laboratory, Wright-Patterson Air Force Base, Dayton, Ohio.

REFERENCES

Bauch, H. 1956. Die Schwingungsform der Basilarmembran bei Erregung durch Impulse und Geräusche, gemessen an einem elektrischen Model des Innenohres. Frequenz. 10, 222-234.
Békésy, G. von. 1960. Experiments in hearing. McGraw-Hill Book Co., New York.
Fletcher, H. 1951. On the dynamics of the cochlea. J. Acoust. Soc. Am. 23, 637-645.
Fletcher, H. 1952. The dynamics of the middle ear and its relation to the acuity of hearing. J. Acoust. Soc. Am. 24, 129-131.
Miller, G.A. and Licklider, J.C.R. 1950. The intelligibility of interrupted speech. J. Acoust. Soc. Am. 22, 167-173.
Peterson, L.C. and Bogert, B.P. 1950. A dynamical theory of the cochlea. J. Acoust. Soc. Am. 22, 369-381.
Stewart, J.L. 1961. A model for hearing. This volume, p. 213.
Turin, G.L. 1960. An introduction to matched filters. IRE Trans. Information Theory IT-6, 311-329. (Also see Stewart, J.L. 1960. Fundamentals of signal theory, Chap. 11, McGraw-Hill Book Co., New York.)
Wiener, F.M. and Ross, D.A. 1946. The pressure distribution in the auditory canal in a progressive sound field. J. Acoust. Soc. Am. 18, 401-408.
Zwislocki, J. 1948. Theorie der Schneckenmechanik. Acta Oto-Laryng. Suppl. 72, 1-76.
Zwislocki, J. 1950. Theory of the acoustical action of the cochlea. J. Acoust. Soc. Am. 22, 778-784.

AN ELECTRONIC MODEL OF THE LIMULUS EYE

D. Hildebrand

Bionics Unit, Advanced Electronics Center, Cornell University
General Electric Company, Ithaca, New York

The electronic model is based on the concept of mutual inhibition. This concept is developed and the model described. A computer program to simulate the Limulus eye and the results of several experiments are discussed. Some possible applications are outlined.

One might ask at this point: "What is mutual inhibition?" Mutual inhibition is the interaction of the outputs of biological sensor elements and, while it appears immediately adjacent to the receptors themselves, as in the eye of Limulus, it can be described and discussed separately from the receptors.

The mutual inhibition among the receptors of the lateral eye of the Limulus, as reported by Hartline and Ratliff (1957, 1958) and Hartline et al. (1936) has led many researchers in a new and exciting direction in the study of neural systems. Evidence of mutual inhibition has been reported in human vision (von Békésy, 1960). The spatial frequency-response curves reported (Lowry and DePalma, 1961) for the human eye are analogous to those obtained from a mutually inhibitory system.

The concept of spatial summation of inhibitory influences, as developed by Hartline and his coworkers, will be described with the aid of the block diagram shown in Fig. 1. In the real physical world, the interface between the receptors and the mutually inhibitory network is not usually available to the experimenter. It will be shown later how measurements can be made indirectly at this point. The following discussion of mutual inhibition will be limited to the block labeled "Mutually Inhibitory Network." The "magnitude" of a response or a stimulus means the frequency or reciprocal of the average interval between neural impulses. The inputs to the mutually inhibitory network are the outputs of the group of receptors feeding it, and the output of the network is a trunk of nerve fibers. An inhibitory unit is defined, for convenience of discussion, as an input line, its associated output line, and the inhibitory interconnections to the other units in the system.

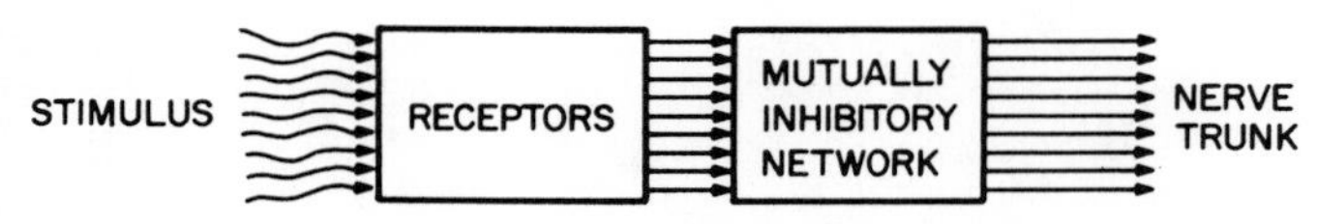

Fig. 1. Block diagram of mutually inhibitory network.

A mutually inhibitory network is shown schematically in Fig. 2. This system consists of three units, A, B and C, arranged so that B and C can inhibit A, but B and C do not inhibit each other (in Limulus this uncoupling of B and C can be achieved by choosing units that are widely separated on the eye). An input I_A is applied to A only and its output, O_A, measured. It is found that I_A is equal to O_A; now an input I_B is applied to B and the output of A and B measured. The output of A, O_A, is now found to be less than in the previous case and is expressed by

$$O_A = I_A - \Delta_B \tag{1}$$

By experimentation it was found that Δ_B is a constant fraction of O_B. A constant called "the coefficient of the inhibitory action" was defined by Hartline. This constant, K_{AB}, is a measure of the inhibitory action of unit B on unit A. When Δ_B is expressed in terms of K_{AB} and O_B we have

$$O_A = I_A - K_{AB}O_B \tag{2}$$

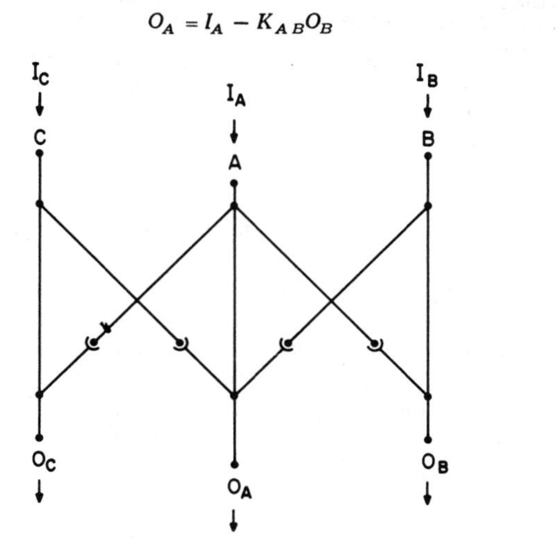

Fig. 2. Schematic of mutually inhibitory network.

The same experiment is performed with unit C in place of B and the constant K_{AC} determined. Now an input is applied to both B and C and it is found that O_A is diminished by an amount Δ_{BC} which is equal to the sum of Δ_B and Δ_C. By varying the inputs to B and C it is observed that Δ_{BC} can be expressed by

$$\Delta_{BC} = K_{AB}O_B + K_{AC}O_C \tag{3}$$

The output of A is now seen to be determined by

$$O_A = I_A - (K_{AB}O_B - K_{AC}O_C) \tag{4}$$

The restriction that B and C cannot interact can now be removed if one is careful to observe that it is the outputs of B and C that inhibit A, and, to achieve the desired output from any unit, it is necessary to take into account the inhibitory influences from the other two. Output functions for B and C analogous to that for A can be written, defining a system of simultaneous linear equations.

Our mutually inhibitory network can now be expanded to a system of n units and the equations written in the form of

$$O_p = I_p - \sum_{\substack{j=1 \\ j \neq p}}^{n} K_{pj}O_j \tag{5}$$

Note that the term under the summation for $p = j$ is not included. This is the term that corresponds to a unit's inhibition of itself. There is some evidence that such self-inhibition exists, but for the present it will be assumed there is none.

As in all neural studies there are thresholds and limits that must be taken into account. It has been found that there is a threshold of the inhibitory action of one cell on another; that is, unless the output of a cell is greater than a certain minimum, there is no inhibitory effect from that cell. This is shown by

$$O_p = I_p - \sum_{\substack{j=1 \\ j \neq p}}^{M} K_{pj}(O_j - O_{pj}^0) \tag{6}$$

Thus O_{pj}^0 is the threshold of the inhibitory action of the jth cell on the pth cell. If O_{pj}^0 is greater than O_j, there is no inhibition and zero is substituted for the term $(O_j - O_{pj}^0)$. Also the output of a unit is limited to magnitudes greater than or equal to zero.

It was previously mentioned that it is possible to measure the inputs to the mutually inhibitory network indirectly. If a stimulus is applied to only one receptor, there will only be one input line to the network activated. No other units except the one with an input can have any output and its output must, therefore, be identical in magnitude to its input.

The electronic model of the Limulus eye that we have constructed is a special-purpose analog computer which can solve the equations describing a ten-unit mutually inhibitory network. There are ten summing amplifiers in the model, each consisting of a two-stage negative-feedback-stabilized ac-coupled transistor amplifier. The first stage of the amplifier is a voltage amplifier with 180° phase shift. The input impedance was intentionally made low for reasons which will be shown later. The voltage across the collector-load resistor is amplified in an emitter-follower stage. The gain of each amplifier was adjusted for unity when an input voltage was applied in series with a 10,000-ohm resistor. The inhibitory connections are made by connecting a resistor from the output of the inhibiting amplifier to the input of the amplifier to be inhibited. The value of this resistor is determined by the numerical value of the coefficient of inhibitory action desired.

The reason for the low-input impedance is now clear. Each of the inputs to the amplifier causes a current to flow in the input impedance and the voltage caused by these currents is proportional to their algebraic sum. This voltage, when amplified and inverted, appears as the output of the amplifier. The output now has the correct magnitude and sign to be fed back to other amplifiers as an inhibitory input, and to be measured to determine the unit's output. The inhibitory resistors are mounted on a circuit board with their leads brought to a 20-pin connector. A connector on the model connects these resistors to the inputs and outputs of the amplifiers. In this manner the coefficients of inhibitory action can be easily changed by changing the circuit board.

Because of the complete freedom in connecting the inhibitory resistors, the units can be interconnected in any desired manner. A linear array of the ten units has been used in all the experiments to date, and several boards with different coefficients of inhibitory action have been constructed. The inputs to the network are 400-cycle ac voltages which can be varied with a potentiometer at each of the ten inputs. The inputs and outputs of the network are displayed on an oscilloscope with a scanning switch. The vertical height of each block represents the magnitude of the input or output for each unit. Figures 3 and 4 show some representative examples. The effect of mutual inhibition can easily be observed. There is a definite accentuation of the edges or steps in the input pattern. Such a device could well be used to accentuate the edges and other details in the input pattern from an array of IR detectors or other similar device.

If the set of numbers making up the inputs is considered as a sampling of an intensity distribution function and the output considered in a like manner, it can be shown that the output function is the autocorrelation function of the input and a function defined by the coefficients of inhibitory action. This leads to equations similar to those found in electrical-filter theory. The model constructed can be studied with linear-filter theory and its limitations defined. As the model does

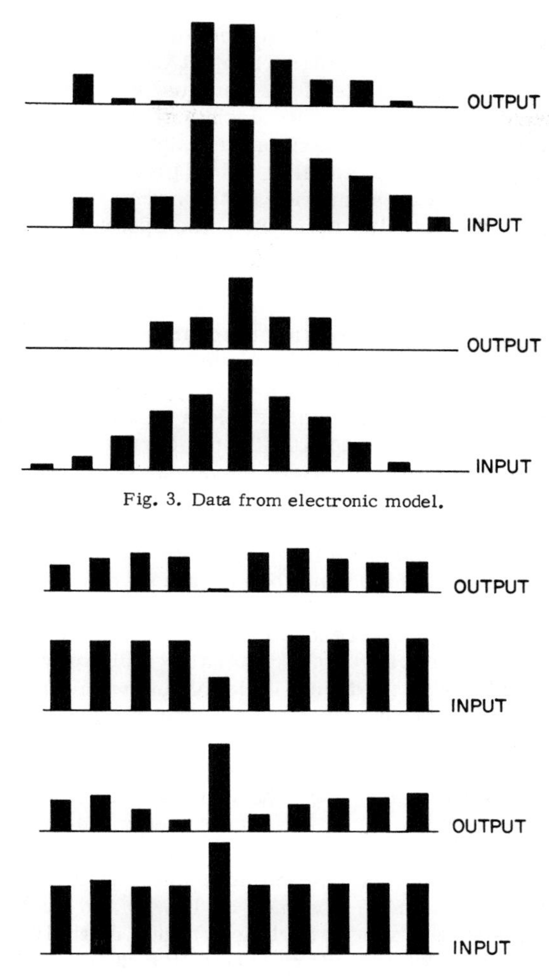

Fig. 3. Data from electronic model.

Fig. 4. Data from electronic model.

not incorporate the thresholds and limits implicit in Hartline's mathematical model, a digital computer was programmed to simulate a mutually inhibitory network and determine the effect of the limits and thresholds. Linear-filter theory clearly defines the limits of performance of a linear filter, but in the case of a nonlinear filter this cannot be done. The computer simulation has already shown an unexpected and as yet unexplainable effect of the inhibition threshold. This threshold has a large effect on the average value of the output, almost an order of magnitude more than might be expected, and in the opposite direction from what had been supposed. In some cases this effect is only in the dc level of the output (that is, the relative values remain unchanged); however, in other instances it modifies the relative values as well, but to a lesser degree. The limiting of the output to positive numbers is, for the most part, manifested as a clipping action, but does have a small effect on the relative values of the positive responses.

The phenomenon of "simultaneous brightness induction," (Heinemann, 1955) was suggested as a possible manifestation of mutual inhibition in the human visual system. Briefly, Heinemann's experiment is as follows: The subject is shown an illuminated disk with an illuminated annulus surrounding it. Separated from this is another disk on which the subject can control the brightness. The experimenter varies the brightness of the annulus, keeping the disk it surrounds at a constant level of brightness. For each setting of the annulus, the subject adjusts the brightness of the comparison disk until it appears the same as that of the disk surrounded by the annulus. This gives a measure of the apparent brightness of the test disk as a function of the actual brightness of the annulus. As the brightness of the annulus increases, the apparent brightness of the disk increases slightly until the disk and the annulus have the same actual brightness. Then the apparent brightness of the disk decreases very rapidly until it is quite dark.

A similar experiment was run with the computer program using a section across the disk-annulus as a stimulus. When the size of the disk was less than the "refractory width," as defined by von Békésy (1960), curves similar to those of Heinemann were obtained, but when the width of the disk was greater than the refractory width, a bright spot appeared in the center. This experiment may be a means to measure the refractory width in humans by observing the appearance of the bright spot in the center of the disk. An additional observation is that when the calculations on the computer are made without limits and thresholds, the apparent brightness of the disk simply increases with the brightness of the annulus. Thus, it seems that mutual inhibition is not sufficient in itself to explain this phenomenon; the effects of limits and thresholds must also be considered.

A second experiment of interest is one which was designed to measure the spatial frequency-response curve of a mutually inhibitory network. The electronic model of Limulus was modified. A delay line with ten equally spaced taps was connected to the input of the network, one tap going to each input line. A sine-wave voltage, applied at the input of the delay line, could be sampled at the ten taps, thus converting a voltage function in time to one in space, the spatial dimension being along the delay line. The wave would travel across the input of the mutually inhibitory network. By measuring the amplitude of the input to one of the units and the amplitude of the corresponding output, the gain at any particular spatial frequency could be determined. Curves obtained from this experiment are remarkably like those obtained by Lowry and DePalma (1961) for the human eye. From this experiment, it is obvious that a mutually inhibitory network with a set of coefficients of inhibitory action like those used in the experiment will give a maximum response to a range of spatial frequencies, and much diminished response to frequencies above and below this range.

Several devices and applications employing mutual inhibition can be suggested. A device operating on the video signal of a TV or radar system, which would sharpen and refocus the image and enhance edges and contours, would seem to be possible. Experiments are presently in progress to prove the feasibility of such a device and to obtain design data. At present this consists of a set of tapped delay lines to store the video signal and a mutually inhibitory network much like the one used in the model of the Limulus eye. Eventually it is hoped that a thin-film device, much like a light amplifier, could be developed which could be used as the screen of a cathode ray tube. Recalling that the output function of a mutually inhibitory network is an autocorrelation function, one could, by proper choice of the coefficients of inhibitory action, make a device capable of target or character recognition.

Mutual inhibition, having been shown to be valid for simple biological systems, might well be extended to more complex and diverse systems. The mathematical model, with suitable modifications, could well be useful in studying human vision and other sensory modalities.

REFERENCES

von Békésy, G. 1960. Neural inhibitory units of the eye and skin. Quantitative description of contrast phenomena. J. Opt. Soc. Am. 50, 11, 1060.

Hartline, H. K. and Ratliff, F. 1957. Inhibitory interaction of receptor units in the eye of Limulus. J. Gen. Physiol. 40, 357.

Hartline, H. K. and Ratliff, F. 1958. Spatial summation of inhibitory influences in the eye of the Limulus. J. Gen. Physiol. 41, 5, 1049-1066.

Hartline, H. K., Wagner, H. G., and Ratliff, F. 1956. Inhibition in the eye of Limulus. J. Gen. Physiol. 39, 651.

Heinemann, E. G. 1955. Simultaneous brightness induction as a function of inducing—and test field luminances. J. Exp. Psychol. 50, 2, 89.

Lowry, E. M. and DePalma, J. J. 1961. Sine wave response of the visual system. I. The Mach phenomenon. J. Opt. Soc. Am. 51, 7, 740.

RECOGNITION OF THE SPOKEN WORD BY MACHINE

Harry F. Olson and Herbert Belar

RCA Laboratories, Princeton, New Jersey

The purpose of this paper is to describe the automatic recognition of speech by machine. Work in this field has been carried on by a number of investigators. This paper describes the progress made at the Acoustical and Electromechanical Research Laboratory of the RCA Laboratories and, in conformance with the aims of this Bionics Conference, with particular emphasis on this aspect of the subject.

The transducing of the information contained in the spoken word into the printed form can, of course, be performed by a human operator, but just how this is done is not completely known. Obviously, before speech is recognized by a person, the information is processed in the physiological sense. There are still some gaps in the knowledge of the sensation of hearing, in spite of much that is now understood. The most accurate information now available pertains to physical analysis of the sounds of speech, because the means for measurement have been developed. With these reservations, reference may be made to Fig. 1, which depicts the bionics of a person or a machine that types in response to the spoken word. In trying to use human faculties as models for the operation of a machine, there are well-known pitfalls that have to be avoided. Human functions can not always be explained in physical terms before the physical processes themselves are understood. There is also the likelihood of not doing what is natural to the machine, and in many cases it may be desirable to depart from the human model so that advantage can be taken of the greater accuracy with which a machine can determine absolute quantities, endurance can be traded for complexity, and so forth. Those who have worked in the field of acoustical engineering as long as the authors may remember the first automatic record changers. They followed the steps of a human operator. The record was picked up, carried to the turntable, placed thereon, played, lifted up, turned over, again placed on the turntable, played again, and finally taken off the turntable and placed into another container. Modern record changers are very simple indeed by comparison. Human operations are more complex than the most sophisticated machine ever built, but a machine can be made more precise and consistent and it does not tire in the same way. A human operator would not like to hold a pile of records on a spindle while they are being played and drop them one by one, nor would human fingers be suited to count off records from the inside of a little hole. More about the different ways of humans and machines will be outlined in later sections.

Figure 1 indicates the Bionics of a person/machine that types in response to the spoken word. A grossly simplified description of the human system is as follows: receptor, nerve, brain; and brain, nerve, effector. In this case the receptor is the ear and the effector is the finger that operates the typewriter.

The Outer and Middle Ear

The machine counterparts of the human system are the microphone, audio amplifier, and audio compressor and limiter. The ear canal helps to match the impedance of the air to that of the eardrum and affects the frequency response principally by deemphasizing low frequencies. The mechanical motion produced in the eardrum is transmitted and transformed in order to match the impedance of the liquid-filled cochlea by means of the small bones interposed, which move as levers in a nonlinear manner. The signal is compressed; that is, greater amplitudes are reduced proportionately more than smaller ones. The nonlinear motion gives rise to the subjective harmonics. In the machine counterpart, the generation of the equivalent of subjective harmonics is avoided when an audio compressor is used which varies the gain at a rate slower than the frequency that is amplified. Much work was done on compressors for speech machines, as their requirements differ in many respects from other audio uses. In an audio system the criterion is that the compressor should not cause audible distortion. In a speech recognition machine it is desired that variations in loudness of speaking or distances from the microphone have the least effect upon the analysis obtained. Tests were also made with nonlinear amplifiers that come closer to the action of the inner ear. Amplifiers were employed that delivered an audio output with an average value proportional to the logarithm of the average value of the input signal. In such a system the distortion in the form of harmonics is proportional to the amplitude of the signal, and the harmonics diminish rapidly with their order. Good results were obtained when certain critical threshold levels were observed in the detectors following the use of such a compressor. In those cases it was also desirable to add high-frequency preemphasis before the nonlinear amplifier, as in the ear. This was not required when conventional audio compressors, which do not cause harmonic distortion were used. It may be noted that only one ear is shown on Fig. 1. It was reasoned that although a human observer would obtain superior results with two ears by using his binaural sense to concentrate on the sound from the desired direction, it is also possible for a person to understand speech with one ear. This simplified the machine for the time being, but considerations have been given to binaural systems. Such a system would extract a greater amount of information from the sound field generated by the speaker and would allow greater discrimination between speakers or between speech and noise. A binaural system would also reduce beats due to reflections in the room. For such a system the directional response of the microphones would have to be changed to avoid an ambiguity in directional response. The pinnae or auricles of the human ear perform this function by acting as reflectors of high-frequency sounds coming from in front of the head. This can be observed, according to Stewart and Lindsay, by holding a watch (the tick of which contains some high-frequency components) first in front of and then behind the head.

The Inner Ear

The oval window in the cochlea receives the vibrations transmitted by the middle ear and transmits them to the fluid of the cochlea (shown extended in Fig. 1). This part of the figure has been taken from a book by one of the authors (Olson, 1952), and in it is shown the frequency scale that can be established along the cochlea. The inner ear is, in effect, a sound analyzer. A good musical ear is capable of distinguishing 1500 separate frequencies. No known linear electrical system with the rapid response of the ear is capable of resolving this number of frequencies in the audio-frequency range. On the other hand, even a simple machine can determine some parameters more accurately than the best ear. The analysis obtained in the cochlea is fed to the brain by 4000 nerve fibers. Not shown on Fig. 1 is the organ of Corti, which terminates the nerve fibers in the form of small hairs extending into the canal of the cochlea.

The machine counterparts of the inner ear are the frequency analyzers and quantizing detectors. The latest laboratory model phonetic typewriter employs only eight frequency channels. So did the first model, but models were built with 16 channels and even greater numbers were tried. This was done in an effort to

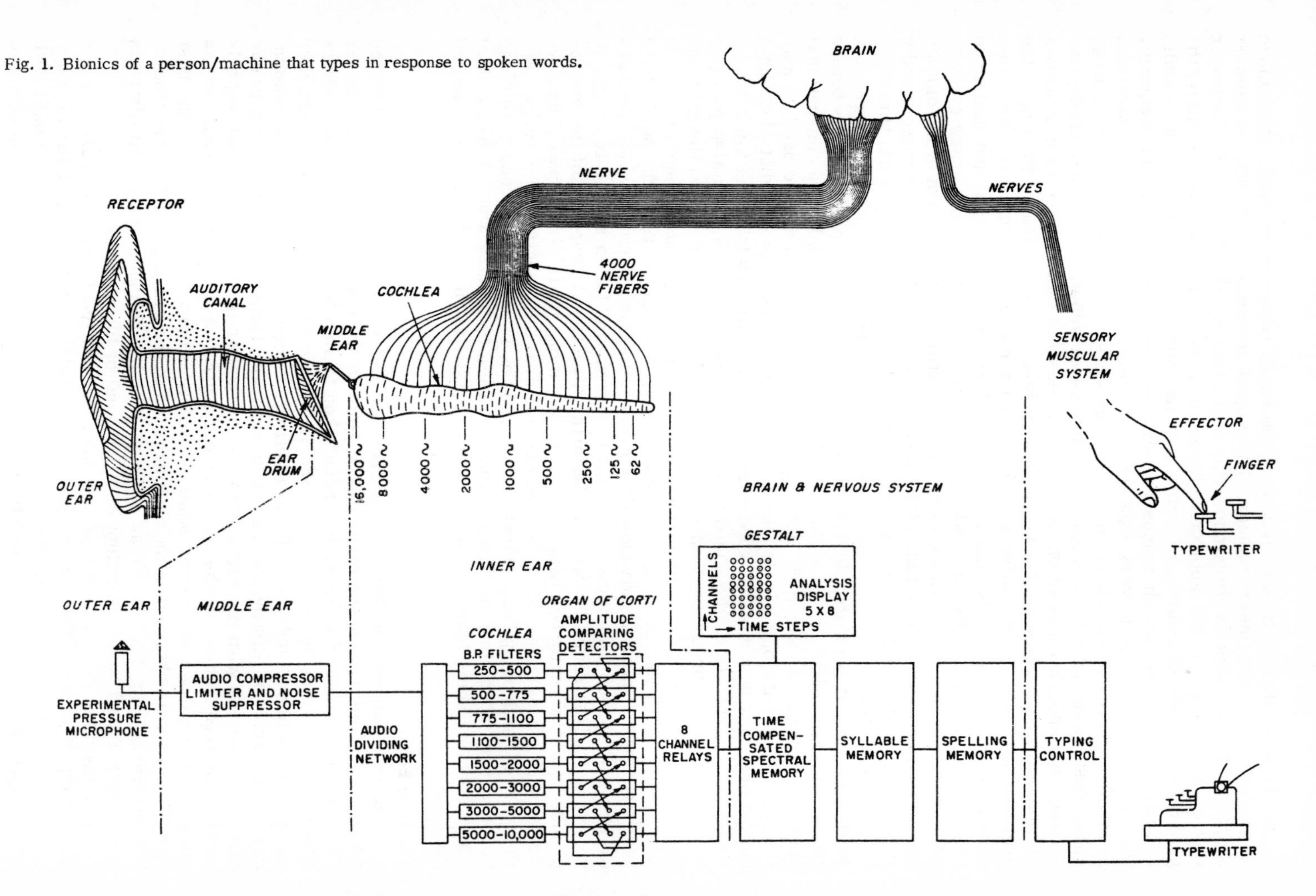

Fig. 1. Bionics of a person/machine that types in response to spoken words.

increase the resolving power of the machine and in order to distinguish between certain words, which the eight channel machine could not do. But the dilemma presented to the designer is that eight channels are already too many in some respects. That is, eight channels quantized in a simple off-on manner show variations in speaking for sucessive phonations of the same sound by the same speaker, even if the speaker makes an effort to speak the same way each time. In the phonetic typewriter Model III, an improvement in this respect was obtained by an amplitude-comparing network. It consists of positive and negative output rectifiers which measure the level in each channel. They are so interconnected that the relay corresponding to a channel is operated only if the level in that channel is greater than the average of the levels in the two adjacent ones. In a way this can be thought to represent the second derivative of the spectral response with respect to frequency by finite differences. The machine analogy with hearing does not necessarily end with the amplitude-comparing network, as it is thought that the human nervous system also performs comparisons by adding excitatory and inhibitory inputs.

The Brain

Stated in greatly simplified terms, the human brain receives information from the ear, processes it, makes decisions, and directs the finger to type. At the present state of the art it may be presumptuous to delineate any portion of the machine as the counterpart of a human brain. However, it is possible to describe what the machine does as it processes the signals received from the analyzer and finally causes a typewriter to type. The amplitude-compared and quantized output of the frequency analyzer is fed in the form of an eight-channel off-on code (eight-bit binary code) to the time-compensated spectral memory (Fig. 1). This sets up a pattern of eight frequency channels and five time steps for each syllable or word spoken. The 40-bit matrix for each spoken syllable or word is not read out into the syllable memory until it has been completely set up. If the smallest elements by which speech can be described are called phonemes, then most syllables or words will contain more than one phoneme. The reason for recognizing speech by groups of phonemes as they occur in syllables is the difficulty of recognizing many phonemes out of context. The recognition of a syllable display by the syllable memory is a form of sorting process. The display in the 40-bit matrix can also be considered a binary number. There are over one trillion such numbers in a 40-bit matrix. The set of numbers corresponding to different voicings of the same syllable or word, as determined from many tests, is wired into the memory, following procedures described by the authors. The syllable, once recognized in this manner, causes a spelling-memory relay associated with that syllable or word to be operated. This relay is wired to sequencing buses and letter-code buses of the typing control unit, which steps one sequence at a time in accordance with feedback pulses received from the remote-operated electric typewriter. The word is thus typed in accordance with a predetermined spelling, which of necessity must be the same for words that sound the same. Hence, the reason for the name, phonetic typewriter. To attain a closer approach to conventional spelling would require a much larger memory—large enough to include sentence structure and so forth.

The Flow of Information in the Laboratory Model Phonetic Typewriter Model III

Another way of explaining the performance of a machine such as the phonetic typewriter Model III is by following the flow of information. Assume that the first letter of the alphabet, which is also the indefinite article, a, and therefore a word, is spoken into a microphone. The signal output of the microphone will then be a function of amplitude versus time, as shown by the trace depicted in Fig. 2. When this signal is fed to the spectral analyzer, where it is transformed

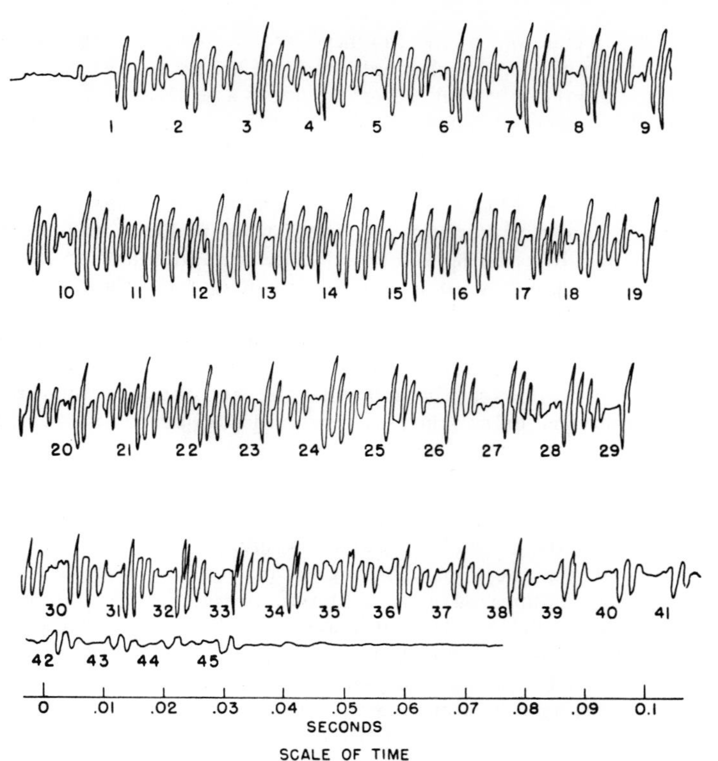

Fig. 2. Trace of speech wave of "a" spoken by H.B.

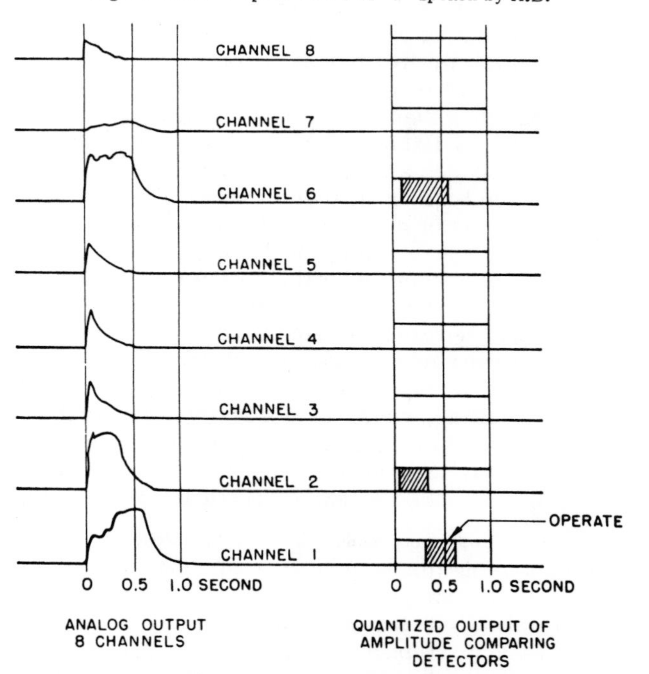

Fig. 3. Signal-amplitudes-and-relay-operations spectral analyzer, Model III, voicing "a" by H.B.

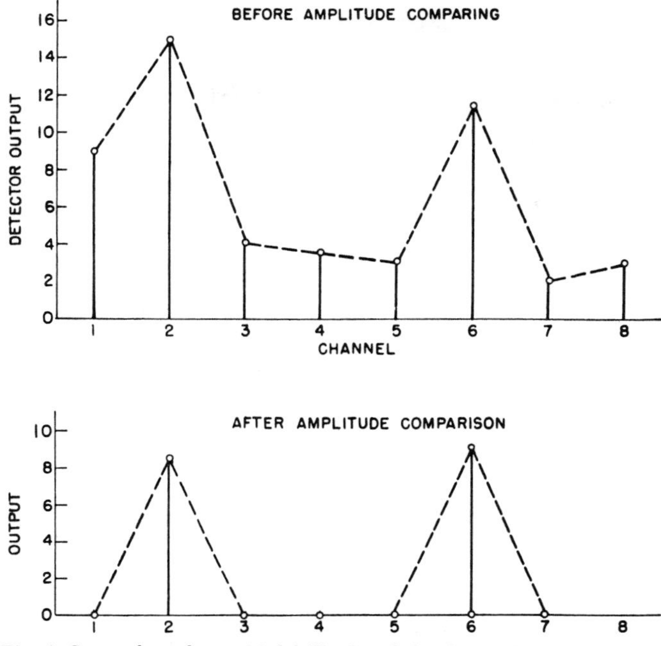

Fig. 4. Spectral analyzer Model III. Signal levels in detector circuits 0.2 sec after start of voicing of "a" by H.B.

into a quantized frequency-amplitude-time function, the rectified output in the various frequency bands will be found to vary as shown in Fig. 3. In order to explain the action of the amplitude-comparing detector circuits, the signals existing in eight channels before and after amplitude comparison are shown for one instance of time in Fig. 4. The advantage of the amplitude-comparing system

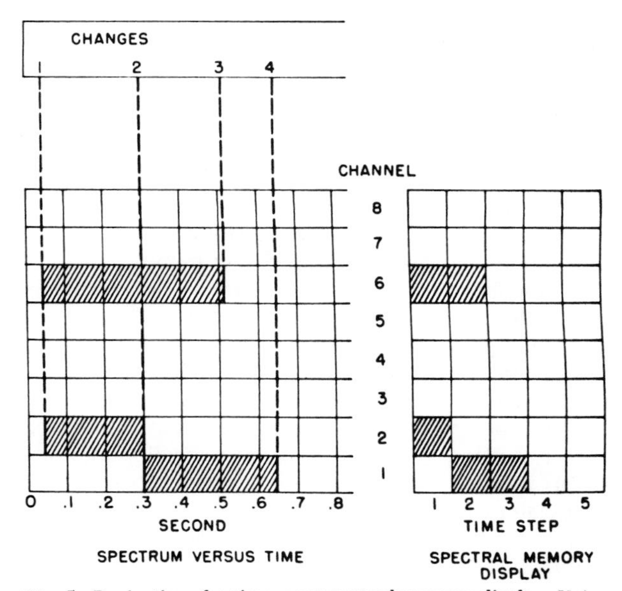

Fig. 5. Derivation of a time-compensated memory display. Voicing of "a" by H.B.

can be seen in Fig. 4 by the sharper definition of the peaks. The quantized output of the spectral analyzer and the information fed into the spectral memory, in steps determined by changes in the quantized spectrum, are both shown in Fig. 5. Figures 3 to 5 portray the acoustically derived information from a unique but typical voicing of "a." If the same speaker spoke it again, he might or might not produce the same results again. Speech is subject to variations, not all of which are under the control of the speaker. The effects of these variations are reduced by the normalizing processes, but some still remain. The number of variations in the analyzer output depends on the number of steps in which the information is quantized. In general, the greater the number of steps, the greater the number of variations. They also depend on the speaker, on the language, and on the word or syllable. For example, 100 voicings of "a" by H.B. result in 14 different displays, as depicted in Fig. 6 in the order of their frequency of occurrence. The

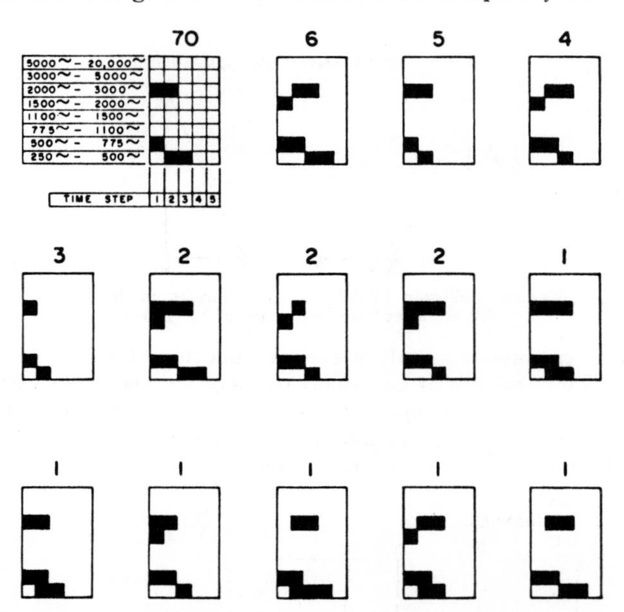

Fig. 6. Fourteen different displays obtained in 100 voicings of "a," as in RCA, by H.B.

most frequent display occurring in 70 out of 100 voicings is also the same as the typical voicing described in Figs. 3 to 5. A study of the 14 different displays in Fig. 6 shows that there are some features common to all 14. For instance, the field in the second row from the bottom in column one is always operated. In the bottom row, either column two or three, or both, are always operated. The same is true for the sixth row from the bottom, where either column one or two, or both, are always operated. On the other hand, there are four other fields that may be either operated or not operated. They are denoted by X's on Fig. 7. All other fields must not be operated. A wiring schematic that serves to recognize the set of numbers resulting in the above-mentioned displays for the 100 voicings of "a" is also shown on Fig. 7. As stated before, the output of the syllable memory consists of a connection to a bus associated with the syllable that was recognized. The explanation given above for the circuits that perform the recognition has been greatly simplified. Many other factors are included in the course of work to design these circuits to perform at a predicted accuracy, etc. The analyses of other words are not always as uniform as the "a" given as an example. For

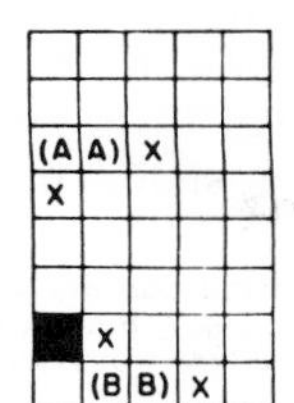

SYMBOLIC NOTATION
■ = RELAY MUST OPERATE
X = RELAY MAY BE OPERATED
(A A) = AT LEAST ONE MUST OPERATE
(B B) = AT LEAST ONE MUST OPERATE
□ = RELAY DOES NOT OPERATE

WIRING OF SYLLABLE MEMORY RELAYS
(RELAY COILS NOT SHOWN, RELAYS SHOWN NOT OPERATED)

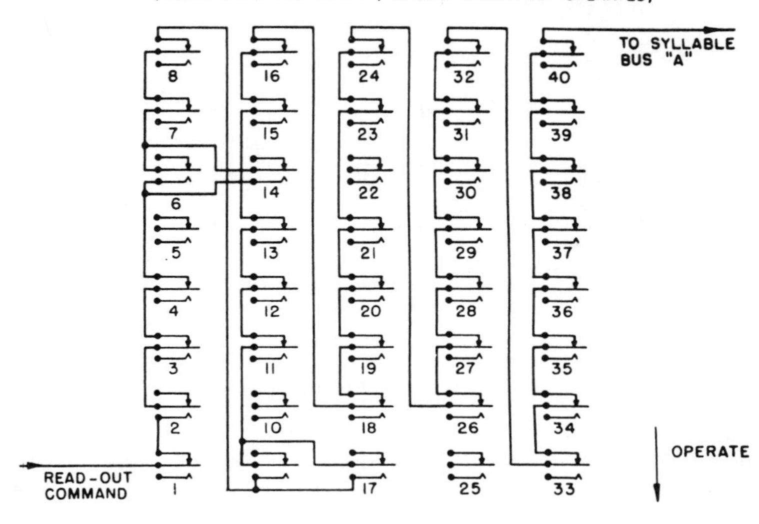

Fig. 7. Syllable-memory wiring to recognize "a" spoken by H.B. Phonetic typewriter Model III.

Fig. 8. RCA Laboratories phonetic typewriter Model III.

instance, 100 voicings of "I" by the same speaker results in 30 different displays.

A photograph of the Phonetic Typewriter Model III is shown in Fig. 8 and the disposition of the various units of the assembly is shown in Fig. 9.

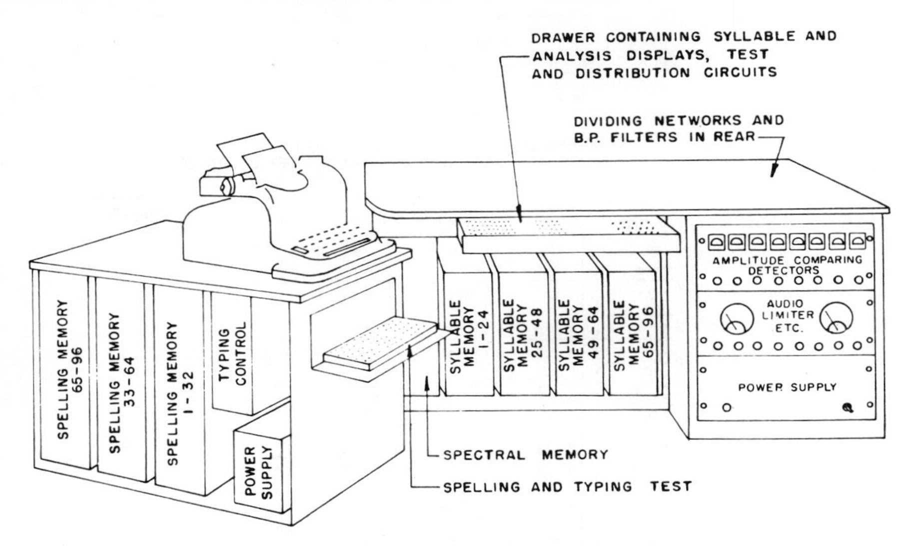

Fig. 9. Perspective view of phonetic typewriter Model III.

Conclusions

Machines have been built and described that are complete operating models in the sense that they type in response to words spoken into a microphone; however, they are still rudimentary in terms of vocabulary. To understand English with the equivalent of a syllable-articulation index of 98% will require a vocabulary of about 2000 syllables. The development of such machines entails much more than mere expansion of present designs. Further research is needed in the field of speech processing and this research will be helped by a better knowledge of the speech process in the human nervous system.

REFERENCES

Olson, H. F. 1952. Musical engineering. McGraw-Hill Book Co., Inc., New York.

Olson, H. F. and Belar, H. A print-out system for the automatic recording of the spectral analysis of spoken syllables. J. Acoust. Soc. Am., February, 1962.

Stewart, G. W. and Lindsay, R. B. Acoustics. D. Van Nostrand Co., Inc., Princeton, New Jersey.

STABILIZED RETINAL IMAGES AND VISUAL PERCEPTION

Roy M. Pritchard

McGill University

INTRODUCTION

Earlier investigations of eye movements have shown that when a subject "fixates" on a stationary target, small involuntary rotations of the eyeball persist (Lord and Wright, 1950; Ratliff and Riggs, 1950; Barlow, 1952; Ditchburn and Ginsborg, 1953; Riggs, 1958). As a result, the image of the target on the retina is in continuous motion. A slow drift, which carries the image away from the center of the fovea, is terminated and corrected for by an impulsive change in the direction of the optic axis of the eyeball. High-frequency oscillatory movements are superimposed on the drift motion (Ditchburn, 1955; Cornsweet, 1956; Fender, 1956) (Fig. 1).

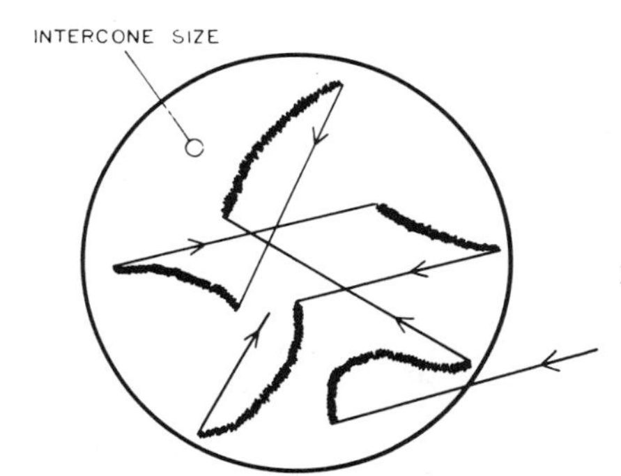

Fig. 1. Drift motion of the optic axis of the eyeball.

Recent researches have shown that the extremely small involuntary rotations play a significant role in the visual process. Several optical devices have been developed which produce a target whose image does not move across the retinal receptors in response to eye movements (Ditchburn and Ginsborg, 1952; Riggs et al., 1953; Ditchburn and Fender, 1955; Ditchburn and Pritchard, 1956; Cornsweet, 1956; Yarbus, 1956; Krauskopf, 1957; Clowes and Ditchburn, 1959). Such an image is called a stabilized retinal image. When the motion of the image upon the retina is prevented, the stabilized image is perceived only intermittently (Ditchburn and Ginsborg, 1952; Riggs et al., 1953). Imposed movements similar to the low-frequency components of the natural oscillatory motions restore and maintain normal continuous vision (Krauskopf, 1957; Ditchburn et al., 1959).

When a stabilized image is first presented it is seen as in normal vision. After several seconds it disappears from view and a gray structureless field is perceived. Later, the gray field may be replaced by an intense black field. The image regenerates either in whole or in part and is followed by alternate disappearances and regenerations. At McGill University, D.O. Hebb, Woodburn Heron, and I have been investigating the nature of the fragmentation, or the alternate partial disappearance and partial regeneration, as a function of the character and content of the image itself. Our findings give support to more than one major theory of visual perception and emphasize that a modern theory must incorporate some of the concepts from both analytic and holistic theories (Pritchard, Heron, and Hebb, 1960).

OBSERVATIONS

The stabilizing system used in the studies reported in the present paper consists of a tight-fitting contact lens on which is mounted a miniature self-contained optical projector (Pritchard, 1961) (Fig. 2). The target, a 5-mm disc

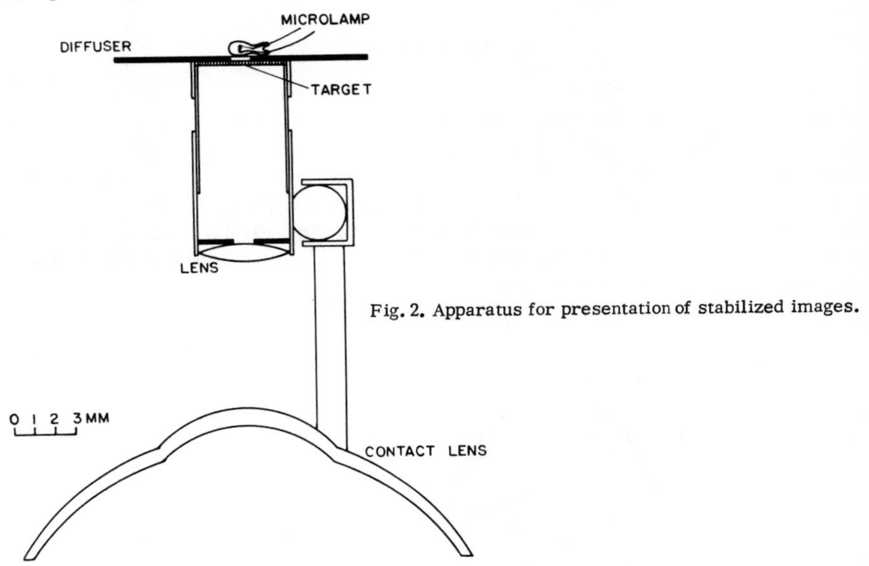

Fig. 2. Apparatus for presentation of stabilized images.

of photographic negative, is maintained in the focal plane of a high-power positive lens and is viewed against a diffuse field of light. The 5° circular field of the diffuser is illuminated by either an attached miniature surgical bulb or focused radiation from a dc ribbon-filament lamp. The rest of the diffuser is blackened to shield the eye from stray light. The projector is mounted by a ball-and-socket joint to a stalk carried on the contact lens. The contact lens, previously ground to produce normal vision, adheres to the subject's eyeball because of a reduction in the hydrostatic pressure beneath the lens surface. While the contact lens continues to follow the involuntary movements of the eyeball, so, also, does the projector. In consequence, the image of the target is fixed relative to the retina. The targets are viewed by the subject through the high-power lens and, thus, are seen as if located at infinity. They are in focus on the retina, therefore, for a normal relaxed eye.

In the present investigation the subject lay on a couch in a darkened and partly soundproofed room. The luminance of the brightest parts of the target was maintained at approximately 25 millilamberts. All observations were monocular, the other eye being occluded. A continuous recording was made of the subjects verbal report and compared with control observations recorded under identical conditions, but without attaching the projector to the contact lens, so that the image was not stabilized. The results quoted here are from four experienced observers and have been independently reported by each without a knowledge of the reports made by the others.

When a naive subject first sees a stabilized image, it is perceived as in normal vision. At the initial occurrences of fragmentation and regeneration, the subject inevitably tries to look at the region that has suddenly vanished or reappeared. Gross eye movements are associated with these attempts for, when in normal vision he wishes to focus attention upon a specific region of the visual field, he rotates his eye to bring the image of the selected region into the center of the fovea. Training observation periods are necessary, therefore, to teach a subject that he is unable to alter the geometrical placing of a stabilized image on the fovea and that he should cease to try. After he has learned to view the image passively he discovers he can still transfer his attention from one region of the image to another, although unable to alter the relation between his retina and the image. The transfer of attention is effective only over a limited visual field. All targets were presented within this stabilized attention field, which is about 2° for naive subjects but which expands with prolonged experience of stabilized vision.

Examination of complex patterns in the stabilized condition reveals that perception of the image is related to the structure of the target itself. The image of a simple figure, such as a single line, vanishes as a complete image and later reappears. With continuous viewing the alternate vanishing and reappearing of the complete image persists and a steady state is achieved when the configuration is perceived for less than 10% of the total viewing time (Fig. 3). A more complex

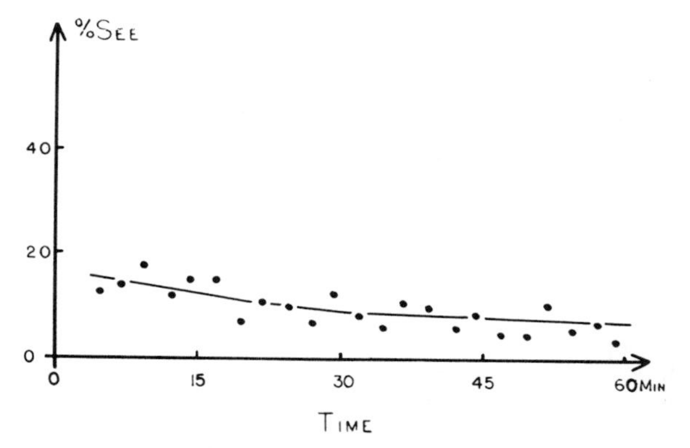

Fig. 3. Perception of a simple figure.

pattern may also vanish as a whole but, in addition, it may fragment and one or more of its parts vanish independently. Further, a complex pattern is perceived, in whole or in part, for a much greater percentage of the viewing time. The outline figure of the human profile inevitably vanishes and regenerates in separate discrete organized units. The front of the face, the back of the head, the assembly around the eye, or that around the ear vanish and reappear as entities, separately and in various combinations (Fig. 4). In contrast, on first presentation a figure composed of many curlicues arranged together in an unorganized fashion is reported as an extremely active figure. The individual curlicues vanish and regenerate rapidly and the subject perceives almost every configuration that can be derived from the original figure. The changes are so rapid that no accurate report can be given by the subject. After prolonged viewing small groups of curlicues vanish and reappear as single entities. The newly formed combinations persist for longer periods than others and the figure can no longer be considered unorganized.

The importance of past experience to visual perception is apparent when a highly organized meaningful figure is viewed in the stabilized condition. The monogram formed from the letters H and B includes several symbols, such as H, B, P, 3, 4, etc., and these rapidly supersede one another within the field of

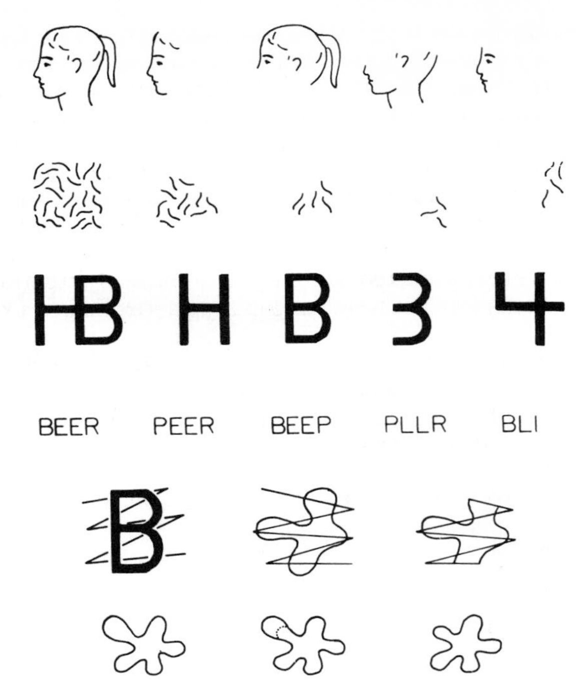

Fig. 4. Perception of complex figures.

view. One or more of them is visible when any part of the figure is perceived. When entire words are presented, the partial fragmentation of the individual letters can cause different words to be perceived. However, the letters appear to fragment independently and there is a high probability of seeing meaningless groupings of letters. When a symbol obscured by hatching lines is viewed, the subject sees either the intact symbol or the hatching lines independently, or the two elements are seen in different planes when perceived together. The separate vanishing of two elements is also reported when the hatching lines obscure a less meaningful shape, such as an amoeba. In the latter case, however, it is usual for parts of both the lines and shape to vanish while the remnants combine to form a new composite figure which is a more compact and rounded configuration.

The observations described to date strongly support the analytic or "cell assembly" theory of visual perception (Hebb, 1949; Milner, 1957; Lashley, 1958). According to the theory, experience is essential in the development of perception. Separate neural impressions are established in the brain which correspond to various learned elements, and a pattern is believed to be perceived through a synthesis of parts. The "organized" and "meaningful" parts of a pattern are considered to correspond to elements that have been learned and established by experience. Thus these perceptual, as opposed to purely sensory, elements can be expected to have been excited by a stabilized image. Also, the integration of these elements requires the additional information usually derived from the movements of the image across the retina. For the originally unorganized curlicue pattern, time is necessary to first establish certain perceptual elements, which then operate as units. The formation of a composite figure from the amoeba and hatching-lines pattern suggests that the holistic or Gestalt theory of perception must also be considered (Kohler, 1929; Koffka, 1935). According to

Gestalt theory, perception is innately determined and a pattern is seen as a whole due to an unlearned ability to perceive certain basic qualities such as "form," "wholeness," and "organization." The appearance of the more compact and rounded configuration conforms with Gestalt ideas.

When only an amoeba shape is presented as a stabilized image, parts of the figure vanish; these are usually the larger limbs and distorting elements of the figure. After their disappearance, closure occurs to produce a symmetrical and more compact figure. In general, a smooth, well-rounded figure vanishes and regenerates more as a whole than does a jagged, irregular one.

The importance of linear organization as a determinant of the groups within a complete figure that operate together is emphasized by the fragmentation of a stabilized image composed of rows of squares (Fig. 5). A complete horizontal,

Fig. 5. Fragmentation of stabilized images.

vertical, or diagonal row is usually left visible and this subsequently disappears to leave a single isolated square in the field of view. Occasionally, one common side of all of the squares in the pattern vanishes and a field of squarish u's, c's, or n's is seen. A random collection of dots may vanish to leave a series that lies approximately along a line and the linear relationship may not be obvious until after the other dots have vanished. As Gestalt theory would predict, contiguity and similarity determine the functioning of subgroups derived from a complete figure. However, the acceptance of some cell-assembly concepts is made inevitable by the independent action of separate lines which constitute a more complex figure. When simple straight-line drawings are viewed, the lines act independently and breakages occur at intersections. A line vanishes and reappears as a whole either alone or in association with others, i.e., parallel lines often operate together. In a three-dimensional figure, such as a necker cube, a line may still act as a unit and a parallel-line effect is also observed but with the lines defining a plane. Thus, parallel planes may remain in view while the additional lines vanish. The corner replaces the line as the unit of independent action when solid-tone figures are substituted for simple line drawings. The fading of the stabilized image starts at the center and the sharply outlined corners vanish in succession. Regeneration produces a complete or partial image with the corners again sharply defined.

The influence of a visual object beyond the area of actual stimulation is observed when two figures are presented simultaneously and stabilized. Each figure may vanish independently or fragment. Parallel segments, one from each figure, are seen when fragmentation occurs and this conforms with a field effect postulated in Gestalt theory. Finally, further support for the theory is derived from the functioning of the whole as a perceptual entity. Although the fragmentation of each pattern has been described above, it must be emphasized that the original pattern may function as a single unit, disappearing and reappearing as a whole.

COMMENT

The observations made when viewing stabilized complex patterns have been shown to support two theoretical approaches to perception, namely, the cell-assembly and Gestalt concepts. The latter receives strong support from the functioning of wholes, the functioning of groups of entities, the production of "good" compact figures by closures, and, also, field effects. But it is the independent action of parts which predominates over the whole in stabilized vision and forces the acceptance of a modified cell-assembly theory and the perceptual elements it postulates. Yet the perceptual elements themselves appear as organized entities, which is a Gestalt concept. Whereas Gestalt ideas can be assimilated by the analytic approach, it is impossible to reconcile most of the experimental observations with holistic concepts. The question that now arises concerns the capacity to perceive "form," "wholeness," "organization," etc., as postulated in Gestalt theory and observed in both normal and stabilized vision. Are these summary rules of perception also learned—if so, how, and at what stage of development? Are the Gestalt concepts merely gross neural impressions established in the brain by learning which monitor and control the numerous smaller cell-assemblies corresponding to various learned elements? Is it sheer exposure to our highly organized and stable world that establishes them so strongly? The visible structures within our environment conform to the basic laws of physics which formularize the behavior of the surrounding matter. Hills, trees, clouds, waves, and any man-made structure are all subject to strict physical conditions which emphasize and impose stability. In turn, stability and compactness imply continuance and, thus, stable objects are rendered observable for long periods of time. It is only the stable, compact, and organized world that we are continuously stimulated by.

In conclusion, I will comment on the first physiological experiments to parallel the stabilized-image studies. The recent measurement of small involuntary eye movements in the cat (Pritchard and Heron, 1960; Hebbard and Marg, 1960) have led to an investigation of the activity of cortical neurons in response to both stabilized and unstabilized visual stimuli (Burns, Heron, and Pritchard, 1962). A continuously illuminated simple pattern is focused upon the retina of a cat. This image can be moved in a controlled manner after paralyzing the animal. Responses of single cortical cells are recorded by means of a microelectrode inserted into the visual cortex of the unanaesthetized isolated forebrain. The mean discharge frequency of a cell when the retina is in complete darkness is found to be the same as that when the pattern is stabilized upon the retina. As soon as the pattern is oscillated the mean discharge level of the cell is considerably altered (Fig. 6). Thus, the subjective reports obtained during the stabilized

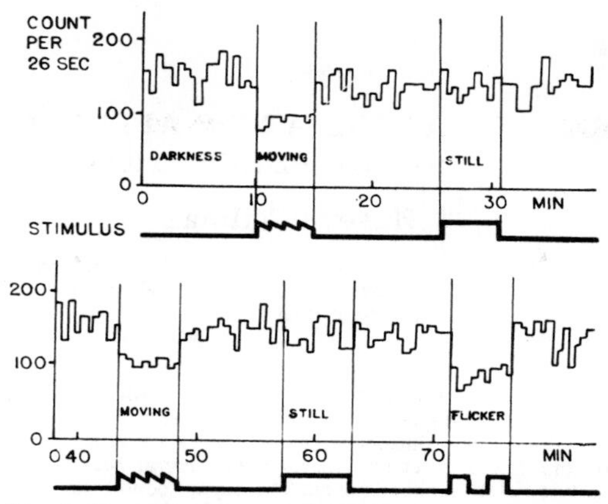

Fig. 6. Response of cortical neurons to stabilized and unstabilized visual stimuli.

viewing of simple patterns are substantiated by the associated activity of cortical neurons. From observations of cortical activity only, the disappearance of a simple stabilized image could be postulated. The cortical activity in response to complex-pattern stimulation is now being studied and may provide additional information on the fragmentation of the stabilized image.

ACKNOWLEDGMENT

The research of this paper was supported, in part, by the Defence Research Board of Canada, Grant number 9401-11.

REFERENCES

Barlow, H. B. 1952. Eye movements during fixation. J. Physiol. 116, 290-306.
Burns, B.D., Heron, W., and Pritchard, R.M. 1962. Physiological excitation of the visual cortex in the cat's unanaesthetized isolated forebrain. J. Neurophysiol. (In press.)
Clowes, M.B. and Ditchburn, R.W. 1959. An improved apparatus for producing a stabilized retinal image. Opt. Acta 6, 128-133.
Cornsweet, T.N. 1956. Determination of the stimuli for involuntary drifts and saccadic eye movements. J. Opt. Soc. Am. 46, 987-993.
Ditchburn, R.W. 1955. Eye movements in relation to retinal action. Opt. Acta 1, 171-176.
Ditchburn, R.W. and Fender, D.H. 1955. The stabilized retinal image. Opt. Acta 2, 128-133.
Ditchburn, R.W., Fender, D.H., and Mayne, S. 1959. Vision with controlled movements of the retinal image. J. Physiol. 145, 98-107.
Ditchburn, R.W. and Ginsborg, B. 1952. Vision with a stabilized retinal image. Nature 170, 36-37.
Ditchburn, R.W. and Ginsborg, B. 1953. Involuntary eye movements during fixation. J. Physiol. 119, 1-17.
Ditchburn, R.W. and Pritchard, R.M. 1956. Stabilized interference fringes on the retina. Nature 177, 434.
Fender, D.H. 1956. The function of eye movements in the visual process. Unpublished doctoral thesis, University of Reading.
Hebb, D.O. 1949. The organization of behavior. John Wiley & Sons, New York.
Hebbard, F.W. and Marg, E. 1960. Physiological nystagmus in the cat. J. Opt. Soc. Am. 50, 151-155.
Koffka, K. 1935. Principles of Gestalt psychology. Harcourt, Brace and Co., New York.
Kohler, W. 1929. Gestalt psychology. Liveright, New York.
Krauskopf, J. 1957. Effects of retinal image motion on contrast thresholds for maintained vision. J. Opt. Soc. Am. 47, 740-744.
Lashley, K.S. 1958. Cerebral organization and behavior. Res. Publ. Assoc. Nerv. Ment. Dis. 35, 1-18.
Lord, M.P. and Wright, W.D. 1950. The investigation of eye movements. Rep. Progr. Phys. 13, 1-23.
Milner, P.M. 1957. The cell assembly: Mark II. Psychol. Rev. 64, 242-252.
Pritchard, R.M. 1961. A collimator stabilizing system. Quart. J. Exp. Psychol. 13, 181-183.
Pritchard, R.M. and Heron, W. 1960. Small eye movements of the cat. Canad. J. Psychol. 14, 131-137.
Pritchard, R.M., Heron, W., and Hebb, D.O. 1960. Visual perception approaches by the method of stabilized images. Canad. J. Psychol. 14, 67-77.
Ratliff, F. and Riggs, L.A. 1950. Involuntary motions of the eye during monocular fixation. J. Exp. Psychol. 40, 687-701.
Riggs, L.A. 1958. Vision. Ann. Rev. Psychol. 9, 19-46.
Riggs, L.A., Ratliff, F., Cornsweet, J.C., and Cornsweet, T.N. 1953. The disappearance of steadily fixated test-objects. J. Opt. Soc. Am. 43, 495-501.
Yarbus, A.L. 1956. Perception of a stationary retinal image. Biofizika 1, 435-437.

COLOR VISION AND A NEW APPROACH TO GENERAL PERCEPTION

Huseyin Yilmaz

Applied Research Laboratory, Sylvania Electronic Systems
A Division of Sylvania Electric Products, Inc.
Waltham, Massachusetts

A simple theory of color vision which explains Edwin H. Land's recent two-color projections as well as the classical color mixing experiments is presented. The theory is developed on the basis of evolutionary requirements and leads to a set of transformations similar to the Lorentz transformations of special relativity. This suggests that color is essentially a relative phenomenon. The experimental justifications of the theory and the relation of its underlying postulates to the theory of evolution are discussed. Various consequences with regard to contrast enhancement, aperture colors, and two-color projections are presented. Ways of testing the evolutionary theory using the newly developed perceptrons and adaptive electronic devices are suggested. In the opinion of the author, the approach to perception followed in this paper is a new science having its own class of phenomena, fundamentals, principles, logical structure, and its own experimental methods to test the validity of its deductions.

I. INTRODUCTION

In this paper an attempt is made to deduce the properties of human color perception from evolutionary arguments. The essence of the approach is as follows. Consider the physical properties of light and its natural daily distribution. Consider also the evolutionary needs of the organism in terms of food and protection. Given suitable neural material and processes, and also given enough time to act, we then postulate that evolution will produce an optimum detection and recognition device for the organism. The ideal form of such a device may be anticipated logically, irrespective of the particular biochemical reactions used or neural processes adopted. This *ideal* form would be what the organism strives for in the course of its evolution. Of course, the actual perception device may differ from the ideal form because of incomplete evolution, inability to find the most suitable combinations, or the changing of the early natural conditions, whose effects are fixed by heredity. It may be expected, however, that the general over-all properties of the actual perception device will be closely consistent with the logically derived ones. The end result must be obtained one way or other, at least approximately, otherwise the organism cannot survive. In this article we will endeavor to show that in color perception this is, to a considerable degree of approximation, indeed so. It may be claimed, with considerable justification, that the approach put forward in this paper constitutes a new science, which may be called *Percevonics*. This science looks at the problem of perception in a wide sense, defines its subject matter and the class of phenomena entering its field, formulates principles, derives conclusions, and tests such conclusions by new and unquestionable experimental techniques.

II. THEORY OF COLOR PERCEPTION

a. Electromagnetic radiation being the carrier of visual information, we consider first the physical properties of radiation. Since the electromagnetic field is a vector field, we must know the polarization and intensity for each wavelength in order to specify a distribution (since natural sunlight is phase-incoherent, we do not need to consider phase). In other words, we have three variables, P, I, and λ, to work with. Normal human vision, however, is insensitive to polarization. Evolutionally, this is understandable because the only natural polarizers are certain tourmaline crystals, which have no survival value. We will, therefore, drop polarization and consider only the intensity and wavelength. If we put ourselves in the position of an engineer who is trying to design an eye for the human need, we immediately appreciate the fact that the eye does not have to be sensitive to all wavelengths in the same proportion. Extremely short wavelengths, namely, the γ-rays and x-rays are not suitable as carriers since they are scarce and do not interact strongly with tissues. Similarly, available energy in the extremely long wavelength region is small, and the resolving power of the device gets lower as the wavelength increases. In other words, the detection of a small object with large wavelengths is difficult because of poor resolution. Therefore, a certain intermediate range called the "visible spectrum" must be selected. The fact that the actual visible spectrum is adjacent to the ultraviolet, where a reasonable interaction exists without the wavelengths becoming larger than the neural diameters, and coincides closely with the maximum energy region of daylight illumination is no accident (Fig. 1). Any sensible designer would select about the same region.

b. Having chosen a range for the operation of our device, the next question is the recognition of objects via the spectral distribution of light reflected from these objects. Under a given illumination a definite energy distribution from each object reaches the eye. The problem is then to recognize various distributions in this range. Since the energy distribution is a function $F(\lambda)$ of the wavelength (Fig. 1), we may represent this distribution with a Fourier series. For

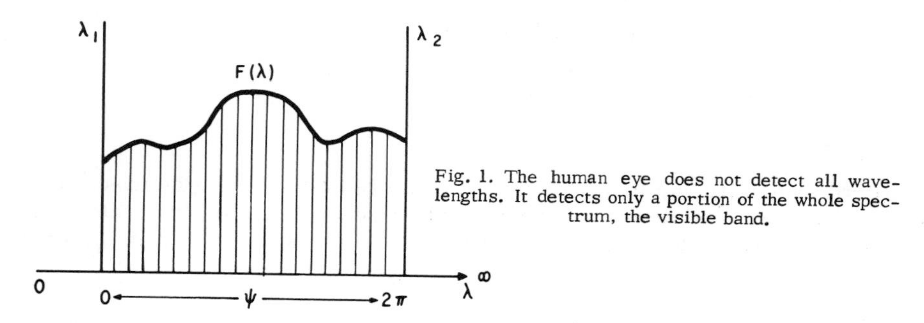

Fig. 1. The human eye does not detect all wavelengths. It detects only a portion of the whole spectrum, the visible band.

this purpose we define a hue angle $\phi(\lambda)$ as a function of wavelength so that the range λ_1 to λ_2 is mapped into 0 to 2π*. (This step is nothing but a change of variable.) The function $F(\lambda) = F(\phi)$ may then be expanded as

$$F(\phi) = \boxed{\gamma + \alpha \sin \phi + \beta \cos \phi} + \mu \sin 2\phi + \cdots \tag{1}$$

In order to recognize all possible distributions separately, one needs an infinite number of terms. Since these terms are linearly independent quantities, the eye then needs an infinite number of channels to the brain in order to recognize all possible light distributions. This is clearly impossible. We must stop somewhere in the expansion. We assert that the normal human eye uses only the first three terms. This makes the eye a rather poor Fourier analyzer. In this way the normal human color vision may be said to operate in a three-dimensional space, a subspace of an infinite-dimensional Hilbert space.

*Remember that this is an idealized model of the eye. In the actual eye, one-to-one mapping is accomplished over somewhat less than $-\pi$ to π; the gap is filled by the purple region. For further detail and a more realistic model, see section IV of this article and also the extensive article on the subject by the author in Mathematical Biophysics, to appear in the April 1962 issue.

c. The justification of this interpretation lies in the three psychological attributes of color, namely, the brightness, hue, and saturation. These three independent attributes may be characterized in terms of α, β, and γ as follows (Fig. 2):

$$\begin{aligned} &\gamma \rightarrow \text{brightness} \\ &\phi = \tan^{-1}\frac{\beta}{\alpha} \rightarrow \text{hue} \\ &\sigma = \frac{(\alpha^2+\beta^2)^{1/2}}{\gamma} \rightarrow \text{saturation} \end{aligned} \tag{2}$$

From the figure it is seen clearly that if α, β, and γ are the Cartesian coordinates of a light sample, then the psychological attributes are the polar-coordinates representation of the same sample. The facts that brightness is always

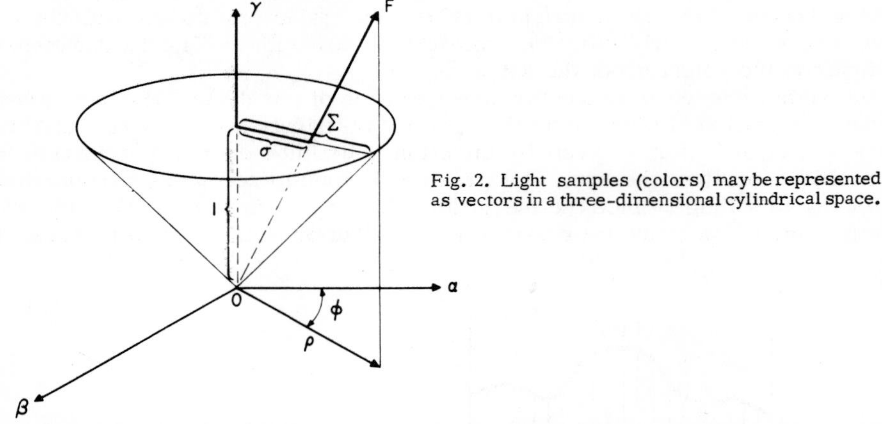

Fig. 2. Light samples (colors) may be represented as vectors in a three-dimensional cylindrical space.

a positive quantity and that hues can be arranged circularly (the so-called color wheel) are implicit in the representation. Since $F(\lambda)$ is positive (intensity), the vector is defined with positive γ components and lies inside a limiting cone given by

$$\alpha^2 + \beta^2 = \Sigma^2\gamma^2 \tag{3}$$

The origin O corresponds to the absence of light, that is, to black, and the γ-axis is the loci of grays and whites. The saturation $\sigma = (\alpha^2 + \beta^2)^{1/2}/\gamma$ reaches a maximum Σ at the cone and describes the limiting case of maximum psychological saturation. Note that ϕ and Σ are defined as ratios, whereas γ is not a ratio. From an evolutionary point of view, the sensation of absolute physical magnitudes is not essential or even desirable. From one situation to another, only the relative differences or ratios are of survival value. For this reason the psychological brightness sensation should not be assumed to be proportional to γ. Although the actual dependence is difficult to deduce, a reasonable form is a logarithmic dependence:*

$$\text{Brightness sensation} \sim \log\frac{\gamma}{\gamma_0} \tag{4}$$

where γ_0 is a threshold value. This so-called Weber-Fechner form is dependent on a ratio and the sensitivity increases as the stimulus gets smaller. This is a desirable feature biologically, since it tends to normalize the sensation. These

*Recently the logarithmic dependence was criticized and a power law $\sim(\gamma/\gamma_0)^{0.35}$ was defended by various investigators. However, in the region where the normal color vision operates, these two curves are fairly close to each other.

summarize the main features of what is usually referred to as the "Classical Color Theory."

d. Color perception under different illuminations and viewing conditions induces a transformation of α, β, and γ into α', β', and γ', which to a first approximation may be assumed linear:

$$\alpha' = \Omega_{11}\alpha + \Omega_{12}\beta + \Omega_{13}\gamma + \xi$$

$$\beta' = \Omega_{21}\alpha + \Omega_{22}\beta + \Omega_{23}\gamma + \eta \qquad (5)$$

$$\gamma' = \Omega_{31}\alpha + \Omega_{32}\beta + \Omega_{33}\gamma + \zeta$$

Here Ω_{ik} are constant coefficients and ξ, η, and ζ are small quantities. Such a transformation is necessary biologically because the important things for the organism are the objects and their correct classification and recognition. From one illuminant to another the light reflected from each object changes. Under this change, object-color identities and their interrelationships must not change. Therefore, the transformations (4) must be such that the change in the physical characteristics due to the change in the illuminant is compensated by the transformations so as to leave object-colors and their interrelationships invariant. This may be interpreted as follows. To each illuminant I (an illuminant is here defined as a light source containing all wavelengths in the visible region but with intensity varying as a function of wavelength) there corresponds a coordinate system, S. The change from one illuminant to another is nothing but a transformation from one coordinate system to another (Fig. 3). In nature such changes in the illuminant light take place quite often. For example, if a cloud passes between us and the sun, the illumination changes from direct-sunlight (yellowish in nature) to blue-sky illumination. Under such a change a white page that we may be reading must stay white, as it does. Similarly the appearance of a highly chromatic object (high saturation) must not change. These two conditions, together with the fact that γ must always stay positive, determine the nature of the transformations (4). Indeed, the well-known Lorentz transformations of the special theory of relativity satisfy these requirements.

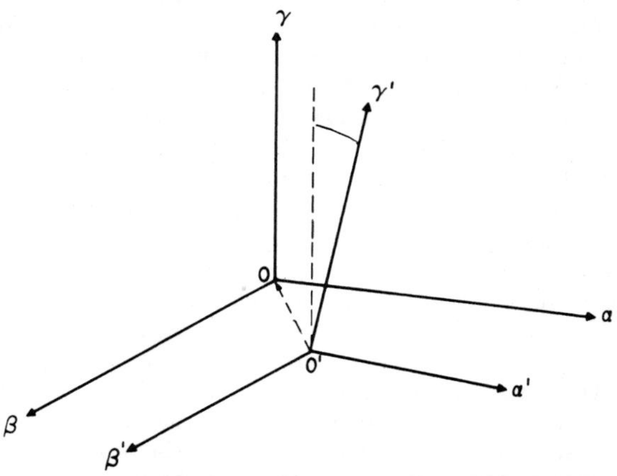

Fig. 3. The general transformation l_0 may be represented as a shift of the origin plus a rotation of coordinate axes.

To see how the analogy works, notice that all permissible colors lie inside a cone of maximum saturation Σ (Fig. 2). The γ-axis represents all achromatic colors from black to white. The γ-axis represents also the quality of the illuminant light since a white paper reflects exactly the illuminant quality. Transformation of white into white means that after the transformation, the achromatic axis lies in the direction of the new illuminant and the transformation of highly saturated objects into highly saturated objects means the invariance of the maximum saturation cone.* This argument is clearly analogous to the derivation of the Lorentz transformations from the principle of relativity and the invariance of the velocity of light. Neglecting the small quantities ξ, η, and ζ, the transformations are therefore of the form

$$\begin{aligned} \alpha' &= \frac{\alpha - \sigma\gamma}{\sqrt{1-(\sigma/\Sigma)^2}} \\ \beta' &= \beta \\ \gamma' &= \frac{\gamma - (\sigma/\Sigma^2)\alpha}{\sqrt{1-(\sigma/\Sigma)^2}} \end{aligned} \tag{6}$$

where σ is the relative saturation of the old illuminant with respect to the new illuminant and Σ is the maximum saturation. Here the two illuminants are assumed to be in the α-γ plane, so that in this special case β is not affected by the transformation.

e. The terms ξ, η, and ζ are small in magnitude and in general may be neglected. However, in certain particular situations, such as the two-color projections of Edwin H. Land, they lead to large qualitative effects. For this reason we will keep them as part of the transformations, although in ordinary cases their effects are small. The evolutionary reason for the existence of these small terms will be clear from the following considerations. Suppose there is a blue object in a given illuminant. If we change to a rather chromatic yellow illumination, the intensity reflected from the blue object will be considerably lessened. To compensate for this, the transformation must be so as to restore the brightness of the blue object, as well as its hue and saturation. This results in a shift of the coordinate axes by ξ, η, and ζ (Fig. 3). The direction of the shift is easily understood from the argument. For example, ξ and η are opposite to prevailing colors and ζ is always positive (Helmholtz' intrinsic light of the eye—Helmholtz, 1924). Also, the fact that they are small and apparent only for dark objects is connected to the Weber-Fechner law. According to this law, sensation-wise the brighter objects do not change much in appearance; hence, there is no need for compensation in this range. For darker objects, however, the compensation is effected by only a small shift. Following Edwin H. Land, we call the shift of origin the "shift of the fulcrum" (Land, 1959).

Geometrically the transformations (4) may be interpreted as a translation of the coordinate axes by ξ, η, and ζ, plus a rotation by Ω_{ik}. This concept explains the recent two-color projections of Edwin H. Land, as well as the classically known behavior for color transformations (Land, 1959).

f. If the scene in the whole visual field is white or achromatic, the determination of the achromatic axis is simple, since it will be the quality of the illuminant. However, if the illuminant is not visible and if the visual field is covered with large patches of colored areas, we need a procedure to determine the achromatic axis. Following the example of the complete achromatic field, we may assume that the eye tends to interpret the sum of all light reaching the eye as achromatic; that is

$$\Sigma S_i \alpha_i' = 0 \qquad \Sigma S_i \beta_i' = 0 \tag{7}$$

*The invariance of maximum saturation cone does not necessarily mean the invariance of spectral saturations. Spectral saturations may fall considerably inside of the psychological maximum saturation circle as in the case of yellows, then invariance of spectrum yellow is approximate.

where S_i are the solid angles in the visual field corresponding to the light sample $F_i(\lambda)$. From this a formula may be derived for the so-called contrast enhancement. In a given illumination and achromatic background, let small chips of colors have the coordinates α_i, β_i, and γ_i. If we bring large areas of the same colors and fill the whole visual field with them, there will be a complex interaction amongst them and their appearance will change due to (7); a transformation occurs and a new achromatic axis is set up. Let the relative saturation of the new axis with respect to the old one be σ_0. Then from (6) we can see that σ_0 will be found as

$$\sigma_{0\alpha} = \frac{\Sigma S_i \alpha_i}{\Sigma S_i \gamma_i} \qquad \sigma_{0\beta} = \frac{\Sigma S_i \beta_i}{\Sigma S_i \gamma_i} \tag{8}$$

This is the so-called contrast enhancement or simultaneous contrast phenomenon. This effect is usually treated as a separate subject in color vision, whereas here it appears as a consequence of our transformation theory. We must also note at once that (8) is actually a simplified form, since it gives the same weight to all areas in the visual field irrespective of the mutual proximity of various colors in space and in time of viewing.

Our theory is now complete, conceptually. Although it may be an idealized form, describing the actual human color perception only approximately, it is, nevertheless, a logically self-contained system embodying the physical, biological, and evolutionary requirements. We now proceed to show experimentally that the over-all effects predicted by the theory are, in fact, present in the normal color perception of the human eye. Two identical rooms R_1 and R_2, separated by a common wall, are illuminated by the sources S_1 and S_2. Both rooms are painted with a nonselective white paint. A piece of white paper is divided into two and the pieces are placed in the rooms so that an observer can see them simultaneously, one directly, the other through a hole in the thin common wall (Fig. 4). The colors seen are then compared with a set of Munsell chips illu-

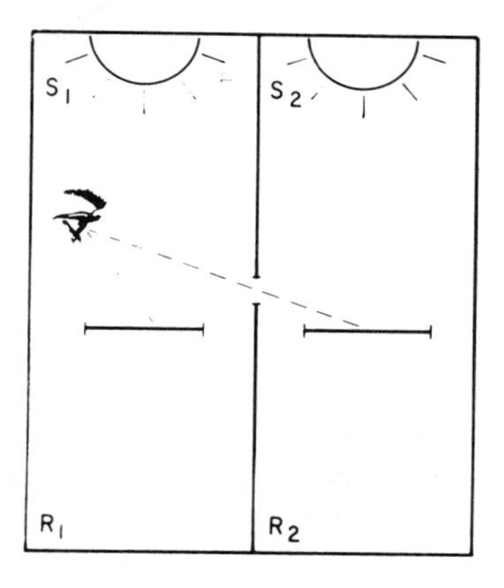

Fig. 4. Colors are relative. The psychological attributes of a given light sample are different in different illuminations.

minated by a standard C illuminant. The light sources S_1 and S_2 can be chosen to correspond to any point on the Munsell chromaticity scale. We will give the results for a typical situation (Fig. 5).

1. If the sources S_1 and S_2 are chosen to be two different illuminants, I and I', then each room is white to its own observer but the other room, as seen through the hole, appears colored. Furthermore, if R_2 appears with the saturation σ from R_1, then R_1 appears with the saturation $-\sigma$ from R_2, the minus sign indicating that the hue is complementary to the former case. This experiment

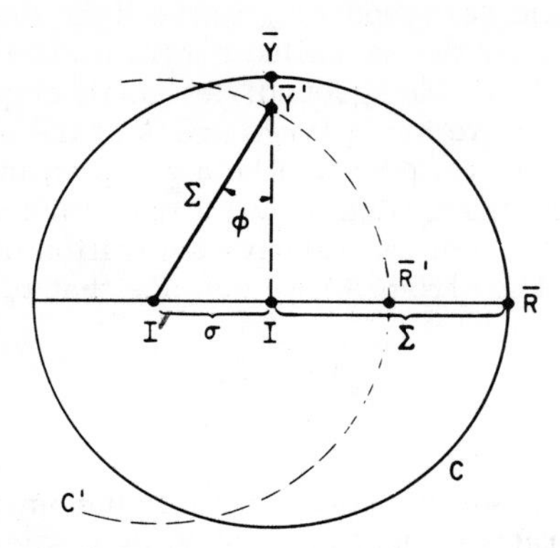

Fig. 5. From one illuminant to another, the limiting saturation Σ remains almost unchanged.

corresponds to the transformations (6) first order in σ/Σ and indicates clearly the relativity of color perception.

2. If S_2 is chosen to be a spectral color, say, spectral red $\bar{R}$ (Fig. 5), then the saturation Σ observed through the hole (observer being in R_1) remains practically the same if we change the illuminant from I to I' in R_1. This experiment indicates the invariance of the maximum saturation Σ.

3. Let S_2 be the spectral yellow $\bar{Y}$ perpendicular to red on the color wheel (Fig. 5). Then if we change the illuminant in R_1 from I to I' the hue of $\bar{Y}$ is seen to change by an amount $\sin\phi \simeq \sigma/\Sigma$. No variation seems to take place in its saturation. This effect is similar to the aberration effect in special relativity.

4. Let S_2 be turned off. If now we use, say, a rather chromatic source in R_1, the hole (aperture) does not look completely black. It appears as a deep, dark green, roughly complementary in hue to that of the source in R_1. This experiment demonstrates the existence of the fulcrum shift. The homogeneous parts of equations (5) alone cannot explain this since they would always map black into black.

5. The influence of the second-order terms $(\sigma/\Sigma)^2$ is more difficult to detect in individual observations, but when a large number of measurements is made and averaged out we find that the effect is there. For example, in transforming I into I' we have

$$\gamma' = \frac{\gamma}{[1 - (\sigma/\Sigma)^2]^{1/2}} \tag{9}$$

since $\alpha = \beta = 0$ for I. If now we take a wide variety of pairs with relative saturation σ and average out γ and γ', we find that on the average γ' is larger than γ by an amount approximately given by (9). Thus, "the grass on the other side of the fence" looks not only greener but also brighter!

We would like to add at once that perfect accuracy of these results is not claimed. They hold fairly well for illuminants of moderate saturation, but if the illuminant is highly chromatic they break down. Also, for some hues they seem to work better than others. In the violet and blue region the effects seem to be brightness-dependent and for better results the brightness of the blue illuminant must be chosen to be somewhat lower than that of the yellow illuminant. Although our method of comparison (Munsell chips) cannot be considered perfect, these effects are unquestionably there.

III. TWO-COLOR PROJECTIONS OF EDWIN H. LAND

In this section we would like to apply the foregoing theory to an interesting case which recently aroused considerable excitement. Let two color-separation

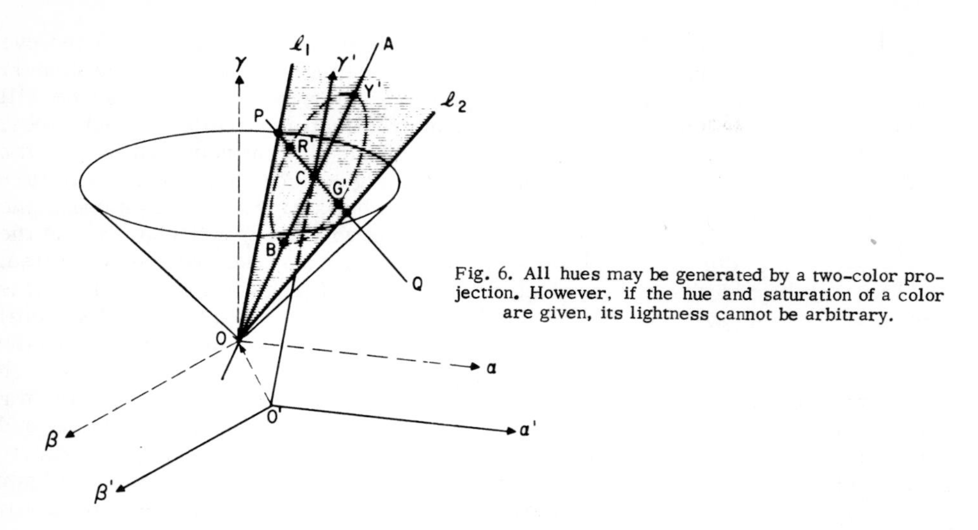

Fig. 6. All hues may be generated by a two-color projection. However, if the hue and saturation of a color are given, its lightness cannot be arbitrary.

positives of a natural scene, one taken through a red filter, the other through yellow-green, be projected with their respective filters in exact registration (Land, 1959). On the screen the colors of the original scene are observed in their proper places. These colors appear somewhat distorted and pale but they are distinctly yellow, green, red, blue, etc. Let the saturations corresponding to our filters be σ_1 and σ_2. In terms of the coordinates α, β, and γ they would be described as the straight lines l_1 and l_2 (Fig. 6). Therefore all possible light samples producible in this way fall on the shaded plane area $l_1 O l_2$. Judged from this original coordinate system, these light samples would appear as the various mixtures of red and yellow-green. However, the eye does not function that way. Looking at the figure we see that the origin O is shifted to O' by the coordinates ξ, η, ζ and the achromatic axis $O\gamma$ is tilted to $O'\gamma'$ by an amount given by (8). The net result is that from the new reference system, light samples spanning the shaded area will now appear to have all hues. However, all possible colors are not generated since very bright blues and dark oranges will be missing. This is because the equation of the plane may be written

$$A\alpha' + B\beta' + C\gamma' + D = 0 \tag{10}$$

so that if the hue and the saturation of a sample on this plane are given, its brightness cannot be arbitrary.

Note that the form of equation (10) is invariant under the transformations (6). In other words, if new transformations are induced by turning on the lights of the room or by providing contrast and surround with the help of other colored areas and scenes, the appearance of a given image will remain practically the same. This is because, along with the equation of the plane, the mutual interrelationships of its points will also remain invariant in form, so that the color classifications of the objects within the image will be preserved. This leads to an important conclusion, first expressed by Land, that "different color worlds can coexist side by side or one within another."

From these simple considerations, various other properties of Land's projections follow. For example, exchanging the two filters reverses some colors to their complements since this reflects the closed curve $R'Y'B'$ in Fig. 6. If one uses identical transparencies in both projectors, one obtains a straight line OR on the shaded area intersecting the achromatic axis. If in one projector we use the negative of the transparency used in the other projector, we obtain another straight line PQ, again intersecting the achromatic axis. In such cases the eye will evidently see only the various shades of the same color and its complement since all directions are not generated. In the former case the whole scene will be almost hueless since OA and $O'\gamma'$ are approximately parallel to each other. It would be quite wrong, however, to conclude that all continuous curves on the shaded area will correspond to achromatic images. For instance one can take as the original scene a color wheel which traces out a closed curve on our plane when all light samples are plotted. This curve will necessarily go around the achromatic axis due to (8). Then it is evident that all hues will be generated.

The stability of the observed colors against large variations of intensities follow from the logarithmic Weber-Fechner law between sensations and stimuli. When two different sensations are compared, they tend to be proportional to the logarithms of their physical intensity. If one of the intensities is increased ten times, the sensation increases only by the logarithm of ten. This explains the relative insensitivity of Land's projections to the variations of intensity and contrast. Also, this consideration appears to be the basis of the new coordinate system of Land. This rather qualitative coordinate system is a mapping of our shaded plane on a logarithmic paper. That this system is inadequate to describe all possible colors with all possible lightness is evident from its basic two-dimensionality.

The explanation of the range of colors producible by various pairs of wavelengths (Land's color map of the eye) follows from similar considerations. For example if l_1 and l_2 are parallel or if they are in the same plane with $O'\gamma'$, the range of colors will be restricted (these are the cases of parallel and antiparallel hues on a chromaticity diagram). Also, if we always use the same pair of separation positives and vary only the wavelengths, we see that there will be a reversal of colors around the wavelength corresponding to blue, since this is where shorter wavelengths start getting a reddish hue which originally belonged to very large wavelengths. Comparison of these and various other consequences of the theory shows a satisfying over-all agreement with the experimental results of Land.

In concluding this section we may add that the choice of orangish red and yellowish green as the pair of filters is better than others because the resulting colors are then brighter in yellows and darker in blues. This simulates the common psychological color image that the best yellows are bright and the best blues are dark. The color quality of Land projections can also be improved by increasing the contrast and by adding to the screen a uniform bluish light (not necessarily projected). This later operation accentuates the effects of the transformations, although a uniform light does not carry any new information from the original scene that was photographed.

IV. A MORE REALISTIC MODEL

In the previous pages we have presented an idealized theory of color perception and indicated that the over-all consequences of this theory are in satisfactory agreement with the observed facts of normal color vision of the human eye. In idealizing the model to utmost simplicity, we have also committed some errors which we now intend to correct. This will result in a more realistic model of human color perception but we must emphasize that, conceptually, nothing new will be added. Only, the model and the formulae, presented above, will be modified to fit the evolutionary arguments and the observational results better than the previous idealized model.

a. We start with the expansion (1) of a light sample. In this expansion the sensitivity curve for brightness is tacitly assumed to be constant for all wave-

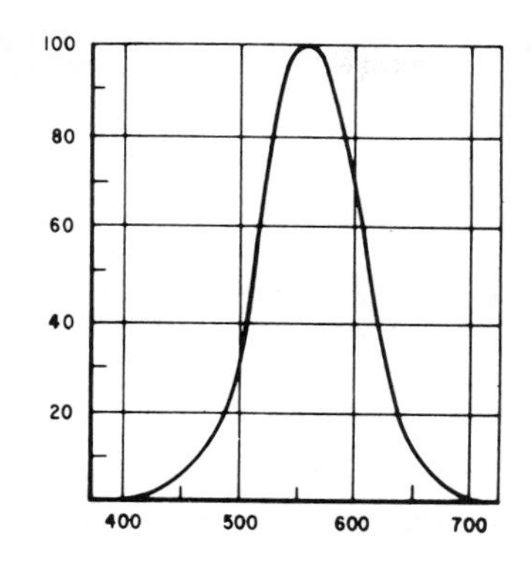

Fig. 7. Brightness sensitivity curve of the human eye.

lengths in the visible region. This is, of course, not true in the actual eye. Sensitivity to brightness is rather a Gaussian-looking curve, as a function of frequency, having a maximum at about a wavelength of 552 mμ, and practically vanishing at 400 mμ and 800 mμ (Fig. 7). This is understandable, because in the rays of sun the energy is distributed in about the same way.* Furthermore, for the reasons given in section II, as the wavelength approaches 800 mμ and 400 mμ, its perceptive value decreases. As a result, the sensitivity of the eye is proportionately lower for these wavelengths. Let us then assume that the expansion is of the form

$$F(\lambda) = \gamma\bar{\gamma} + \alpha\bar{\alpha} + \beta\bar{\beta} + \ldots \tag{11}$$

where $\bar{\gamma} = e^{-u^2/2}$ with $u = 7500(1/\lambda - 1/552)$. This fits the brightness sensitivity curve rather well. Taking $\bar{\gamma} = e^{-u^2/2}$ as the first function in the expansion into eigenfunctions we now find that

$$\bar{\alpha} = \sqrt{2}\, u e^{-u^2/2} \qquad \bar{\beta} = \frac{1}{\sqrt{2}}(2u^2 - 1)\, e^{-u^2/2} \tag{12}$$

This way the sensitivity functions become the first three eigenfunctions of a linear harmonic oscillator (Fig. 8). Note the qualitative similarity of these functions to the earlier functions $\bar{\gamma} = 1$, $\bar{\alpha} = \sin\phi$, $\bar{\beta} = \cos\phi$ in the visible range. The

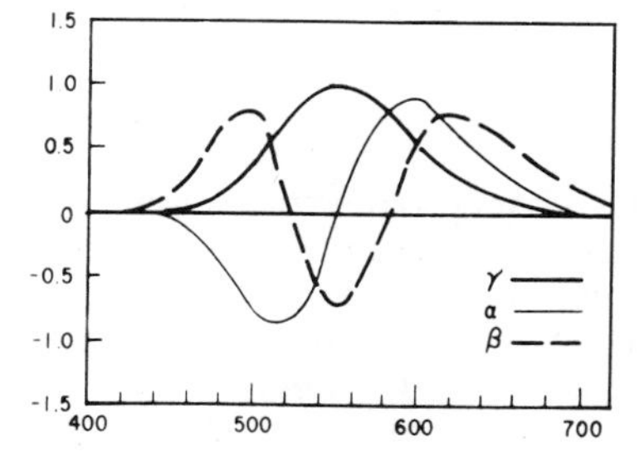

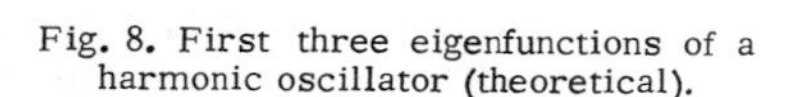
Fig. 8. First three eigenfunctions of a harmonic oscillator (theoretical).

*The sensitivity curve, $\bar{\gamma}$, for brightness may be deduced. Consider the statistical average of all objects. With respect to color this will be an achromatic object reflecting the illuminant quality. Now, evolution requires that on the average the sensation is as large as possible. Thus,

$$\int I(\nu)\bar{\gamma}(\nu)\, d\nu \rightarrow \max$$

From this we find that $\bar{\gamma}(\nu)$ has the same form as the illuminant, which here is the sunlight distribution.

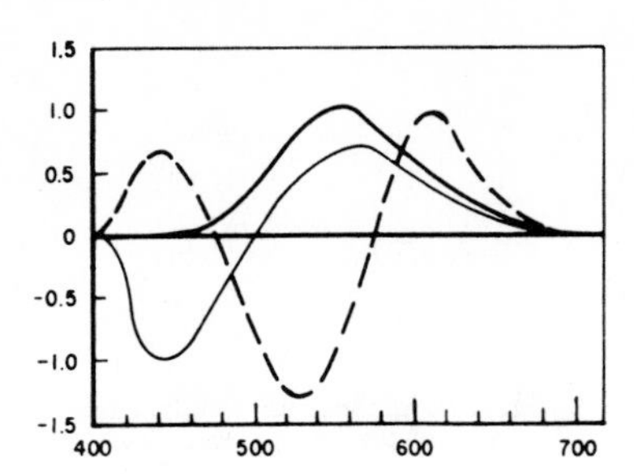

Fig. 9. Hering opponent-colors sensitivity curves (experimental).

sensitivity curves for an opponent-colors theory of Hering type are given in Fig. 9. These are obtained from the standard C.I.E. curves. The closeness in appearance of these curves to the theoretically derived ones lends great support for the basic assumptions of the theory.

Another way of bringing the meaning of the modification just made into light is to compute the curves corresponding to the C.I.E. curves from the theoretical functions. In Fig. 10 we have plotted the functions

$$\bar{x} = \bar{\gamma} + \frac{\bar{\beta}}{2} - 1.3\bar{a}$$

$$\bar{y} = \bar{\gamma}$$

$$\bar{z} = \bar{\gamma} + \frac{\bar{\beta}}{4} + 1.2\bar{a}$$

and in Fig. 11 we have constructed the resulting chromaticity diagram. This diagram shows clearly all the characteristics of the experimental chromaticity diagram.

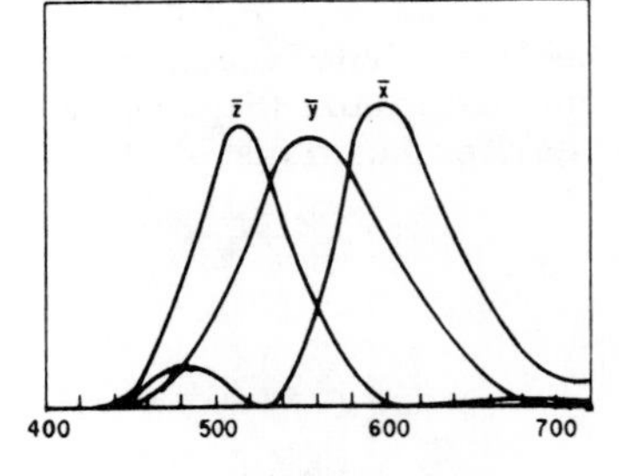

Fig. 10. Theoretically deduced C.I.E.-type color sensitivity curves.

b. The change from the Fourier harmonics to the new eigenfunctions results in a change of the circular character of the cone (Fig. 2) of maximum saturations. This means that for large saturations, $\sigma \to \Sigma$, the equations (6) become inapplicable. In other words, the transformations break down before the previous ideal limit Σ; and due to the noncircular character of the cone, the strict isotropy implied in the idealized model is no longer valid. But for small relative saturations those formulae hold quite well, and their use is warranted due to this good approximation and the theoretical simplicity inherent in the model.

c. The terms ξ and η are treated on an equal footing according to the idealized model. Now, the brightness curve is not uniform over all wavelengths. Therefore, the colors produced by the fulcrum shift must be more marked in the directions (on the chromaticity diagram) complementary to wavelengths of

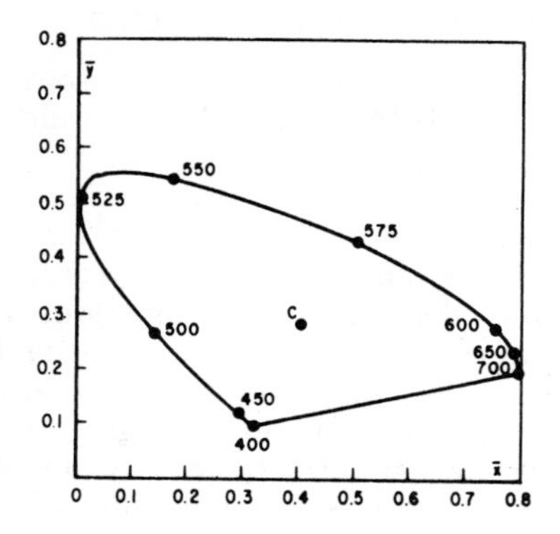

Fig. 11. Theoretically deduced chromaticity diagram.

high-brightness sensitivity. This prediction is indeed an experimental fact. In the aperture experiment of section II, the colors produced by the fulcrum tend towards the purple more than other directions. The common psychological association mentioned earlier (best yellows are brighter, best blues, darker) is also a consequence of the new expansion (11). These are the distortions on the original model imposed by the Gaussian nature of the brightness curve. This causes the original ideal model to deviate from being strictly isotropic and metric; but, the relativity requirements for colors are apparently included in actual vision as much as required by the organism.

d. The formulae (8) for contrast enhancement must also be modified due to the foregoing considerations. Since, however, these formulae are the consequence of the transformations (6), the considerations of the previous paragraph apply here just as well. Namely, formulae (8) are valid for small relative saturations. Furthermore, these formulae, together with the fulcrum shift phenomenon, are the reasons why Land projections work. It follows that Land projections will work better if the over-all light quality is yellowish on the screen, and consequently the fulcrum shift produces blues and purples better. This corresponds exactly to what is observed. The formulae (8) are inaccurate for one other reason: namely, as was mentioned earlier, the same weight was given to all areas in the visual field, irrespective of mutual proximity of color patches. Biologically, the foveal region may be more important than others. Also, mutually close patches can be resolved better if they have higher contrast than the over-all formula predicts. Therefore, further refinement of (8), by introducing a weight function depending on the position on the retina, and the mutual proximity of images will improve the model. Here we do not want to go into it in any further detail since it is quite complicated and does not add anything new to our fundamental understanding of the subject of color perception.

With these modifications the theory is now closer to the actual color perception of the human eye, but still preserves its original conceptual structure. It is still complete and logically self-contained. This does not mean, of course, that there exist no other interesting phenomena involving the human eye. For example, the human eye sees light and color when struck, and it behaves in a certain way when the light intensity increases or decreases indefinitely. In the next section we will try to argue that such features do not belong to the theory of perception. The theory of perception gives the mathematical properties of an optimum perception device, irrespective of what material is used to make it or what processes are adopted to make it work. For example, if the human color perception device was made using photocells and electronic circuitry, the theoretical properties we have derived would still be there, although it would not see light and color when struck.

V. NONPERCEPTUAL FEATURES OF THE HUMAN EYE

The arguments just given indicate the need for defining what is a perceptual feature and what is a nonperceptual effect. Before we do this we would like to give more examples.

a. As the intensity of a given light sample increases, its saturation decreases. In fact, extremely intense light tends to appear white even if composed of spectral colors such as yellows and greens. What may be the evolutionary reason for this? The phenomenon clearly indicates that sensitivity functions are dependent on the intensity of light and that the functions (12) reach saturation before the brightness sensitivity function $\bar{\gamma}$. We would tend to think that evolutionally this is not a desirable feature since it may lead to confusion at high intensities. Therefore, unless we find a survival value for this effect, we may classify the phenomenon as a deficiency of the eye rather than as a special power at which to marvel.

b. Another effect to consider is the so-called Bezold-Brucke phenomenon. As the intensity of a light sample increases, the orange and yellow-green hues shift towards yellow, and violets and blue-greens shift towards blue. This effect may be explained easily by assuming that the red-green sensitivity function $\bar{\beta}$ reaches saturation before the yellow-blue function $\bar{\alpha}$. Again there does not seem to be an advantage for survival in designing the eye this way. Apparently, in the course of its evolution, the organism could not find better materials or processes to avoid these undesirable features. The situation here is similar to the situation of the color television industry, where the finding of a phosphorus with certain properties would improve the quality of the pictures, but until such material is found or a completely new approach is discovered, we have to content ourselves with the imperfect device. Such considerations help us in defining the subject of perception in a more useful manner. A device of perception uses a form of energy as its stimulus (in our case, the sun's electromagnetic radiation) and is constructed for a purpose (in our case, the survival of the organism). Medium and purpose determine the mathematical properties of the device, and these properties may be called the *laws of perception*. They are independent of the way one wants to implement the device. In constructing the device with the materials we can find at the time, we may not be able to realize it perfectly, thus giving rise to imperfections and deficiencies. Hence, it is important to classify in the human visual system the effects of perceptual and nonperceptual nature. The mathematical theory of perception deals only with the perceptual phenomena. In this light the Bezold-Brucke phenomenon is a nonperceptual effect, whereas the colored shadows are of perceptual origin, although they are traditionally regarded as a deception of the eye. These arise from the transformation formulae (8) (i.e., relativity of colors) and truly belong to the perceptual class of phenomena. Similarly, the recent two-color projections of Edwin H. Land are not the results of certain unnatural deceptions of the human eye, but belong to the domain of the mathematical theory of perception.

Before we conclude this section, we would like to mention, for the sake of completeness, that the human eye could have some other effects of a perceptual nature, but it does not have them at the present time. We mentioned at the beginning that the electromagnetic radiation has another variable, namely, polarization. If, in the past, some of the objects important for survival were polarizers, the human eye most likely would have developed a polarization sensitivity and the color space would have been four-dimensional. Since at different times of the day the polarization of the light coming from different parts of the sky is different, the transformations (6) would be applicable even for polarization. Thus, we come to the conclusion that in the idealized form of section II the color perception space would have to be similar to a Minkowsky space of four dimensions. Such a color space may yet be evolved in the future if various industrial products of a polarizing nature become of widespread use and importance. It is interesting to note in this connection that bees perceive polarization. The usual explanation of this development in bees is that they make use of it in determining the position of the sun even when the sun is not directly visible. Bees find their way with the help of this information. We would like to add here that bees deal with sugar and certain sugar solutions which are known to rotate the polarization angle right or left according to their molecular structure. This fact may have enhanced the development of polarization sensitivity in bees.

VI. ON A GENERAL THEORY OF PERCEPTION

Throughout this article we have tried to stress the mathematical and postulational nature of the approach being followed. We have insisted in every occasion that the perceptual aspects are independent of the way the perception device is made. In other words, there is a general theory of perception with its own abstract principles which gives the over-all properties such devices have to fulfill. After these properties are defined, the construction of the device proceeds by trying to find the best way of realizing it with the materials which are available and usable. Furthermore, a perception device does not have to be exclusively of a biological construction. We can just as well imagine an electronic color perceptor. Such a machine may use filters, photocells, and electric wires, instead of color receptors and neural networks. But, given the purpose of human need in the human environment, when the eye evolves, it will have the same perceptual properties as the human eye. In fact it is possible to use such electronic machines to test the evolutionary theories pertaining to perception. For example, we can build an electronic perceptron (Rosenblatt, 1960) and train it to recognize such important and natural objects as plants, animals, fruits, stones, etc., under the natural sunlight illumination and at various times of the day. After a long time the perceptron will develop a color space. It will then be possible to study this space to see if it has the same general properties as the human color space. If it does, then this can be counted as evidence in favor of the evolutionary theory. If not, some of the assumptions of the theory must be wrong. With new assumptions, one then tries again. In this new light, the color theory we have proposed becomes a particular theory to be tested. If it is wrong we try over again until we find the correct theory. Thus, it is possible to advance a new science, the science of perception, with its own class of phenomena, with its own class of principles and theories, and with its own methods of observation and experimentation to prove or disprove such theories. This science may be called Percevonics, meaning the science of perception in its evolutionary perspective.

After this generalization it is evident that the science of perception is not restricted to color or visual perception alone. The perception of shapes and patterns, sounds and speeches, smells, tastes, and tactile sense perceptions fall into the same class. Furthermore, certain forms of perception which are not familiar to human beings may be included. For example, an electric eel sets up an electrostatic field and this field is modified by the objects around in a certain way. From this modification the fish perceives the configuration of objects. No doubt this is a form of perception. On the other hand, the sense of balance or one's knowing where one's feet and hands are may be rather ambiguous. These and other cases, such as the sense of well-being, depression, etc., should probably be classified into a separate domain and given a new name. The name introception may be a suitable term for such inner perceptions. The term perception then would be reserved strictly for the case where the state of the exterior world is perceived. Here we may emphasize that the difficulty of defining the subject of perception at the borderline of introception should not be considered a grave objection. After all, we can also ask: Where does physics stop and chemistry begin? Does the problem of chemical bond belong to physics or chemistry? Such questions indicate that the human experience is probably an indivisible whole. Classification is used only because of convenience in treating closely related groups of phenomena.

In concluding this section, we may point out the relationship of perception theory to cybernetics. In a sense, the situation is analogous to the relationship between thermodynamics and statistical mechanics. Perception bypasses the microscopic details of nervous structure and operation and concerns itself with the prediction of the final over-all results, under the evolutionary constraints of optimum survival value. Like thermodynamics, it is interested in a set of macroscopic principles which govern the over-all equilibrium properties (final evolutionary goal) of the organism rather than the microscopic transitional details as functions of time. Cybernetics is, therefore, the counterpart of statistical mechanics. It studies the regulatory processes, whether perceptive or not, and aspires to give us microscopic details of how such regulation is achieved and evolved in time.

VII. DISCUSSION

In this article, a summary of the earlier work on two-color projection is omitted since a recent article by Deane B. Judd fulfills this need to our satisfaction (Judd, 1960). As to the relation of the present attempt to previous work, we acknowledge at once that most of the background information used to build the theory is well known experimentally, although the interpretations given here to some of these facts may be different. The principle that object-colors remain invariant under various illuminations and that for each illumination there exists a reference point is due mainly to Helson (Helson, 1938). Helson was also the first investigator to point out that it is impossible for the eye to accept a pure monochromatic source as illuminant. In our theory this is explained by saying that in the limit $\sigma \to \Sigma$ the transformation from one illuminant to another becomes indeterminate. Our theory emphasizes the invariance of color interrelationships, namely, the interrelationships among a set of color samples rather than strict object-color constancy. However, the observed approximate object-color constancy follows from our theory, as is easily seen by computing for each illuminant the light sample coming from an object and putting it into our transformations.

The effects of neighboring colors on a given light sample were investigated by various workers (Jeansch, 1921). This so-called contrast enhancement was usually treated as a separate phenomenon. Our treatment shows the close connection between this and the transformation under change of illuminant. From our point of view, contrast enhancement is essentially a consequence of the transformations.

The nonhomogeneous terms in the transformation (5) are small and usually may be neglected. Their omission, however, would eliminate the faint blues, blue-greens, and purples observed in the Land projections. To our knowledge these nonhomogeneous terms appeared for the first time in the work of Burnham, Evans, and Newhall (1957), although the aperture color experiment was known in Helmholtz's time (Helmholtz, 1924).

It must be stressed that our transformations are fundamentally different from von Kries' coefficient law. The validity of the coefficient law, as finally developed by Judd, Helson, and Warren (1953), was re-examined by Burnham, Evans, and Newhall (1957), and by MacAdam (1956) on the basis of a method suggested by Brewer (1954). It was found that the law is untenable or at least needs drastic modification. A set of three fundamental response functions satisfying a coefficient law was not consistent with the careful experiments that were performed. MacAdam concluded that the experiments cannot be explained unless five or more response functions are postulated. It would be interesting to see if the present laws (6), which are linear transformation laws, agree with the experiment without further modification.

As to the mechanism producing the transformations, one usually thinks in terms of after-images and retinal adaptations. The author is of the opinion that the small nonhomogeneous terms ξ, η, and ζ might be related to the retinal or after-image mechanism, but the primary part of the transformation, namely, the tilt of the γ-axis (Fig. 3), may essentially be cortical and act almost instantly.* In this connection, consider the following experiment. One looks at a large yellow paper with a white dot in the center for a few seconds. When one turns the eye immediately to a gray field, one sees, as the after-image, a gray field with a yellow dot! This experiment is hard to explain with the ordinary after-image theory, which predicts a blue field with a white dot as the result. It can easily be explained, however, with our transformations if the homogeneous part is assumed to act much faster than the nonhomogeneous part. The process producing the information for the homogeneous part of the transformations could perhaps be attributed to various interconnections, directly or through bipolars, between the retinal cones. This may result in an average stimulus which could be carried to the visual cortex via bipolars. Unfortunately, our knowledge of these neurophysiological activities is so crude that it is perhaps impossible to say anything really convincing at the present time. Besides, our approach is essentially perceptual in nature and does not pretend to go into neurological matters.

ACKNOWLEDGMENTS

The author would like to express his gratitude to Drs. Leonard Sheingold and James Storer for support and encouragement, to Dr. Deane B. Judd for an inspiring discussion, and to Drs. Donald Brick, Seymour Stein, and Ronald Row and Messrs. Robert Lucy, Edward Smith, and Stanley Schneider for help and discussions.

REFERENCES

Brewer, W. L. 1954. J. Opt. Soc. Am. 44, 207.

Burnham, R. W., Evans, R. M., and Newhall, S. M. 1957. J. Opt. Soc. Am. 47, 35. See also Wassef, G. T. 1955. Optica Acta (Paris) 2, 144.

Helmholtz, H. V. 1924. Physiological Optics. Vol. II, p. 275. Opt. Soc. Am.

Helson, H. 1938. J. Exp. Psychol. 23, 439.

Helson, H., Judd, D. B., and Warren, M. 1953. Illum. Eng. 47, 221.

Jeansch, E. R. 1921. Über den Farbencontrast und die sog. Berücksichtigung der Farbigen Beleuchtung, Z. Sinnesphysiol. 52, 165.

Judd, D. B. 1960. J. Opt. Soc. Am. 50, 254.

Land, E. H. 1959. Proc. Natl. Acad. Sci. 45, 115, 636. Sci. Am. 200, 84, 1959: Fox, W. F. and Hickey, W. H. 1914. British Pat. No. 636.

MacAdam, D. L. 1956. J. Soc. Motion Picture Television Engrs. 65, 455.

Rosenblatt, F. 1960. Perceptrons and the theory of brain mechanisms. Cornell Aeronautical Laboratory No. VG-1196-8.

*See comments by E. H. Land on D. B. Judd's summary article (Judd, 1960).

NEUROMIME MODELING OF SENSORY PATHWAYS

E. B. Johnston*

ITT Communication Systems, Inc., Paramus, New Jersey

Progress in physiological modeling has been closely associated with progress in the disciplines that provide its tools. Because these tools provide understanding of living processes, many of the secrets they yield can be used to create more tools. Thus, the cycle has begun; from it is born bionics.

This paper does not treat a neuron model, but rather a neuronal function. Two forms of circuit elements are interconnected with no appreciable alternation in the results. The paper does contribute knowledge to the following dilemma: "When we record neuroactivity from a bundle or group of neurons, individual events are extremely difficult if not impossible to decipher, and if we record from neuroelectrodes to one or a small number of neurons, the knowledge is so meager compared to the complexity of the higher order nervous system that little is gained."

In 1956 Fishkopf et al. postulated a neuron model system concerning statistical-distribution-evoked response from a controlled stimulus from a neuron population of "neuron units" of fluctuating threshold. Thus, the distribution of response is related to the statistical properties of a "summed response" for the population. In investigating noise in communication circuits, the work of S. O. Rice (1945), J. M. Whittaker (1936), N. Campbell (1909), and others was reviewed. Their work explains noise in vacuum tube circuits as a summation of individual waveforms or "shot-noise" series.

C. E. T. Krakau (1956) and M. H. Goldstein et al. (1960) relate neuronal noise to elemental waveforms by statistical variations, much as does Rice. Gross responses are thereby treated as a summation of incremental discrete wave potentials.

The work in "Agathe Tyche" and "Reliable Responses from Unreliable Nets," and the assessments of the reticular system by W. S. McCulloch and W. A. Rosenblith et al. provided the challenge for a sensory model.

The primary purpose of this investigation was the feasibility of developing an animated (analog) display from limited digital information. However, the investigation soon took on the form of sensory pathways of either the photo or tactile process.

The original model contained photosensors arranged in a matrix. Each of these activated a multivibrator of constant threshold (Fig. 1). These neuromimes

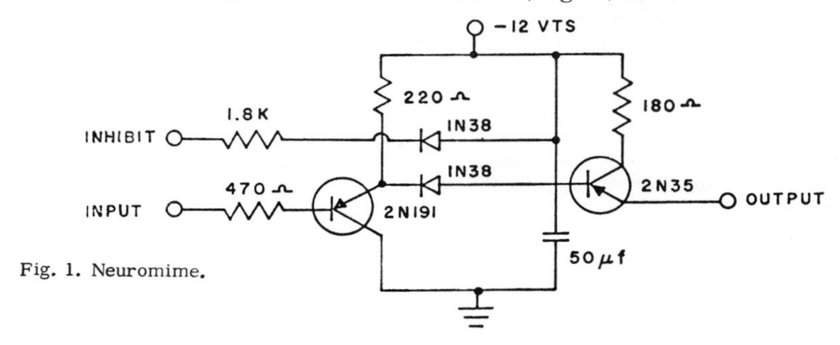

Fig. 1. Neuromime.

*Present address: ITT Federal Laboratories, San Fernando, California.

in turn activated a neuromime in a network of neuromimes of the type shown in Fig. 2. These units have the properties of variable threshold, all-or-none response, inhibition, and summation (by diode logic) usually attributed to neurons.

The output of each neuromime is sufficient to "fire" the next. Synapsis throughout the networks was by diode "and" and "or" logic. Early in the investigation it was recognized that to program the neuromime's ability to fire was incompatible with nature. Therefore, two measures were initiated to assure randomness. First, the outputs of all neuromimes are clamped below their

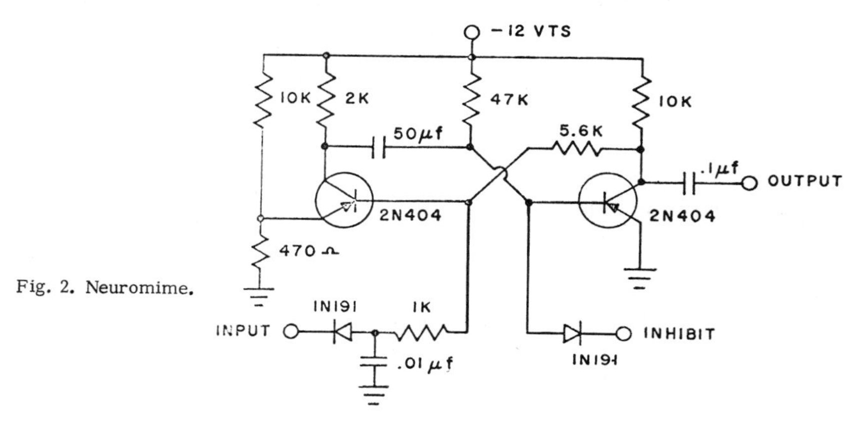

Fig. 2. Neuromime.

nominal threshold. Second, a white noise source (Fig. 3) is used to raise some units to the subliminal fringe. By appropriate "and" connections, the summation of a noise pulse and a signal pulse exceeds threshold and the neuromime conducts. The length of the impulse was purposely made long, approximately $1\frac{1}{2}$ sec in the unstable state, so closer subjective observations could be made. Variations in refraction time added nothing to the investigation, and were not used. However, they can be added by introducing white noise to the inhibitory input of either Fig. 1 or Fig. 2.

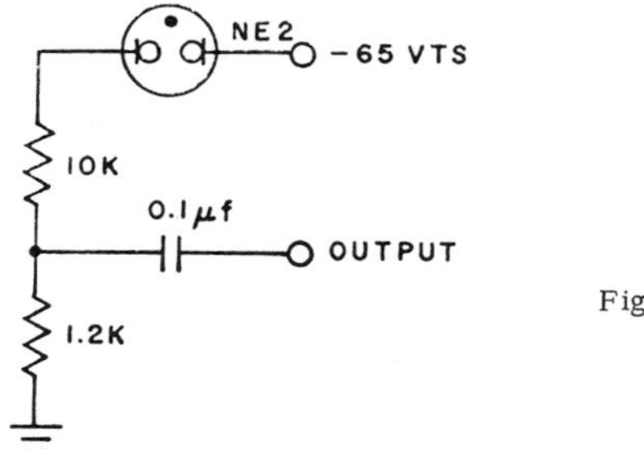

Fig. 3. Noise generator.

The first model consisted of 53 neuromimes interconnected by diodes. A photoreceptor and its flip-flop constituted the input. This input was coupled to three neuromimes in such a way that as one "fired," its output inhibited all others in that level. The output also passed to one of three in the next level, and the same response and inhibition resulted. In this level were 27 neuromimes. The process continues; however, convergence takes place until one output results. The order is then 1-3-9-27-9'-3'-1'. The only stipulations are if the sensor is stimulated, there must be an output from No. 1 neuromime, and if any of the final three are stimulated, there must be an output from 1'.

It should be pointed out that one could equate an "evoked response" to the distribution of the noise. Statistically, the output will occur as a response to an input 2186 times out of 2187 tries. Emperically a response occurred for 1689 consecutive tries in one test set.

From this background a 5×5 matrix of twenty-five sensors and 1325 neuromimes was constructed. The empirical results were a matrix display consistent with the input. It can be shown that for any time $t_2, t_3, \ldots, t_n$ where $T_1 =$ start, there are N neuromimes in the subliminal fringe capable of firing. The chances of two neuromimes firing at the same instant are of the form

$$P_0\ (N,T) = \frac{\int_0^t f(t)dt \cdot \exp\left[\int_0^t -f(t)dt\right]}{N!}$$

which is the Poisson distribution for any level or any pathway at any time $\Delta t < t_2$, where $N!$ is the probability of N firings at the same time.

The next possibility to be investigated was the interconnection of the individual pathways in the 5 by 5 matrix. Diode channel crossings were made as diagramed in Figs. 1 and 2 of the appendix. The empirical results of an output resulting from an input in an adjacent channel were 1 in 286 tries as an average for five tries. This differs considerably with the analysis presented. Note that if an output results in an adjacent channel, there may or may not be an output in the stimulated channel. The inhibitory network of one channel does not connect to the adjacent channels.

Another arrangement which yields similar results is diagramed in Figs. 3 and 4 of the appendix. In these, the outside or interchannel connections are direct in the four rows which contain only 25 instead of 27 neuromimes. The resultant probability is the same as for the previous case.

A final arrangement was tried using 100 sensors in a 10 by 10 matrix and 1700 neuromimes. The order was 1-3-9-3'-1'. Interchannel connections were made at the 3-to-9 and 9-to-3' levels only. Again, diodes were used. In this arrangement, a condenser was charged by the output and added to the input of each neuromime fired. This reduced the threshold in a roundabout manner by adding to the noise component, with the result that the required amplitude of a signal impulse was reduced. In this manner a pathway through any channel was established. It was the purpose of this setup to create some semblance of self-organization. Attempts at modeling "moving edge detection," as defined by Lettvin et al. (1959), were made. The size of the receptors made "net convergence" impractical.

The results of the edge detection were not astounding. A moving edge detection did evoke a response. However, the edge had to be parallel to the arrangement of the receptors in the matrix.

The conclusions made from this project are somewhat inconclusive. For a system similar to this, a reliable output is obtained for an input. There need not be the redundancy of channel pathways described in the 5 by 5 matrix to obtain the same order of reliability. There can be an animated or moving display from limited digital data. If there is a retentivity of output greater than unity, where unity is impulse duration of the neuromime, the animation progresses more smoothly. Finally, a neuromime model can be constructed of a statistical process of "shot noise" or "summed bursts" contributing to an "evoked response." Much more work is needed before the dilemma mentioned is resolved.

I wish to thank Dr. D. I. Epstein for his help and work in the analysis of our models.

APPENDIX: THE PROBABILITY OF IMPULSE ESCAPE

D. I. Epstein

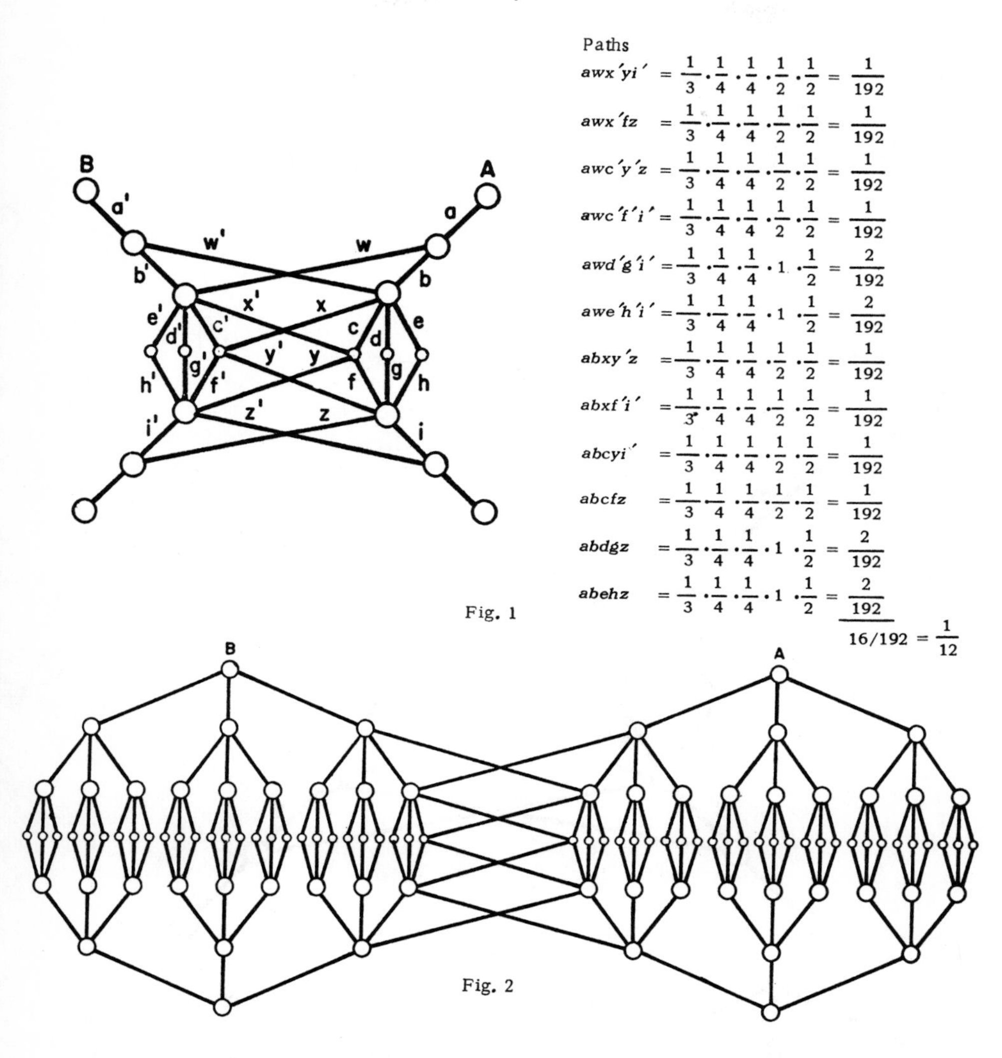

Paths

$$awx'yi' = \frac{1}{3}\cdot\frac{1}{4}\cdot\frac{1}{4}\cdot\frac{1}{2}\cdot\frac{1}{2} = \frac{1}{192}$$

$$awx'fz = \frac{1}{3}\cdot\frac{1}{4}\cdot\frac{1}{4}\cdot\frac{1}{2}\cdot\frac{1}{2} = \frac{1}{192}$$

$$awc'y'z = \frac{1}{3}\cdot\frac{1}{4}\cdot\frac{1}{4}\cdot\frac{1}{2}\cdot\frac{1}{2} = \frac{1}{192}$$

$$awc'f'i' = \frac{1}{3}\cdot\frac{1}{4}\cdot\frac{1}{4}\cdot\frac{1}{2}\cdot\frac{1}{2} = \frac{1}{192}$$

$$awd'g'i' = \frac{1}{3}\cdot\frac{1}{4}\cdot\frac{1}{4}\cdot 1\cdot\frac{1}{2} = \frac{2}{192}$$

$$awe'h'i' = \frac{1}{3}\cdot\frac{1}{4}\cdot\frac{1}{4}\cdot 1\cdot\frac{1}{2} = \frac{2}{192}$$

$$abxy'z = \frac{1}{3}\cdot\frac{1}{4}\cdot\frac{1}{4}\cdot\frac{1}{2}\cdot\frac{1}{2} = \frac{1}{192}$$

$$abxf'i' = \frac{1}{3}\cdot\frac{1}{4}\cdot\frac{1}{4}\cdot\frac{1}{2}\cdot\frac{1}{2} = \frac{1}{192}$$

$$abcyi' = \frac{1}{3}\cdot\frac{1}{4}\cdot\frac{1}{4}\cdot\frac{1}{2}\cdot\frac{1}{2} = \frac{1}{192}$$

$$abcfz = \frac{1}{3}\cdot\frac{1}{4}\cdot\frac{1}{4}\cdot\frac{1}{2}\cdot\frac{1}{2} = \frac{1}{192}$$

$$abdgz = \frac{1}{3}\cdot\frac{1}{4}\cdot\frac{1}{4}\cdot 1\cdot\frac{1}{2} = \frac{2}{192}$$

$$abehz = \frac{1}{3}\cdot\frac{1}{4}\cdot\frac{1}{4}\cdot 1\cdot\frac{1}{2} = \frac{2}{192}$$

$$16/192 = \frac{1}{12}$$

Fig. 1

Fig. 2

Two nets are connected as shown in Fig. 1. The problem is to determine the probability that an impulse entering the input of net *A* will appear at the output of net *B*.

Several restrictions are imposed on the transmission of the impulse. First, at each step the impulse must move into a different node (no delays). Second, at each step the impulse must move to a node on the next lower level; thus, the same link cannot be traversed twice. Third, the probability that the impulse leaves a node along a particular admissible link is equal to $1/k$, where k is the number of admissible links incident on the node.

Figure 2 shows only that part of the total structure presented in Fig. 1 which would provide the impulse with an opportunity for escaping from *A* to *B*. There are 12 paths which lead from the input of net *A* to the output of net *B* (more

Paths

$$awx'yg' = \frac{1}{3}\cdot\frac{1}{4}\cdot\frac{1}{3}\cdot\frac{1}{2}\cdot\frac{1}{2} = \frac{1}{144}$$

$$awx'cz = \frac{1}{3}\cdot\frac{1}{4}\cdot\frac{1}{3}\cdot\frac{1}{2}\cdot\frac{1}{2} = \frac{1}{144}$$

$$awc'y'z = \frac{1}{3}\cdot\frac{1}{4}\cdot\frac{1}{3}\cdot\frac{1}{2}\cdot\frac{1}{2} = \frac{1}{144}$$

$$awc'e'g' = \frac{1}{3}\cdot\frac{1}{4}\cdot\frac{1}{3}\cdot\frac{1}{2}\cdot\frac{1}{2} = \frac{1}{144}$$

$$awd'f'g' = \frac{1}{3}\cdot\frac{1}{4}\cdot\frac{1}{3}\cdot 1\cdot\frac{1}{2} = \frac{2}{144}$$

$$abxy'z = \frac{1}{3}\cdot\frac{1}{4}\cdot\frac{1}{3}\cdot\frac{1}{2}\cdot\frac{1}{2} = \frac{1}{144}$$

$$abxe'g' = \frac{1}{3}\cdot\frac{1}{4}\cdot\frac{1}{3}\cdot\frac{1}{2}\cdot\frac{1}{2} = \frac{1}{144}$$

$$abcyg' = \frac{1}{3}\cdot\frac{1}{4}\cdot\frac{1}{3}\cdot\frac{1}{2}\cdot\frac{1}{2} = \frac{1}{144}$$

$$abcez = \frac{1}{3}\cdot\frac{1}{4}\cdot\frac{1}{3}\cdot\frac{1}{2}\cdot\frac{1}{2} = \frac{1}{144}$$

$$abdfz = \frac{1}{3}\cdot\frac{1}{4}\cdot\frac{1}{3}\cdot 1\cdot\frac{1}{2} = \frac{2}{144}$$

$$12/144 = \frac{1}{12}$$

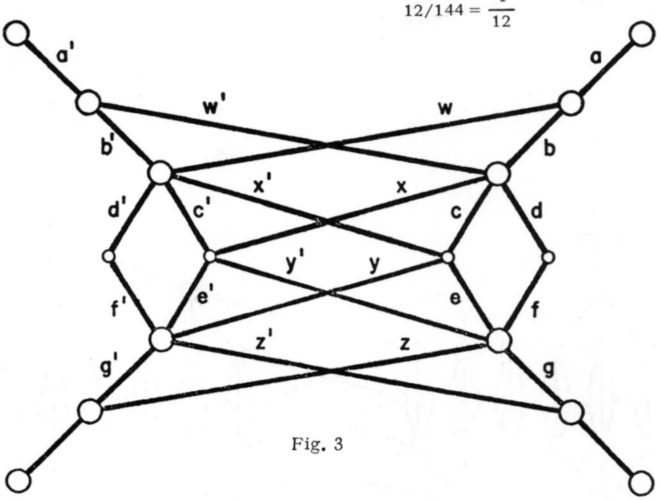

Fig. 3

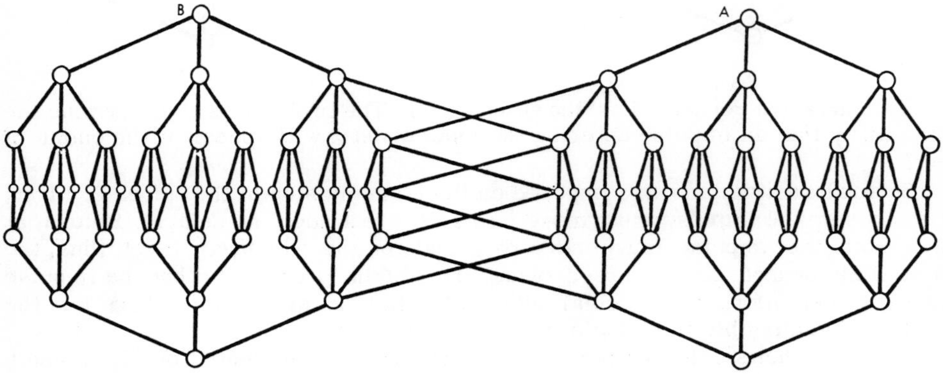

Fig. 4

precisely, to the node marked *X*, from which the impulse has no choice but to proceed to the output of *B*). These 12 paths are identified by means of the lettering scheme, and their respective probabilities calculated. The probability that an impulse entering the input of net *A* will appear at the output of net *B* is $1/12$.

Although it has not been shown, there is another net, *C*, to the right of *A*. *A* and *C* are connected in the same way as *B* and *A*. It is of interest to calculate, also, the probability that an impulse entering the input of net *A* will appear at the output of net *C*. However, in view of the symmetry of the over-all structure, this is the same as asking for the probability that an impulse entering the input of *B* will appear at the output of *A*. But, again because of symmetry, this is the same as the probability that has been calculated above, for example, $1/12$. Therefore, the probability that an impulse entering the input of net *A* will appear at the output of one of its two neighboring nets is $1/6$.

Figures 3 and 4 treat a similar model in which the number of nodes is reduced by one at the highest level. The probability that an impulse will escape is the same as for the previous net.

ACTIVITY LEVELS AND OSCILLATION MODES IN NEURAL NETS

D. R. Smith

National Physical Laboratory, Teddington, Middlesex, England

and

C. H. Davidson

Department of Electrical Engineering, University of Wisconsin

Based on both engineering and biological arguments, a "probabilistic" approach toward analysis of networks of simulated neurons is taken, rather than the more conventional "deterministic" one. Such networks are shown by both theoretical analysis and digital computer simulation to be capable of supporting self-maintaining activities of several sorts. The results of Shimbel and Rapoport, Allanson, and Beurle are extended, and a number of new cases considered. Both steady-state and oscillatory activity are considered and related to several of the parameters of the individual elements and of the network as a whole.

It is shown that a mode of regularly repeated activity called "cycling" may exist in either of the above cases, even when the network is made up of elements of quite widely differing properties. One new phenomenon is reported which seems to merit the description of "self-organization" of network activity.

Some possible roles of these types of behavior in neural activity are discussed briefly in the conclusion.

BACKGROUND

One of the specific outgrowths of the University of Wisconsin Interdisciplinary Research Program in Artificial Intelligence, which has brought together a productive collaboration of electrical engineers, mathematicians, neurophysiologists, and psychologists, has been a growing conviction that computers are too exact.

Although reliance on completely deterministic interconnection of similarly deterministic logic elements has produced some fantastically successful machines, the construction and maintenance requirements of this sort of system are becoming more and more staggering. In an electronic computer, the logical design must spell out precisely where each of the 10^7, or better, connections must go; if even one is incorrect or missing, complete nonsense may emerge. Furthermore, even if all are initially correct, failure of one component or a deterioration of one connection may reduce the entire machine to impotence.

It is amply established that nature does not place the same reliance on exact determinism. The logic elements she employs in the central nervous system seem to be far more erratic than their electronic counterparts. Evidence from genetics, neurophysiology, and other investigations supports the view that the wiring diagram seems to allow for a great deal of "local option" in the assembly process; i.e., there appears to be a considerable degree of randomness in the connections, rather than having all of them completely predetermined.

This lack of preciseness in the specification of the connection says, for one thing, that the response of the system must be (at least at first) very unpredictable. It is only by a process of training and growth that the system eventually learns to produce a consistent response from a given class of stimuli.

The over-all reliability achieved by the biological computing device in the face of this further implies a large amount of redundancy in the elements and their interconnections, so that the output is a statistical function of the joint behavior of many parts, rather than being critically dependent upon the behavior of any one.

Still further evidence of the biological computer's escape from determinism is its known ability to continue or recover in the face of disease or injury. Even when tissue known to be a vital link is irreplaceably damaged, brains can be retrained to establish essentially equivalent behavior patterns as before.

Recent investigations into the analysis and modeling of neural circuits fall roughly into these two classes: the "deterministic" school, started by the classical paper of McCulloch and Pitts (1943); and the "probabilistic" school, based upon the work of Shimbel and Rapoport (1948), who first proposed the application of statistical techniques to the study of nerve-like structures.

As far as applicability to the study of biological systems is concerned, most of the deterministic systems proposed fail in plausibility. Their behavior does not possess the flexibility of biological systems; their detailed specification is unlikely from genetic and comparative anatomical considerations; and their construction, when allied with the reliability-increasing techniques, would often require more cells than exist in the entire nervous system. In addition, to be purely pragmatic, the logical method of analysis, based as it is on the exact knowledge of the connections of each individual element, becomes prohibitive or impossible for systems with extremely large numbers of elements.

As a basis both for biological study and possible eventual computer design, we turn instead to the "probabilistic" approach which, for present purposes, amounts to first postulating a net of a large number of neural-like elements, whose interconnections are random or specified only by a probability distribution, and then examining the types of behavior which this net might yield. The examination employs both an analytical approach from discrete probability theory, and simulation studies using the digital computer. Although an eventual goal will be a study of the possibility of cognitive processes in such a net, the first phase of our investigation is merely to examine the types of behavior such a net can support.

In this, we recognize the extensive early work of Rapoport and Shimbel (1948, 1950, 1952); the demonstration by Allanson (1955), using numerical solution of the possibility of oscillation in neural nets; the showing by Beurle (1956) that such nets could support wave motion; and the introduction by Rochester (1956), Frankel (1955), and Farley and Clark (1954, 1960) of the digital computer as a simulation tool.

Comparatively little analysis has been done to discover how oscillatory neural behavior is related to the constituent cell properties (and what part it might play, if any, in cognitive processes). Perhaps the two most comprehensive papers on this subject, those of Beurle (1956) and Allanson (1956), are mutually contradictory on the rather basic point of whether a stable equilibrium of continuous random activity can exist. The present work attempts to answer some of the simpler questions involved in such a network activity.

PROPERTIES OF THE NETWORK UNDER STUDY

The properties of the neuron-like elements, which we will consider in our model, are summarized symbolically in electrical schematic form in Fig. 1: a monostable element is controlled by a threshold gate; at the input, afferent stimuli are summed spatially (from several other cells) and temporally (by means of an integrating network); when the combined input exceeds the threshold, the cell fires, emitting a single constant-amplitude pulse of either excitatory or inhibitory effect, which is transmitted essentially undiminished to other similar elements; furthermore, a feedback path from the output of the cell raises its own threshold

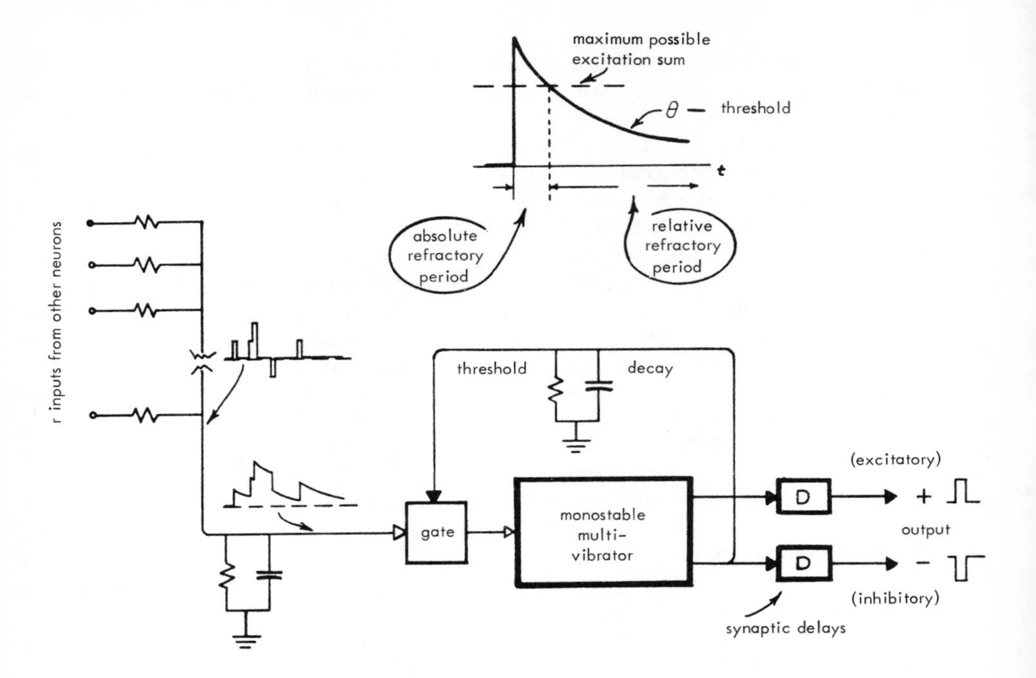

Fig. 1. Simulated neuron properties, symbolic diagram.

to a more or less refractory state for a certain period, from which it eventually returns to its original condition.

Three time delays are implied in the above description: (1) the propagation time of a pulse to the next element (including any synaptic delay time involved); (2) the latent summation period over which incoming stimuli can be effective; and (3) the refractory period during which the cell threshold is above normal. It is customary in such analyses to divide up the time scale, allowing firing to occur only at discrete intervals. If these intervals are taken to correspond to the propagation delay times, this approach avoids most of the conditional probability problem, and leads to equations that lend themselves reasonably well to both numerical analysis and digital computer simulation. If, furthermore, the second and third of these delays are defined and measured in terms of the first, the propagation delay time, and if that time is short in comparison with the other two, it is hoped that this procedure approximates a more continuous model.

Although time delays two and three—the afferent summation period and the cell refractory period—can be postulated to have almost any conceivable time course, three specific decay patterns will be allowed for each, as shown in Fig. 2. In both the first pair, the step function, and the second, the exponential decay, each element is assumed to have exactly identical properties with its neighbors; in the third, a statistical spread in the properties among the elements is allowed, assigned according to a precalculated probability distribution function.

Although all three versions are used in the simulation studies, most of the analysis is limited to the "step function" approximation corresponding to a constant latent summation period s, and an absolute refractory period T. This is an unfortunate necessity for a manageable analysis, but the more salient conclusions carry over to the more complex systems.

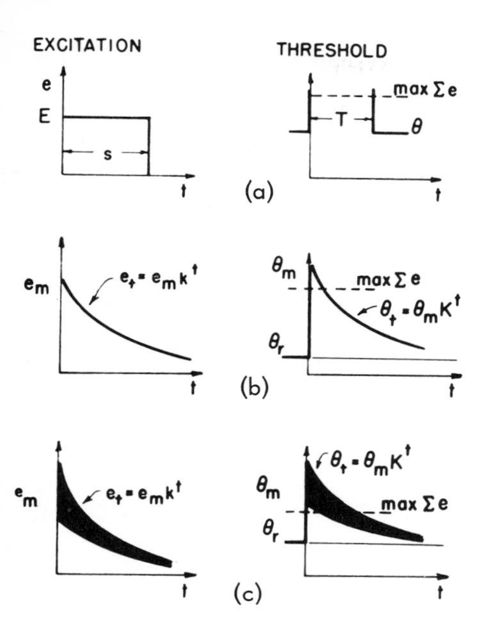

Fig. 2. Excitation and threshold decays.

STEADY STATES

Since the connections between our elements are assigned at random (or more properly by a pseudo-random-number generating program), it is not possible to write exact equations to determine the exact behavior of the network in response to a certain stimulus. In fact, even though equations for the probable behavior can be written with the help of discrete probability theory, it turns out that only for a few simple cases can meaningful answers be extracted. One such group is the set of equilibrium values at which an approximately constant level of activity maintains itself. Inasmuch as a simple method of analysis can be applied to these equilibria, they form a convenient point of departure for study.

EXCITATORY CONNECTIONS ONLY

Initially, nets having excitatory connections only, and no refractory properties, are considered. If the number of elements in the net is assumed large, the probability that a given cell has received i units of excitation over the preceding s time intervals is

$$p_i = \binom{sE}{i} \phi^i (1-\phi)^{sE-i} \tag{1}$$

where E is the number of excitatory input connections and ϕ the instantaneous activity, or fraction of cells firing at a particular time. If this is now summed over all values of i equal to or greater than the threshold θ, it should give the total fraction firing the next instant of time. For the activity to be in equilibrium, this should be the same as the last time:

$$\phi = \sum_{i=\theta}^{sE} \binom{sE}{i} \phi^i (1-\phi)^{sE-i} \tag{2}$$

This is equivalent to saying that for ϕ nearly constant, ϕ can be calculated as a function of ϕ, which function we here call the right side, R_E:

$$\phi = f(\phi) = R_E \tag{3}$$

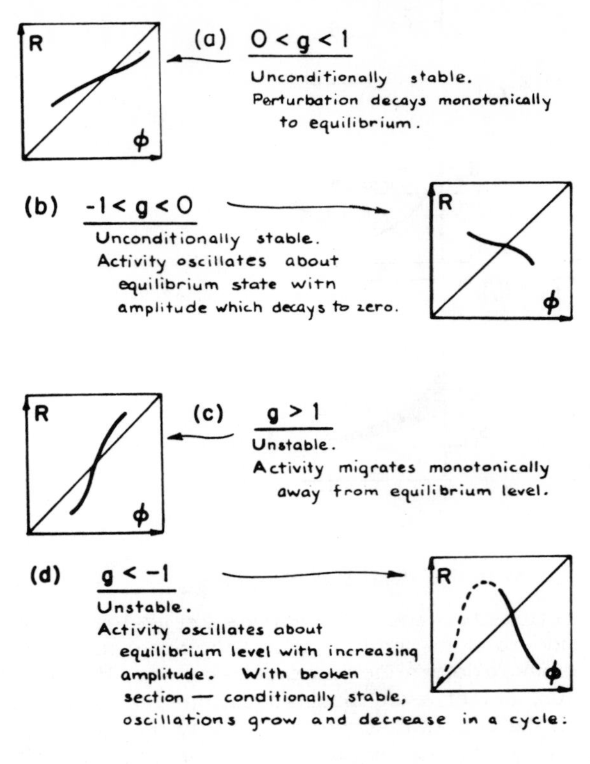

(g = GRADIENT OF R AT INTERSECTION)
R
ϕ
(a) 0 < g < 1
Unconditionally stable.
Perturbation decays monotonically to equilibrium.
(b) -1 < g < 0
Unconditionally stable.
Activity oscillates about equilibrium state with amplitude which decays to zero.
(c) g > 1
Unstable.
Activity migrates monotonically away from equilibrium level.
(d) g < -1
Unstable.
Activity oscillates about equilibrium level with increasing amplitude. With broken section — conditionally stable, oscillations grow and decrease in a cycle.

Fig. 3. Stability classes.

Values of ϕ satisfying this equation will be equilibrium states; here we find that for $\theta \geq 1$, $\phi_1 = 0$, and for $\theta \leq sE$, $\phi_2 = 1$.

The stability of such equilibria is often pictured graphically by plotting separately the left- and right-hand sides of equation (2), as shown in the four cases of Fig. 3. As can be seen, the conclusion to be drawn from the study of the various cases is that where the slope of the right-hand side g at the intersection is equal to or less than one in absolute value, the solution will be stable at that point, and presumably for a small region around.

Differentiation of equation (2) shows that the above roots are stable for $\theta \geq 2$ and $\theta \leq E - 1$, respectively.

It can be shown that a third equilibrium level ϕ_3 exists between the other two, but since both the first two roots are stable, the slope of R_E at the third intersection point must be such that the intermediate root must be unstable (see Fig. 4). This means that small perturbations from the value ϕ_3 will grow monotonically until one of the other equilibrium levels is reached. Since ϕ_1 and ϕ_2 represent no activity and maximum activity, this intermediate unstable equilibrium has been interpreted as an "ignition point."

It can also be shown analytically that the value of ϕ_3 is directly dependent upon θ, and that a rise in the threshold produces a rise in the corresponding ignition point, as would be expected.

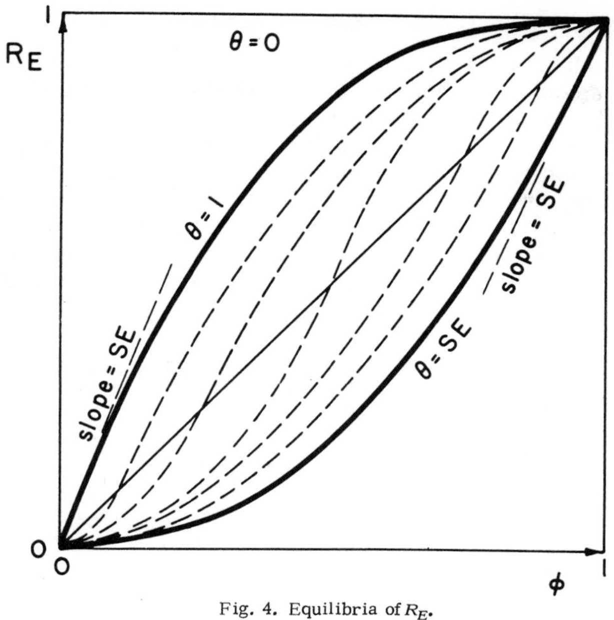

Fig. 4. Equilibria of R_E.

EXCITATORY AND INHIBITORY CONNECTIONS

The inclusion of inhibitory connections in the network raises the maximum number of equilibrium states. Among the new possibilities are systems which show two intersections with slope less than one in absolute value, indicating the existence of two nonzero stable states (e.g., A and E in Fig. 5).

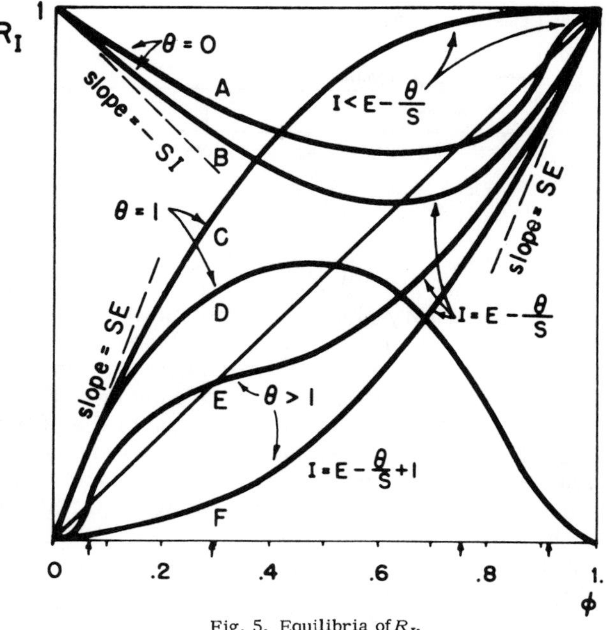

Fig. 5. Equilibria of R_I.

COMPUTER SIMULATION

Simulation studies on the digital computer have corroborated all the findings reported above: the all-or-none type of network activity, necessarily characteristic of the all-excitatory net; the existence and calculated value of ignition points, and their variation with θ; and the existence of the bistable behavior predicted for the nets with both excitatory and inhibitory connections (see Fig. 6). Quantitative agreement has been very good, except that the experimental levels of continued activity tend to be a little higher than the theoretical levels. Apart from this discrepancy, about which more will be said in the next section, it may be concluded that the analytical model is a true representation of the behavior of nets of these types.

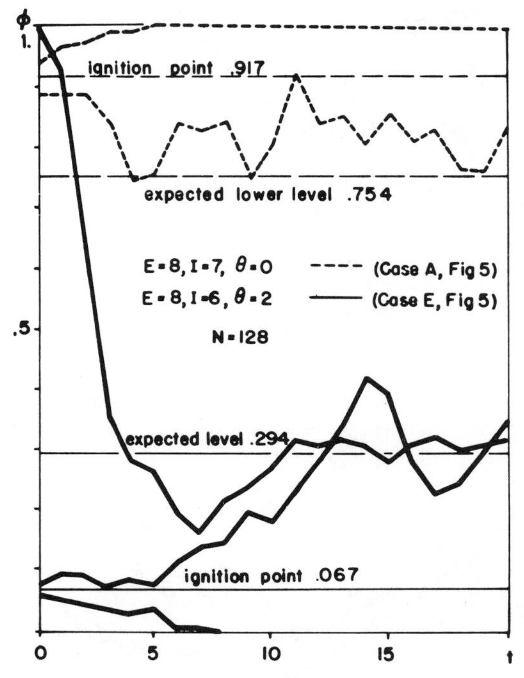

Fig. 6. Simulation of nonrefractory nets.

REFRACTORY NETS

The introduction of refractory elements complicates the analysis with conditional probability problems which have often been insufficiently appreciated in the literature (Smith and Davidson, 1962). Although equations corresponding to the preceding ones can be derived, they can be solved analytically only for certain simple cases (e.g., $s = 1$, $T = 2$, where s is the duration of the afferent summation period, and T that of the absolutely refractory period—see Fig. 2, case a). When this is done, a treatment similar to that for the nonrefractory nets above gives exactly similar results, except that the upper stable equilibrium value is less than one.

However, when these theoretical analyses were compared with the simulation studies of nets with the same step decays on both the refractory and afferent summation properties, results of the type shown in Fig. 7 were consistently obtained. Immediately subsequent to the randomly chosen initial state, the activity levels are close to the chance values, but thereafter grow and finally assume steady levels which are much greater. That a similar situation prevails in networks of more complicated cells seems to be indicated by the similar behavior shown in Fig. 10, case D, where the refractive property not only decays exponentially, but differs from cell to cell. Even though analytical solutions are not possible for these complex nets, as for the simpler ones of Fig. 7, the similarity in their behavior patterns is quite striking. These patterns, in fact, are quite general for a large number of different networks simulated.

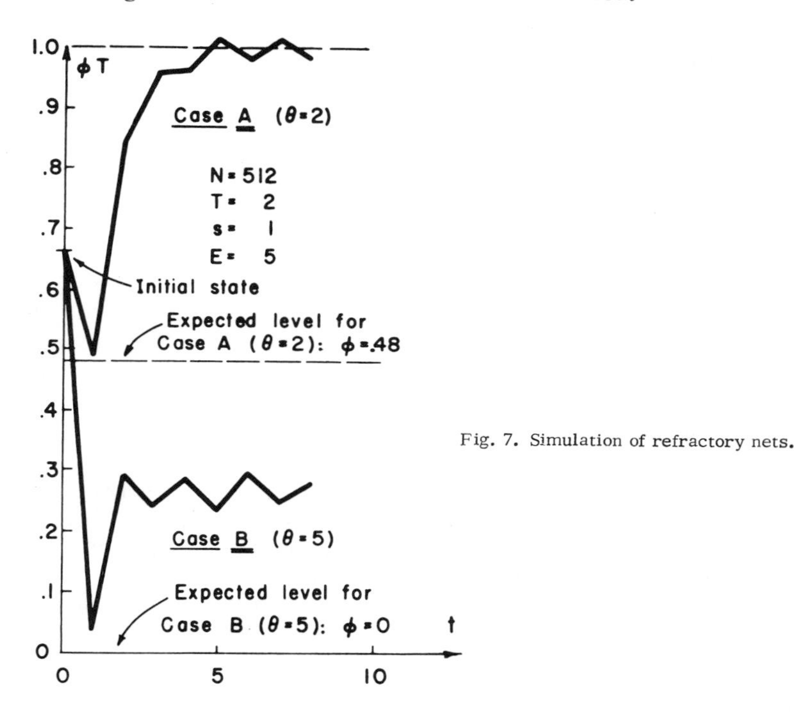

Fig. 7. Simulation of refractory nets.

This behavior can be described, if not explained, by saying that after starting from an initially disorganized state, the activity tends to "organize" itself, so that the simple probability considerations of this elementary treatment no longer apply. The result is that in almost all cases the final maintained activity levels are significantly higher than those expected from straight probability calculations.

CYCLING

Cells with refractory properties appreciably slower than their temporal summation properties tend to be conditioned primarily by their release from their refractory condition. Under these conditions, cells fire as soon as they are released, so that each cell ends up firing at its maximum rate. Therefore, the time relationships between the firings of different cells will remain constant, and the same firing subsets will be reactivated at intervals equal to the refractory period. This type of activity turns out to be quite frequently encountered, and we have named it "cycling." It can be shown to occur in both oscillatory and steady-state types of activity, although it is more commonly associated with oscillations of the same period. Specifically, the simulation examples of Figs. 7A, 10B, and 10D exhibit repeated sequence activity, while those of 7B, 10A, and 10C do not.

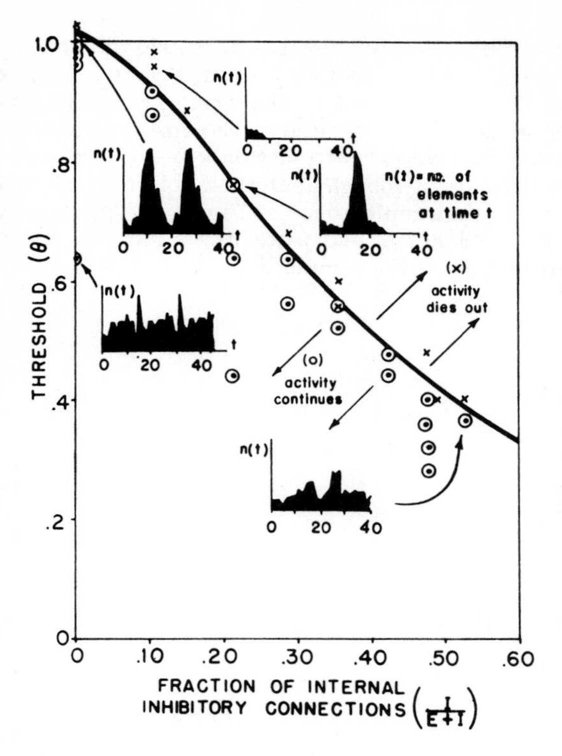

Fig. 8. Boundary of continued activity.

An extended simulation study of some 30 to 40 systems illustrates (in Fig. 8) some parameter relationships which find intuitive corroboration but which have not been expressable in quantitative form as yet. The systems examined were composed of 512 identical cells having five inputs, refractory step functions, and an excitation decay such that an excitation contribution was reduced by 80% in approximately one-third T (case b-a, Fig. 2). The inset activity vs time diagrams demonstrate typical behavior of nets whose parameters correspond to the region in which the inset diagram appears.

Looking first at the all-excitatory nets along the left margin, it is seen that for a sufficiently low threshold, the nets tend to maintain a fairly pronounced activity level with some fluctuations around that value. Nevertheless, the envelope shows very little regular oscillation. As the threshold is increased, the oscillation becomes more pronounced and eventually explosive. As the threshold passes some critical value, the amplitude of the first large burst becomes so great that not enough cells remain unrefractory to maintain activity, and the activity dies out completely.

In either case, the mechanism is as follows: for a period immediately after the application of the initial randomly chosen set of stimuli, the cells are firing at a rate less than their maximum, and the time relations are changing and shifting, until a pattern of activity eventually emerges and provides enough excitation so that all cells are firing at their maximum rate. At this point, the activity "locks in" to a cycling pattern which from then on is preserved and maintained. Not apparent from the diagram, and perhaps a bit surprising, is the fact that whether the net exhibits large amplitude oscillations or more regular sustained activity, cycling sets in at approximately the same time after the initial state.

When the fraction of inhibitory connections in the net is increased, however, an interesting phenomenon takes place: the eventual cycling condition takes longer to set in. Figure 9 shows that there is a fairly smooth increasing relationship between the fraction of inhibitory connections in the net and the time taken for the activity to become organized to a cycling state. The sharply increasing slope of this curve further implies that there will be values of inhibition fraction for which the net will never lock in, but will continue to support activity. These properties have some interesting potentialities in one of the possible roles played by these oscillations in neural activity, as will be mentioned later.

Just as too high a threshold causes the activity to die out completely, so does too much inhibition. Figure 8 shows a very clearly marked boundary between the regions representing conditions of threshold and inhibition which will support continued activity and regions which will not. An important factor in controlling the ability to continue is the amount of activity in the first deep trough. Some attempts, only partially successful, have been made at working this into a quantitative expression.

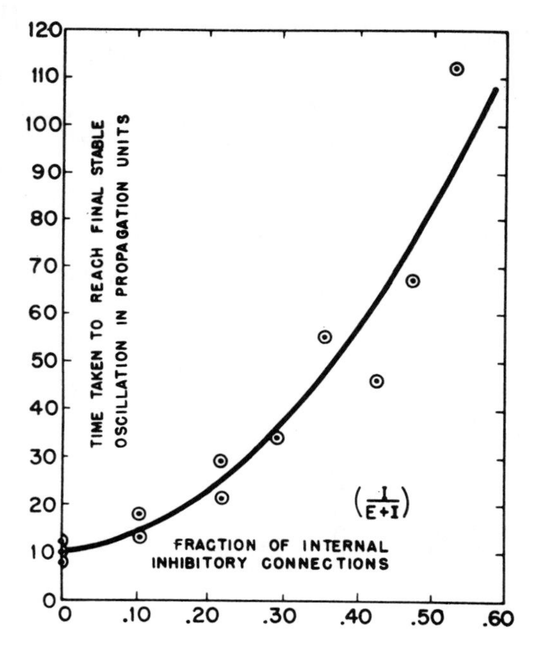

Fig. 9. Lock-in time.

RELATIVELY REFRACTORY NETS

The mechanism of cycling discussed in the previous section was predicated upon a precise period during which each cell is refractory, at the end of which time the cell is suddenly ready to fire again with the same ease as originally. In the somewhat more realistic model exemplified by case b-b, Fig. 2, the cell may undergo a period during which the threshold is so high that even the maximum available excitation cannot fire it, but it emerges from this more gradually, passing through a period during which it may be fired with increasing ease. Under these circumstances, the refractory period varies from cell to cell, depending upon connections, and the mechanism for maintaining firing relations among the cells is not so clear-cut. In such nets, one would expect many more cases of continuing noncycling activity, both steady and oscillatory, and that is exactly what was encountered. What is perhaps more surprising is that a significant number of cycling activity patterns were found. Figure 10 shows examples of all four combinations of activity, both steady state and oscillatory, in each case

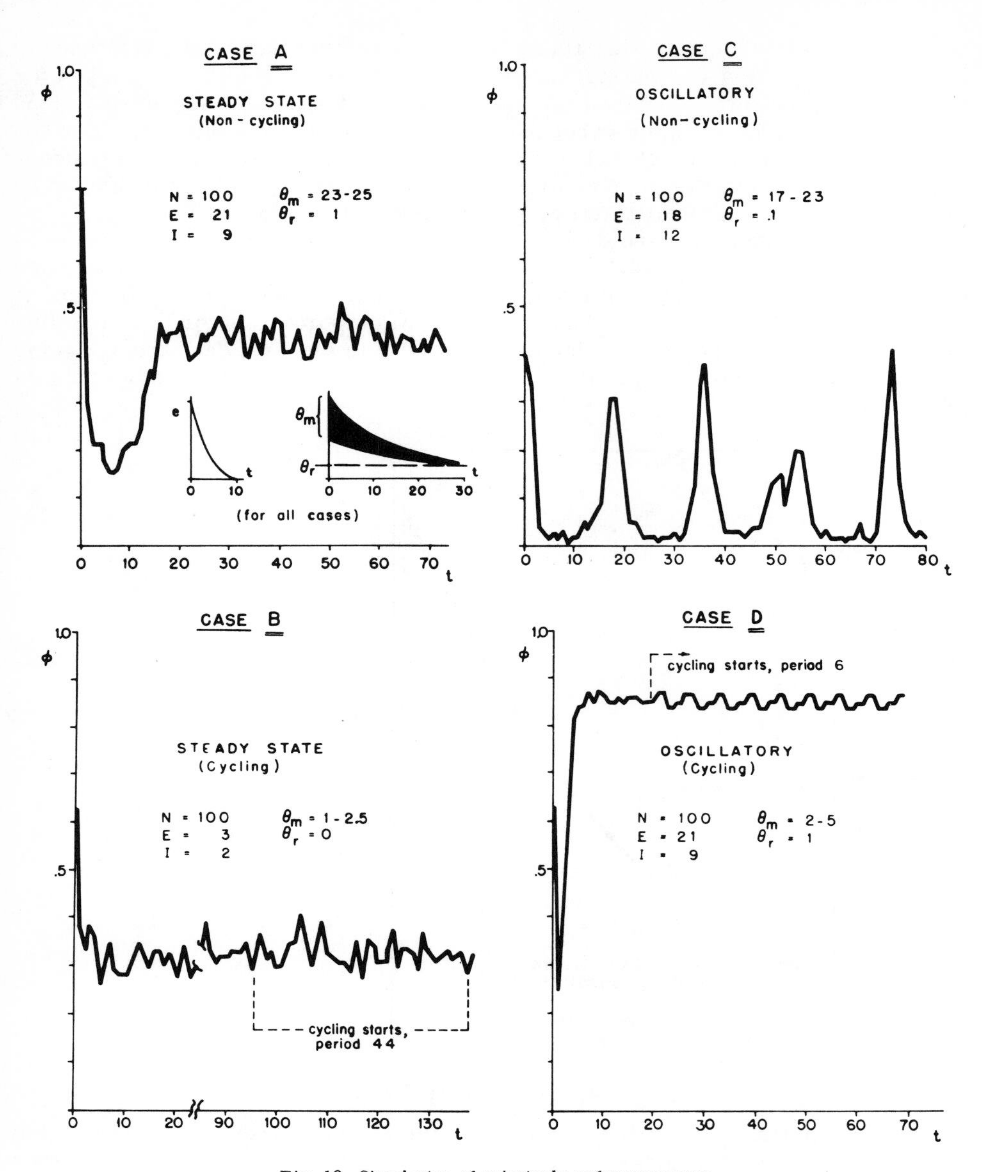

Fig. 10. Simulation of relatively refractory nets.

with and without cycling patterns. Note that in Fig. 10 a statistical variation in one cell property was deliberately introduced, namely, the maximum height to which the threshold rises immediately after firing—so that these are examples of case b-c, Fig. 2. The significant result is that, even with such a "sloppy" net, cycling oscillations will take place (Fig. 10, case D). Because of the high activity level in this cycling behavior, it is apparent that on the average each cell fires several times per cycle, as compared with once per cycle in the oscillations of the previous section. Hence, the term "higher mode" cycling has been applied. More detailed investigations into the nature and mechanism of this cycling are currently going actively forward.

SIGNIFICANCE

At this stage, no attempt is made to correlate the nets studied here with any specific physiological feature, save to reiterate that biological nervous systems show a more random, less exact structure and behavior than do their contemporary electronic counterparts. It is the conviction of the authors that the engineer and the biologist alike will profit by an investigation into the behavior of such systems, specified in whole or in part in terms of probability distributions, rather than subject to a strictly logical design.

More specifically, the phenomena of oscillation and cycling demonstrated here offer possibilities as information storage mechanisms. Experiments on such oscillating nets indicate that the final state attained is a very sensitive function of initial activity, and hence, conceivably of stimuli applied to the net. Mechanisms for entering information need to be worked out; one possibility is the effectiveness, shown in Fig. 9, of an increase in the number of inhibitory connections in a net in "unlocking" a cycling activity. Such a change would move the operating point to the right in that diagram, causing the activity to drop out of cycling and continue at a less-than-saturated level. During this time, the firing relations would undergo perturbation, so that when the stimulus is removed, the activity would presumably drop into a different cycle from its previous state.

Suggested possible roles for network oscillations include information storage, conversion from temporal sequence to spatial pattern, and even a short-term dynamic memory, preserving received information for a sufficient length of time for it to be transferred to a more permanent store, perhaps by a mechanism of slow synaptic growth.

Although some slight increase in the understanding of the behavior of artificial neural nets has been acquired, much more work is certainly called for. The combination of analysis and simulation described here is recommended as a particularly effective technique.

REFERENCES

Allanson, J. T. 1956. Some properties of randomly connected neural networks. Presented at 3rd London Symposium on Information Theory, 1955. Published in Information Theory, Butterworths, p. 303.

Beurle, R. L. 1956. Properties of a mass of cells capable of regenerating pulses. Phil. Trans. of Royal Soc. B, 55.

Farley, B. G. and Clark, W. A. 1954. Simulation of self-organizing systems by digital computer. IRE Trans PGIT-4, 76-84.

Farley, B. G. and Clark, W. A. 1960. Activity in networks of neuron-like elements. 4th London Symposium on Info. Theory, 1960.

Frankel, S. 1955. On the design of automata and the interpretation of cerebral behaviors. Psychometrika 20, No. 2.

McCulloch, W. S. and Pitts, W. 1943. A logical calculus of the ideas immanent in nervous activity. Bull. Math. Biophysics, May, 115-133.

Rochester, N., Holland, J. H., Haibt, L. H., and Duda, W. L. 1956. Tests of a cell assembly theory of the brain, using a large digital computer. IRE-PGIT-2, Sept., 80-93.

Shimbel, A. and Rapoport, A. 1948. A statistical approach to the theory of the central nervous system. Bull. Math. Biophysics, March, 41.

Smith, D. R., Davidson, C. H. 1962. Maintained activity in neural nets. J. ACM (in press).

ASSOCIATIVE STORAGE AND RETRIEVAL OF DIGITAL INFORMATION IN NETWORKS OF ADAPTIVE "NEURONS"

Bernard Widrow and Marcian E. Hoff

Department of Electrical Engineering, Stanford University
Stanford, California

ABSTRACT

An adaptive logical element, called the ADALINE "neuron," which consists of a set of variable weights, a threshold, and adaptation machinery for automatically adjusting its weights, has been described previously.* Proofs of convergence of its learning processes and derivations of learning rates have been made. It has been demonstrated analytically and empirically that a single ADALINE can be "trained" to recognize geometric patterns, perform logical functions, and store digital information.

Machines capable of being trained to solve multistage decision problems require associative memories which permit the abstraction of previous experiences similar to current problem situations. Networks of ADALINEs can perform the associative memory function. Three types of networks are considered.

One system stores incident information in available memory registers. Classification is accomplished in the read-out process after storage by means of adaptive-neuron classifiers attached to each register. Associative retrieval is accomplished by simultaneously training the classifiers, then causing all registers to transpond to a central control if their contents fall in the desired class.

Another form of memory allows some classification of information to take place during storage, and some during retrieval. A tree-like structure, connected as a traffic control system, can be trained to route input information according to class into many storage bins, where it is recorded and possibly further classified. At each juncture in the tree, a neuron acts like an "adaptive traffic cop," controlling (gating) the choice of propagation path. After training, each class of input pattern excites a characteristic connection path or "trace" through the tree.

In a third memory system, information is stored directly in a bank of adaptive neurons and is classified as it is stored. This system is trained to produce a set of D binary output digits in response to an input set of N binary digits, and has the ability to generalize in that input stimuli that are similar to the training experiences evoke the same responses. The number of experiences required to train the neuron memory equals several times the product ND. This type of memory tends to forget previous experiences exponentially. A set of experiences, in order to be completely remembered, has to be repeated over and over again until it "sinks in," i.e., until the training process converges. The similarity to animal memory is striking.

*Widrow, B., and Hoff, M.E. Adaptive Switching Circuits, 1960 Wescon Convention Record, Part 4.

A SEMANTICALLY ASSOCIATIVE MEMORY

Roger L. Boyell

Pennsylvania Research Associates, Inc.
Philadelphia, Pennsylvania

Whereas associative memories have usually been based on the syntax of the contents of cells in the memory (such as on specific bit configurations), a model is proposed in which the associations between entries in the cells are characterized independently of their contents. For example, the entries "three," "five," and "multiplication" can be construed as being associated jointly with the entry "fifteen." This association by semantic content is invariant under the transformation to the respective equivalents "3," "5," "x," and "15."

The memory model consists of entries conceptually placed at the nodes of a network, the numeric strengths of the links between entries in the network representing the degree of direct association, by meaning, between the entries. Linking strengths may be increased between any two entries by the temporal proximity of reference to those entries, corresponding to conditioning of the memory. Constraints may be imposed in the model according to the use to which the memory is being put; exponential decays in the linking strengths may represent forgetting, and so on.

A quantitive measure of the organization of the memory at any time is suggested, and it is shown to have certain intuitively satisfying properties. The criterion of maximal organization is derived, and it is shown how the distribution of links of the same total strength may affect the measure of organization. Using linking strengths of only unity and zero, a technique is suggested for determining the total degree of association between any two entries in the memory. Correspondences between use of the "association matrix" thus formed and apparent behavior of animal memories are indicated.

INTRODUCTION

This is a preliminary report on some work in progress at Pennsylvania Research Associates on self-organizing memories. The aspect reported is that of the formulation of a memory model which can be used to study entire behavior patterns rather than merely relations between inputs and prescribed or observable responses. The work thus falls under Simon's (1961) fourth simulation category—less concern with pattern recognition and more concern with the non-numerical, mathematical properties of the bionic model.

It may be of interest to determine the conditions under which a supposedly self-organizing system tends to achieve correctness or optimality of behavior. Certainly it would not be said that a system which cyclically returns to the same state or structure is truly self-organizing. On the other hand, a given cycle may be repeated only until externally stimulated, at which point the system goes into a more actively "organizing" behavior pattern until a new cycle of activity again occurs. Evidently the stimulus has affected the system, and thus one may say that a "memory" of the stimulus remains. But the memory is inherent in the behavior of the system and is not explicit in the content of a memory location. The work of Davidson and Smith (1960) exemplifies this interest in behavior patterns of neural networks.

A useful model for study of these response patterns of a memory must be freed from the syntactic constraints so common to associative memories described in the literature. An example of a syntactically associative memory was given by Seeber (1960) in which access was by numerical comparison of a key with each entry in the memory. Certainly retrieval here is by content and not by location, and such a memory could be easily used by a digital computer.

However, such a technique is not really applicable to construction of, for example, an automated library of documents. As discussed by Stiles (1961), the construction of a large retrieval system involves building up a tremendous number of relationships between descriptors and documents, these relationships changing with new accessions to the library and through utilization of the system. It may be said that there are associations built in many more ways than could be conveniently coded into similarity of bit patterns representing each entry.

The name "semantically associative" is thus given to a memory whose relationships between entries are invariant under transformations to equivalent but not identical contents. For example, the entries "three," "five," and "multiplication" can be construed as being associated jointly with the entry "fifteen." This association by semantic content is invariant under the transformation to the respective equivalents "3," "5," "×," and "15." A memory model is proposed which is a tool for study of subjective or internal behavior (Bishop, 1960).

FORMULATION OF THE MODEL

The entries or cells in the memory are conceptually placed at the nodes of a network, with the branches of the network representing associations or relationships between respective entries at any time. In the automated library example, these entries may be both descriptors and document titles, the associations among them varying in strength with use of the system.

On the other hand, the entries may be concepts learned by an animal. In this event, it is seen that conditioning of behavior would be modeled by increasing the strength of the link between the entries "food" and "bell" in the classic Pavlov experiment, with the strength of the link between "food" and "salivation" large because of the extensive prior reinforcement the dog has undergone. Thus, there is a secondary association formed between "bell" and "salivation"—a relationship is built between two otherwise unconnected entries by virtue of their strong connection to a common entry or node.

This conditioning may increase linking strength by temporal proximity of the stimulus, as in the classic Pavlov experiment, or any of a number of other procedures for modifying the links may be invoked. The semantic association thus modified is reflected in the branches of the network, and is independent of the syntax, or means of representation of the entries, at the nodes.

Forgetting in this memory may be modeled by exponential decays in the linking strengths. For complex models, the time constant of decay may itself be made a function of the degree of importance to the system of the association represented. Further, each entry in this semantically associative memory can represent not just a single concept or percept, but also may be an entry in another entire memory. In this manner, a hierarchy of memories may be constructed.

Kabrisky (1961) suggests that the animal brain is interpretable as a transition between sensory input and mechanical output, and that its capability should increase smoothly with increases in the number of elements in the structure. The present model embodies this by allowing relatively distinct memory networks for the sensory coding and effector decoding (Wiener, 1948), as well as the other level functions, with the information transmission between these networks being performed by means of entries common to more than one network. In this manner, the model corresponds to Kabrisky's requirement for memory to be distributed throughout the bionic "computing" system, again being independent of the particular method of representation of the "data" at any point.

Having discussed the model and some of its extensions in rather vague terms, it is desirable to apply a bit of rigor in characterizing it. This is performed in the next two sections.

A MEASURE OF ORGANIZATION

Consider a memory consisting of $N+1$ entries, in which the important characteristic is the "relatedness" between one entry (the query) and another (the retrieved item). As an initial simplification, assume that two entries are either directly related or completely unrelated—equivalently, that a link joining the two entries respectively does or does not exist. It is desirable to have a measure of the degree to which the memory is organized—the degree to which, on the average, a query will evoke a useful set of retrieved items. One such measure can be defined strictly in terms of the number of links that exist at any time, the $N+1$ entries being connectable by a minimum of zero links and a maximum of $N+(N-1)+(N-2)+\cdots+1=\frac{N(N+1)}{2}$ links.

Analogous to the definition of entropy of an information source, a definition of degree of organization is sought with certain intuitively desirable characteristics. The measure should be proportional to the logarithm of the number of entries in the memory for a linking scheme which forms independent groups of entries that do not interact. This is reflective of the desire to measure increment ratios rather than absolute increments in capability. On the other hand, the measure should be proportional to the number of entries in the memory, for a maximally organized memory whose linking scheme associates each new entry with the optimum number of old entries. Most important, a set of links joining a given entry with all N others, or the absence of any links including a given new entry, should not represent any greater organization.

In the manner of Shannon's (1959) definition of entropy, these requirements are satisfied by defining the absolute organization to be

$$G=-\sum_{i=1}^{N+1} p_i \log p_i$$

where p_i is the ratio of the actual number n_i of links including entry i, to the possible number N of links to that entry. This may also be expressed as

$$G=-\sum_{i=1}^{N+1}\frac{n_i}{N}\log\frac{n_i}{N}=-\frac{1}{N}\sum_{i=1}^{N+1}\left(n_i\log n_i+n_i\log\frac{1}{N}\right)=-\frac{1}{N}\log\frac{1}{N}\sum_{i=1}^{N+1}n_i-\frac{1}{N}\sum_{i=1}^{N+1}n_i\log n_i$$

Then the relative organization of a memory of $N+1$ entries may be defined as the ratio G/G_{max}, where G_{max} is the maximum absolute organization the memory can attain.

Returning to the original definition of organization

$$G=-\sum_{i=1}^{N+1} p_i \log p_i$$

note that, in analogy to the definition of entropy of an information source, $0\leq p_i\leq 1$; on the other hand, there is no analogous value of the summation of the p_i except that $0\leq\Sigma\, p_i\leq N(N+1)$, since there are $N+1$ entries, each of which may be included in N links.

When no links exist including entry i, $p_i=0$, and no organization involving that entry is measured. Similarly, when all N links exist including entry i, $p_i=1$, $\log p_i=0$, and no organization involving that entry is measured. This means that, if an entry is related either to all or to none of the other entries, its presence affords no aid in evoking a useful selection of retrieved items.

If a link joins two otherwise unlinked entries, $p_i = 1/N$ for each of these entries, and the organization added by each such link is $(2/N) \log N$. If all entries are linked pairwise, $p_i = 1/N$ for all $N+1$ entries (if N is odd), and the organization is $G = [(N+1)/N] \log N$. (If N is even, of course, there is one entry left over, and the organization is just $G = \log N$.)

To find the condition for maximum organization, set the derivatives of G with respect to each of the p_i equal to zero, obtaining the $N+1$ simultaneous equations

$$\frac{dG}{dp_j} = -\frac{d}{dp_j} \sum_{i=1}^{N+1} p_i \log p_i = 0 \qquad j = 1, 2, 3, \ldots, N+1$$

For any particular j

$$\frac{dG}{dp_j} = -\frac{d}{dp_j}(p_j \log p_j) - \frac{d}{dp_j} \sum_{i \neq j} p_i \log p_i = -\log e - \log p_j - 0 = 0$$

$$\log p_j = -\log e = \log 1/e$$

Thus for maximum organization, the linkage ratio $p_i = 1/e$ (where $e = 2.71828\ldots$) for all i. It is of interest to plot the organization as a function of a linkage ratio which is the same for all i. That is, for the constant linkage ratio p, the organization is

$$G_p = (N+1)\, p \log \frac{1}{p}$$

The maximum organization, as found above, occurs for $p = 1/e$, or

$$G_{max} = (N+1) \frac{1}{e} \log e$$

A convenience of using relative, rather than absolute, organization, is that it eliminates the requirement for stating the base of the system of logarithms chosen. It is instructive to plot the relative organization G_p/G_{max} as a function of the constant linkage ratio p (Fig. 1). It can be seen that organization of the memory, according to this definition, is within about 5% of maximum when the constant linkage ratio $1/4 < p < 1/2$.

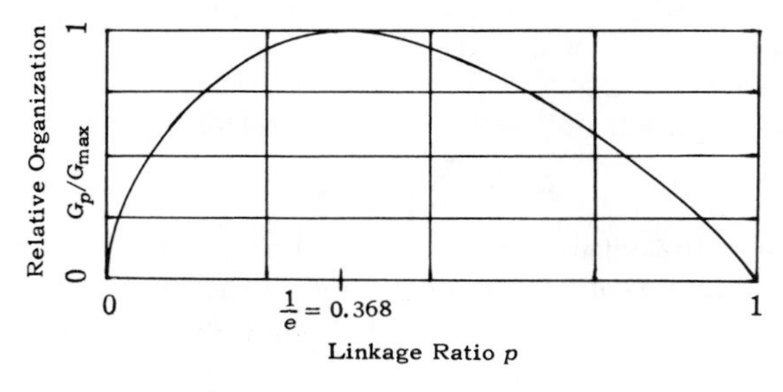

Fig. 1

Consider, then, the merits of small tightly linked sections of the memory compared with large loosely linked sections. For illustrative purposes, compare the following two configurations of two links for $N+1 = 4$ entries:

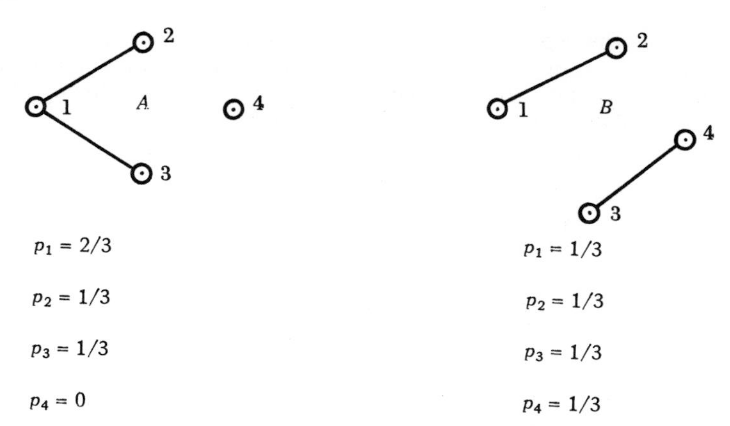

The relative organization of configuration *A* is 0.64, while that of configuration *B* is 1.00, to two decimal places. This example seems to illustrate the principle that it is more useful to have the links include more entries in the memory, with the number of links per entry more nearly constant than would be the case if the links tended to be concentrated about relatively few entries. That is, it is more useful to retrieve some items for all queries than to retrieve a large number of items for only a few queries.

It is apparent that even with this simple measure of memory organization, a number of such interesting comparisons can be made. The next stage would probably be to allow the linkage ratio to include the effect of two items being only partly related. That is, the number of links including any entry i would not be used, but the quantity

$$n_i = \sum_{j \neq i} m_{i,j}$$

where $m_{i,j} = m_{j,i}$ is the degree of relatedness (or linking strength) between entries i and j, would characterize the links including i. Then p_i would represent relative total linking strength (instead of number of links) including entry i in the formula.

THE ASSOCIATION MATRIX

Consider a memory comprising linked entries, in which the strength of each link is either unity or zero. Such a memory may be queried by starting with one entry (the key) and determining the degree of association between it and all other entries; those other entries having the greatest degree of association form the result of the query.

For this purpose the degree of association between two entries is taken as unity if they are joined by a link (of strength unity in this simplified formulation), as a fraction thereof (say, a half) if they are joined by a pair of links in series, and as a similar fraction (thus, a fourth) if there are three links between them.

Then in the linking scheme of Fig. 2, entry *A* is associated with entry *D* by two paths of strength $\frac{1}{2}$, entry *B* is associated with entry *F* by a path of strength 1 and a path of strength $\frac{1}{2}$, and so on. Paths comprising more than three links in series are neglected. (It must be emphasized that the strengths 1, $\frac{1}{2}$, $\frac{1}{4}$ could be a geometric progression of any common ratio, and there is no a priori reason to use paths only up to three links in length.)

Suppose the query were used to find the entry most strongly associated with entry *A*. In Fig. 2 are shown the single-link paths to the adjacent entries in the memory. Then in Fig. 3 the double-link paths are added by extending each of the directed single-link paths, indicating the strengths to be $\frac{1}{2}$. Further, in Fig. 4

the triple-link paths are shown with the strengths $^1/_4$. Note that these paths may overlap, perhaps with opposite directions, indicating that an association between entries is built of all possible linking paths joining them, up through length three in this example.

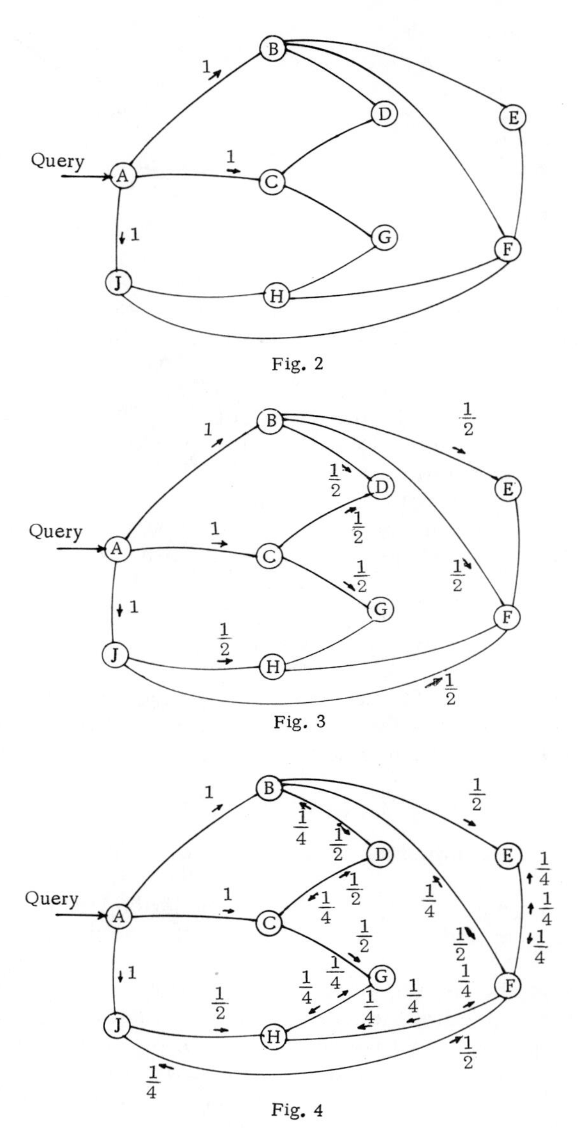

Fig. 2

Fig. 3

Fig. 4

From Fig. 4 a table may be made of the total linking strengths between entry *A* and the other entries:

A	*B*	*C*	*D*	*E*	*F*	*G*	*H*	*J*
Query	1½	1¼	1	1	1½	¾	1¼	1¼

from which it is apparent that, by the above rules, entry *A* is most strongly related to entries *B* and *F*.

In similar manner, tables may be made of total linking strengths between any given entry and all others. These tables may be stacked to form the *association matrix* $||a_{ij}||$ in which the degree of association between entry i and entry j in the memory is given by the matrix entry a_{ij}. This matrix completely characterizes the memory, being formed by tracing all paths of length 1, 2, 3, etc., between entries and summing the weighted linking strength between each pair by these paths.

It is apparent that $a_{ij} = a_{ji}$, for $i \neq j$ (for the present, a_{ii} is undefined). Since the link joining entries i and j can be traced in both directions, it should be counted as a link *to* both entries, rather than as a single link. In the above definition of organization of the memory, this is just what was done—the number of links *to* each entry was counted. It was shown, moreover, that the method of apportionment of any given number of links among a given number of entries affected the organization; the basis for this can be appreciated upon calculating the entries in the association matrix $|| a_{ij} ||$.

It was seen that, in the linking scheme diagramed, $a_{AB} = a_{AF} > a_{Aj}$ for all $j \neq A \vee B \vee F$ (where the symbol $\vee$ represents logical union). But then consider the inverse, or the use of entry B or F as the query. It is apparent that $a_{BA} = a_{FA} = 1\frac{1}{2}$, but it can also be calculated from Fig. 5 that, although $a_{BJ} = a_{BE} = 1\frac{1}{2}$ similarly, $a_{BF} = 1\frac{3}{4} > a_{Bj}$ for all $j \neq B \vee F$.

This means that if entry A is queried, entries B and F are equally associated results. However, if entry B is queried, entry F is the single most associated result. But then if entry F is queried, it can be calculated that entries B and now J are the equally associated results. This shows the interesting property that there is not necessarily reciprocity between query and result; the row maxima and column maxima of the matrix are not necessarily in transposition.

It may be of interest to calculate the relative organization of the linking scheme of Figs. 2 to 5 used for the foregoing discussion. In this example there are $N + 1 = 9$ entries.

$$\frac{G}{G_{\max}} = \frac{-\sum_{i=1}^{N+1} p_i \log p_i}{(N + 1)(1/e)\log e} \qquad p_i = \frac{n_i}{N}$$

i	n_i	p_i	$-\log_e p_i$	$-p_i \log_e p_i$
A	3	3/8	0.981	0.368
B	4	1/2	0.693	0.347
C	3	3/8	0.981	0.368
D	2	1/4	1.386	0.346
E	2	1/4	1.386	0.346
F	4	1/2	0.693	0.347
G	2	1/4	1.386	0.346
H	3	3/8	0.981	0.368
J	3	3/8	0.981	0.368

$-\Sigma p_i \log_e p_i = 2.204$

Thus,

$$\frac{G}{G_{\max}} = \frac{2.204}{9/e} = 0.676$$

or about $\frac{2}{3}$ the possible organization for 9 entries.

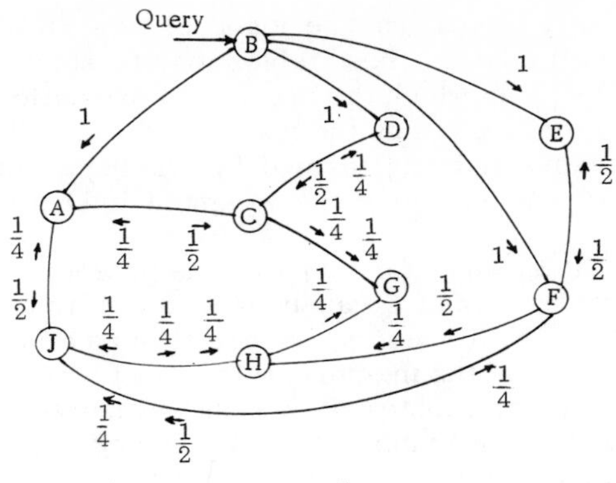

Fig. 5

As before, the obvious extension to this formation of the association matrix is to allow the linking strengths to be anywhere in the interval [0, 1], rather than calculating the association matrix only on the basis of presence or absence of individual links between entries.

CONCLUSION

It must be emphasized that the degree of organization and the association matrix characterizing the memory may vary with time; indeed, the learning process may be considered merely modification of the association matrix. Remembering that this matrix indicates the total degree of association between each entry and any other, a query to the memory may consist of many items in different amounts, represented by a query vector. That is, a query to a retrieval system may list several descriptors with different weights, these weights forming the vector. Upon multiplying by the association matrix, the result will similarly be a vector—those other descriptors and those documents of high relevance will have large components. But the result of a query will embody all the direct entry-to-entry associations and their weights that may exist within the system at the time.

The operation of the memory by querying an entry and determining the most associated entry (the maximum in a given row of the association matrix) is independent of the particular means of representing the data. Each entry could itself be a list of equivalent representations, a computational algorithm, the title of a document, or a mental concept. Consider only the fact that a query breeds a result. By the nonreciprocity seen above, using that result as a query will not necessarily produce the original query as the result. Here we have a model of the "chain of associations" familiar to psychologists—each concept gives rise to another because of some common element. On the other hand, with no external stimuli either accessing or modifying the linkage of the memory, cyclic behavior will eventually be produced. This is the phenomenon that occurs to psychological subjects who are divorced as far as possible from all sensory inputs—a concept takes hold like a familiar melody and cannot be unthought.

Chains of associations, free-running cycles of thought, time-sharing of mental tasks, and probabilistic behavior suggest that animal memories constitute complex interconnections, perhaps on several hierarchal levels, between the entries representing elements of a concept. There is apparently no analogy to the conventional computer's separation of numerical or logical processing from memory operation; the processing is implicit in the results of memory accesses. This type of behavior may have been what von Neumann (1958) meant when he said that the language of the nervous system is probably entirely different from the language in which conventional computers and mathematics operate, but it is conceivable in terms of a semantically associative memory.

It is interesting to speculate on some of the ramifications of the model. Just as instinctive motor reflexes may be the manifestation of inherited neural structures, so a racial memory may be explained by postulating prefabricated neural links. That is, the behavior pattern of migrating birds may be just as explainable by the linking structure of their nervous system as the reflex to squawk when hurt. Rote memory in the model would consist of strengthening links by repetition, just as conditioned memory would consist of strengthening links by, say, temporal proximity of the stimuli. Evidence that the mechanisms of animal memories are actually such relatively permanent chemical or structural modifications is given by Gerard (1953).

The goal is to formulate an associative memory that demonstrates quasi-human behavior. It is felt that the semantic memory model described above has greater possibilities than a conventional syntactic memory to emulate the behavior discussed by Mach (1959):

> When once the inquiring intellect has formed, through adaptation, the habit of connecting two things, A and B, in thought, it tries to retain this habit as far as possible, even where the circumstances are slightly altered. Wherever A appears, B is added in thought. The principle thus expressed, which had its root in an effort for economy, and is particularly noticeable in the work of the great investigators, may be termed the principle of continuity.
>
> . . . . .
>
> The tree with its hard, rough, grey trunk, its many branches swayed by the wind, its smooth, soft, shining leaves, appears to us at first a single, indivisible whole. In like manner, we regard the sweet, round, yellow fruit, the warm, bright fire, with its manifold moving tongues, as a single thing. One name designates the whole, one word draws forth from the depths of oblivion all the associated memories at once, as if they were strung upon a single thread.

It must be emphasized that a great deal of work remains to be performed in the mathematical description of semantically associative memories and their evaluation, as well as, of course, in their mechanization.

REFERENCES

Bishop, G.H. 1960. Feedback through the environment as an analog of brain functioning, p. 122. In: Self-organizing systems. Pergamon Press, New York.
Davidson, C.H. and Smith, D.R. 1960. Oscillation characteristics of large neural networks. Presented at 15th Annual Conference of the Association for Computing Machinery, Milwaukee.
Gerard, R.W. 1953. What is memory? Sci. Am. 189, 3, 118.
Kabrisky, M. 1961. A spatially iterated memory organ patterned after the cerebral cortex. Presented at the 16th Annual Conference of the Association for Computing Machinery, Los Angeles.
Mach, E. 1959. The analysis of sensations. (Trans.) Dover Publications, New York.
Seeber, R.R. 1960. Cryogenic associative memory. Presented at the 15th Annual Conference of the Association for Computing Machinery, Milwaukee.
Shannon, C.E. and Weaver, W. 1959. The mathematical theory of communication. Univ. of Illinois Press, Urbana, Illinois.
Simon, H.A. 1961. Modeling human mental processes. The RAND Corporation Report P-2221.
Stiles, H.E. 1961. The association factor in information retrieval. J. Assoc. Computing Mach. 8, 2, 271.
von Neumann, J. 1958. The computer and the brain. Yale Univ. Press, New Haven, Connecticut.
Wiener, N. 1948. Time, communication, and the nervous system. Ann. N.Y. Acad. Sci. 50, Rept. 4, 197.

ELECTRONIC SIMULATION OF THE BIOLOGICAL CLOCK

A. P. Sage and J. L. Melsa

Department of Electrical Engineering
The University of Arizona, Tucson, Arizona

INTRODUCTION

The term biological clock has been given to the phenomenon displayed by organisms, both plants and animals, that pace their functions in a cyclic fashion related in some way to environmental stimuli.

In this discussion, we shall be dealing primarily with formulation of a model for the timing mechanism by which organisms mark the passage of the hours of the day and with the external stimuli which influence this timing mechanism.

To determine the biological effects which describe the action of the "clock" phenomenon, an extensive survey of the available literature was made. Emphasis was placed on the general trend and qualitative nature of the results rather than on specific or quantitative factors. For simplicity, data are presented for nocturnal animals only and are intended to be typical of all nocturnal animals rather than indicative of any particular species. It is expected that simple modifications, such as changing the sign for certain variables, will allow the data to be extended to diurnal animals.

In some cases, contradictory results were obtained by different experimenters, who were often using different techniques. In these cases, an attempt was made to determine the best results on the basis of other observed effects. Until these discrepancies can be resolved, quantitative accuracy of the model can never be assured.

Light and temperature will be the only external stimuli considered in this report. The response due to light stimuli will be shown for (1) continuous light or dark signals, (2) periodic light-dark regimes, and (3) nonperiodic and random light shocks.

The light effects were studied under conditions of constant temperature; the temperature effects were examined both with and without a light regime present.

LIGHT STIMULI

Continuous Light or Dark

To study the results of continuous light or dark, animals were kept in constant dark for a control period, then subjected to constant light, and finally returned to constant dark. Experiments of this type are the starting point for most biological studies of the "clock."

In constant dark, most nocturnal animals display a period of less than 24 hr. The period in constant dark has been defined as the endogenous period for a nocturnal animal. In constant light, most nocturnal animals display a basic period greater than 24 hr (Pittendrigh, 1958). This is accomplished by delaying the onset of activity each day. Typical results are shown in Fig. 1a.

In contrast, some nocturnal animals display a period greater than 24 hr both in constant dark and constant light; however, the period in constant light must always be greater than the period in constant dark (Bruce, 1960). Figure 1b shows typical results for this type of animal.

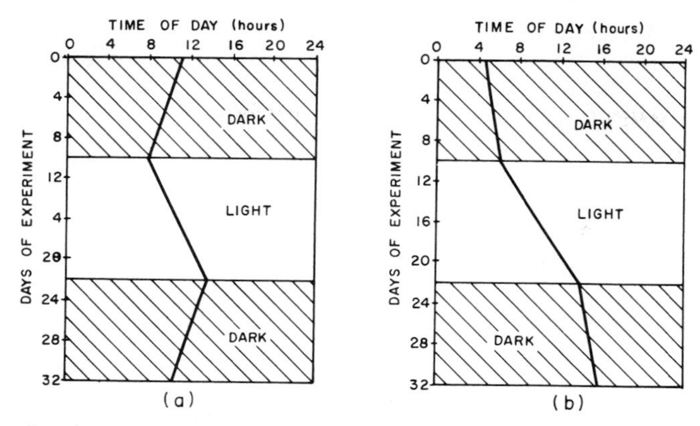

Fig. 1. Free-running periods for nocturnal animals in constant light or constant dark.

In general, each animal exhibits its own characteristic endogenous period within a range of perhaps $23\frac{1}{2}$ to $24\frac{1}{2}$ hr (Bruce, 1960). Figure 2 presents a typical distribution of periods for nocturnal animals in constant light and constant dark. It should be noted that there is a trend toward endogenous periods of less than 24 hr.

For the most part, the free-running periods in constant conditions remain at some fixed value unless a temporary disturbance occurs. There are, however,

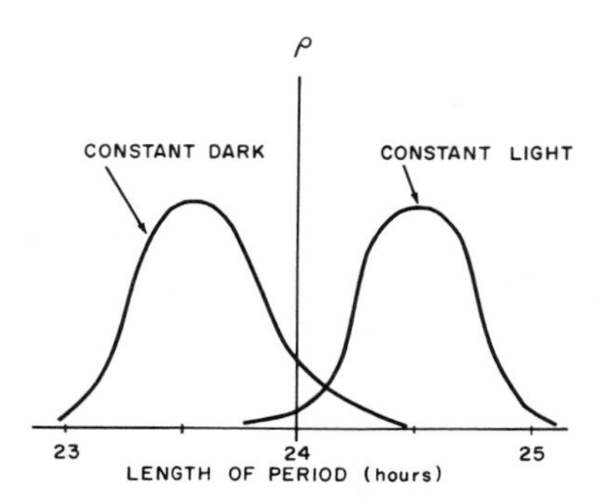

Fig. 2. Probability density function for free-running period in constant light or constant dark.

several cases when the endogenous period apparently changed spontaneously. This phenomenon was noted by both Roberts (1959) and DeCoursey (1960). It is maintained that these period changes reflect some unknown change internal to the animal since no known disturbance of the environment occurred simultaneously.

Periodic Light-Dark Regimes

The experiments in the area of periodic light-dark regimes can be divided into two basic classes by the type of period considered: (1) exact 24-hr period, and (2) non-24-hr periods. Each class can be further subdivided into four basic experiments: (1) entrainment with gradual light-dark transitions, (2) entrainment with abrupt transitions, (3) variation of light-dark ratio, and (4) frequency demultiplication. The experimental results are presented so that the variation of each factor (i.e., period, light-dark ratio) is made separately in an attempt to demonstrate each effect of the "clock" phenomenon more explicitly. In all of the experiments, the intensity of light is low enough that no inhibition of activity occurs.

Twenty-Four-Hour Entrainment With Gradual Transitions

To study the entrainment process in nocturnal animals for gradual light-dark transitions, animals were maintained for several days in constant dark and then exposed to an artificial day of 10 hr of light and 14 hr of dark. The light was turned on and off gradually, and initially interrupted the active period of the animals. The animals were returned to constant dark following the experiment.

Figure 3a presents the results of this experiment for animals with an endogenous period of less than 24 hr. The leading edge of the activity cycle was entrained with the dusk (light-to-dark) transition. It should be noted that the amount of daily phase delay was relatively constant throughout the approach to entrainment (DeCoursey, 1959).

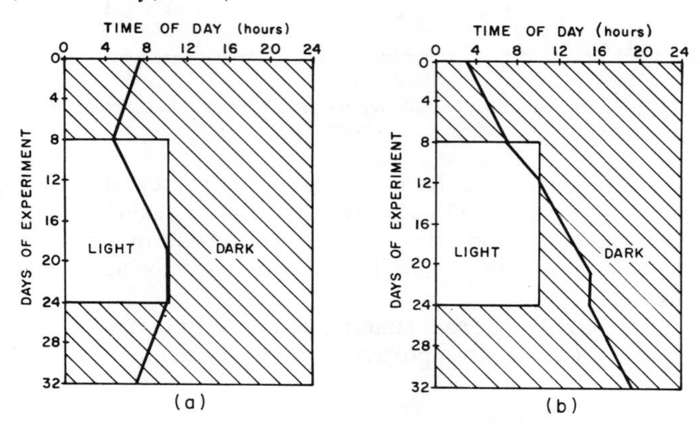

Fig. 3. Entrainment of nocturnal animals to 24-hr periodic light-dark cycles.

Figure 3b shows the result of the same experiment for nocturnal animals with an endogenous period of greater than 24 hr. In this case, the trailing edge of the activity cycle was entrained with the dawn (dark-to-light) transition.

Figure 4 presents the results of a similar experiment, except that the light did not initially interrupt the leading edge of the activity cycle but did interrupt the trailing edge. Entrainment was the same as above in both cases.

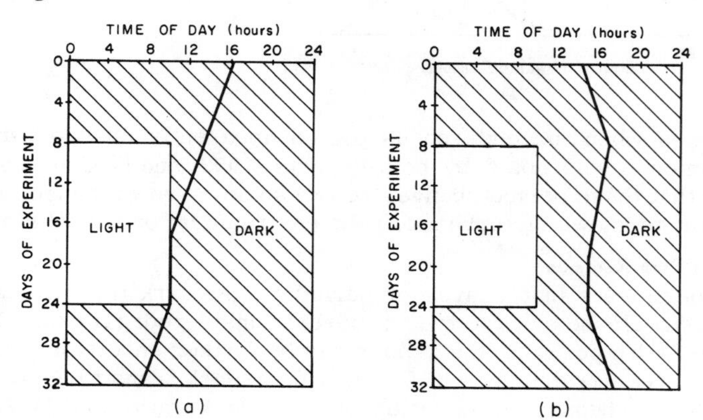

Fig. 4. Entrainment of nocturnal animals to 24-hr periodic light-dark cycles.

Entrainment With Abrupt Transitions

Experiments very similar to the ones described above were used to study the entrainment of nocturnal animals with abrupt transitions of light to dark

(DeCoursey, 1959). The only change was that abrupt rather than gradual transitions were used when the light was turned on and off. The entrainment process was identical with the previous results, except for a characteristic overshoot which is present in each case. Again, the amount of delay or advance per day was relatively constant throughout the entrainment process.

Variation of Light-Dark Ratio

For a nocturnal animal, the length of the activity period depends in part upon the length of the dark cycle and the animal's normal activity period (Bruce, 1960). It is possible to entrain both the onset and termination of daily activity by making the duration of the dark cycle shorter than the duration of the animal's normal activity cycle. Figure 5 presents the results of an experiment used to illustrate this phenomenon.

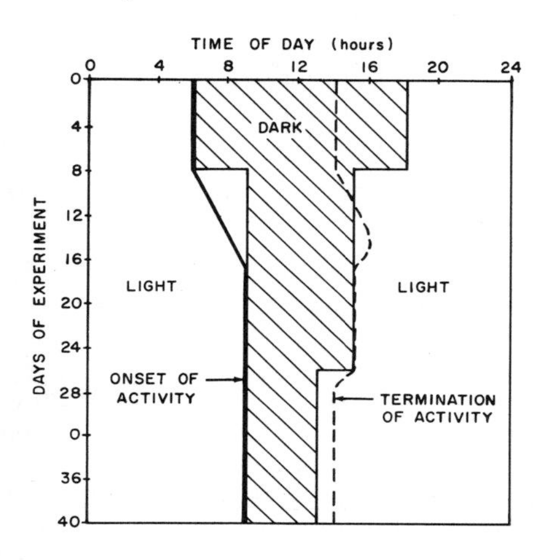

Fig. 5. Entrainment of a nocturnal animal to 24-hr periodic light-dark cycles.

An animal with a normal activity period of 8 hr was initially placed in an artificial day of 12 hr of light and 12 hr of dark. Entrainment was with the dusk transition. When the duration of the dark period was abruptly changed to 1 hr, both the onset and termination of the activity period were entrained.

The duration of the dark period was then abruptly changed to 4 hr. The entrainment of the onset of activity to the light-dark transition was retained, but the termination of activity was not entrained, indicating some minimum period for which the animal must be active.

Frequency Demultiplication

The experiments demonstrating frequency demultiplication (Bruce, 1960) are a natural outgrowth of the variation of light-dark ratio experiments. In this case, animals were subjected to periodic signals which were submultiples (i.e., $\frac{1}{2}$, $\frac{1}{3}$) of 24 hr.

Figure 6 shows the results of a frequency demultiplication experiment. Initially the period was 24 hr and entrainment was with the dusk transition. As the period was changed to 12, 8, and then 6 hr, entrainment was maintained. Again, the animal's minimum period of 5 hr becomes evident. When the period was finally reduced to 4 hr, entrainment is no longer possible, and the animal delays the onset of activity on each day.

It should be noted that the termination of daily activity is normally not as regular as the onset of activity; therefore, the smooth curves for termination of activity shown in Figs. 5 and 6 are not an exact representation of the biological data.

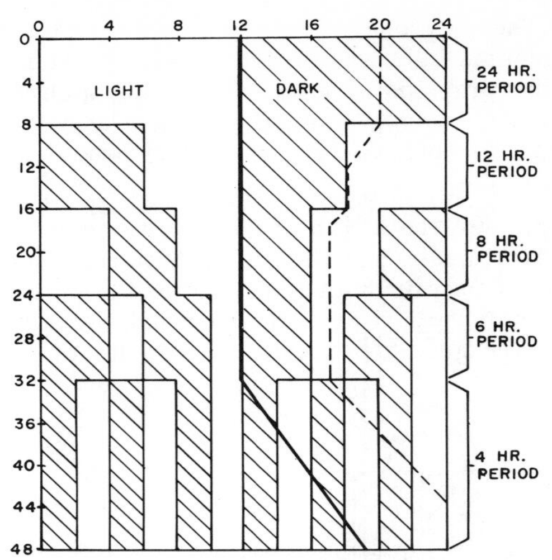

Fig. 6. Frequency demultiplication.

Non-24-hour Periods

To study the entrainment process for non-24-hr periods, animals were subjected to artificial days with periods ranging from 22 to 26 hr (Bruce, 1960). The results of this experiment are shown in Fig. 7. Entrainment was possible for periods from 23 to 25 hr.

For periods greater than the animal's endogenous period, the leading edge of the activity cycle was entrained with the dusk transition, whereas for periods less than the animal's endogenous period, the trailing edge of the activity cycle was entrained with the dawn transition. The inability to entrain to periods greater than 25 and less than 23 hr may indicate that there is some maximum amount of phase shift both advancing and delaying for each animal. In this case, the maximum amount appears to be approximately 1 hr.

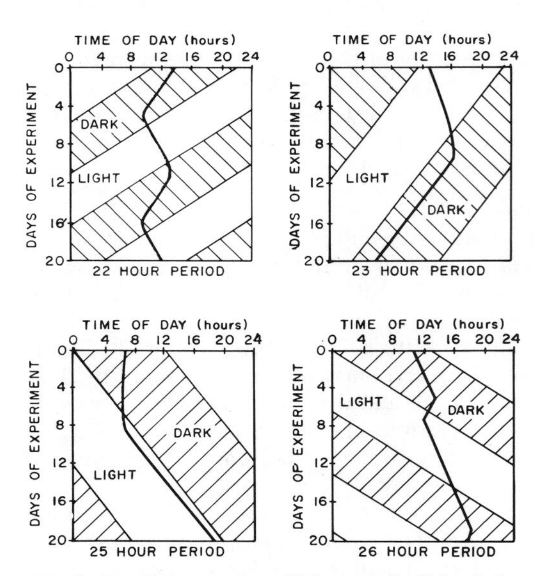

Fig. 7. Entrainment to non-24-hr periodic light-dark cycles.

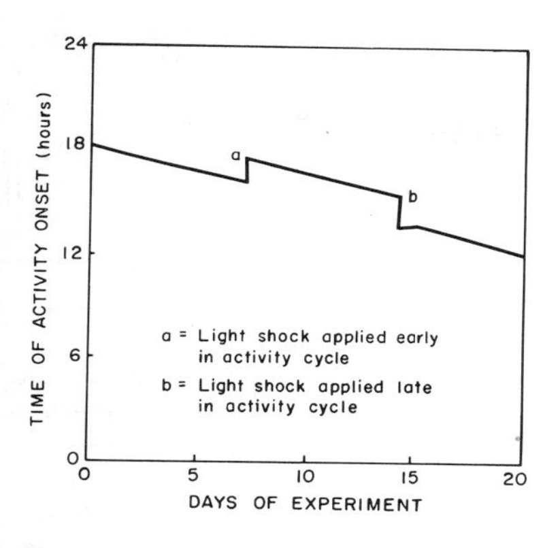

Fig. 8. Effect of 10-min light shocks of a given intensity.

Light Shocks

Animals were subjected to light shocks of varying intensity and duration in order to determine the transient effects of light upon the basic clock mechanism. An exact measure of the effects of a light shock on the "clock" can be made by determining the difference between the expected and actual time of onset of activity on the night after the shock. The expected time of onset may be determined by extrapolation of the average period during the preceding period of constant dark. Typical results from an experiment of this type are shown in Fig. 8.

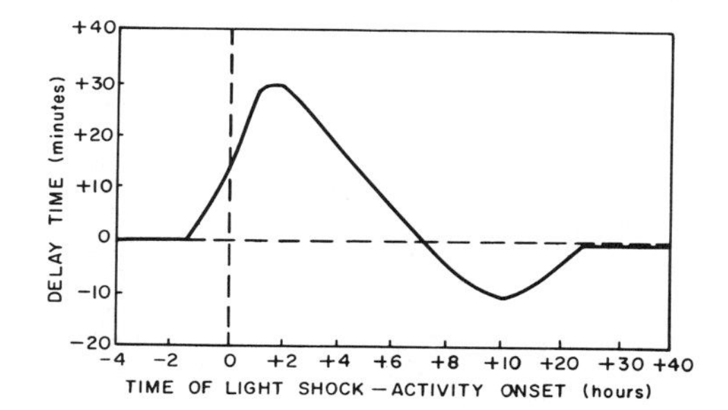

Fig. 9. Sensitivity of clock to light shocks.

By use of many such experiments, it is possible to develop a plot of the amount of delaying or advancing phase shift for a light shock versus the time at which the shock was applied relative to the onset of activity. This plot is commonly called a sensitivity curve; a typical sensitivity curve is shown in Fig. 9. DeCoursey (1959) has attempted to determine whether the zero portion of the curve was due to the animal's inactivity by awakening the animal before application of the light shock. Although her results are not conclusive, they tend to indicate that the insensitivity is not due to the animal's inactivity.

The light-shock technique can also be used to study the effects of the intensity of light in causing phase shifts (DeCoursey, 1959). Figure 10 shows the effect

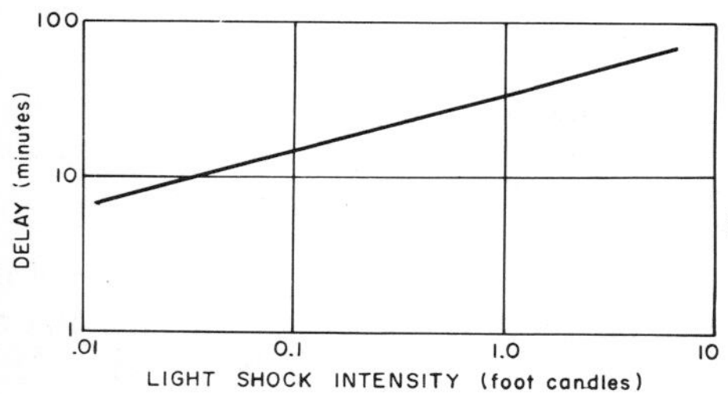

Fig. 10. Effect of light intensity in resetting clock.

of light intensity on the resetting of the "clock." There appears to be some level at which saturation occurs (i.e., further increase of intensity will have no effect). For some animals this saturation level is very low and may be the reason that some researchers have concluded that the intensity of light had no effect.

By varying the duration of the light shock while maintaining a constant intensity and time of application, it is possible to plot a curve of shock duration versus amount of delay (DeCoursey, 1959). Figure 11 presents such a curve and clearly indicates that the duration of the shock has little effect on the amount of phase shift.

DeCoursey (1959) has shown that when an animal is subjected to multiple short-duration shocks on any given day, the total phase shift is somewhat less than the sum of the phase shift for the same light shocks given on different days. However, the effect is greater than that for a single shock lasting for the total test period. The length of dark period necessary between shocks to allow summation was not determined.

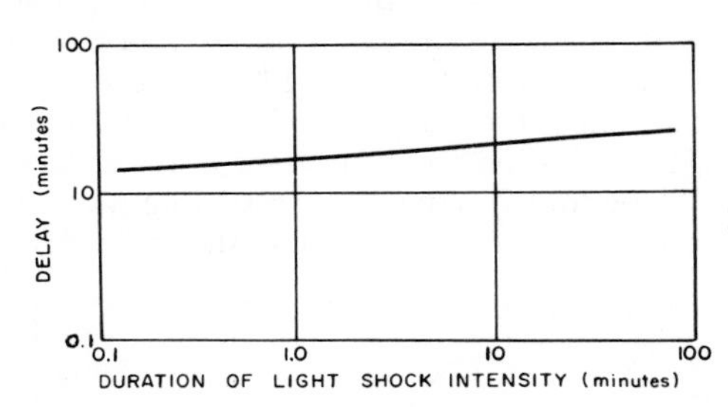

Fig. 11. Effect of light-shock duration upon phase delay.

For example, if three 10-min light shocks are given at 1, 3, and 4 hr after the onset of activity, one would expect from Fig. 11 a total phase delay of 29 + 27 + 22 = 78 min. The actual phase delay may be on the order of 55 to 75 min. A single light shock of 30-min duration, starting 1 hr after onset of activity, would produce a phase delay of approximately 30 min.

When a delay shock and advancing shock are given in the same activity period, the response is equal to a delay shock alone, indicating that a delaying signal overrides the advancing signal.

TEMPERATURE EFFECTS

Pittendrigh (1954) has presented convincing arguments suggesting that light will generally be the most reliable and best perceived phase giver. This argument hinges on the assumption of the relatively precise timing and easy perception of the light-to-dark and dark-to-light transition, in contrast to the greater day to day variability of changes in temperature. It has been demonstrated that the light regime is generally a powerful entraining agent, although temperature has also been shown to have an effect (great or small) in most cases. The study of temperature effects has been made both with and without a light regime present.

Temperature Entrainment in Constant Dark

Subjected to a 24-hr temperature oscillation in constant darkness, a nocturnal animal will reset its phase and follow a steady-state rhythm with a 24-hr period. The time of onset of activity will shift to a point coinciding with the high point of the temperature curve (Roberts, 1959).

Figure 12 shows the effect of a sinusoidal temperature variation upon the time of onset of activity. The phase of the rhythm shifts in such a way that the onset of activity occurs at the high point of the temperature cycle.

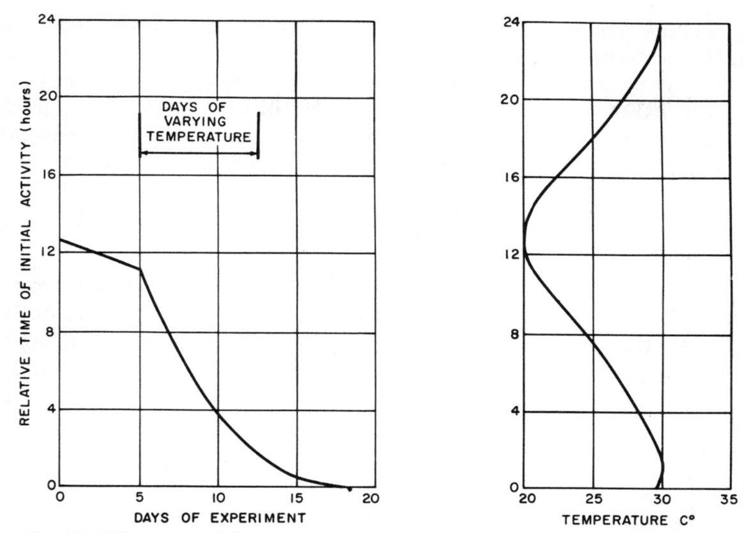

Fig. 12. Effect of 24-hr temperature cycle on activity rhythm in constant darkness.

Conflicting Light and Temperature Signals

The two distinct entraining agents of light and temperature operate simultaneously in nature and generally give congruent or nonconflicting information. Sunset and the high point of the temperature curve are roughly coincident. Under laboratory conditions, however, it is possible to study the effects of simultaneous light and temperature cycles in which the high point of the temperature cycle occurs at any pre-established point in the light cycle.

Pittendrigh et al. (1958) have shown that when animals or organisms are subjected to simultaneous light and temperature cycles in varying degrees of phase conflict, a "jump" phenomenon occurs when the temperature and light cycles are in approximately 12-hr conflict. As illustrated in Fig. 13, the onset

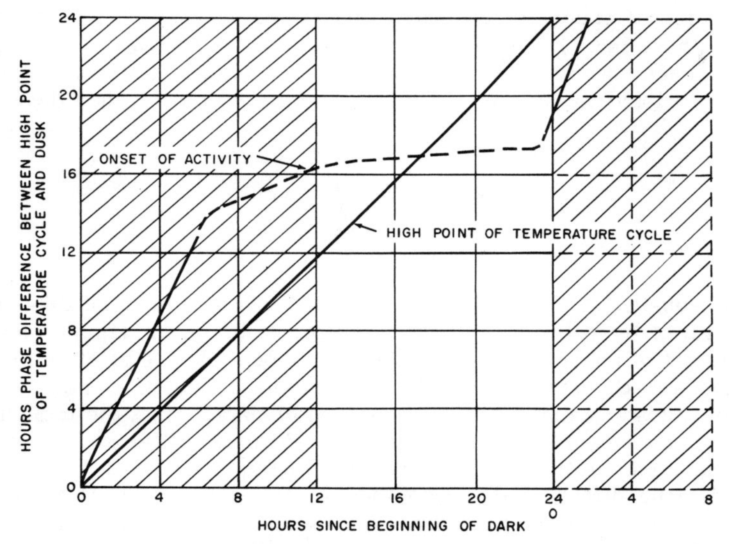

Fig. 13. Steady-state onset of activity as a function of phase difference between conflicting light and temperature regimes.

of activity in the steady state follows the high point of the temperature cycle until the light and temperature are in maximum conflict, at which time the phase of the clock rhythm shifts abruptly about 12 hr to the time of the next dusk signal. This again shows the predominance of light as the phase giver. In this case, it appears impossible to shift the phase of the clock so that the animals' onset of activity occurs during the light portion of the light-dark cycle.

DEVELOPMENT OF THE MATHEMATICAL MODEL

Light Stimuli

Since light has been shown to be the most important phase giver, a model for light stimuli only will be considered first. The problem is basically twofold in nature. First, the time of onset of activity, and second, the time for termination of activity must be determined. Many other authors have attempted to develop a model in which both of these factors were highly interrelated (Pittendrigh and Bruce), and the difficulties experienced should point out the reasons for developing a noninteracting solution to each of these problems.

Time of Onset of Activity

As noted earlier, the time of onset of activity is determined by the animal's endogenous period and the amount of phase shift accumulated on the previous days. For the majority of animals studied, transients induced by light shocks are essentially one day in duration. The ultimate phase shift is thus reached on the day after the light shock is applied. Since the endogenous period is assumed to be an innate and constant characteristic of each animal, the determination of the time of onset is, basically, a determination of the phase shift caused by external stimuli. The problem may then be simply stated: Should a phase shift be made; if so, should it be an advance or a delay, and how much?

The first two parts of the problem can be answered in a digital manner—by a simple yes or no answer—while the third question will need an analog answer—one in which a solution must be generated continuously.

Two Historical Theories

Several theories have been postulated for computing the amount of phase shift that should be received from some given light stimuli. The two most prominent of these have been integral action and differential action (Pittendrigh, 1960).

The proponents of the integral action theory argue that the amount of phase shift is proportional to the area under the sensitivity curve when the light is on. That is

$$\text{Phase shift} \propto \int_{t_0}^{t} c(t)\, dt$$

where $c(t)$ = sensitivity curve shown in Fig. 9. The inadequacy of this theory can be demonstrated by reference to the multiple-light-shock data. It can be noted that the amount of phase shift for the 30-min shock given 1 hr after onset would be much greater than the three 10-min shocks according to the above theory. This is not substantiated by the experimental data. Also, the lack of relation between the amount of phase shift and the duration of the shock, as shown in Fig. 11, is unexplained by the integral action theory.

Basically, the differential action theory states that light affects the system only at its initiation and termination. This would indicate that there would be no phase shift for constant light—an obvious contradiction of experimental data. If the light is turned on gradually, when should the phase be determined?

A thorough investigation of the biological data indicated that the above theories did not provide a complete solution; therefore, the development of a new model was undertaken.

In general, it is easier to characterize a linear time-varying system by its impulse response than by its steady-state response. For this reason, light-shock data, rather than entrainment information, will initially be used in the development of the model.

The Peak-Holding Theory

A peak-holding theory for determination of the amount of phase shift will be presented in this report. To date, the authors have found no mention of any similar theory and, therefore, some background for this decision needs to be presented.

Basically, the amount of delay will depend on three factors: (1) intensity of light, (2) time at which the shock is applied, and (3) duration. Symbolically, the phase shift $= f(i,t,d)$, where $i =$ intensity, $t =$ time at which the shock is applied, and $d =$ duration of shock.

From Fig. 10, it appears that the amount of phase shift should be proportional to the effective intensity of light to some power "K" if all other variables are held constant. The effective light intensity may be different than the actual intensity due to saturation effects. Then

$$\text{Phase shift} \propto i_e^K$$

where $i_e =$ effective light intensity.

The sensitivity curve describes the relation between the amount of phase shift and the time at which the shock is applied. Then for a very short shock (i.e., short enough that the duration will be unimportant), the phase shift will be given by

$$\text{Phase shift} = I_e^K (t)\ C\ (t)$$

where $I_e =$ normalized effective light intensity. The relation of shock duration to the amount of phase shift was not as easily established. Figure 11 indicates that the amount of phase shift is practically independent of shock duration. This information does not tell which value of phase shift given by the above equation to use if a light shock extends for a long duration. The most logical solution that could be found was that the animal would use the maximum amount of phase shift available. Thus, the peak-holding theory was formed. As has been noted previously, there appears to be some maximum amount of phase shift that an animal can receive on any given day. Thus, the amount of phase shift for any given day from a single light shock will be given by

$$\text{Phase shift} = |I_e^K\ c\ (t)|_{max}$$

$$\text{Phase shift} \leq \text{Maximum possible phase shift}$$

For multiple light shocks, the amount of phase shift will be the summation of the phase shift received from each shock, again subject to some constraint on the maximum amount of phase shift for any given day.

Digital Model

The following logical equations have been developed from the biological data to decide when an advancing or delaying phase shift should be made:

(1) The animal should receive a delaying phase shift if he is awake, the light is on, and the time is during the positive part of his sensitivity curve.

(2) The animal should receive an advancing phase shift if he is awake, the light is on, the time is during the negative portion of the sensitivity curve, and there has been no delaying signal on this day.

The above equations are simply a logical form of previous statements in the biological data section. The above equations describe a problem in sequential logic and standard techniques (Caldwell, 1958) may be used in its solution. The results of this solution are shown in symbolic logic form below.

$$D = slc$$

$$A = slc'f$$

where

$$F = s(f + lc + lg)$$

$$G = sl'(cf' + g) + sc'g$$

Table I gives a list of the symbols used and a definition of their logical "1" state.

By use of the above logic equations and the peak-holding theory, it is possible to determine the phase shift to be received from any light stimuli.

Termination of Activity

The determination of the time for termination of activity is a digital problem involving the animal's minimum and normal activity periods, and light stimuli. The animal will become inactive if he has been awake for his normal active period or if the light is on after he has been awake for his minimum active period. In symbolic logic form

$$I_n = x' + ly'$$

A list of the preceding symbols and the definition of their logical "1" state is given in Table II.

Table I. Logic Symbols and Definitions

Symbol	Represents	Definition of logical "1" state
S	Animal state	Animal is awake
L	Light	Light is on
C	Sensitivity function	$c(t)$ is positive
D	Delay	Delaying phase shift should be made
A	Advance	Advancing phase shift should be made
F, G	Secondary states	

Table II. Logical Symbols and Definitions

Symbol	Represents	Definition of logical "1" state
I_n	Determination of activity	The animal should terminate activity for given day
x	Normal activity period	Animal has not been awake for normal activity period
y	Minimum active period	Animal has not been awake for minimum active period
L	Light	Light is on

Temperature Stimuli

A mathematical model for temperature stimuli has the same qualitative form as that for light stimuli. This model will be presented in a future report.

ELECTRONIC SIMULATION

The oscillator models for the "clock" that have been proposed by other authors (Pittendrigh and Bruce; Klotter, 1960; Wever, 1960) have two basic limitations when actual electronic simulation is attempted. First, it is very difficult to control the phase and, in some cases, the period of an oscillator without creating undesirable transients. The second problem, which was mentioned previously in the discussion of the mathematical model, is the interaction of the onset and termination of activity inherent in the oscillator models.

The electronic model presented in this report has attempted to circumvent these difficulties. This model parallels very closely the mathematical model in relation to determining the times for onset and termination of activity as separate problems.

A general block diagram of the proposed electronic model is shown in Fig. 14. Basically, the model consists of three functional units: (1) an endogenous clock unit, (2) a conditional response unit, and (3) decision units.

The endogenous clock unit includes the master clock and trigger, the activity control, and the animal state circuits. These circuits are used to pace the animal's internal rhythms and to supply information concerning the animal's present state to the conditional response and decision units.

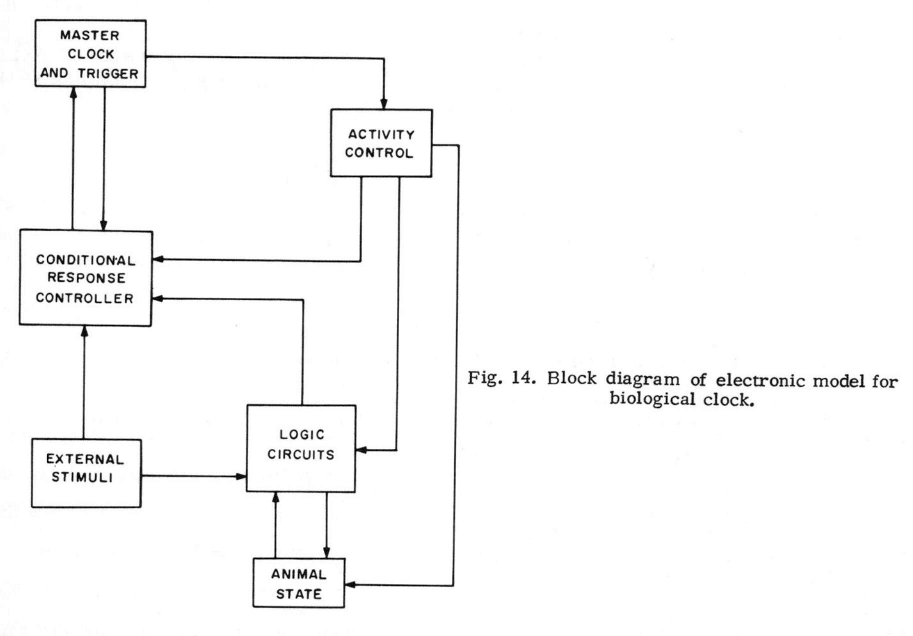

Fig. 14. Block diagram of electronic model for biological clock.

The conditional response unit comprises the analog portion of the model and is used to determine the amount of phase shift that should be applied, while the decision or logic units make all of the required decisions for the model in terms of past and present information concerning the endogenous clock unit and external stimuli.

In typical operation of the model, an advancing or delaying signal in the form of a positive or negative voltage level will be added with a voltage sweep generated by the master clock. When the combination of the two voltages reaches some preset value, the output of a comparitor indicates the onset of activity. If no advancing or delaying signal is present, the time between any two successive onsets of activity will be equal to the endogenous period of the animal.

At an onset of activity signal, the activity control begins counting the animal's normal and minimum active periods.

The logic circuits determine whether the animal should advance or delay his onset of activity or become inactive. After the logic circuits have determined that a delay or advance should be made, the conditional response controller determines the amount of phase shift to be applied to the endogenous clock unit.

COMMENTS

There is no reason for believing that this proposed model for the biological clock is the only model possible or the best model. Indeed, the form of our model is due largely to the techniques developed for digital computing and mathematical logic. The duties of the sequential logic circuitry include the interpretation of external sensory stimuli and of reports of the physical state of the clock, the control of locomotor activities, and the memory or learning function, with its very complicated procedures for the transformation of and the search for information. A conditional response controller which is hybrid in nature determines the amount and duration of the control to be exerted on the basic clock mechanism.

Thus, it appears that our model represents a rather complex hybrid adaptive control system, a type of system which hopefully may lead to improvements in the performance of many existing control and communications systems.

Current investigations of the biological clock at the University of Arizona are attempting to explain the action of the clock on a cellular level and to include the learning process in the electronic model.

ACKNOWLEDGMENT

Work reported here was accomplished under sponsorship of the Bionics and Computer Branch, Electronic Technology Laboratory, Aeronautical Systems Division, Air Force Systems Command, United States Air Force.

REFERENCES

Bruce, V.C. 1960. Environmental entrainment of circadian rhythms, p. 29-48. In: Symposia on quantitative biology, Vol. 25. Long Island Biol. Assoc., Long Island, N.Y.

Caldwell, S.H. 1958. Switching circuits and logical design. John Wiley and Sons, Inc., New York.

DeCoursey, P.J. 1959. Daily activity rhythms in the flying squirrel. Ph.D. thesis, Univ. Wis., Madison, Wis.

DeCoursey, P.J. 1960. Phase control of activity in a rodent, p. 49-55. In: Symposia on quantitative biology, Vol. 25. Long Island Biol. Assoc., Long Island, N.Y.

Klotter, K. 1960. Theoretical analysis of some biological models, p. 189-196. In: Symposia on quantitative biology, Vol. 25. Long Island Biol. Assoc., Long Island, N.Y.

Pittendrigh, C.S. 1954. On temperature independence in the clock system controlling emergence time in Drosophila. Proc. Nat. Acad. Sci. 40, 10, 1018-1029.

Pittendrigh, C.S. 1958. Perspectives in the study of biological clocks, p. 239-268. In: Symposium on perspectives in marine biology. Univ. Calif. Press, Berkeley.

Pittendrigh, C.S. 1960. Circadian rhythms and the circadian organization of timing systems, p. 159-184. In: Symposia on quantitative biology, Vol. 25. Long Island Biol. Assoc., Long Island, N.Y.

Pittendrigh, C.S. and Bruce, V.C. An oscillator model for biological clocks, p. 75-109. In: Rhythmic and synthetic processes in growth. Princeton Univ. Press, Princeton.

Pittendrigh, C.S. et al. 1958. On the significance of transients in daily rhythms. Proc. Nat. Acad. Sci. 44, 9, 965-973.

Roberts, S.K. 1959. Circadian activity rhythms in cockroaches. Ph.D. thesis, Princeton Univ.

Roberts, S.K. Circadian activity rhythms in cockroaches. J. Cell. Comp. Physiol. 55, 99-110.

Wever, R. 1960. Possibilities of phase-control, demonstrated by an electronic model, p. 197-206. In: Symposia on quantitative biology, Vol. 25. Long Island Biol. Assoc., Long Island, N.Y.

STRUCTURAL, HYDRAULIC, AND "ECONOMIC" ASPECTS OF LEAF VENATION AND SHAPE

Howard C. Howland

State University of New York
Oyster Bay, Long Island, New York

I would like to begin by outlining the relationships between the methods of this investigation and the central bionic hypothesis.

The evaluation of efficiency of a system is inexorably bound up with a teleological statement about that system. The efficiency of an energy converting process is usually defined as the ratio of output energy to input energy of the system. It necessarily distinguishes "useful" energy, the output, from "wasted" energy. This distinction can only be based upon some knowledge of the purpose of the system, the recognizable output. If we are to design "efficient and effective systems" by basing them on biological prototypes, then it is incumbent upon us to select prototypical organisms whose "purposes" are in some sense in accord with the purpose of the machine we wish to build.

Now the investigation of the "final causes," the purposes, of living organisms has for the last century or so been largely overshadowed by the inquiry into their efficient causes. While few of us have reason to regret this, yet we may agree with D'Arcy Thompson (1952) when he writes "... like the warp and the woof, mechanism and teleology are interwoven together, and we must not cleave to the one nor despise the other, for their union is rooted in the very nature of totality."

I think that this fundamental union follows in some part from the fact that natural selection is the manufactory of teleological organisms, that is to say, of organisms which act as if they were designed to fulfill a purpose, and that all organisms have as one attribute of their final causes the common injunction that they shall reproduce. Aristotle teaches us that the different species of organisms embody final causes which are unique collections of attributes; yet because many of these attributes are shared among organisms, there exists a science of final causes.

The bionic hypothesis takes for granted that natural selection produces "efficient" organisms. There is, of course, no a priori basis for predicting how close to perfection the plan of a given organism may have evolved. But where we think we know quite well the intent of nature—in certain examples of mimicry where nature copies herself, as it were—we obtain support for the intuition that the process which produced such noble creatures as ourselves has not been neglectful in its other offices.

While it may be difficult or impossible to make statements about the most efficient design of a given organism, we are in a rather better position with respect to relative efficiencies of organisms which live in competition with one another. It would seem that among organisms whose final causes are very similar to one another, similar functions are performed with similar efficiencies.

The method of this investigation may be formulated as follows: A hypothesis is made regarding the attributes of the final cause, or purpose, of the organism or group of organisms, and measurements are made of the structures or processes by which these ends are fulfilled. The ratio of measures characteristic of the actual organism and the "ideal" design is calculated. This "figure of merit" is a number which is analogous to the efficiency defined above. The general aim is to obtain a statement of final cause such that the resulting calculated "efficiency" of organisms with similar causes may be found to be similar, and that the "figure of merit" or efficiency of their parts may be similar. Lastly, the statement of the final cause should be such that the measured efficiencies approach as closely as possible to those which might be expected if nature were striving mathematically to maximize efficiency.

This study of leaf shape was suggested in a conversation with my father, W. E. Howland, who is an engineer. It occurred to us that the very regular patterns of venation of our common tree leaves probably reflect optimized economic "pipeline" designs, such as those he discussed with me in connection with his paper, which presents a cost theorem (referred to below) on the economic design of straight line structures (Howland, 1952).

I have since found in D'Arcy Thompson's book, "Growth and Form" (1952), a report of several studies on vertebrate circulatory systems which are antecedent to my father's paper on the cost theorem, but much less general. (It is to be noted that the theorem which my father hit upon had been discovered and published long before in an entirely different field.)

Thompson tells us that Roux formulated the following empirical rules for the branching of arteries:

1. "If an artery bifurcates into two equal branches, these branches come off at equal angles to the main stem."

2. "If one of the two branches be smaller than the other, then the main branch or continuation of the original artery makes with the latter a smaller angle than does the smaller or lateral branch."

3. "All branches which are so small that they scarcely seem to weaken or diminish the main stem come off from it at a large angle, from seventy to ninety degrees."

An explanation of these rules was given by W. Hess, who assumed that the energy loss of the blood flowing through a part of the system is minimized.

In Fig. 1, if AC is a main vessel and PB and $P'B$ are alternative paths of a branch leading from the main vessel to point B, we assume that the optimum

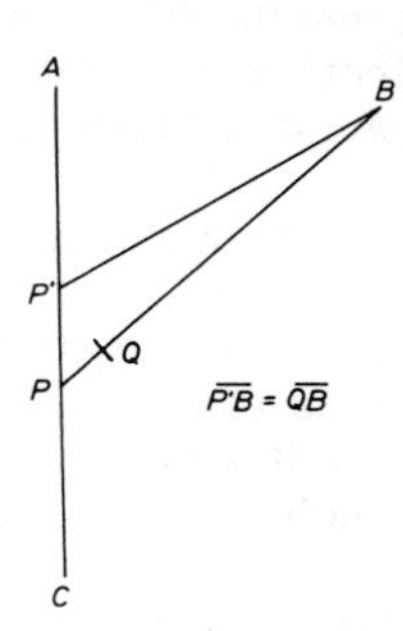

Fig. 1

junction lies somewhere between P and P'. If points P and P' are chosen on AC such that the energy loss of the blood in PP' is equal to the energy loss of the blood in PQ, then equal amounts of energy are dissipated by the blood along paths $PP'B$ and PQB. (This is a condition for the minimum loss of energy of the blood flow from C to B, but not for the system as a whole.)

We may imagine that P and P' are chosen to be closer and closer together until the optimum path is more and more closely bracketed. At the limit

$$\frac{\text{Energy loss in } PP' \text{ per unit length}}{\text{Energy loss in } PQ \text{ per unit length}} = \cos\theta$$

this being

$$\frac{E_C}{E_B} = \cos\theta \qquad (1)$$

where E_C is the energy loss per unit length in the line from the junction to C and E_B is the energy loss per unit length in the line from the junction to B, and θ is the acute angle subtended between the main vein and the branch vein.

W. E. Howland independently arrived at the following general theorem: "When straight line structures such as pipes are to extend between certain fixed points on a plane surface, then the cost of the system of lines will be a minimum when the angles between three lines at their junction are the same as between three concurrent forces in equilibrium whose magnitudes are the corresponding unit costs of the three lines respectively."

An elementary proof of this theorem follows from some basic considerations of mechanics.

Figure 2 represents a force table of the sort that might be used in an elementary physics course. Three weights W_1, W_2, and W_3 are suspended by strings

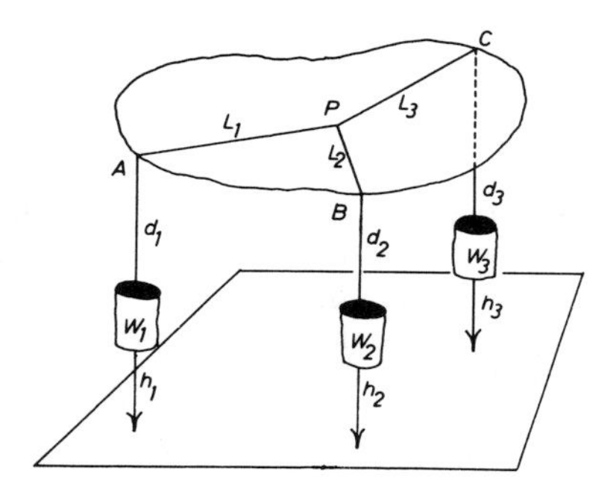

Fig. 2

which are tied together at point P. The strings extend outward from point P and pass over the rounded, perfectly smooth edge of the table at points A, B, and C.

When the system is in equilibrium, the potential energy of the system is at a minimum and the quantity $W_1h_1 + W_2h_2 + W_3h_3$ is minimized where the d's represent the various heights of the respective weights off the floor.

Since the height from the table to the floor is a constant, the quantity $W_1d_1 + W_2d_2 + W_3d_3$ is maximized where the d's represent the respective distances of the weights from the top of the table.

Since the lengths of the strings are invariant, the quantity $W_1L_1 + W_2L_2 + W_3L_3$ is minimized where the L's are the respective lengths of the portions of strings on the flat top of the table, which are equivalent to the lengths of the actual straight line structure, in this case, pipes.

Hence, if the weights are chosen to be proportional to the cost per unit length of the structure, then the equilibrium arrangement of the strings represents the minimum cost configuration.

Returning to Hess' argument, let us assume a configuration of vessels as in Fig. 3. The main vessel, AC, again gives rise to a branch, PB. We also assume that points APC must lie on a straight line.

The vertical components of the vector diagram must balance. Thus if E_A is the unit cost of the line to A, E_B of the line to B, and E_C of the line to C then

$$E_A + E_B \cos\theta = E_C \qquad (2)$$

or

$$\cos\theta = \frac{E_C - E_A}{E_B} \tag{2a}$$

Which is to say that the cosine of the angle subtended by the branch vessel with the main vessel is equal to the difference in cost in the main vessel before and after the branch was given off, divided by the cost of the branch vessel, cost always referring to cost per unit length. Now if E_C, E_A, and E_B are considered to be proportional to the energy loss per foot, as in Hess' formulation, it is clear that his equation (1) and equation (3) are in agreement only if E_A, the cost per unit length of the continuation of the main vessel, is disregarded or is zero. In

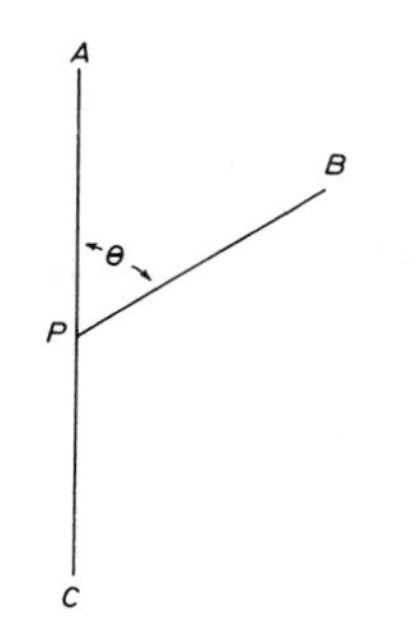

Fig. 3

other words, the formula supplied by Hess considers the energy loss only in two flow channels, not in the entire system, which consists of three flow channels. This would seem to be a serious limitation of the Hess formulation.

While we do not know what determines the "cost" of a leaf vein, it seems reasonable to express it as some function of leaf area. We chose as a first approximation

$$\text{Cost} = (\text{Area})^N \tag{3}$$

If the costs of the vessels are dictated by hydraulic considerations alone, it is possible to make some guesses regarding their cost per unit length.

If the flow is by diffusion or by osmosis we might expect the rate of flow to increase directly with the cross-sectional area of the vein. Assuming that the cost increases with the diameter squared of the vein, then we may write the proportionality

$$\text{Area served by vein} \propto \text{Rate of flow} \propto \text{Cross-sectional area} \propto d^2 \propto \text{Cost} \tag{I}$$

where d is the outside diameter of the vein. If cost is directly proportional to area served by the vein, then $N = 1$ in equation (3).

Poiseuille's law states for laminar flow

$$Q = \frac{\pi R^4}{\eta} \cdot \frac{\Delta P}{L} \tag{4}$$

For constant headloss per unit length, $\Delta P/L$, and viscosity, η, Q is proportional to R^4 and hence to d^4. Hence, from (I)

$$Q \propto \text{Area served} \propto (\text{Cost})^2 \tag{II}$$

Thus, the value of N in equation (3) would be 0.5.

Since the flow in the vascular tissue of dicotyledonous leaves, we suspect, is neither entirely diffusive nor entirely laminar, we may expect a value of N somewhere between 0.5 and 1.

If A is the area served by the main vein above a junction on one side of a pinnately veined leaf,* and B is the area served by the branch vein at that junction, then by our above assumption and the cost theorem we may write

$$A^N + (B^N \cdot \cos\theta) = (A + B)^N \tag{5}$$

Substituting $K = B/A$ we have

$$A^N + K^N \cdot A^N \cos\theta = A^N (1 + K)^N \tag{6}$$

or

$$\cos\theta = \frac{(1 + K)^N - 1}{K^N} \tag{7}$$

This function of N versus $\cos\theta$ for various values of K has been computed and is graphed in Fig. 4.

Using this graph it is relatively easy to determine values of N for a given leaf, and we are in the process of accurately measuring these values for the leaves of temperate forest trees.

(Incidentally it is very easy to confirm Roux's laws for blood vessels with the graph of Fig. 4.) If N is constant, then as the size of the branch vessel decreases with respect to the main vessel (decreasing K), the angle the branch vessel makes with the main vessel should increase (decreasing $\cos\theta$).

For the large leaf of Magnolia tripetela we find N to be 0.775 ± 0.005 for

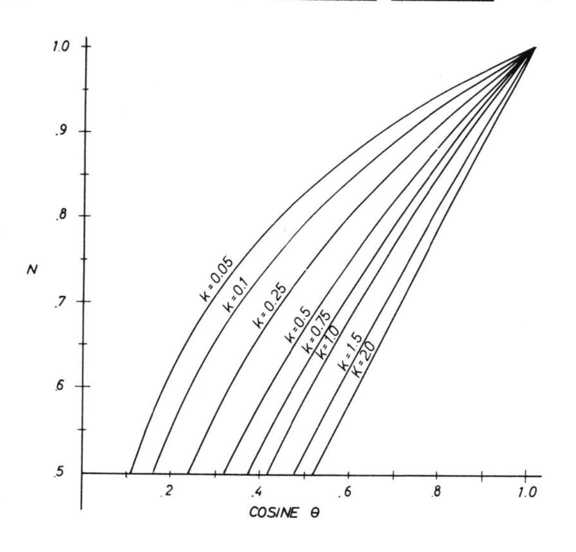

Fig. 4

values of K from 0.5 to 0.05 and we are encouraged by the constancy of the value of N over the large range of K.

For a species of horse chestnut, Aesculus hippocastanum, a palmately compound leaf, we find the value of N to be 0.844 ± 0.012 for values of K from 0.07 to 1.5 in the leaflets. Again the constancy of N is heartening.

Thus, we think that we have in this cost function a powerful tool for measuring one significant characteristic of a leaf, the "efficiency" of its venation, and we are anxious to see a complete tabulation of N for temperate forest species.

*Note that we take only the area on one side of the leaf, as if all leaves were oppositely veined and at each junction two lateral veins were given off in opposite directions. This assumption works for alternately veined leaves since the direction of the main vein is measured over many junctions.

There are other considerations, however, which we suspect determine in part the shape of leaves, and I have attempted to appraise some of them this summer while the leaves were still on the trees.

Some of the same tissues which conduct fluids in the leaf also help mechanically to support the leaf. On the very large leaf of Magnolia macrophylla, I have attempted to test the hypothesis that the main vein of the leaf is an equistrength member. For an equistrength member the section modulus should be directly proportional to the bending moment. This guarantees that the horizontal unit stresses at the top and bottom of the beam are everywhere equal. Thus

$$s = \frac{Mc}{I} \tag{8}$$

where s is the horizontal unit stress at a given point on the outside of the member, M is the bending moment at that section, and I/c is the section modulus. Thus, the condition for an equistrength member is

$$\frac{I}{c} = kM \tag{9}$$

where k is constant; for then s will also be equal to a constant.

Now for beams with similar circular cross sections, whether hollow or not, the section modulus I/c is proportional to the cube of the outside diameter of the beam.

Hence, if the main vein of the leaf is an equistrength member, we would expect that a plot of bending moment M versus the outside diameter of the main vein cubed, d^3, would yield a straight line on log-log paper with a slope of 1.

This graph is given in Fig. 5 and should be interpreted with the following reservations. In the first place, I have measured the static bending moment,

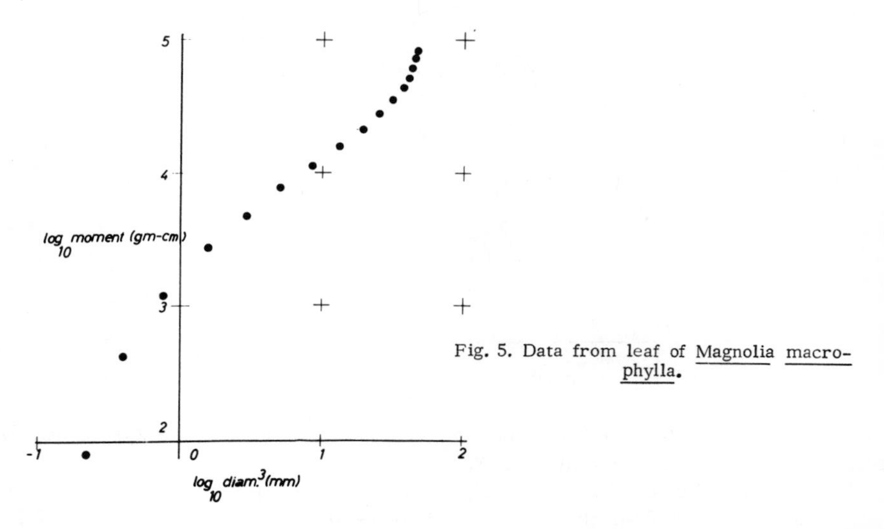

Fig. 5. Data from leaf of Magnolia macrophylla.

not the dynamic moment. While we would expect aerodynamic loading to follow the static loading fairly closely, still it is not possible to predict the stresses due to various modes of oscillation. Secondly, in computing the bending moment, sections were cut perpendicularly to the main vein, and the supporting role of the secondary veins was ignored. Lastly, the relative strength of the main vein is not precisely reflected by the quantity d^3 in the proximal portion of the leaf. This is due to the inclusion of lightweight parenchyma cells in the center of the proximal portion of the vein. This is reflected in the gradual reduction in density of the main vein from the distal to the proximal end of the leaf. This density change is shown in Fig. 6.

While these measurements give us some indication that the magnolia leaf main vein is in part an equistrength structure, this aspect of the study will benefit by direct measurements of the main-vein breaking strength.

We may shed some light on the structural aspects of leaf economy by dimensional considerations alone. For leaves of similar shape, but of different sizes, assuming that the thickness of the blade does not change and ignoring the weight of the main vein, we may expect the bending moment of the leaf at similar points

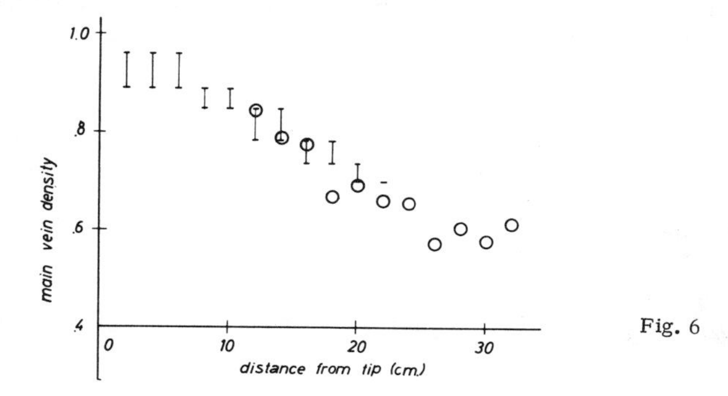

Fig. 6

on the petiole to increase with L^3, where L is some characteristic dimension of the leaf blade. Thus the diameter cubed of the petiole should increase directly with L^3 (assuming equistrength structures) and, hence, the diameter of the main vein, d, would increase directly with L. Equating "cost" to mass, we would expect the cost of the blade of the leaf (whose thickness remains constant) to increase with d^2 and the cost of the petiole with d^3. (This ignores the parenchyma cell economy noted in Magnolia macrophylla.) Thus the quotient

$$\frac{\text{Cost of blade}}{\text{Cost of petiole and main vein}} \propto \frac{1}{L} \qquad \text{(III)}$$

Since the blade is photosynthetically productive and the petiole is not, or is much less so, lower values of this quotient indicate lower efficiencies of the leaf. To estimate the efficiency of the entire organism, the "cost" of the supporting structures of twigs, branches, trunk, and roots would, of course, also have to be taken into consideration.

As a result of these considerations, which tell us simply that similar cantilevered structures become more uneconomical as they get larger, we might expect that the photosynthetic material of leaves is laid down first and most economically next to the branch. Thus, we would not be surprised to find leaves radiating out in circular whorls from the ends of branches, with the area around the branch completely covered by leaf blades.

This is essentially the plan of most trees in the tropical rain forest, where the leaves of all species show a tremendous convergence to one shape, roughly that of a rhododendron leaf with a "drip tip" (Richards, 1952).

Such leaves are also found in the temperate forest, but they are less abundant there, their place being taken by leaves of widely different shapes. All of these other leaves, these temperate forest types, show in comparison to tropical forest leaves, either longer petioles, reduced surface areas, or both.

The possibility that temperate forest leaves are modified tropical forest types leads to the following argument: If the tropical leaves have been modified by the loss of proximal blade area (thus reducing aerodynamic load and increasing the flexibility of the petiole), we might expect to find in temperate forest leaves an increase in petiole length correlated with an increase in ratio of breadth to length of the leaf blade. Of course the petioles of temperate leaves might simply get longer, while at the same time the leaves became broader, which would amount to the same thing. In both situations the restriction on breadth of the leaf is imposed by the presence of neighboring leaves whose petioles maintain constant angles with themselves and the branch.

Figure 7 shows a plot of petiole length/blade length versus maximum blade width/blade length. This shows rather clearly the lack of broad leaves with short petioles and narrow leaves with long petioles, a lack which I have no other a priori grounds for expecting.

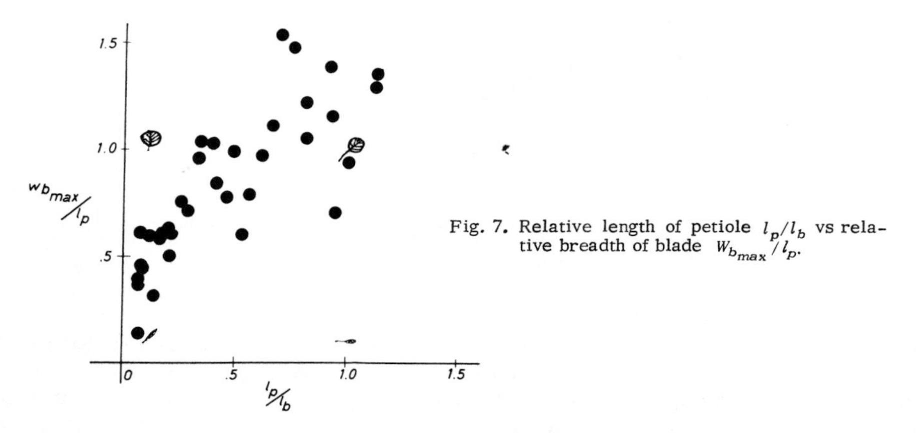

Fig. 7. Relative length of petiole l_p/l_b vs relative breadth of blade $W_{b_{max}}/l_p$.

Among the temperate forest leaves we can distinguish four tendencies or serial gradations. The first is illustrated by the oaks, whose leaves range from obovate, almost entire leaves, as in Querous marilandica (Muenchhausen), to ovate leaves as of Quercus imbricaria (Michaux.), or to the deeply lobed leaves of Quercus rubra (L.).

The second is illustrated by the birches, whose leaves grade from oval, as in Betula lutea (Michaux. filius), to deltoid, as of Betula populifolia (Marshall).

The third series is illustrated by the common sassafras and mulberry leaves, which are sometimes ovate and sometimes palmately lobed.

The fourth is illustrated by the maples, which are sometimes palmately simple and sometimes compound.

These relationships are diagramed in Fig. 8.

Further evidence that the tropical rain forest leaf is primitive is provided by fossil leaves. Arnold (1947) lists three angiosperm tree genera whose fossils exhibit changing leaf shapes. They are:

1. The oaks, the primitive forms being unlobed.
2. Plane trees, the primitive form being a shallowly lobed leaf with a cuneate base (like sassafras) changing to a leaf with large lobes and a cordate base.
3. Cercidiphyllum, the Japanese katsura tree, whose primitive leaves are ovate with cuneate bases, and whose later forms are round with deltoid and finally cordate bases.

I have included these trees in Fig. 8, and have indicated their direction of change with arrows.

While the data of Fig. 8 hint at the evolution of the temperate forests from the tropical rain forest, it may be that these series are simply a reflection in the leaves of the fact that there exists today a gradation of climates, and that

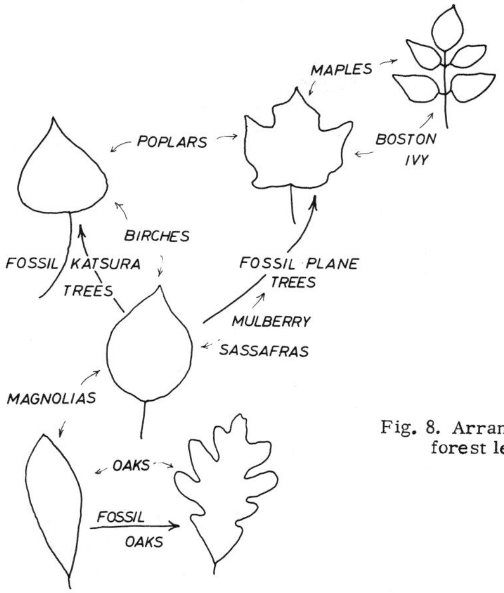

Fig. 8. Arrangement of leaf types. Tropical rain forest leaf is at bottom left of diagram.

any family of large dicotyledons would assume in a relatively short evolutional span the leaf shape appropriate to that particular climate.

Be that as it may, the existence of a "standard tropical rain forest leaf," the convergent form of many families, coupled with a graded series of temperate forest leaves, leads us to believe that if we can grasp the significance of this basic shape, we will have opened the door to understanding the more complicated temperate forest shapes.

In summary, we may note that this investigation has proceeded along three lines which we hope in their pursuit and eventual synthesis will yield the multiple causes of leaf shape. These three lines are the hydraulic, the structural, and the comparative analyses of leaf shapes. Our view of the leaf is that of a well-designed economic structure whose form reflects its function if we can but discover what these manifold functions are, and the relative importance of each to the organism.

In particular, it has been shown for one leaf that a significant portion of its main vein varies in cross section in accordance with the calculated mechanical requirements for strength—considering it as a cantilever beam carrying the measured weights of the appropriate portions of leaf. Also, it has been shown that the angles between the main vein and secondary veins of two leaves from different families vary consistently with a theory for economic design of pipe systems taken from fluid mechanics. Lastly, we have noted a strong correlation between the relative length of petioles and relative breadth of leaves for 32 species of some 16 families of temperate forest deciduous leaves, and we have discussed the economic implications of this correlation.

REFERENCES

Arnold, C. A. 1947. An introduction to paleobotany. McGraw-Hill, New York.
Howland, W. E. 1958. Economic pipe routes and other straight line structures. Industrial Wastes. Mar.-Apr.
Richards, P. W. 1952. The tropical rain forest, an ecological study. Cambridge Univ. Press.
Thompson, D. W. 1952. Growth and form. Cambridge Univ. Press.

GENERAL PRINCIPLES OF OPERATIONS IN NEURON NETS WITH APPLICATION TO ACOUSTICAL PATTERN RECOGNITION

P. Mueller

Eastern Pennsylvania Psychiatric Institute
Basic Research Department

and

T. Martin and F. Putzrath

Radio Corporation of America
Defense Electronic Products, Applied Research Department

THEORY OF NEURON NET DESIGN AND OPERATION

This report presents general principles of operations in neuron networks and is composed of two parts. One is concerned with the theoretical aspects of operations in neuron nets; the other is concerned with the application of some of these principles to the particular problem of speech recognition by artificial neurons. The term "neuron" is used without distinction for real neurons—those found in the brain—and for artificial neurons—those made from electronic components. It is possible to construct artificial neurons which are, as far as input-output relations are concerned, complete analogs of their biological counterpart (Mueller, 1958). The networks shown in the figures in this report have been assembled and tested using artificial neurons.

The object of the theoretical part of the report is to define the neuron as a logical device, to arrive at some classification of possible operations in neuron networks, to construct networks which realize some of these operations, and to present methods which enable quantitative calculations of input-output relations in networks.

The Neuron As a Logic Device

In order to evaluate the operations the neuron is capable of performing, we must analyze its input-output characteristics. The quantities of interest are the output as a function of input and the output as function of the input and time. The symbols used in the networks to be described are shown in Fig. 1.

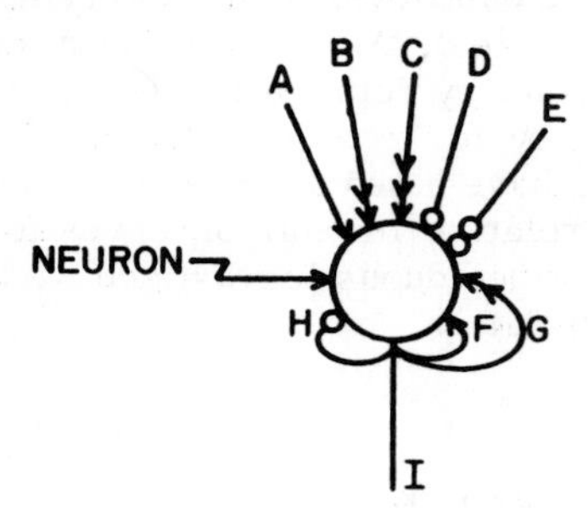

Fig. 1. Neural network symbology: A, excitatory input; B, excitatory input, large intensity; C, excitatory input, very large intensity; D, inhibitory input; E, inhibitory input, large intensity; F, excitatory feedback to produce the maximum firing rate for the time during which an excitatory input exceeds the threshold; G, excitatory feedback that permanently produces the maximum firing rate once the neuron has begun firing (in order for cessation to occur, the neuron must be reset by inhibitory input); H, inhibitory feedback; I, output.

The fact that the output from neurons, as it is usually observed in the brain, appears in the form of pulses of uniform voltage has led to the development of theories which emphasized the digital aspects of operation and employ Boolean algebra as a tool for a quantitative treatment of input-output (McCulloch and

Pitts, 1943; McCulloch, 1959). However, it is sufficiently evident that a neuron sees the output of its neighbors only after integration at the synapse. That is, as far as the individual neuron is concerned, there exist no pulses. Its input and output are voltages which continue through varying periods of time and which are, within limits, continuously variable (Eccles, 1953; Preston and Kennedy, 1959). The transformation of its output voltage into frequency seems to be mainly an elegant way the system devised to avoid the difficulties of transmitting small voltages accurately through conductors of extremely high resistance. (The internal longitudinal resistance of a single A-fiber going from the spinal cord to the foot is larger than 10^{10} ohms, while for C-fibers it is larger than 10^{13} ohms.) By the transformation of output voltages into frequencies, the transmission becomes independent of the characteristics of the amplifier stations along the fiber (Nodes of Ranvier).

We thus will proceed under the assumption that for the logic operation of the central nervous system, the individual pulses (action potentials) are irrelevant. The neuron functions essentially as a nonlinear amplifier having a lower and upper bound and whose characteristics can be controlled by external connections (feedback). Figure 2A shows some typical input-output curves obtained by measuring the voltage integral of the pulses at the synapse of artificial neurons such as that shown in Fig. 9. The curves in the figure represent the integrated output pulses of a neuron plotted versus the integrated input pulses, or time. Input pulses are integrated by the *RC* circuit of the synapse; output pulses are integrated at the synapse of a succeeding neuron. The input-output characteristics, normally almost logarithmic, can be varied by positive or negative feedback (through "recurrent collaterals" in neurophysiological language) from linearity to a complete step function, as seen in Fig. 2A. Time functions can also be controlled by the nature of the synapse (Fig. 2B). There are usually two discontinuity steps in the input-output curve. One corresponds to the familiar threshold (θ) and the other is the minimum output voltage at threshold input. While the input can be both positive and negative (stimulation and inhibition), the output is always positive. Actually, however, the positive output becomes inverted at an inhibitory synapse, and in our later neuron models we have incorporated a negative and positive output instead of using negative and positive input points. Both methods are formally identical.

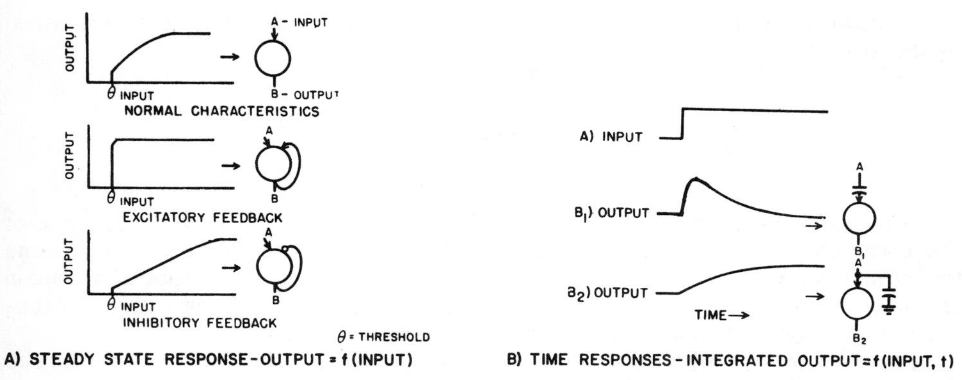

Fig. 2. Input-output characteristics of neuron.

Variables and Operations

Assuming that there are no additional ("mysterious") input-output functions of the individual neuron which cannot be described in terms of voltage and time, we can specify the possible variables and basic operations of a system of neurons. The output of neurons within a net can (1) have a certain voltage, (2) have a certain duration, or occur at a certain time, and (3) have an extension in space (i.e., involve a number of neurons), or occur at a certain place. Thus, there are only three variables or domains on which the system can operate, energy (V), time (t), and space (s). Energy enters receptor fields in the form of sound, light, etc., in one dimension, as in the cochlea, or in two dimensions, as in the retina, and is distributed in time. It is carried through the system in the form of the product of voltage and charge, where the amount of charge is given by the area and charge density at the synapse.

The basic operations on the variables s, t, V are those of addition and subtraction in space or time (integration), and the so-called sentential connection ($\supset$) "if, then," which is a consequence of the transmission of energy from one neuron to the next. All other arithmetic operations result from addition and subtraction performed with analog quantities. The discontinuity (quantization) in space or in the input-output characteristics (threshold) make logical operations of the Boolean or Post type possible.

At the input, the first operation the system has to perform is to obtain a measure of the input variables. Energy enters as a quantity; time and space, however, must be operated on as Δt or Δs (these operations are discussed below). All further operations are then on a quantity of Δs, Δt, or V and will be designated $q(s)$, $q(t)$, $q(V)$. We define q as the projection of the external quantity of the variable Δs, Δt, or V into the limits given by the characteristics of the neuron for that particular variable. Generally it refers to any quantity Δs, Δt, or V within the neuron net and contrasts with the same quantities in the outside world. For energy and space these limits are obviously much smaller than in the external world, while time can be carried through without scaling.

However, the variables s and t can also be represented as such (i.e., not as quantity Δs or Δt) within the system. Under these conditions, events or regions can represent "points" in t or s [in the following referred to as $p(s)$ and $p(t)$] and can be ordered according to their sequence in space or time. For this type of operation, the beginning or end of the event or region has to be recognized. This can be done by operations such as obtaining

$$\frac{dv}{dt}, \frac{dv}{ds} \quad \text{or} \quad \frac{dq(s)}{dt}, \frac{dq(t)}{ds}, \text{ etc.} \tag{1}$$

The following questions and combinations of these questions can thus be answered by the system

When ?	$p(t)$
Where ?	$p(s)$
How long ?	$q(t)$
How far ?	$q(s)$
How much ?	V

The answers to these questions can, in turn, be represented in any one of the three domains and their derived functions. Thus, $_Tq_V(s)$, for example, means the transformation of a q of space into the q of V; the voltage output of a neuron is proportional to a distance or a spatial pattern in the input space. Transformations will be discussed in more detail below.

Some of the simpler operations have been classified in Table I according to the domain of input variables and whether they are logic or algebraic. Transformations are classified separately. Within one neuron, logic operations can be mixed freely and often simultaneously with algebraic operations. For instance, neuron C fires if the input difference $(a-b) > \theta$ (θ = threshold), while the output of C is proportional to $q(a-b)$. Some of the logic operations require ternary or higher-valued logic.

Table I. Operations in Space, s, Time, t, and Energy, V

Domains of Input*	Space	Time	Energy	Space–time	Space–energy	Time–energy	Space–time–energy
Required normalization	t, V	s, V	t, s	V	t	s	None
Examples of entries or features that can be extracted by quantitative (analog) operations	$q(s)$ (distance length)	$q(t)$ (duration)	$q(V)$ (amplitude)	$q(ds/dt)$ (speed of movement) $q[dq(s)/dt]$ (space expansion) $q[dq(t)/ds]$	$q(dV/ds)$ (slope)	$q(dV/dt)$ (frequency)	$q(ds/dt, dt/dV$, etc.)
Required quantization	s	t	V	s, t	s, V	t, V	s, t, V
Examples of entities or patterns that can be extracted by Boolean or m-valued logic operations	$p(s)$ (position, order) $q(s) \gtreqless q(x)$	$p(t)$ (moment, sequence; long, short, long, etc.) $q(t) \gtreqless q(x)$	$q(V) \gtreqless q(s)$	Combined time sequence and space order a=before, after, during b b=longer, shorter, as long as b $q(ds/dt) \gtreqless q(x)$	Combined V, s pattern $q(dV/ds)$ $\gtreqless q(x)$	Combined t, V pattern $q(dV/dt)$ $\gtreqless q(x)$	Combined s, t, V pattern $q(ds/dt, dt/dV$, etc.) $\gtreqless q(x)$
Transformations	$\tau s(s)$ $\tau V(s)$ $\tau t(s)$	$\tau t(t)$ $\tau s(t)$ $\tau V(t)$	$\tau V(V)$ $\tau t(V)$ $\tau s(V)$				

* Some basic features which can be extracted from inputs to neuron nets by either analog or logic operations are classified according to the domain which is represented (space, time, or energy) and their combinations. Normalization of the domains not represented makes the extracted function invariant under changes occurring in nonrepresented domains. In addition to this normalization, logic operations require the quantization of the input variable.

Operations in less than three domains require a normalization of the domains not represented. For instance, operations in $q(V)$ alone must be invariant under changes of t and s. Examples of actual circuits which can perform these normalizations are presented in Fig. 3. Obviously, operations will become more complex as more domains are involved.

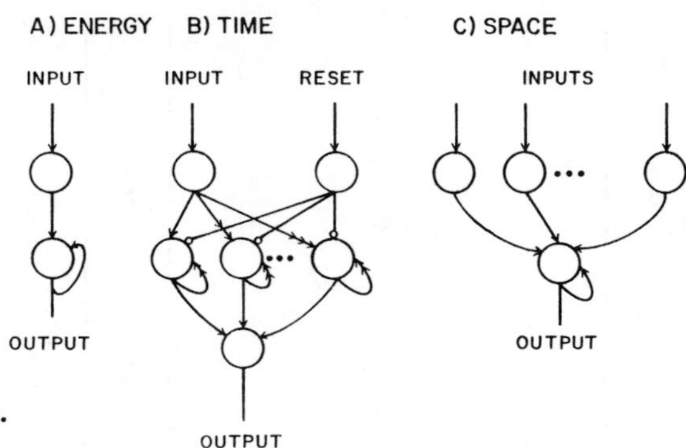

Fig. 3. Normalization of input domain.

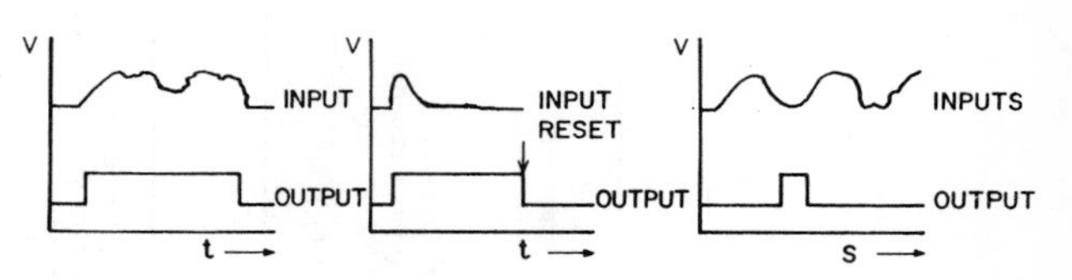

For the arithmetical operations, all quantities (q) are carried as continuous entities. No quantization to binary or n-ary digits occurs and operations are performed by what is commonly known as analog computation. Multiplication and division are made possible by neurons with logarithmic input-output functions. Some network examples for the operations $q(ds/dt)$, etc., are shown in Fig. 4. In the figure the output voltage of each net is a measure of the quantity of the indicated input function. For each of the operations shown, the nonrepresented input variables have been previously normalized.

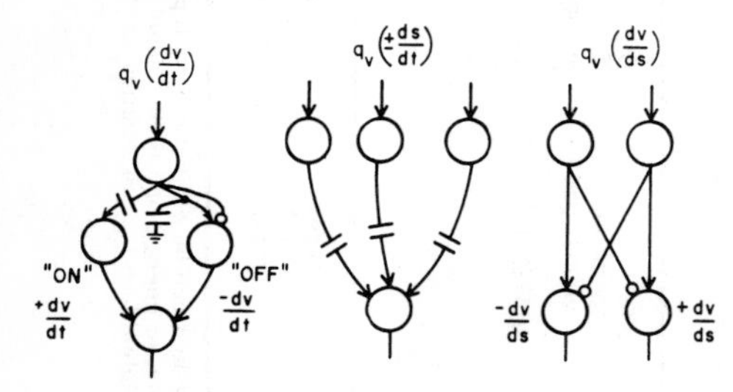

Fig. 4. Some examples of quantitative operations in two domains.

Logic operations in Boolean or n-valued logic (Post, 1921; Rosenbloom, 1942) require quantization of $q(s, V, t)$. The number of different quantized values into which the variable is broken up will determine the value of m in the corresponding logic.

Given below are two examples in which $m = 3$ for operations on Δs or Δt and for operations in s or t (space or time sequences).

1. A particular value of $q(s)$ representing, for example, a distance in the visual field can be larger, smaller, or equal to a particular value x of $q(s)$. In this case m would be equal to 3. Similarly, a particular value of $q(t)$ (duration) or

$q(V)$ can be smaller, larger, or equal to x. In addition, a particular event normalized with respect to V and s and representing a particular $p(t)$ can occur before, after, or during another event. And again, an event normalized with respect to t and V and representing a $p(s)$ can occur spatially on the left or right or in the same place with respect to event x.

The simple diagram below illustrates the first case.

$qD(a) > qD(x)$

$qD(a) < qD(x)$

$$D = V,\ s,\ \text{or}\ t \qquad (2)$$

$qD(a) = qD(x)$

$qD(x)$

The quantity $qD(a)$ can be larger, smaller, or equal to $qD(x)$ where D represents either the space, time, or energy domain. If $D = s$, the operation would be that of comparing the lengths of straight lines with a particular length $qs(x)$ and classifying them according to $<, >, =$. The different lines could follow each other in time or space. If $D = t$, $qt(a)$ could represent the length of a tone and could be compared with an internal standard $qt(x)$; and, finally, if $D = V$, the operation could represent the scaling of an input, such as light intensity, with respect to $qV(x)$.

2. The other example of a three-valued logic operation in one domain mentioned above could be illustrated as follows:

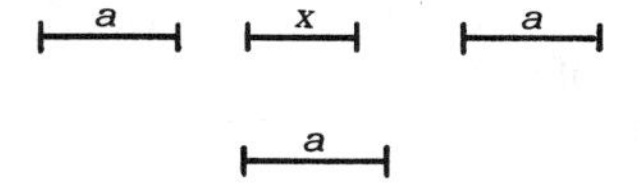

Event a, which can be normalized with respect to t, V, or s, can occur before, after, or during event x, which is likewise normalized with respect to s, t, or V. This operation requires the quantization of Δs or Δt between the end of the event and the beginning of event x, or between the end of x and the beginning of a. Such operations can determine the sequence of events in time or space which are quantized between the events. This type of operation, however, is meaningless in the energy domain since energy enters the system as ΔV (potential difference between two points in space · charge).

The actual operation of quantization, i.e., breakdown of $q(s)$, $q(V)$, and $q(t)$ into quanta, depends on the number of quanta and on which domain is to be quantized. Space is already quantized and one convenient way for quantizing V and t is to transform both variables into space. A simple quantization of V into two values is possible by positive feedback of the output (see Fig. 2A). In this case the output (V) is either at 0 or at its maximum, a quantization necessary and sufficient for Boolean operations. Quantization of time by a ring of neurons is also possible. Each neuron in the ring gives an "on" response, as in Fig. 5. The period of the output pulses is proportional to the number of neurons in the closed loop. For the three-valued logic of the $\gtreqless$ type, the operations of subtraction and classification of the results into plus and 0 are sufficient and especially useful if conducted in the V domain. As a matter of fact, this scheme can be extended to a quantization of any number of steps by using a series of internal standards having different values of outputs.

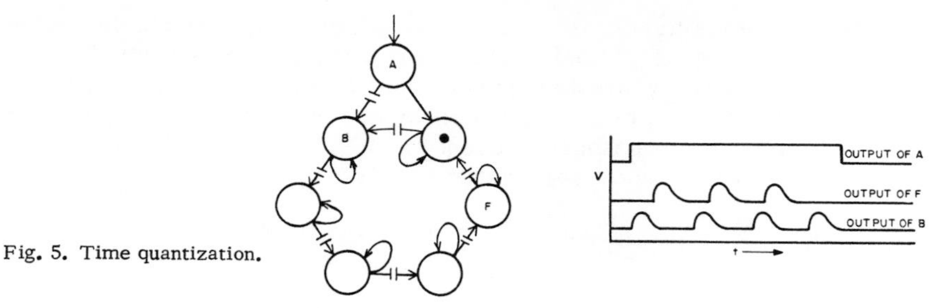

Fig. 5. Time quantization.

Any operation dealing with $q(s)$, $q(t)$, or $q(V)$ requires a measure of the variable in question. As was mentioned above, V is already available as a quantity. To establish a quantity for space and time, it is necessary to determine Δs and Δt. To do this, the system must be able to recognize the beginning and end of the region in s or the event in t and have a measure of distance or time from these two points. The mode by which this is achieved depends on the domain in which the measurement is taken. If $q(s)$ or $q(t)$ are to be expressed as V, the transformation $\tau q_V(s)$ or $\tau q_V(t)$ is made simultaneously with the measurement. Also, both the requirements mentioned above, i.e., recognition of the start and end of the event or region and "measurement" of the distance or time from these points, are met by one operation. The essential feature of this operation is a "sloppy" differentiation of the quantity that changes at the beginning of the event or region, e.g., dV/dt or dV/ds. The "on" or "off" response (Fig. 2B) exemplifies this case best. The output V of the measuring neuron starts at the beginning of the event and decreases in time. Its amplitude, $q(V)$, is a measure of t after the beginning of the event. The same holds for the "off" response, and, as we have shown above, this is sufficient and necessary for the measure of $q(t)$ and any interval between two events in terms of its transform, $\tau q_V(t)$. A similar situation exists in the space domain and an example is given in Fig. 6B. These two operations of $\tau q_V(s)$ and $\tau q_V(t)$, that is, measure of time or space and transformation into V, are of outstanding importance at the primary input neurons in the central nervous system. The connections of the primary neuron in the eye of Limulus are essentially the same as those in the primary neurons in Fig. 6B (Hartline et al., 1958), and "on-off" responses are characteristic for certain neurons in the retina. Obviously, the first operation the system has to perform is to obtain a measure of the input variables.

Logic operations in combined domains follow from those for the single domains described above. The simplest class of such combined operations is that commonly used in binary computers where the amplitude is quantized into two values, and space or time is quantized into equal steps (drum locations).

Quantization of V into more than two steps, and operations with quantized $q(s)$ or $q(t)$ lead to more complex operations which make it possible to recognize any combined $V-p(s)$, $V-q(s)$, etc., pattern. Finally, combinations of any pair of the two-domain operations is sufficient for the operations in all three domains.

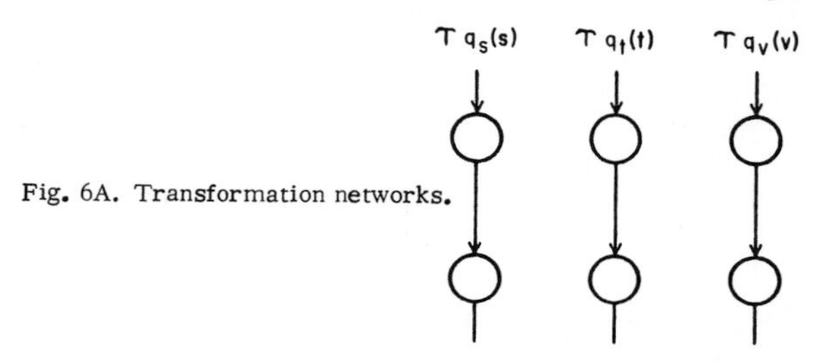

Fig. 6A. Transformation networks.

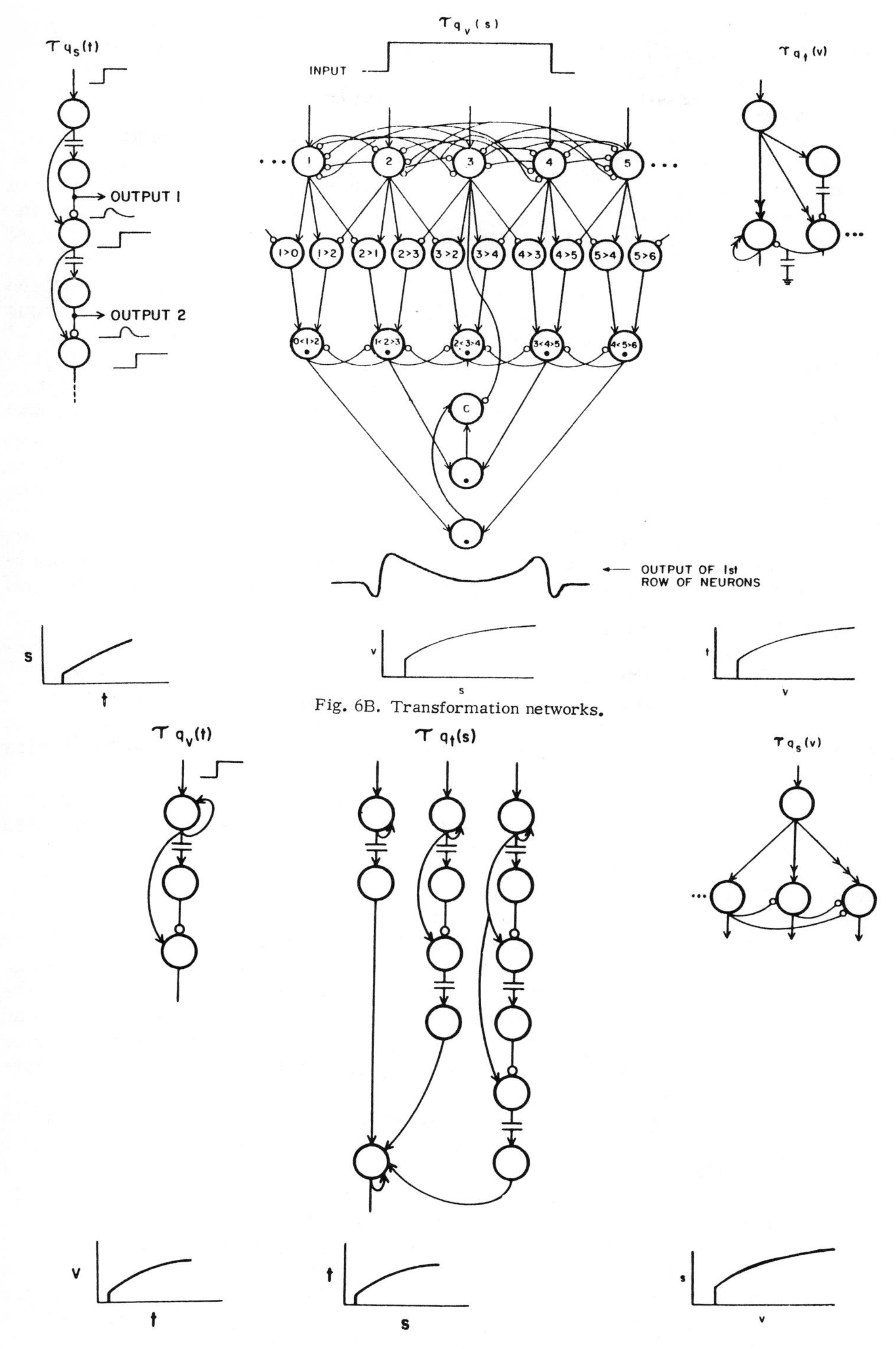

Fig. 6B. Transformation networks.

Fig. 6C. Transformation networks.

Examples of such combined operations have been found in the frog retina (Lettvin et al., 1959; Maturana et al., 1960) and are used in the acoustical pattern-recognizing networks shown in Fig. 14.

Domain Transformations

As was mentioned above, the system can readily transform a quantity appearing in one domain into any of the two other domains. There are six such non-identical transformations (see Table I) and there are two particular sets of three transformations which will give all six by successive operation. For instance, $\tau V(t)$ can be obtained by $\tau s(t) \cdot \tau V(s)$. These two sets are shown in Fig. 6. The domain transformations combined with the identical members $\tau s(s)$, (Fig. 6A) etc., have the properties of a group. In Fig. 6 the q refers to both the input and the output domains. Domains not represented are assumed normalized at previous stages. The ordinates represent the input variable to be transformed.

The networks shown in Fig. 6 refer to transformations of a quantity (q) of one domain into a quantity of another domain. This is indicated by the notation $\tau q_V(s)$, etc. Transformation of a point or region of space, $p(s)$, or a moment in time, $p(t)$, into either quantities of s, V, t or moments and points has not been illustrated in detail. One example is presented in Fig. 6B [$\tau q_s(t)$], where transformations $\tau q_s(t)$ and $\tau p_s(qt)$ are performed by neurons located at different points in the network.

Domain transformations can greatly simplify certain operations; however, transformations of two domains into a common one in which subsequent operations are performed will reduce the degrees of freedom and information content.

Two- and Three-Dimensional Space

In classifying the various operations, we neglected the higher dimensions of space. It is apparent that two-dimensional space would introduce more complexities into the operations without, however, changing the general classification. This is also the reason why, in our practical application, we restricted ourselves to the problem of acoustical pattern recognition where space along the cochlea has only one dimension.

It is questionable whether the central nervous system is capable of coping with three-dimensional space patterns. Certainly the optical input is represented only in two dimensions.

Memory

So far we have made no mention of the problem of memory. To the extent that the term "memory" refers to the storage of information in terms of patterns in the three domains, it falls under the heading of time normalization. The other aspect of memory, usually referred to as "conditioning," implies a change in the operations performed by the system (flexible logic). In its simplest form it can be represented, for example, by $(a \cdot b) \supset C \to (a + b) \supset C$, where the arrow indicates a change in the logic operations within the system, depending on previous operations.

We have investigated the incorporation of memory aspects and flexible logic into our artificial nets by using an electrochemical device composed of two silver wires with different areas dipping into a sodium iodide solution. Current flow towards the large electrode increases the resistance between the two electrodes permanently and in proportion to the amount of current flow. In order to achieve their purpose, these memory elements must be incorporated in such a way that they either lower the threshold of a neuron as a function of stimulation or increase the stimulating value of a synapse other than the one which caused the change in resistance. A resistance change influencing the synaptic strength of the synapse that caused this resistance change is not sufficient.

Quantitative Calculations of Input-Output in Nets

Having reduced some of the complexities of input-output characteristics of the individual neuron by assuming that the pulses are irrelevant, we can now try to calculate quantitatively the input-output of nets.

We consider two neurons, a and b; a is stimulating b. Let the output of a be a_0. We then define f_i as that function of a_0 which determines the input voltage to b, b_i. Thus

$$b_i = f_i \, a_0 \tag{3}$$

The properties of the synapse between a and b determine f_i; b_i is in turn related to the output of b, b_0 by the function f_0; that is,

$$b_0 = f_0 \, b_i \tag{4}$$

In biological neurons, f_0 is determined by the membrane properties of the cell body and axon hillock, i.e., those membrane segments which determine the transformation of the synaptic potential into a firing frequency of the cell. In addition, secondary modifications of f_0 can be brought about by recurrent collaterals making inhibitory or excitatory feedback connections to the same neuron. In our artificial neurons, f_0 depends on the circuit elements and feedback connections.

Going back to the input-output characteristics shown in Fig. 2A, we can now set up the following boundary conditions: If b_i is below the threshold, θ, $b_0 = 0$. Therefore

$$b_i < \theta \supset f_0 b_i = 0 \tag{5}$$

At $b_i = \theta$, b_0 is at its lower bound, L (determined by feedback conditions), and we can write

$$b_i = \theta \supset f_0 b_i = L \tag{6}$$

There is also an upper bound U, for b_0 as well as for a_0, which is due to the maximum voltage the system can deliver (100-120 mv for biological neurons; 12 v in our electronic units). Furthermore,

$$f_i \, a_0 \leq a_0 \tag{7}$$

so that

$$a_0 = U \supset b_i \leq U \tag{8}$$

and

$$b_i \geq U \supset f_0 b_i \leq U \tag{9}$$

If there are n inputs to b from neurons $a_1, a_2, \ldots, a_n$,

$$b_i = \sum_{k=1}^{k=n} f_{ik} \, a_{ko} \tag{10}$$

This however is only a first approximation. Actually, only the impedances of the individual synapses and not their voltages are added and a more accurate representation of the input voltage as a function of a number of active synapses can be obtained by considering the network below.

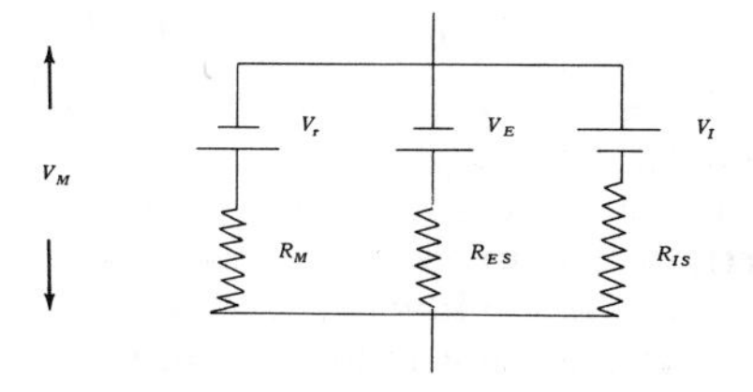

V_M = the membrane potential of a biological neuron, or input voltage of an artificial neuron.
V_r = the resting membrane potential when no synapses are active.
V_E = the voltage of an active excitatory synapse.
V_I = the voltage of an active inhibitory synapse.
R_M = the membrane resistance.

$$R_{ES} = \frac{1}{\sum_{j=1}^{j=n_E} (1/R_{Ej})} \tag{11}$$

$$R_{IS} = \frac{1}{\sum_{j=1}^{j=n_I} (1/R_{Ij})} \tag{12}$$

Both V_E and V_I can be time dependent, although the synaptic integrating capacity has been omitted in the diagram. The quantities n_E and n_I are the number of active excitatory and inhibitory synapses, respectively, and R_{Ej} and R_{Ij} are the resistance of the jth excitatory and inhibitory synaptic membrane, given by the area of the synapse (or the synaptic resistance in the input network of an artificial neuron). Also, if R_{Mr} is the resting membrane resistance (no synapses are active), then

$$\frac{1}{R_M} = \frac{1}{R_{Mr}} - \left(\frac{1}{R_{IS}} + \frac{1}{R_{ES}}\right) \tag{13}$$

If we assume that the voltages of all active excitatory synapses are equal and that the same is true for all inhibitory synapses, we can calculate V_M from

$$V_M = \frac{V_r}{1 + \frac{R_M(R_{ES} + R_{IS})}{R_{ES} \cdot R_{IS}}} + \frac{V_E}{1 + \frac{R_{ES}(R_M + R_{IS})}{R_M \cdot R_{IS}}} - \frac{V_I}{1 + \frac{R_{IS}(R_{ES} + R_M)}{R_{ES} \cdot R_M}} \tag{14}$$

This, however, is valid only for the steady state. If V_E and V_I of the individual synapses are independent time functions, each synaptic potential and impedance must be evaluated independently and its contribution to V_M calculated as in equation (14).

If f_i and f_0 are known (in artificial neurons they can be varied at will), input-output of any net can be calculated. An example is shown in Fig. 8, which represents the calculated output from neuron c in the "AND" gate circuit shown in Fig. 7 as a function of outputs from neurons a and b according to the equation

$$c_0 = f_{0c}[f_{ica}\,a_0 + f_{icb}\,b_0 - f_{icd}\,f_{0d}(f_{ida}\,a_0 - f_{idb}\,b_0) - f_{ice}\,f_{0e}(f_{ieb}\,b_0 - f_{iea}\,a_0)] \tag{15}$$

The subscripts of f_i indicate the neurons which are connected by the synapse whose input function is given.

In our example,

$$\theta = 1 \qquad U = 10 \qquad f_{0c} = 0.5 \qquad f_{idb} = 1.75 \qquad f_{iea} = 1.75 \tag{16}$$

and all other f_i and $f_0 = 1$. These values were derived from the ratio of the synaptic input resistors in the actual circuit.

Brackets in equation (15) enclose terms which represent the sum of the synaptic inputs to a particular neuron. The boundary conditions represented by equations (5) through (9) must be applied to these terms. Brackets are necessary because the distributive law does not hold. The agreement between the actually measured input-output functions and those calculated from equation (15) is good, considering that such simple parameters were chosen for the calculations.

This circuit represents a true "AND" function since the output of c is zero as long as one of the two inputs, a or b, is below a certain value. If both inputs are larger than this value, the output of c is within a central region and is a function of both a and b. In other regions, where the ratio of the two outputs exceeds a limiting value, the output follows only the smaller of the two inputs.

The above type of algebra can predict outputs of any nets at any point, provided all inputs and the properties of neurons and connections are given. This includes time functions, provided the time function of the individual synapse is specified (usually simple exponentials and their sums).

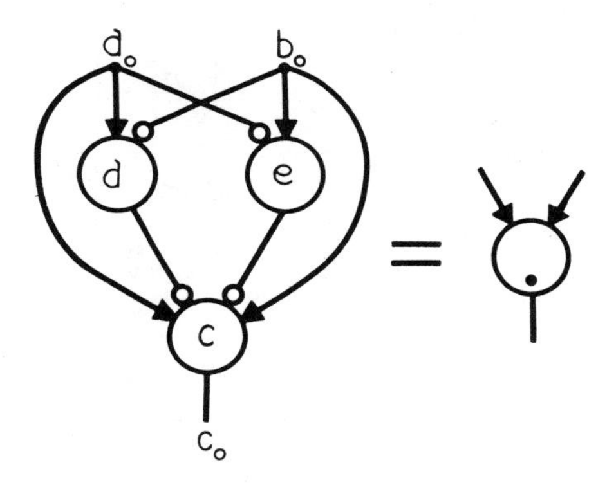

Fig. 7. Neural "AND" gate.

The unusual features of this algebra can be illustrated by a few very simple examples involving variations of the circuit of Fig. 7, assuming that all f_0 and $f_i = 1$. Thus, for instance

$$c_0 = a_0 + (b_0 - a_0) - (a_0 - b_0) = b_0 \tag{17}$$

or

$$c_0 = a_0 + (b_0 - a_0) = b_0 + (a_0 - b_0) = \begin{cases} a_0 & \text{if } a_0 > b_0 \\ b_0 & \text{if } b_0 > a_0 \end{cases} \tag{18}$$

and

$$c_0 = a_0 - (a_0 - b_0) = b_0 - (b_0 - a_0) = \begin{cases} a_0 & \text{if } a_0 < b_0 \\ b_0 & \text{if } b_0 < a_0 \end{cases} \tag{19}$$

In the last two examples, the output of c follows either the larger [equation (18)] or the smaller [equation (19)] of the two inputs a or b, and is independent of the value of the other input.

Any operation in neuron nets can be described in terms of this algebra. If in equation (6) $L = U$, the algebra is Boolean. However, an analytical treatment of this type of algebra has not yet been attempted. If it were successful, it could become a powerful tool in network construction and reduction.

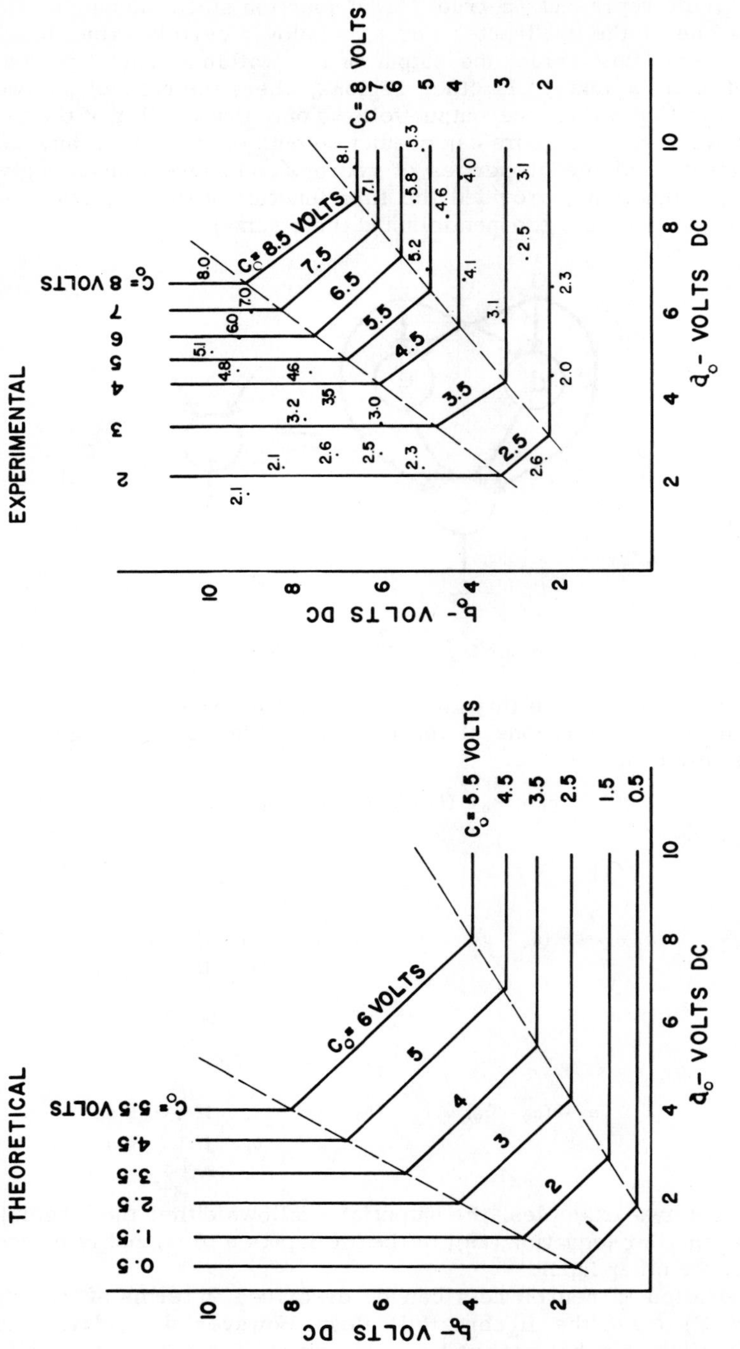

Fig. 8. Example of calculated and actually recorded input-output of a neural net ("AND" gate).

Stability of Operations

A great deal of attention has been paid to the problem of stability and various solutions have been offered. Most of them have employed multiplexing of neurons or connections, and probability logic (Cowan, 1960; McCulloch, 1959; Verbeek, 1960).

We should like to add here another principle which is not so wasteful in terms of material, especially when it comes to constructing nets with artificial neurons. This principle can be best explained by considering a set of Boolean functions of n variables, although the principle holds for all logic functions and operations listed in Table I, as well as their combinations. Consider any function f_B within this set which is represented by an output of one or more neurons. If the number of exclusive conjunctions in this function is m, there exist in the complete set of 2^{2^n} functions, $2^{(2^n)-m}$ antinomial functions (contradictions). The neurons representing those antinomies can each be connected with a strong inhibitory synapse to the neurons representing f_B. Within any arbitrary set of logic functions represented by neurons, the number of inhibitory synaptic connections to any neuron could be at least equal to the number of antinomial functions within that set.

This principle has been applied quite successfully in actual nets and an example is provided by Fig. 14. Already in this relatively simple network the average ratio of inhibitory to excitatory connections is greater than five.

Remarks

Before discussing the application of some of the principles presented in the preceding section, we should like to add some remarks concerning the general analytical capabilities of a brain which operates on these principles. It was assumed that the number of basic variables which can be represented within the system are restricted to three, s, t, and V, and, furthermore, that only a restricted number of basic operations can be performed on these variables. The question, then, is whether such a system can give a complete and noncontradictory description of the universe, including itself. Two possible situations must be distinguished.

1. It is conceivable that the universe contains more variables or basic operations than the analyzing brain can master or perform. In this case, the extra variables and operations must be transformed into the set of represented domains and operations, and any analysis would be incomplete. That is, while the relations between s, t, and V could be worked out, their relations to the possible additional domains or operations cannot be analyzed. This situation can be exemplified by considering a digital computer which, operating on normalized and quantized V and quantized space, has to transform all inputs into these restricted domains and can interpret and describe a universe only in terms of its own variables and operations.

Depending on the nature of the additional variables, it might even be impossible to produce a consistent and noncontradictory description of the universe. The dilemmas of modern physics could well be a manifestation of such a situation.

2. The second possibility, namely, that all domains and basic operations in the universe can be mastered or performed by the brain, still does not guarantee a consistent and complete description. For instance, if a brain can express its analysis of another brain or of the universe in terms of formulas connecting operations and variables, Gödels theorem (Gödel, 1931) would apply. This states that the formulas, as well as statements about the formulas, cannot be mapped into a mathematical system of Gödel numbers, and that any such system is incomplete. For example, there are truths which cannot be derived from the axioms. Furthermore, the nature of any of the domains can be analyzed only after transformation into the other domains. No further reduction is possible and any state-

ments regarding the "true nature" of space, time, and energy, i.e., the universe, must be tautologies.

APPLICATION OF NEURON NET PRINCIPLES TO ACOUSTICAL PATTERN RECOGNITION

Some of the theoretical principles described have been applied to the problem of acoustical pattern recognition. This problem was chosen from among the higher sensory functions because space is represented in only one dimension, yet all three domains are represented in the input pattern.

Neuron Model

The neural networks that have been developed for acoustical pattern recognition have been constructed with a transistorized neuron model, as shown in Fig. 9. The model approximates the basic properties of the biological neuron and has evolved from earlier versions (Mueller, 1958). The circuit contains several properties that have been found necessary when constructing large networks for experimental purposes. Some of these properties are:

1. Low output and input impedances to minimize sneak paths through the logic nets and allow many connections to each neuron.
2. Integration and refractory time constants that are independent of the number and strength of the input connections to a neuron.
3. Stable thresholds (variations less than 1%).

Although it was stated at the beginning that pulses are irrelevant, they have been incorporated into the model. The characteristics of this neuron model have been described in greater detail in another publication (McGrogan, 1961).

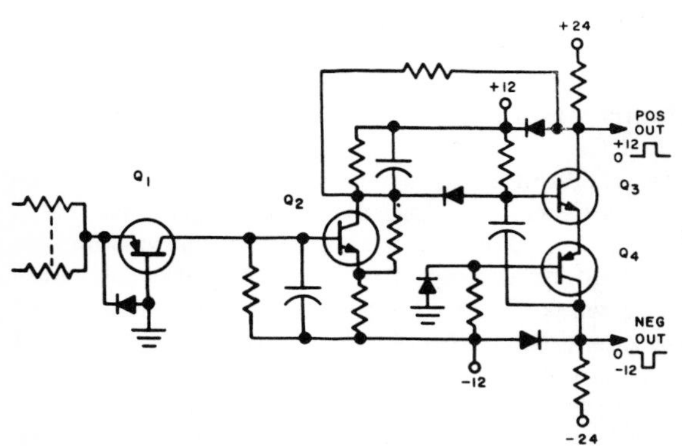

Fig. 9. Circuit diagram of artificial neuron.

Simulated Cochlea and Initial Levels of Neurons

The initial transformation of auditory patterns to neural signals in the biological hearing system is performed by the cochlea and initial levels of neurons. This transformation has many nonlinear characteristics that result in neurophysiological and psychoacoustic effects such as masking, equal loudness sensation, etc. A model of this initial transformation has been conceived in order to study some of the characteristics of this initial processing. The importance of such study may be realized by considering that a child learns to enunciate from his mother, who indicates when the word as spoken by the child fits the norm as she recognizes it. The characteristics of the human auditory system and associated neural structures that perform the speech recognition thereby determine the standards. We may, thus, assume that our speech is formed somewhat to match the human recognition system. The incorporation of these effects into a model makes it possible to study acoustic patterns from a new perspective. Such an investigation may extract basic features of speech patterns that are not readily apparent in approaches that utilize bandpass filter segmentation of speech patterns.

The initial transformation of the auditory pattern to neural signals can be duplicated through the use of a simulated cochlea and artificial neural networks. The movement of the basilar membrane and the corresponding microphonics closely resemble the characteristics of a distributed low-pass structure (Tasaki, Davis, and Legouix, 1952). These effects can be approximated by a RLC transmission line, as shown in Fig. 10. Several levels of artificial neurons are connected to the transmission line to accomplish the desired preprocessing. The primary neurons are excited or inhibited by the signal voltages impressed upon the distributed line, and the secondary neurons are stimulated by the primary row. The neurons near the input end of the distributed line are excited by the total energy of the acoustic spectrum, while those neurons close to the end of the line are excited only by the lowest frequency components of the incoming speech.

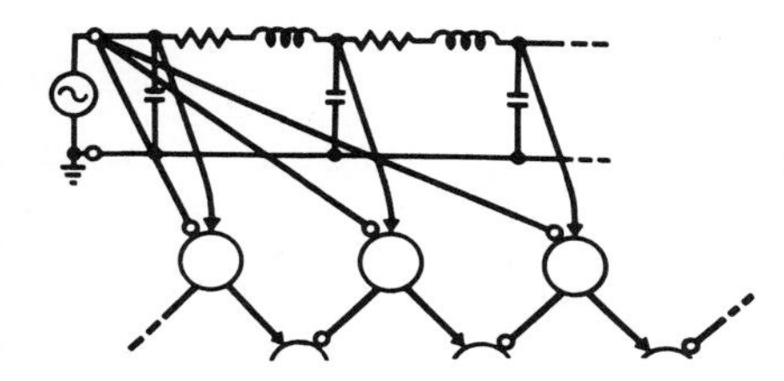

Fig. 10. Cochlea model and primary neuron levels.

Frequency Discrimination in Distributed Network

Frequency discrimination is achieved in the second level of neurons in Fig. 10 by differential neural stimulation. This process can be explained by considering the response of a neuron positioned halfway along the length of the distributed line. A very-high-frequency input signal is attenuated rapidly and does not reach the halfway point. Similarly, a very-low-frequency signal is passed with constant attenuation, except near the extreme end of the line. In this case, the excitation to the second-level neuron (near the center) is canceled by the weighted inhibition of the adjacent neuron farther down the line. Response will occur, however, for an input signal whose frequency is close to the cutoff frequency corresponding to the position of the excitatory input to the neuron. This response occurs because the neuron is positioned where the onset of rapid attenuation of the signal causes a large difference in first-level neuron firing rates. Thus, the sample neuron is more heavily excited than inhibited, thereby producing the condition for firing.

Second-Level Neural Response

Galambos and Davis (1943) have measured the responses of second-level neurons in the cochlear nucleus of the cat. They found that each second-level neuron was attuned to a particular frequency with a typical characteristic, as shown in Fig. 11. Near the threshold level, the neuron responds to a very narrow band of frequencies. As the intensity of the stimulus is increased, the neuron responds to a broader band of frequencies. The maximum firing rate, however, is achieved at the characteristic frequency of the neuron. This effect is precisely what occurs in the second-level neurons shown in Fig. 10. The minimum signal level that produces a response must be exactly at the characteristic frequency in order for differential stimulation to result in excitation which exceeds

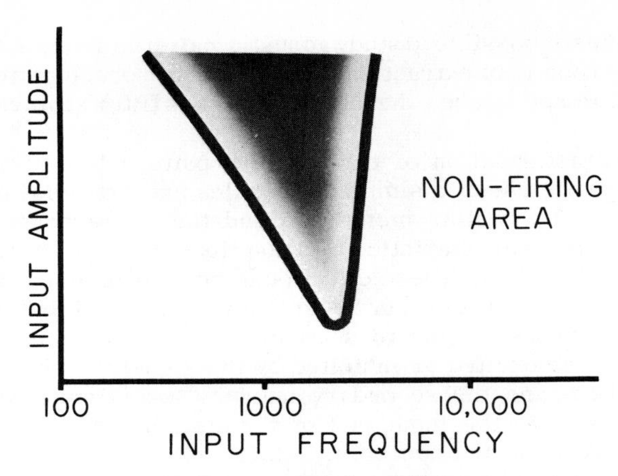

Fig. 11. Response area for single neuron.

the neuron threshold. However, for larger amplitudes the frequency of the input signal may vary over a wider range and still cause the neuron to fire.

Masking

The network of Fig. 10 can also partially explain masking effects, which are very important in determining what we hear. Generally, masking is the phenomenon whereby the presence of one tone obscures or masks the presence of another tone. In sounds of high intensity, low-frequency signals tend to mask the sounds of higher-frequency signals. This effect occurs in the primary neurons of Fig. 10 and is attributable to the nonlinear response of the neuron to an input stimulus. Figure 12 shows the firing rates of the primary neurons along the cochlea model vs distance from the input end. A high-frequency signal produces the firing pattern shown in Fig. 12A. When a high-level low-frequency signal is added to the high-frequency signal, the firing pattern is that of Fig. 12B. The low-frequency signal causes the neurons to operate in the region where the input-output characteristic tends to saturate or level off. As a result, the differential signal produced at the second level of neurons is smaller, thereby masking the presence of the higher-frequency signal. Another method of including the masking effect is to inhibit the high-frequency neurons by the lower-frequency neurons. This can be done with weighted connections so that inhibition is strongest for those higher-frequency neurons in the immediate vicinity of the lower-frequency neurons.

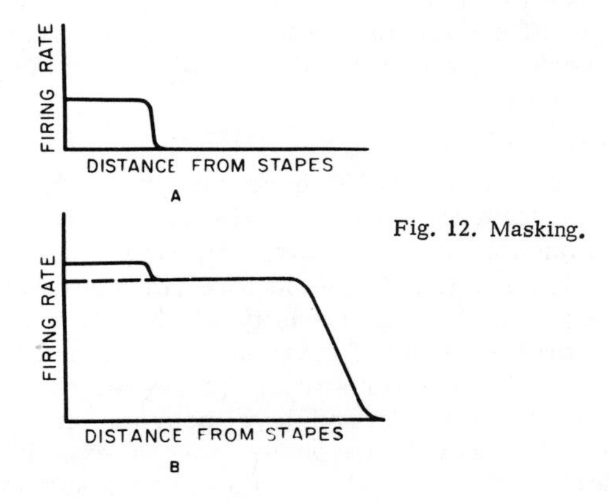

Fig. 12. Masking.

Space-Energy Pattern Abstraction

Having transformed one part of the input, frequency, into linear space, the system must be able to abstract the various three-domain features from acoustic patterns. The experimental networks that have been developed for this purpose have been limited to operations in the two domains of linear space and energy; the time domain has been given only preliminary consideration. The network for the first stages of combined space-energy pattern abstraction is shown in Fig. 13.

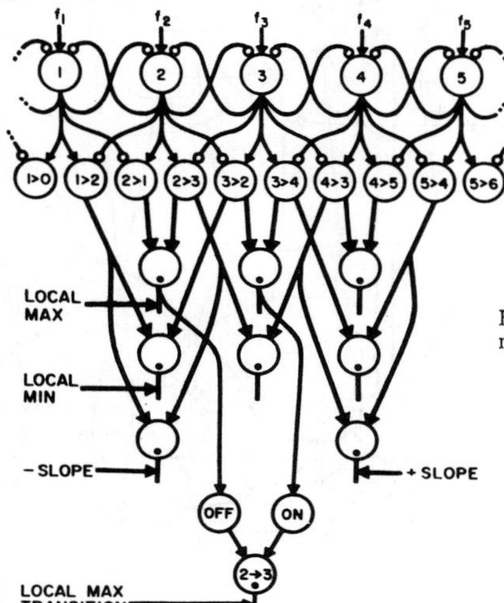

Fig. 13. Section of simplified diagram of primary stages of network used for the recognition of space-amplitude distributions.

Five of the inputs to the primary neurons from the cochlea model are shown in Fig. 13, although a larger number is necessary to cover the entire speech spectrum. The primary row of neurons is mutually inhibited in order to enhance small differences in adjacent channels. The second level of neural processing selects the larger output of two neighboring neurons. The notation inside the individual neurons states the conditions for firing. From the information contained at this level of processing, it is possible to abstract from the input pattern the location along the linear input space of the local maxima, minima, and positive and negative slopes. An example of each of these properties is shown in the final levels of Fig. 13. The local maximum shown occurs if $1 < 2 > 3$, the local minimum if $1 > 2 < 3$, the positive slope if $3 < 4 < 5$, and the negative slope if $1 > 2 > 3$. Since the transfer characteristic of the neuron is a close approximation to a logarithmic relationship, the abstraction of these features can be achieved somewhat independently of the over-all amplitude level of the primary inputs. The output of a primary neuron stimulated by an input, a_j, is approximately $\log a_j$. The differential stimulation of the second-level neurons is then given approximately by

$$\Sigma \text{ inputs} = \log a_i - \log b_i = \log \frac{a_i}{b_i} \tag{20}$$

where a_i = excitatory input to neuron i and b_i = inhibitory input to neuron i. Since the summation of the excitatory and inhibitory inputs to a second-level neuron is approximately $\log a_i/b_i$, any constant multiplier of both a_i and b_i produces the same net stimulus to the neuron. It is thereby possible to achieve a degree of amplitude-independent frequency recognition.

Also shown in Fig. 13 is a network using the ON-OFF responses to indicate when the location of a local maximum shifts from the position of neuron 2 to

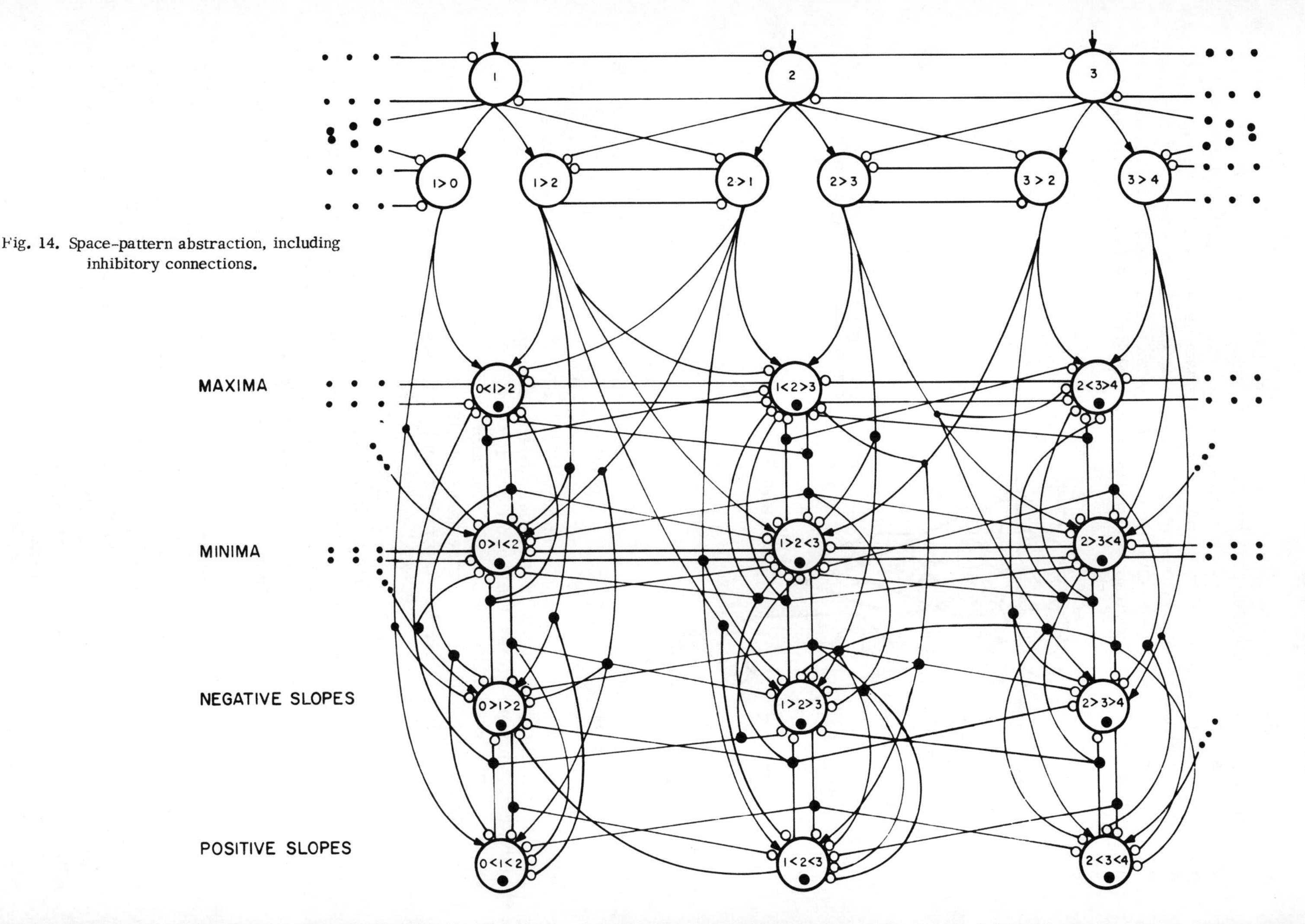

Fig. 14. Space-pattern abstraction, including inhibitory connections.

neuron 3. This type of connection can be used to indicate the local transitions of the maxima, minima, and slopes, and actually involves operations in the three domains, t, s, and V. The output of the neuron indicating the transition is proportional to

$$\left\{\left[\frac{+\,d\,(V_3/V_4)\,(V_3/V_2)}{dt}\right]\left[\frac{+\,d\,(V_2/V_1)\,(V_2/V_3)}{dt}\right]\right\}\frac{ds}{dt} \tag{21}$$

Recognition of simple vowels and some consonants has been achieved with networks similar to that shown in Fig. 14, which includes the inhibitory connections necessary for logical stability. The inputs to this network are either from the primary neuron levels associated with the cochlea model shown in Fig. 10 or are from bandpass filters. The constructed network had ten primary neurons and sections, only three of which are shown in Fig. 14. The further elaboration of the scheme shown in Fig. 14 would imply comparison and ordering of the primary voltage maxima, minima, or slopes, and the movements of these quantities along the input space in either direction according to their intensities and speeds.

For n inputs there are $n(\log_2 n)$ possible secondary, ternary, etc., maxima (i.e., maxima which are derived from comparison of neighboring maxima). The same is true for minima. Generally, for primary maxima or minima extending over h neurons, there are $n(\log_{h-1} n)$ derived maxima or minima. For positive or negative slopes extending over p neurons, where p increases from 2 to n, the number of possible slope orders (i.e., slope a steeper than slope b) is given by

$$n\sum_{p=2}^{p=n}[n-(p-1)] = \frac{n^2(n-1)}{2} \tag{22}$$

A similar treatment would be required for a complete ordering of the transitions (movements) of these quantities according to their speeds.

It is evident that a complete representation and analysis of space—time—voltage patterns, even for a small number of primary neurons (500–1000), is not feasible. At this point we must decide how far to carry such an analysis.

Is the analysis of higher-order maxima, minima, etc., important for speech pattern recognition? To what extent must time patterns be evaluated? These are questions that can be answered only by experiment, and ideally should be answered by direct evidence from properly obtained neurophysiological data.

REFERENCES

Cowan, G.D. 1960. Towards a proper logic for parallel computation in the presence of noise. Bionics Symposium, Wright Air Development Division, Ohio, p. 93.

Eccles, G.C. 1953. The neurophysiological basis of mind. Oxford Clarendon Press, p. 191.

Galambos, R. and Davis, H. 1943. The response of single auditory-nerve fibers to acoustic stimulation. J. Neurophysiol. 6, 39.

Gödel, K. 1931. Über Nichtunterscheidbare Sätze der Principia Mathematica und Verwandter Systeme. Monatsch. Math. Phys. 38, 173.

Hartline, H.K. and Ratliff, F. 1958. Spatial summation of inhibitory influences in the eye of Limulus and the mutual interaction of receptor units. J. Gen. Physiol. 21, 1049.

Lettvin, J.Y., Maturana, H.R., McCulloch, W.S., and Pitts, W.H. 1959. What the frog's eye tells the frog's brain. Proc. IRE 47, 1949.

Maturana, H.R., Lettvin, J.Y., McCulloch, W.S., and Pitts, W.H. 1960. Anatomy and Physiology of Vision in the Frog." J. Gen. Physiol. 43, 129.

McCulloch, W.S. and Pitts, W. 1943. A logical calculus of the ideas imminent in nervous activity. Bull. Math. Biophys. 5, 115.

McCulloch, W.S. 1959. Agathe Tyche of nervous nets—the lucky reckoners. Mechanization of Thought Processes, II, 613, Her Majesty's Stationary Office, London.

McGrogan, E. 1961. Improved neuron models. 1961 National Electronics Conference.

Mueller, P. 1958. Prolonged action potentials from single Nodes of Ranvier. J. Gen. Physiol. 42, 137.

Mueller, P. 1958. Effects of external currents on duration and amplitude of normal and prolonged action potentials from single Nodes of Ranvier. J. Gen. Physiol. 42, 163.

Mueller, P. 1958. On the kinetics of potential, electromotance, and chemical change in the excitable system of nerve. J. Gen. Physiol. 42, 193.
Post, E. L. 1921. Introduction to a general theory of elementary propositions. Am. J. Math. 43, 163.
Preston, G. B. and Kennedy, D. 1959. Integrative mechanism in the caudal ganglion of the crayfish. J. Gen. Physiol. 43, 691.
Rosenbloom, P. C. 1942. Post algebras; postulates and general theory. J. of Math. 64, 164.
Tasaki, I., Davis, H., and Legouix, J. 1952. The space-time pattern of the cochlear microphonics (guinea pig), as recorded by differential electrodes. J. Acoustic Soc. of Am. 24, 502.
Verbeek, L. A. M. 1960. Reliable computation with unreliable circuitry. Bionics Symposium, Wright Air Development Division, Ohio, p. 83.

A MODEL FOR HEARING

J. L. Stewart

Bioacoustics Laboratory, Tucson, Arizona

INTRODUCTION

Many so-called theories and models for hearing have been proposed—here is yet another. It differs from most in the sense of mathematical logic; in fact, the present theory is totally based on a system of hypothesized mathematical functions.

At the outset, certain classical concepts of an empirical nature will be reviewed; from this point, a fairly extensive multicomponent model will be evolved. Finally, an approach to achieving ultimate bandwidth compression for speech, based on the derived model, will be described. The model and the deduced bandwidth compression concept bear marked similarities to plausible human processes.

CLASSICAL LAWS

The power-law function for relating physical and subjective measures for intensity is well known (Luce, 1959; Stevens, 1959; Stevens, 1961; Helm et al., 1961). A suitable statement is

$$L = KF^{n/2} \qquad F = \langle f(t)^2 \rangle = \lim_{T\to\infty} \frac{1}{T}\int_{-T/2}^{T/2} f(t)^2\,dt \tag{1}$$

where L is the subjective measure of "loudness," F is the mean-square value of the sustained stimulus, and K is a constant of proportionality. The exponent $n/2$ (often written $m = n/2$) has a value of approximately $n = 1$ ($m = 0.5$) in hearing.

If total stimulus $f(t)$ consists of additive parts $s(t)$ and $n(t)$ with mean-square values S and N, respectively, and if $s(t)$ and $n(t)$ are independent (orthogonal), then $F = S + N$ and there results

$$L = K(S + N)^{n/2} = K'\left(1 + \frac{S}{N}\right)^{n/2} \tag{2}$$

where the second representation is useful for N = constant. As a rule, $s(t)$ denotes a signal and $n(t)$ denotes noise.

The law of equation (1) is an empirical one; the extension of equation (2) is in reality a (rigorous) theoretical extension of the fundamental law of equation (1). A second extension is concerned with usage of the mean-square value in equation (1); this implies infinite time averaging, which cannot, of course, occur in a sensory system. If $n(t)$ is random and for infinite averaging time, L is a constant; for a finite time average, L becomes a statistical variable and, hence, the value of L is subject to statistical hypothesis testing (Swets, 1961; Tanner, 1960). A block-diagram model for loudness thus consists of a "loudness converter" followed by a decision device. Provided that the averaging time is long compared with detailed variations in $f(t)$, central tendencies do not depend on the statistical testing technique. Thus, for generalization in the ensemble sense (at least for stationary stimuli), the representation with infinite averaging time remains valid.

THE LOUDNESS HYPOTHESIS

As with most empirical laws which are deduced by curve fitting, theoretical extension to less familiar phenomena is not self-evident. The principal problem with equation (1) is that different waveform types for $f(t)$ do not lead to modifications in the basic law, as might be expected. The empirical law is found by experiment to be very good for $f(t)$, a Gaussian random variable, and fairly good for a mixture of sine wave and noise. But waveforms which differ drastically from these may very likely lead to significantly different empirical laws. A generalization is required which can handle arbitrary $f(t)$, which can be physically modeled, and which behaves quantitatively as does equation (1) in cases where equation (1) is observed by experiment to be accurate.

A loudness function hypothesis is thus proposed as

$$L = \langle |f(t)|^n \rangle = \langle |s(t) + n(t)|^n \rangle \tag{3}$$

which has the following results (Rice, 1944, 1945; Middleton, 1960):

Case I, $s(t)$ and $n(t)$ independent Gaussian random variables with mean-square values S and N

$$L(S, N, n) = \frac{\Gamma(1+n)}{2^{n/2}\Gamma(1+n/2)} (S+N)^{n/2} = K(S+N)^{n/2} \tag{4}$$

Case II, $s(t) = R \sin \omega t$ (thus $S = R^2/2$), and $n(t)$ as in Case I

$$L(S, N, n) = \frac{\Gamma(1+n)}{\Gamma(1+n/2)}\left(\frac{N}{2}\right)^{n/2} {}_1F_1(-n/2; 1; -S/N) \tag{5}$$

which show L as a function of S, N, and the parameter n.

Equation (4) is a special case of equation (5); for if $S = 0$, the confluent hypergeometric function has unit value and noise mean-square value N may be separated into equivalent additive parts $S + N$. Also, in these equations, it may be observed that restrictions have not been placed on spectra [except of course for $s(t)$, a sine wave].

Although greatly different in appearance, equation (5) behaves quantitatively much like equation (4) (and it reduces to an identity for $n = 2$). In fact, similarities are sufficient to propose that, in detection-type problems, a relatively narrow band of Gaussian noise may approximate a sine wave and vice versa (as least for typical exponent values).

The loudness function of equation (3) may actually be interpreted as a first-order approximation to a quasi-Taylor-series loudness function which is so general as to defy easy criticism, namely

$$L = \langle |f(t)|^n [1 + A_1|f(t)| + A_2|f(t)|^2 + \cdots] \rangle \cong \langle |f(t)|^n \rangle \tag{6}$$

If the approximation of equation (6) is not satisfactory because $|f(t)|$ is too large, it can be said that the sensory system is "saturated" or "overloaded." Since $f(t)$ includes noise internal to the sensory system, ever-present self-saturation is not an impossibility.

A power-series development of equation (4) [and quantitatively similarly for equation (5)] shows

$$L = K'\left(1 + \frac{S}{N}\right)^{n/2} = K'\left[1 + \frac{n}{2}\left(\frac{S}{N}\right) + \frac{n(n-2)}{8}\left(\frac{S}{N}\right)^2 + \cdots\right] \tag{7}$$

which is the square law to $s(t)$ for all exponents n for small S/N. This phenomenon is the basic enabling mechanism in masking (at least for $n < 2$). The reason for this is that the rate of growth of L depends on the signal-to-noise ratio S/N, which depends linearly on S for small S/N and on $S^{n/2}$ for large S/N. The growth rate of S is faster than that of $S^{n/2}$ for $n < 2$.

The importance of the Gaussian random variable in loudness functions should be commented upon. If loudness is due to a large number of neural pulses which may overlap and which are displaced randomly in time, the famous central limit theorem in statistics applies. "The sum variable tends to the Gaussian random variable." Systems which are probabilistic in this sense are usually well enough behaved so as to have valid power-series representations, as in equation (6).

Noise $n(t)$ in the biological system is in part due to the random addition of neural pulses, much as shot noise in a vacuum tube. Also, random variations in synaptic triggering levels may exist (Frishkopf and Rosenblith, 1958).

If the loudness function as defined here results from operation of the central limit theorem, it follows that sensory systems which operate on relatively few neural pulses do not obey these same loudness laws.

It has been stated that averaging time need not be infinite for the present theory to be valid; rather, averaging time need only be long compared with periodicities in $f(t)$. At least from the point of view of ensemble averaging, even this degree of time averaging is not necessary. However, if the duration of the stimulus is shorter than the averaging time, the effect is to diminish L. This can be accounted for adequately with suitable models for temporal auditory summation (Munson, 1947; Zwislocki, 1960).

A NEO-WEBERIAN LAW

The classic Weber law states that the ratio $\Delta S/S$ is constant, where ΔS is the just-noticeable difference. The empirical law is well obeyed for large S/N, provided that saturation is not a factor. The Weber law is not valid at small S/N.

The neo-Weberian hypothesis is

$$\Delta L/L \text{ is independent of } S \tag{8}$$

The increment ΔL is approximated by the differential dL (with respect to S). For equation (4) [and quantitatively similarly for equation (5)]

$$\frac{dL}{L} = \frac{n}{2} \cdot \frac{dS}{S} \cdot \frac{1}{1 + N/S} \tag{9}$$

which is indeed characteristic of the Weber law for large S/N, for then $dL/L \propto dS/S$. If primed values represent the large S/N case, unprimed ones the general case, and making use of the hypothesis of equation (8), it is found that

$$\frac{\Delta S/S}{\Delta S'/S'} = 1 + \frac{1}{S/N} \tag{10}$$

which plots as in Fig. 1, using logarithmic scales. A shift of the curve in Fig. 1 upward to account for finite $\Delta S'/S'$, and a slight horizontal shift to account for differing measures for total noise, compares with the classic measured data by Miller (1947). The dashed extensions in Fig. 1 are supposed to represent what might typically occur as saturation comes into effect at larger signal levels. With allowances for saturation, Fig. 1 typifies many senses other than hearing (Geldard, 1953).

The value of S/N at which an experimental curve is 3 db above its large S/N plateau has special significance; the value of S pertinent to this point is equal to the mean-square noise in the sensory system. Another interesting observation regarding equation (10) is that the exponent n does not appear (although the similar expression for a sine wave in noise shows slight dependence on this exponent). Observe also that equation (10) depends only on the S/N ratio, as has been verified experimentally by Sherrick (1959).

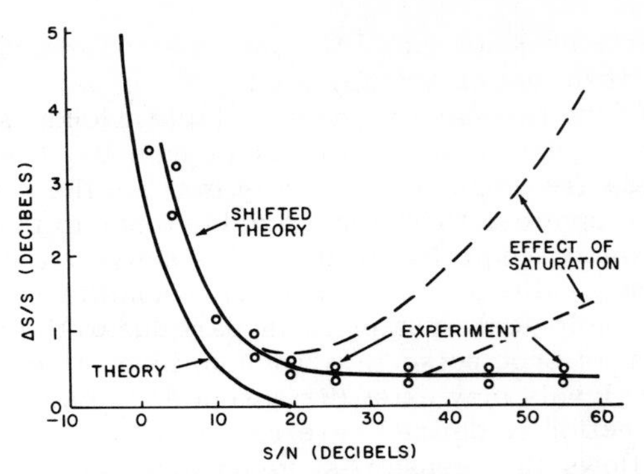

Fig. 1. A generalized plot of $\Delta S/S$ for a Gaussian signal in Gaussian noise with comparison to experiment.

Finally, note that, because the process of averaging is insensitive to the rate of zero crossings in $f(t)$, the neo-Weberian law derived here does not apply to frequency discrimination. Unless the sensory device has frequency-dependent behavior, so that frequency changes are converted to amplitude changes, a mechanism for highly accurate discriminations in frequency is not at all apparent.

No discussion of Weber is complete without bringing up the Fechner "law." This law accumulates units of ΔS in order to obtain $\log S$ as a loudness measure. The analogous procedure here is to add units of ΔL to find $\log L$. But this is senseless because a loudness unit as defined cannot be manipulated to find an entirely different function which means the same thing; this flouts ordinary mathematical logic. It is suggested that a logarithmic approximation to an empirical curve can be replaced with any one of an infinity of entirely different functions (such as ${}_1F_1$?) within the limits of experimental data accuracy.

THE THEORY OF MASKING

Form a recognition function hypothesis as

$$P(S, N, n) = L(S, N, n) - L(0, N, n) \tag{11}$$

which implies merely that recognition depends on the difference between finite- and zero-signal loudness functions for constant noise.

Next, consider the following experiment involving a tone (or equivalent band of noise) in Gaussian noise. Start with an uncorrupted tone and gradually add noise. In order to maintain constant subjective loudness for the tone (not for the tone plus noise), it is necessary to change $s(t)$ by factor δ (or S by δ^2). The starting recognition function $P(S, 0, n)$ is equated to the final function to give

$$P(S, 0, n) = P(\delta^2 S, N, n) \tag{12}$$

Equation (12) may be solved for δ^2 for the case of Gaussian $s(t)$ (and quantitatively similarly for a sine wave) to obtain

$$\delta^2 = \left[1 + \left(\frac{N}{S}\right)^{n/2}\right]^{2/n} - \frac{N}{S} \qquad \left(= 1 + 2\sqrt{\frac{N}{S}} \quad \text{for} \quad n = 1\right) \tag{13}$$

Three cases can occur. For $n < 2$, partial or complete masking is evidenced in that noise reduces the subjective intensity of the tone. For $n = 2$, $\delta = 1$ for all

S/N; in this case, the sensory system is immune to masking. For $n > 2$, "inverse" masking occurs in that noise enhances the signal. This last case may relate to loudness recruitment (albeit confused by other effects such as fatigue) and even suggests that an aid to hearing may consist of noise bias where the noise intensity is relatively large in frequency regions where n is large. So-called center-clipped speech also relates to the $n > 2$ case; intelligibility may actually be improved with noise.

An important application of equation (13) is the experimental determination of exponent n; the curve that best fits empirical masking data provides this determination. If necessary, this technique can determine n without increasing S above threshold by more than a very few db, and, thus, the effects of spurious factors such as adaptation, fatigue, and saturation can be minimized. Because the value of n depends on details of neural summations, it is not unreasonable to suspect that n may constitute a useful comparative measure, or perhaps it may be found to depend on drug action.

Noise $n(t)$ may be composed of two additive parts due to external and internal causes. If these parts are statistically independent, we can write

$$N = N_{ext} + N_{int} \tag{14}$$

where N_{ext} is under control by the experimenter and N_{int} is not. Masking experiments are, in principle, capable of determining N_{int}.

MONAURAL DIPLACUSIS AND PATTERNS

Various observers have noted a change in the subjective frequency of a tone (pitch) when noise is added (Schubert, 1950; Egan and Meyer, 1950). Diplacusis of this type is observed for all frequencies, but regularities are most marked at high frequencies, where the shift in pitch is usually upward. The theory of masking provides an explanation for the phenomenon and, hence, suggests diplacusis measurements for psychoacoustical experiments (and in clinics) as a measure of the asymmetry of the loudness-converted cochlear intensity pattern.

For any sustained sound, a pattern of vibrations occurs along the basilar membrane of the inner ear. Figure 2 shows a pattern for a pure high-frequency tone (or equivalent narrow band of noise) and for relatively white interfering noise. The sum of these two components is not a simple addition of mean-square values because masking varies from point to point along the pattern, depending on the S/N ratio pertinent to the point. Thus, for $n < 2$, points where S/N is large retain intensities not much larger than S, and points where N/S is large remain at about the intensity level for N. After subtracting the pure noise curve from the net suppressed pattern in accordance with the recognition function hypothesis, a resulting signal-estimated pattern obtains which may show a shift in its centroid along the basilar membrane. The amount of shift depends on asymmetry of the

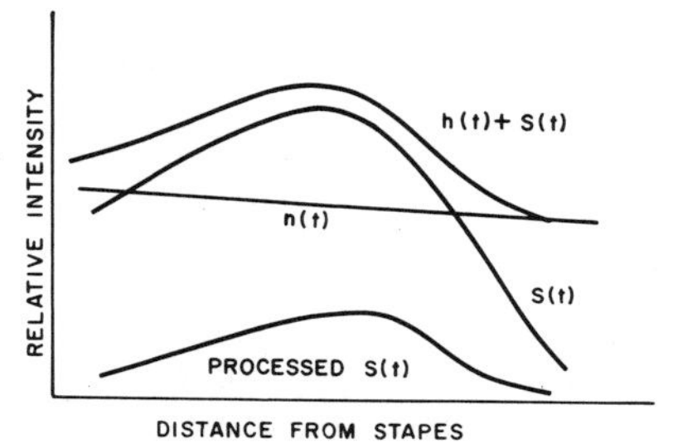

Fig. 2. The concept of differential pattern masking.

cochlear pattern for a pure tone and on regularities (or lack of them) in the pure noise pattern. A shift without excessive distortion in general pattern shape thus corresponds to a pure tone, but at a different frequency than that applied.

Noise suppression does not actually occur at the basilar membrane; rather, it occurs subsequent to conversion to neural form as a detection process. Thus, the suppressed pattern is actually a neural one and, hence, the degree of pattern shift also depends on neural factors in the organ of Corti or in some higher center. The density of active hair cells in the cochlear duct is, thus, an important factor. The incidence of relatively large diplacusis with cochlear nerve damage is, therefore, not unexpected, nor does it appear to be particularly difficult to make quantitative estimates of the extent of nerve damage from diplacusis measurements.

The fact of noise diplacusis raises many additional questions, the most important of which are perhaps associated with the simple loudness converter thus far described. Such a simple device cannot explain cases where different patches of sensory cells in the same sensory organ experience different signal-to-noise ratios. However, the sensory organ can be quantized into patches of cells, each of which experiences a constant S/N ratio.

It is, thus, necessary to quantize the cochlear duct into hair cell patches. The proper excitation of these patches demands use of an artificial cochlea, which in turn must be driven by means of a proper representation for external and middle parts of the ear. There now exist many loudness converters whose outputs collectively excite a single pattern-recognizing device. The "system" is shown in Fig. 3. A fair question to ask is: What is the set of conditions under which the complicated system may be approximated with the simple system, also shown in Fig. 3, so that a simple statistical detection measure can be applied? First, the several loudness converters must have the same power-law exponent and the same averaging time. Most important, they must all experience the same S/N ratio, although absolute values of S may differ. But if the S/N ratio is constant, pattern discrimination can not occur; only simple intensity discriminations are possible. Thus, the use of the simplified system for recognition of other than intensity levels can be seriously questioned.

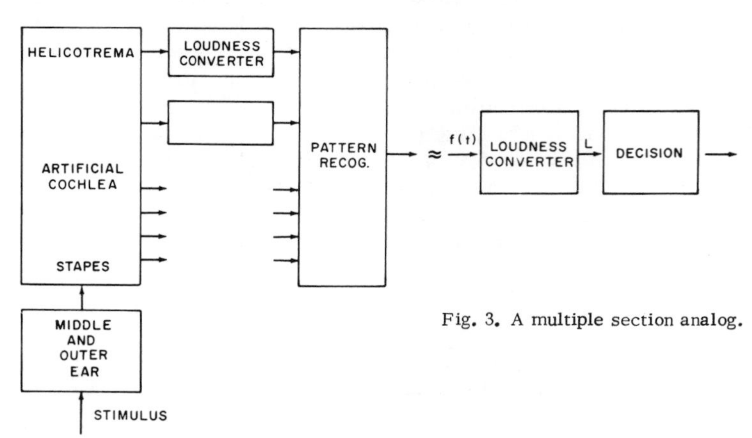

Fig. 3. A multiple section analog.

The model for hearing thus far developed has a marked one-to-one correspondence with the actual ear. Many physiological functions have not yet been introduced, such as fatigue, the stapedial reflex, and so forth. Inasmuch as these factors often are not important at low intensity levels (where speech recognition can readily occur), they constitute second-order factors. Most efferent and cross-connecting fibers in the cochlea are not understood; nevertheless, at small intensity levels where confidence in the loudness function concept is a maximum, these fibers may not play an important role. A "small-signal" approximation as a valid first approach to describing intellectual accomplishments in human hearing is apparently a very reasonable one.

AN APPROACH TO BANDWIDTH COMPRESSION

Optimum methods for achieving pattern recognition in a spatially oriented system, such as that of Fig. 3, are not apparent. However, insight is gained if the spatial coordinate is converted to a time coordinate, which can be done by commutating the outputs from the several loudness converters. The commutation rate must be large enough to retain temporal pattern details; a suitable rate might be of the order of 20 per second (Miller and Licklider, 1950).

The sequence of patterns is applied to the inputs of a number of matched filters which are individually adjusted to cover all pattern shapes that are likely to occur (Turin, 1960; Stewart, 1960). As far as any one filter is concerned, the ensemble of patterns, except for the one to which it is matched, represents approximately Gaussian noise (as a consequence of the central limit theorem). For every pattern presentation, one of the matched filters will have a larger output than any of the rest; this particular filter can be made to generate a specific voltage level. Note that, by selecting the largest output per pattern excitation, problems of pattern amplitude normalization are avoided.

The several matched filters can generate an $N+1$ level waveform (including the zero level) as in Fig. 4a. Every T seconds (about 0.05 second), a different matched filter responds for time-varying speech. The question is: What is the bandwidth of the waveform in Fig. 4a? According to information theory, the capacity of a discrete noiseless channel is $C = 2W \log_2(N+1)$ (Shannon, 1948). The implied information for each selected level of the waveform in Fig. 4, provided all levels are equally probable, is $\log_2(N+1)$. The information rate is, thus, $H = (1/T)\log_2(N+1)$. Thus, the minimum required bandwidth is $W = 1/2T$ (as in the well-known sampling theorem), which is 10 cps for $T = 0.05$.

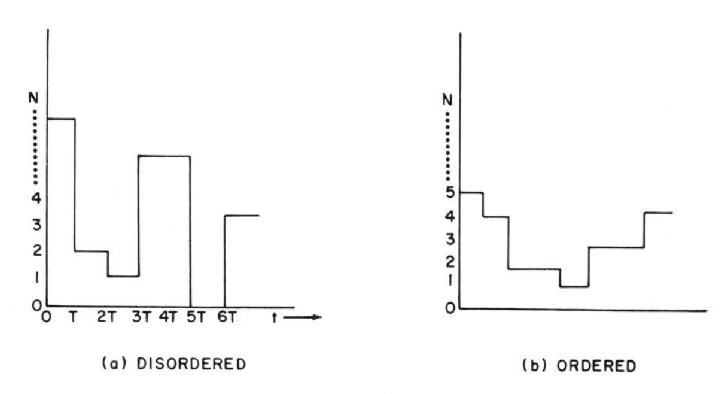

Fig. 4. Quantized level codes.

An alternate approach to the problem is to consider the bandwidth required if a simple RC circuit is employed. The switching transient must reach from a starting level in Fig. 4a to within a half-level of the final value. In a direct manner, it is found that

$$1 - e^{-\alpha T} = \begin{cases} 1 - \dfrac{1/2}{n + 1/2} & \text{for a level transition } n < N \\ 1 - \dfrac{1/2}{N} & \text{for a maximum possible level transition} \end{cases} \tag{15}$$

where the radian bandwidth is $\alpha = 2\pi W$, where W is cyclic bandwidth. From equation (15) there results

$$WT = \begin{cases} \dfrac{\ln(2n+1)}{2\pi k} \\ \dfrac{\ln(2N)}{2\pi k} \end{cases} \tag{16}$$

where ln is the natural logarithm and $k = 1$. Some simple circuits are considerably "faster" than the RC circuit; a fast circuit is represented by equation (16) for $k > 1$ (Valley and Wallman, 1948). Typical k values of the order of 1.3 are reasonable (although a k value which leads to a smaller bandwidth than the theoretical limit given by information theory must be interpreted with caution).

The least possible bandwidth is given when transitions are by no more than one level at a time; in this case the bandwidth is $(\ln 3)/2\pi kt$. In general, for $N+1$ levels, bandwidth limits can be imposed as

$$\frac{\ln 3}{2\pi kT} \leq W \leq \frac{\ln 2N}{2\pi kT} \tag{17}$$

where any bandwidth less than the maximum value implies sequential pattern dependencies such that all transitions are not equally likely.

For $N = 63$ and $T = 1/20$, equation (17) gives limits $3.51/k \leq W \leq 15.3/k$ which for only modest achieves the ultimate bandwidth limit according to the channel capacity formula.

If the ordering of the matched filters in Fig. 4a is random, occasional transitions by a full N levels are likely and, thus, bandwidth $(\ln 2N)/2\pi kT$ is required. A reordering of levels which accounts for adjacent and distant interpattern dependencies minimizes the average and maximum magnitudes of level transitions. This in turn leads to smaller required bandwidth, as is implied with the more slowly varying waveform of Fig. 4b. For $T = 1/20$, $N = 63$, and k near its maximum, a "prudent" guess for the bandwidth of the waveform of Fig. 4b is perhaps 7 or 8 cps.

Suppose that ordered waveforms, as in Fig. 4b, are sent to yet another set of matched filters. Evidently, bandwidth is even further reduced and recognition of complete phonemes and words is mechanized!

A few topics associated with Fig. 4 are worthy additions. First, it is suggested that those who seek to achieve speech reception via alternate sensory routes (as cutaneous) start at the level of Fig. 4a or even Fig. 4b. In order to employ a less "sophisticated" cortical region than the auditory cortex, certain recognition functions may have to be carried out by "prosthesis." In effect, the bandwidth of the message is compressed before application to the biological recognition system. In fact, the cochlea appears to perform this task in hearing prior to transmission to the auditory cortex, although not to the point represented by Fig. 4a.

The effect of noise in Fig. 4 is of interest. Noise larger than a half interval must inevitably cause error; the only way error rate can be reduced is through use of fewer and more widely spaced levels. The effect is not unlike that observed in persons with partial agnosia. Perhaps noise in Fig. 4 is equivalent to cortical confusion.

Small amounts of noise in Fig. 4 can be countered by increasing T so that the transient more closely approaches its final value. However, an increase in T by more than one or two RC time constants is not particularly useful because several time constants exist in each period at the outset, and the resulting percentage increase in T (or reduction in pattern rate) is small. It has often been observed that slowing one's speech does not have a particularly marked effect on intelligibility.

The effect of noise prior to the matched filters is also of interest. In this event, an erroneous level occurs in Fig. 4, although noise per se does not appear. If the noise causes an unlikely level transition, the limited bandwidth associated with the ordered waveform actually reduces the severity of the error. In effect, this amounts to use of intersymbol probabilities in order to reduce the error rate.

Finally, consider the use of a bandwidth in Fig. 4b that is somewhat too small to accept occasional exceptionally large but legitimate transitions. Of course, an error is made but perhaps it is an ignorable one. Articulation test results never seem to reach 100%, even under ideal external conditions.

CONCLUSION

The theory provided here is a relatively extensive one that has been founded insofar as is possible on a minimum number of hypotheses. Phenomena of loudness, difference limens, masking, and noise diplacusis are explained for both Gaussian and sinusoidal excitations. The theory in a collective sense implies a one-to-one model for hearing which can be extended to suggest mechanisms in recognition which lead to bandwidth compression.

Several experimental procedures are suggested by the theory which may have clinical and research applications. One procedure seeks to evaluate noise internal to the sensory system. Another concerns possible pattern symmetries in the inner ear. Yet another evaluates the important power-law exponent. The unique aspect of the theory in regard to testing methods and interpretation of test results is its applicability to the small-signal case where partial masking of a stimulus by internal and/or external noise exists.

ACKNOWLEDGMENT

This research was supported by contract AF 33(616)-7800 between the University of Arizona and Aeronautical Systems Division, Air Force Systems Command. The author is especially grateful to members of the Bio-Acoustics Branch, Aerospace Medical Laboratory, Wright-Patterson Air Force Base, Ohio.

REFERENCES

Egan, J. P. and Meyer, D. R. 1950. Changes in pitch of tones of low frequency as a function of the pattern of excitation produced by a band of noise. J. Acoust. Soc. Am. 22, 827-833.

Frishkopf, L. S. and Rosenblith, W. A. 1958. Fluctuations in neural thresholds. In: Symposium on information theory in biology. Pergamon Press, N.Y.

Geldard, G. A. 1953. The human senses. John Wiley and Sons, N.Y.

Helm, C. E., Messick, S., and Tucker, L. R. 1961. Psychological models for relating discrimination and magnitude estimation scales. Psychol. Rev. 68, 167-177.

Luce, R. D. 1959. On the possible psychophysical laws. Psychol. Rev. 66, 81-95.

Middleton, D. 1960. An introduction to statistical communications theory. McGraw-Hill, N.Y.

Miller, G. A. 1947. Sensitivity to changes in the intensity of white noise and its relation to masking and loudness. J. Acoust. Soc. Am. 19, 607-619.

Miller, G. A. and Licklider, J. C. R. 1950. The intelligibility of interrupted speech. J. Acoust. Soc. Am. 22, 167-173.

Munson, W. A. 1947. The growth of auditory sensation. J. Acoust. Soc. Am. 19, 584-591.

Rice, S. O. 1944 and 1945. Mathematical analysis of random noise. Bell Syst. Tech. J. 23 and 24. Reprinted in Wax, N. (ed.) Noise and stochastic processes. 1954. Dover, N.J.

Schubert, E. D. 1950. The effect of thermal masking noise on the pitch of a pure tone. (abstr.) J. Acoust. Soc. Am. 22, 82.

Shannon, C. E. 1948. A mathematical theory of communication. Bell Syst. Tech. J. 27, 399-423 and 623-656.

Sherrick, C. E., Jr. 1959. Effect of background noise on the auditory intensive difference limen. J. Acoust. Soc. Am. 31, 239-242.

Stevens, S. S. 1959. On the validity of the loudness scale. J. Acoust. Soc. Am. 31, 995-1003.

Stevens, S. S. 1961. Towards a resolution of the Fechner-Thurstone legacy. Psychometrika 26, 35-47.

Stewart, J. L. 1960. Fundamentals of signal theory. McGraw-Hill, N.Y.

Swets, J. A. 1961. Detection theory and psychophysics: a review. Psychometrika 26, 49-63.

Tanner, W. P., Jr. 1960. Theory of signal detectability as an interpretive tool for psychophysical data. J. Acoust. Soc. Am. 32, 1140-1147.

Turin, G. L. 1960. An introduction to matched filters. IRE Trans. Information Theory IT-6, 311-329.

Valley, G. E., Jr. and Wallman, H. (ed.) 1948. Vacuum tube amplifiers. McGraw-Hill, N.Y.

Zwislocki, J. 1960. Theory of temporal auditory summation. J. Acoust. Soc. Am. 32, 1046-1060.

A MATHEMATICAL MODEL FOR VISUAL PERCEPTION

Ming-kuei Hu

Electrical Engineering Department
Syracuse University

INTRODUCTION

The mathematical model for visual perception presented in this paper is a generalization of a simple pattern-recognition model by "moment invariants"* [1]. The pattern-recognition model can identify patterns independently of their position, size, and orientation. The present generalization can perform some other simple human-like functions; it has certain ability to learn, to generalize and to perceive. It learns through a teaching process which consists of a number of simple teaching cycles. Each cycle further consists of three steps: (a) a pattern is shown (visual input), (b) the model's response is observed, (c) if incorrect, the correct name or code is told. By repeating this cycle, association between patterns and names can be established in the model. Specifically, it can learn to do the following:

1. To recognize any geometrical pattern or alphabetical character independently of its position, size, and orientation over a given visual field. For a particular pattern, there are infinitely many possible cases which differ either in position, size, or orientation. Among these cases, only a finite number have to be shown during the teaching process; then the model can generalize to recognize most, if not all, possible cases.
2. To recognize and differentiate between patterns which differ only in position, size, or orientation.
3. To classify a particular pattern into "large" or "small."
4. To perceive "right" and "left" through showing the same "object" at different positions a number of times in the right half or the left half of the sensory field.
5. To recognize and differentiate between the numerals "6" and "9," or the letters "b," "d," "p," "q," in a human-like manner. These can be differentiated independently of position and size, and to a restricted extent in orientation.

MOMENT INVARIANTS AND VISUAL INFORMATION PROCESSING

The two-dimensional $(p+q)$th-order moments of a density distribution function $\rho(x,y)$ are defined in terms of Riemann integrals as

$$m_{pq} = \int_{-\infty}^{\infty}\int_{-\infty}^{\infty} x^p y^q \rho(x,y)\,dx\,dy \qquad p,\ q = 0,\ 1,\ 2,\ldots \tag{1}$$

If it is assumed that $\rho(x,y)$ is a piecewise, continuous, and, therefore, bounded function, and that it can have nonzero values only in the finite part of the xy plane; then there is one and only one $\rho(x,y)$ which can produce the same moments of all orders under the above conditions. In other words, a pattern is completely characterized by all its moments.

The central moments μ_{pq} are defined as

$$\mu_{pq} = \int_{-\infty}^{\infty}\int_{-\infty}^{\infty} (x-\bar{x})^p (y-\bar{y})^q \rho(x,y)\,d(x-\bar{x})\,d(y-\bar{y}) \tag{2}$$

*A systematic study of such moment invariants and their properties, and also of other pattern-recognition models, will appear in a February 1962 special issue of IRE Trans. on Information Theory.

where

$$\bar{x} = m_{10}/m_{00} \qquad \bar{y} = m_{01}/m_{00} \tag{3}$$

It is well known that under the translation of coordinates,

$$x' = x + \alpha \qquad y' = y + \beta \qquad \alpha, \beta \text{ - constants} \tag{4}$$

the central moments are invariants. From (2), it is quite easy to express the central moments in terms of the ordinary moments. For the first four orders, we have

$$\begin{aligned}
&\mu_{00} = m_{00} \equiv \mu \qquad \mu_{10} = \mu_{01} = 0 \\
&\mu_{20} = m_{20} - \mu\bar{x}^2 \qquad \mu_{11} = m_{11} - \mu\bar{x}\bar{y} \qquad \mu_{02} = m_{02} - \mu\bar{y}^2 \\
&\mu_{30} = m_{30} - 3m_{20}\bar{x} + 2\mu\bar{x}^3 \qquad \mu_{21} = m_{21} - m_{20}\bar{y} - 2m_{11}\bar{x} + 2\mu\bar{x}^2\bar{y} \\
&\mu_{12} = m_{12} - m_{02}\bar{x} - 2m_{11}\bar{y} + 2\mu\bar{x}\bar{y}^2 \qquad \mu_{03} = m_{03} - 3m_{02}\bar{y} + 2\mu\bar{y}^3
\end{aligned} \tag{5}$$

Under the similitude transformation, i.e., the change of size,

$$\begin{bmatrix} x' \\ y' \end{bmatrix} = \begin{bmatrix} \alpha & 0 \\ 0 & \alpha \end{bmatrix} \begin{bmatrix} x \\ y \end{bmatrix} \qquad \alpha \text{ - constant} \tag{6}$$

we have

$$\mu' = \alpha^2 \mu \tag{7}$$

and the following similitude moment invariants

$$\frac{\mu'_{pq}}{(\mu')^{(p+q)/2+1}} = \frac{\mu_{pq}}{\mu^{(p+q)/2+1}} \qquad p + q = 2, 3, \ldots \tag{8}$$

Using central moments and the above similitude invariants, pattern identification can easily be accomplished independently of translation and size. The orientation independence is described in the following paragraphs.

Under the following proper orthogonal transformation or rotation,

$$\begin{bmatrix} x' \\ y' \end{bmatrix} = \begin{bmatrix} \cos\theta & \sin\theta \\ -\sin\theta & \cos\theta \end{bmatrix} \begin{bmatrix} x \\ y \end{bmatrix} \qquad \begin{vmatrix} \cos\theta & \sin\theta \\ -\sin\theta & \cos\theta \end{vmatrix} = +1 \tag{9}$$

we obtain, by direct substitution, the relations between the second-order moments

$$\begin{bmatrix} \mu'_{20} \\ \mu'_{11} \\ \mu'_{02} \end{bmatrix} = \begin{bmatrix} \cos^2\theta & 2\cos\theta\sin\theta & \sin^2\theta \\ -\cos\theta\sin\theta & \cos^2\theta - \sin^2\theta & \cos\theta\sin\theta \\ \sin^2\theta & -2\cos\theta\sin\theta & \cos^2\theta \end{bmatrix} \begin{bmatrix} \mu_{20} \\ \mu_{11} \\ \mu_{02} \end{bmatrix} \tag{10}$$

If both sides of (10) are operated upon by the following nonsingular matrix,

$$\begin{bmatrix} 1 & 0 & -1 \\ 0 & 2 & 0 \\ 1 & 0 & 1 \end{bmatrix} \tag{11}$$

we have after simplification

$$\begin{bmatrix} \mu'_{20} - \mu'_{02} \\ 2\mu'_{11} \\ \mu'_{20} + \mu'_{02} \end{bmatrix} = \begin{bmatrix} \cos 2\theta & \sin 2\theta & 0 \\ -\sin 2\theta & \cos 2\theta & 0 \\ 0 & 0 & 1 \end{bmatrix} \begin{bmatrix} \mu_{20} - \mu_{02} \\ 2\mu_{11} \\ \mu_{20} + \mu_{02} \end{bmatrix} \tag{12}$$

There are two ways of using (12) to accomplish pattern identification independently of orientation: (a) The method of principal axes. If the angle θ is determined from the second equation in (12), to make $\mu'_{11} = 0$, we then have

$$\tan 2\theta = \frac{2\mu_{11}}{\mu_{20} - \mu_{02}} \tag{13}$$

The x', y' axes determined by any particular value of θ satisfying (13) are called the principal axes of the pattern. With added restrictions, such as $\mu'_{20} > \mu'_{02}$ and $\mu'_{30} > 0$, θ can be determined uniquely. Moments determined with respect to such a pair of principal axes are independent of orientation. Discussions of certain exceptional cases in which (13) is indeterminate or $\mu'_{30} = 0$ are omitted here. (b) The method of orthogonal moment invariants. Based upon (12), the following two invariant relations can be easily proven:

$$\begin{aligned} \mu'_{20} + \mu'_{02} &= \mu_{20} + \mu_{02} \\ (\mu'_{20} - \mu'_{02})^2 + 4(\mu'_{11})^2 &= (\mu_{20} - \mu_{02})^2 + 4\mu_{11}^2 \end{aligned} \tag{14}$$

These relations can be used directly for orientation-independent pattern identification. For second-order moments, by combining (5), (8), and (14), two moment relations which are invariant under translation, similitude, and rotation can be derived. The simple model to be described is based upon these two invariants only; the numerals "6," "9" or the alphabets "b," "d," "p," "q" cannot be distinguished by this simple model. However, they can be distinguished by using higher order moments and method (a). The value of θ is still determined by (13) but also satisfies the condition $|\theta| < 45°$.

In using method (b), the discrimination property can also be increased by including higher order moment invariants. Similarly, as for the second moments under proper orthogonal transformation, we have for the third moments

$$\begin{bmatrix} \mu'_{30} \\ \mu'_{21} \\ \mu'_{12} \\ \mu'_{03} \end{bmatrix} = \begin{bmatrix} \cos^3\theta & 3\cos^2\theta\sin\theta & 3\cos\theta\sin^2\theta & \sin^3\theta \\ -\cos^2\theta\sin\theta & \cos\theta(\cos^2\theta - 2\sin^2\theta) & -\sin\theta(\sin^2\theta - \cos^2\theta) & \sin^2\theta\cos\theta \\ \cos\theta\sin^2\theta & \sin\theta(\sin^2\theta - 2\cos^2\theta) & \cos\theta(\cos^2\theta - 2\sin^2\theta) & \sin\theta\cos^2\theta \\ -\sin^3\theta & 3\sin^2\theta\cos\theta & -3\sin\theta\cos^2\theta & \cos^3\theta \end{bmatrix} \begin{bmatrix} \mu_{30} \\ \mu_{21} \\ \mu_{12} \\ \mu_{03} \end{bmatrix} \tag{15}$$

If both sides of (15) are operated upon by the following nonsingular matrix,

$$\begin{bmatrix} 1 & 0 & -3 & 0 \\ 0 & 3 & 0 & -1 \\ 1 & 0 & 1 & 0 \\ 0 & 1 & 0 & 1 \end{bmatrix} \tag{16}$$

we have

$$\begin{bmatrix} \mu'_{30} - 3\mu'_{12} \\ 3\mu'_{21} - \mu'_{03} \\ \mu'_{30} + \mu'_{12} \\ \mu'_{21} + \mu'_{03} \end{bmatrix} = \begin{bmatrix} \cos 3\theta & \sin 3\theta & 0 & 0 \\ -\sin 3\theta & \cos 3\theta & 0 & 0 \\ 0 & 0 & \cos\theta & \sin\theta \\ 0 & 0 & -\sin\theta & \cos\theta \end{bmatrix} \begin{bmatrix} \mu_{30} - 3\mu_{12} \\ 3\mu_{21} - \mu_{03} \\ \mu_{30} + \mu_{12} \\ \mu_{21} + \mu_{03} \end{bmatrix} \tag{17}$$

These relations (17) can be used to determine the third-order moments with respect to the principal axes without transforming the input pattern. Based upon (17), we can also derive the following three orthogonal invariants (with only one side of each relation given)

$$(\mu_{30} - 3\mu_{12})^2 + (3\mu_{21} - \mu_{03})^2$$

$$(\mu_{30} + \mu_{12})^2 + (\mu_{21} + \mu_{03})^2$$

and

$$\begin{aligned} &(\mu_{30} - 3\mu_{12})(\mu_{30} + \mu_{12})[(\mu_{30} + \mu_{12})^2 - 3(\mu_{21} + \mu_{03})^2] \\ &+ (3\mu_{21} - \mu_{03})(\mu_{21} + \mu_{03})[3(\mu_{30} + \mu_{12})^2 - (\mu_{21} + \mu_{03})^2] \end{aligned} \tag{18}$$

The invariants given by (14) and (18) are all independent ones; they are invariants not only under proper orthogonal transformation but also under the following improper orthogonal transformation

$$\begin{bmatrix} x' \\ y' \end{bmatrix} = \begin{bmatrix} \cos\theta & \sin\theta \\ \sin\theta & -\cos\theta \end{bmatrix} \begin{bmatrix} x \\ y \end{bmatrix} \qquad \begin{vmatrix} \cos\theta & \sin\theta \\ \sin\theta & -\cos\theta \end{vmatrix} = -1 \tag{19}$$

The expression

$$\begin{aligned} &(3\mu_{21} - \mu_{03})(\mu_{30} + \mu_{12})[(\mu_{30} + \mu_{12})^2 - 3(\mu_{21} + \mu_{03})^2] \\ &- (\mu_{30} - 3\mu_{12})(\mu_{21} + \mu_{03})[3(\mu_{30} + \mu_{12})^2 - (\mu_{21} + \mu_{03})^2] \end{aligned} \tag{20}$$

derived from (17) is also an invariant under proper orthogonal transformation, but it is not an independent one, i.e., there exists an algebraic relation connecting (20) with those given in (18). Expression (20) has another useful property: it changes sign under improper orthogonal transformation. This is useful for distinguishing "mirror images."

Combining second and third moments, one more independent orthogonal invariant can be derived from (12) and (17)

$$(\mu_{20} - \mu_{02})[(\mu_{30} + \mu_{12})^2 - (\mu_{21} + \mu_{03})^2] + 4\mu_{11}(\mu_{30} + \mu_{12})(\mu_{21} + \mu_{03}) \tag{21}$$

All these invariants may be used to increase the discrimination property in method (b). Similarly, higher order orthogonal invariants may be derived.

A SIMPLE PATTERN-RECOGNITION MODEL

A simple pattern-recognition model, using only two moment invariants, may be constructed as follows. No information or properties about the patterns to be recognized are contained in the model itself; it learns to recognize. For a given pattern, the following two moment invariants

$$\begin{aligned} X &= \mu_{20} + \mu_{02} \\ Y &= \sqrt{(\mu_{20} - \mu_{02})^2 + 4\mu_{11}^2} \end{aligned} \tag{22}$$

are computed. The central moments μ_{20}, μ_{11}, μ_{02} used above (normalized with respect to size) are obtained from the ordinary moments by (5). This point (X, Y) in a two-dimensional space is used as a representation of the pattern.

Assume the model has already learned a number of patterns, represented by (X_i, Y_i), $i = 1, 2, \ldots, n$, together with their names. If a new pattern is presented to the model, a new point (X, Y) and the distances

$$d_i = \sqrt{(X - X_i)^2 + (Y - Y_i)^2} \qquad i = 1, 2, \ldots, n \tag{23}$$

between (X, Y) and (X_i, Y_i) are computed. Let the minimum distance $d_{\min}$ be defined as

$$d_{\min} = \min_i d_i \tag{24}$$

The distance d_k satisfying $d_k = d_{\min}$ is selected (if more than one of the distances satisfies the condition, one d_k is selected at random). Then d_k is compared with a preselected recognition level L. (1) If $d_k > L$, the model will not identify by indicating "I do not know," and then wait to learn the name of the new pattern. If a name is now told, the model then stores (X, Y) as (X_{n+1}, Y_{n+1}) together with the assigned name. Hence, a new pattern is learned by the model. (2) If $d_k \leq L$, the model will identify the pattern with (X_k, Y_k) by indicating the name associated.

In this model each pattern, or more correctly, each class of patterns is really represented by a circular region which has the point corresponding to the particular sample learned as the center and L as the radius. If any point corresponding to a particular pattern falls into one of these regions, the pattern will then be identified with that class of patterns. Evidently, such identification is independent of position, size, and orientation. Moreover, because of the use of L, it also allows for other minor variations and a certain amount of noise.

A simulation program of this model has been written for an LGP-30 computer. The visual field used is a 16 by 16 matrix of small squares. A pattern is first projected onto this matrix, then it is digitalized, to the values 0, 2, 4, 6,

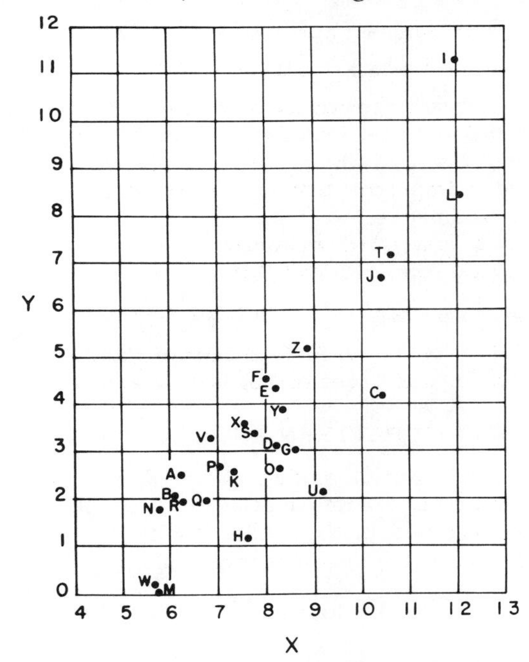

Fig. 1. Point representations of the 26 capital letters.

or 8 for each small square, as the input to the program. The program itself is written according to the description given above.

The program works successfully for a number of geometrical patterns. Twenty-six capital letters from 2-in. Duro Lettering Stencils were also digitalized as inputs to the program. The results, in arbitrary units, are given in Fig. 1; a sample of these inputs is given in Fig. 2. It may be noted that the points for all 26 letters are separated. If digitalized inputs prepared by using the same stencils at different position and orientation are used, the corresponding points are generally not the same as those shown in Fig. 1. For a limited number of cases tried, the maximum variation in terms of distance between two points representing the same letter is of the order of 0.5. Compared with Fig. 1, it is obvious that incorrect identification will occur. The performance may be improved by increasing either the resolution of the visual field, the number of moment invariants used, or both.

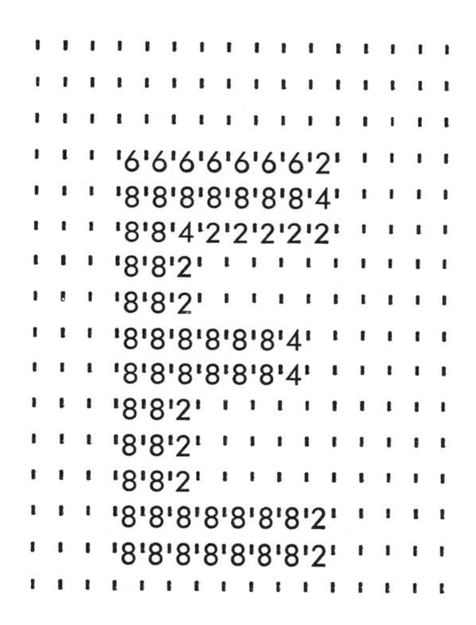

Fig. 2. A digitalized input sample.

In this model, because of the complete orientation-independence property of the moment invariants, it is not possible to distinguish patterns such as "6" and "9." If instead of moment invariants the "principal moments" (i.e., the moments with respect to the principal axes) are used in the model, it is possible to distinguish "6" and "9" with proper determination of the principal axes, as described in the last section.

A MODEL FOR VISUAL PERCEPTION

The pattern-recognition model described in the last section is highly efficient in learning. Once it has learned a given pattern, it can recognize the same pattern at any other position, and in any other size and orientation. This property is inherent in the model; therefore, it can never be taught to differentiate the same pattern at different positions, sizes, and orientations. The following generalization is to remove this limitation and to increase its ability.

In this perception model, the following six quantities are computed for each pattern

$$\mu,\ \bar{x},\ \bar{y},\ \theta,\ \mu'_{20},\ \mu'_{02} \tag{25}$$

Where μ is the total "mass" or "area," it is an indication of the pattern size; $(\bar{x}, \bar{y})$ are the coordinates of the center of gravity, and they give the pattern position; θ is the angle of rotation determined by the auxiliary conditions, $\mu'_{20} > \mu'_{02}$ and $\mu'_{30} > 0$—it may vary from $-\pi$ to $+\pi$ and is an indication of the pattern orientation; μ'_{20} and μ'_{02} are the normalized second-order principal moments—they represent the 'shape' of the pattern. These six quantities will be denoted by $X^1, X^2, \ldots, X^6$ respectively, in the following description. The point $(X) \equiv (X^1, X^2, \ldots, X^6)$ in a six-dimensional space is used as a representation for the pattern.

For each class of patterns, a rectangular recognition region is now used; it is defined by the six linear intervals

$$(X_1^p, X_2^p) \qquad p = 1, 2, \ldots, 6 \tag{26}$$

with

$$\begin{aligned} X_1^p &= \min X^p \\ X_2^p &= \max X^p \end{aligned} \tag{27}$$

where the minimum and maximum are selected from all the samples (of the same class) learned. These 12 numbers, together with the name assigned, are stored for each class of patterns.

As in the last section, assume the model has already learned a number of classes; the corresponding rectangular regions are stored with their names. When a new pattern is presented to the model, a new (X) is computed. If (X) falls inside any one of the rectangular regions, the model then identifies the pattern with the corresponding class by indicating the name associated. If it does not fall inside any of the known regions, the model will indicate this by "I do not know." Now the correct name may be told, and the model will check this name against all the known names. If it is identical to the one already known, the corresponding region is then enlarged according to rule (27); otherwise, a new region (really a point) is formed and stored together with the name just told.

For such a model, it is obvious that it has the ability to learn to differentiate the same pattern at different positions, of different sizes and orientations if different names are given. Each of the rectangular regions is really a single point in this case; identification is by coincidence. On the other hand, if the same pattern is shown many times at different positions, and of different sizes and orientations and giving the same name, it is clear that both μ'_{20} and μ'_{02} will remain unchanged, but the intervals corresponding to μ, $\bar{x}$, $\bar{y}$, and θ will be enlarged as more samples are learned. After such a teaching and learning process, it is likely that the rectangular region is large enough to include most if not all of the points corresponding to the same pattern at different positions, and of different sizes and orientations.

To classify a given pattern into "large" or "small" is done essentially the same way, but now μ is separated into two nonoverlapping classes—the "large" ones fall into one μ-interval and the "small" ones fall into another μ-interval. In the case of perception of "right" and "left," $\bar{x}$ is separated into two classes instead of μ. This can also be extended to the distinction of "vertical" and "horizontal" or a combination of such classifications. Using only the above six quantities is not enough to distinguish 6 and 9. It is necessary to include the four third-order principal moments, μ'_{30}, μ'_{21}, μ'_{12}, and μ'_{03}. Basically, this is still the same, except that more dimensions are involved.

Finally, it is interesting to note that the model may also be modified to increase its learning ability by past experience. As described above, to learn to recognize a pattern, say the letter A, independently of position, size, and orientation, a comparatively large number of samples must be used. Internal to the model, this merely requires an enlargement of the intervals corresponding to

μ, $\overline{x}$, $\overline{y}$ and θ. To learn to recognize another pattern, also independently of position, size, and orientation, the comparatively long teaching process may be replaced by just copying the "intervals" corresponding to μ, $\overline{x}$, $\overline{y}$ and θ of the pattern A for those of the new pattern. The model is told to do this by a code or a statement such as "learn this pattern as the letter A."

ACKNOWLEDGMENT

This work was started as an unsponsored research, and is now supported by Air Force Systems Command, Rome Air Development Center, Griffiss Air Force Base, New York, under Contract No. AF 30(602)-2543.

REFERENCES

1. Hu, M.K. 1961. "Pattern Recognition by Moment Invariants," Correspondence, Proc. IRE, Vol. 49, No. 9, p. 1430, September.

THE SURVIVAL VALUE OF SENSORY PERCEPTION

James J. Gibson

Cornell University, Ithaca, New York

The Modes of Sense

The classical senses, vision, hearing, touch, taste, and smell, were first conceived as the windows of the soul. Later, and even up to the present, they were conceived as distinct channels by which messages were sent to the brain. Each has an obvious and seemingly isolated organ. The simplicity of this scheme began to break up in the nineteenth century. The list of senses had to be extended. Kinaesthesis was added, but it had to include the sense of position of the body as well as of movement. The equilibrium sense was discovered, its organs being part of the inner "ear" or labyrinth. Temperature and pain were added, or else made subdivisions of the skin sense. Touch itself proved to be complex. The senses were classified by Sherrington as exteroceptive, proprioceptive, and interoceptive, but these classes do not now appear to be mutually exclusive.

Instead of a list of sense organs, we must now accept the fact of a complex array of receptive elements grouped into complexes with cross-related functions and structures. There is a structural ear complex and a functional eye-ear complex, for example. Likewise the list of modes of conscious sensations or sense data drawn up by the introspectionists does not seem to stand up, nor does each sense datum neatly correspond with its anatomical receptor.

The Evolution of Receptive Systems

When one studies the evolution of the "senses" in animals, about which a great deal is becoming known, a puzzle appears in that they seem to have evolved not to yield sensations, but perceptions. For example, there is no survival value in being able to distinguish one spectral wavelength from another (pure color), but there is great value in being able to distinguish one pigmented surface from another in variable illumination. Similarly, the distinguishing of pure tones was useless in evolution, although the distinguishing of sounds like those which specify running water, or animal cries, or the vowels of speech were very useful. There was no utility for the chemical senses to identify chemicals, but great utility in identifying the taste or odor of food, species, mate, or young. Until civilized man developed, there was no need for distinguishing geometrical forms, or two-dimensional shapes, but great need for distinguishing different families of perspective transformations, that is, distinguishing objects from one another.

In short, the survival value of the "senses" is found in the ability of animals to register objects, places, events, and other animals; that is, to perceive.

The Supposed Perceptual Process

The question of how sense impressions are converted into perceptions has never been answered. The theories are a hopeless muddle. The controversies over innate ideas, past experience, meaning, constancy, the cues for depth, and the validity of human knowledge are hard to follow. In some respects, men do learn the activity of perceiving, but it is very doubtful that they learn to convert sensations into perceptions.

Perception as a Biological Function

If we turn our attention from men to animals and consider their receptive inputs, we can bypass the anthropomorphic theories. We can suppose that animals register information about their environment by means of "informative" stimuli, that is, those which are specific to their sources in the world. We note that different animals pick up different kinds of stimulus information in accordance with their peculiar way of life. We can assume that the effective stimuli are selected from a flowing array of potential stimulus energies. Thus, we can mean by "sense perception" not just sensation and then perception, but a primitive process which includes all of what we call sensing, knowing, and attending.

It is very doubtful that animals see, hear, touch, smell, and taste as we do. What they can do is select information from the ambient light, sound or mechanical energy, and from certain departures of the medium from its normal composition. The receptive organs become tuned to those stimuli arising from prey or predator, obstacles or shelter, and to the flow of stimulation arising from locomotion or other action. Specifying information can only be conveyed to the receptors by physical energy, of course, but these potential stimuli are better described by the concepts of ecology than those of physics proper. Nevertheless, only physical energies can be stimulus energies. Some animals can detect obstacles by echo-reception but no animal registers "thought waves."

The Information in Stimulation

The information in ambient energy is carried by variables of sequence and arrangement, not simply by variables of intensity or frequency. Unhappily, this makes for difficulty in the quantifying of informative stimuli. The noninformative stimuli for the classical sensations like pure colors and tones and punctate touches or points of light are easy to quantify but meaningless. The relevant stimuli in an array of ambient light, for example, are properties like a gradient in the density of the optical "texture," which is a pattern of patterns and, therefore, something not readily measured in the units of physical optics.

The variables of sequence and arrangement which specify events and objects are *invariant* under the changes of energy which yield the classical sensations.

A Source of Confusion in the Study of Receptive Systems

It is easy to assume that stimuli for the receptors of animals can properly be called *signals* and that the information they carry is *coded* information. A receptive system which carries information about the environment is taken to be analogous to a communication system between men. It is true that we are more familiar with human signals and the coding and decoding of messages than we are with the biology of receptors, but this does not mean that we must interpret the receptive process as a communication process. This commits us to a dubious theory of perception.

I suggest that the receptors of animals are adapted to register *natural* information, not *coded* information. Ordinary stimuli, then, are not signals and the senses do not work by the laws of information transmission that hold for human messages. Men, to be sure, developed a speech code, and later a written code, where the stimuli are arbitrarily related to their objects by convention, but the stimuli for which the senses evolved are related to their objects by laws of ecology, not by convention.

The Tuning of the Receptive Systems

The main problem in understanding sense perception is the mechanism which selects stimulus information out of the vast flux of potential stimulation. The variations in the surrounding sea of energy are piled upon one another and the information is unlimited. In their own ways, animals and men become sensitized to the invariants among these variations, the ones that *specify* or *signify*. The mechanism of selection has to be studied at several different levels:

a. The structure or specialized anatomy of the sense organs for a given species.

b. The maturation or growth of cells in the receptive surface.

c. The development of the adjustments of the sense organs for stimulus exploration. Eye movements, localizing movements, and finger movements depend on neural circuits which enhance the stimulus information for vision, hearing, and touch. This is involuntary attention.

d. The learning of new discriminations. This seems to depend on neural selection in the thalamus and cortex as well as on sense-organ adjustment. It is "voluntary" attention, and it increases sensitivity to abstract variables, small differences, and subtle stimuli. This is what happens when a child learns to distinguish speech sounds.

e. The obtaining of secondhand information by way of words, pictures, and writing. This is truly mediated perception, or comprehension at the most complex level. At this stage we can properly speak of the stimuli as being signals or constituting messages, and, hence, must consider the phenomenon of coding.

A COMPUTER SIMULATION OF PATTERN PERCEPTION AND CONCEPT FORMATION

Charles Vossler

System Development Corporation, Santa Monica, California

and

Leonard Uhr

University of Michigan, Ann Arbor, Michigan

The Organism and Its Environment

Living organisms manage to survive as entities, in a complex environment which continually threatens their disintegration, by their knowledge of this environment, and by their ability to use this knowledge to maintain their own existence. Unlike a stone, whose passive existence is simply the result of its own hardness, and of the fact that few natural forces tend to change it, living organisms, including man, must actively seek certain stable conditions under which their continued existence is possible.

Man's knowledge of the environment and his ability to exploit this knowledge is indeed staggering. How then are we to simulate, for example, on a digital computer, this sort of complex behavior which we describe by the word "intelligent"?

If we consider any particular fact about the external world which is known to an organism, it seems clear that this "knowledge" could only have been acquired by the organism in one of two ways. Either (1) the organism was born with this knowledge, i.e., it was inherited or (2) the knowledge was derived or extracted from the continuing stream of information about the environment entering the organism through its various senses. It seems clear that there is no need to include in the program any knowledge which the machine can derive from its own senses. What must be included in the program are (1) the basic drives and abilities which allow the machine to organize and make use of the incoming flow of information, and (2) any knowledge about the organization of the information which is not implicit within the stream of information itself.

If the stream of information coming to an organism were completely random, then by definition the organism could never come to know anything about this information, that is, it could never learn to predict anything about what would occur next in the input. Similarly, if the information coming from the environment were some completely efficient, nonredundant encoding of relationships existing in the environment, then the organism could learn to understand the environment only if somehow it knew from the beginning what this encoding was. For the fact that the encoding is nonredundant precludes the possibility that the organism could ever learn it; even if by random trial and error it happened onto the correct encoding, it would never have any way of knowing that this was indeed correct.

However, the information coming from the environment to actual living organisms is highly redundant, and this redundancy now at least allows the possibility that the organism can come to learn something about the organization of the information and, hence, about the organization of the environment from which the information is coming, even though originally it knew nothing about this environment. It is this fact, that the organization of information in any sequence of information coming from the real world is to an overwhelming extent implied within the sequence of information itself, that allows us to conclude that the program for an intelligent machine, that is, the knowledge which we must give the machine by preprogramming, may be quite small.

This indicates a special kind of "pattern-discovery" computer that appears to be capable of rather efficient learning over a wide range of problems. The computer, like a living organism, is embedded in a larger system (the "external world"). It is capable of being aware of, and of coming to "know" this world only as the world acts upon its set of input-sensing devices. These sensing devices, then, bombard the computer with several continuing streams of changing values.

The computer discovers, and it discovers *how* to discover, information from the undefined stream of stimuli impinging upon it from the external world. We might think of this as learning to sift the information-bearing aspects from the noise. It is this information that structures the computer's abilities. On the basis of this information itself, the computer learns how to organize and use this information in a continuing process of learning by induction from experience. We might think of this as the patterning or structuring of meaning. This appears to apply not merely to the perceptual processing of inputs by the computer, but to the entire flow of utilization of these inputs by the resultant structure. That is, through these learning processes the computer builds up structures that seem to be sufficient for the entire patterning of its behavior, from the cognitive transformations that we typically label "concept formation" and "problem-solving," to the sequences of response acts that are triggered off by the results of these transformations in the computer's attempts to serve its purposes—to do whatever it has figured out it ought to do.

The computer appears to be capable of learning at least something toward the solution of any problem about which the external world gives any information. That is, unless the flow of bits from the external world is either random or irrelevant (unrelated) to the problem, the computer will discover ways of capturing and making use of pertinent information in this flow. It is thus, for example, capable of learning to recognize sensory patterns, such as alphabets, pictures, and spoken words; natural language patterns, such as grammatical sentences, phrases, and parts of speech; and patterns in strings of recurring symbols, such as algebraic expressions, graphs, and sequential decisions. It further learns, as a part of each problem, the patterns of making appropriate use of the information that it has learned and structured. Thus, for example, it will answer questions posed to it in natural language, or continue a line of discussion with a string of subsequent sentences that develop a theme or suggest pertinent facts or new ways of looking at the question, or it will translate the sentence into an equivalent sentence in some other language that it has learned. Thus, if its problem domain has been games, it will try to make good moves in response to its opponent's moves.

The Model

We propose, then, that an intelligent machine should have the following abilities: (1) the ability to sense the environment; (2) the ability to act upon the environment by means of effectors; (3) the ability to search for redundant patterns within some preprogrammed limits of possible search mechanisms; (4) the ability to form concepts, by grouping symbols or structures of symbols into various equivalence classes, again, within preprogrammed limits on possible rules for forming classes; and (5) the ability to store and make use of symbols and relationships between symbols, where these symbols now include both the basic input symbols and symbols which are the names of any classes the machine can recognize.

The control of the program would be through a system of feedback operating within and between the various levels of the program's activity, directing the search for patterns, the formation of concepts, and the storing of information. Ultimately, the motivating force providing this feedback might simply be the result of an attempt by the program to optimize its ability to predict its input sequence, coupled perhaps with certain other basic drives.

If we consider the computer as having several sense modalities, each of which is being fed a stream of symbols following each other in time, we can see that the computer can initially express, or work with, only simple relations between these symbols. These relationships are of the sort: $R1$, a symbol in sense modality m occurring at the same time as a symbol in sense modality n; or $R2$, a symbol in sense modality m at time t, followed by a symbol in the same modality at time $t+n$. With these relationships the program can express information like $A\ R1\ C$, meaning, for example, that an A in one sense modality occurred at the same time as a C in some other modality.

However, to the extent that the program can group symbols or structures of symbols into classes, it can express more complex relationships between the incoming stream of symbols. Thus, if it can recognize nouns and verbs in a sequence of English words, it can express a relationship like *MAN R27 EATS*, where *R27* might now mean something like a particular noun in relation to the first verb which follows it.

The formation of the first classes allows the computer to describe the input in more detail, and allows it, so to speak, to gain a foothold which it can then use to climb higher.

A few specific algorithms by which a computer might search for patterns may help to illustrate the model.

1. Assume the input to be a single sequence of some set of symbols, e.g., the letters of the alphabet. The computer knows nothing about these symbols, but knows the order in which they are fed in, i.e., that C follows A and B follows C in the sequence ACB . . . , and can distinguish one symbol from another.

An algorithm by which the computer might search for redundant patterns might be as follows: "Store all connected sequences of symbols which have occurred more than once, and store the number of times each sequence has occurred. When a new sequence is composed of already stored sequences, define it in terms of this concatenation of shorter sequences."

If the input to the computer is some written English text, then it is clear that the computer will have stored in memory all words in the text which have occurred more than once. The more frequent words like *bTHEb* (here *b* stands for the symbol for blank) will have high-frequency counts, as will also strings like *INGb* and *bUN*.

If now the computer attempts to determine some rule by which it can predict other strings which as yet have not repeated, but which are likely to repeat, it can find that the rule, "store any sequence in the input having the form, a blank followed by a sequence of symbols not containing a blank followed by a blank," will predict a large number of the repeated strings. The formation of this concept of a word is a pattern-recognition problem and once it has formed this concept it no longer sees the input simply as a sequence of letters, but also as a sequence of words. That is, it has a new unit composed of words which it can use to describe what is going on in the input sequence.

2. Suppose we wish the program to recognize patterns in a 20 by 20 matrix of 0's and 1's, but for some reason instead of preprogramming the computer to recognize a matrix as a basic structure, we let the computer determine this

structure of the information for itself. Let us say that we are feeding into the computer many examples of hand-printed characters, as follows: we feed in the first row of twenty bits for the first character, then the second row for the same character, and so on until the twentieth row. This is then followed by the first row of the next character, and so on. The computer then sees only a one dimensional string of 0's and 1's.

In this case an efficient algorithm by which the computer can reconstruct the connectivity of the original matrix is as follows: "Using each symbol as a starting point, determine the conditional probability of other symbols at fixed distances from the starting point." If the inputs are the hand-printed characters described above then the computer will find that the conditional probability of a 1 occurring at distances of ±1 is higher if the symbol at the starting point is 1 than if it is zero. It will also find that this probability drops off as the distance increases, until the distance is close to ±20, at which point it increases again. From this information the program can reconstruct the original two-dimensional connectivity of the input sequence. (It seems clear that the human brain does not have to go to all this trouble in this particular case, since the visual image on the retina is mapped in its two-dimensional form onto the visual cortex.)

3. Let us assume that the computer has two input channels, into one of which is coming a sequence of words in English, and into the other a sequence of words in Russian. These come into the computer in the form of a pair of sentences describing the same thing, or, equivalently, in the form of a Russian sentence and its English translation. Let us assume that initially the computer can recognize the beginning and end of sentences in each language and can distinguish the individual words in each language.

The program can now begin to learn the equivalents in the two languages in the following way. It first stores, as tentative equivalents, any words which occur at the beginning of the sentences in the two languages and words which occur at the end of the sentences. It also tentatively stores as equivalents any words which either precede or succeed any word which is identical in the two languages (for example, dates like 1835 or 1950 may be identical). These first attempts at forming equivalents may often be wrong, but to the extent that they are correct, they will be reinforced by further occurrences of the same pairs of words. As soon as some of the more frequent words in the two languages have been established as equivalents, these serve as tags in the two languages, and allow the computer to, so to speak, line up the words in the middle of the two sentences, even though the sentences are of different length. This begins to allow the computer to discover, in addition, that pairs of words in one language are associated with single words in the other, and eventually as more and more is learned about the two languages, the computer will become able to associate words, even though the word order is different in the two languages. In fact, determination of the word order in one language from the word order in the other becomes a new problem for the computer.

It is easy to see that if languages were more "efficient" codes, this method of learning to translate from one to the other world be just that much more difficult. It is precisely the redundancy within each language, and the redundancy between the "languages" of the different senses which allows the computer to learn a language or to learn the translation from the language of one sense to that of the other.

The Model as a Generalization of Visual Perception

We have tried to describe a computer that discovers how to extract patterns (or we might say meaningful information) from the world external to it—patterns that are of significance (or we might say of "meaning") to the model. Further, it then makes use of its new abilities, improving upon them as necessary, in its continuing attempts to cope with the external world. This, then, is a model that learns how to be an information-processing system: how to input the appropriate information (and prior to that, what the appropriate information, in fact, is); how to make appropriate use of this information (in restructuring and enriching its memory, in effecting the suggested transformations); how to act appropriately (in making decisions and, through responses that impinge upon the external world, "behaving" in such a way as to affect that world); and how to learn, through reinforcement and other feedbacks (both internal and external) to its responses, to improve upon itself.

We have developed this model with the human brain—its achievements, its functions, its behavior, its introspections, its structure, and its microstructure—in mind. We began with the problem of visual form perception in the human being. Here the over-all fit of model to observation seems reasonably good. From what is known about the visual nervous system, the model looks as plausible as any (more so, we would argue). It is a simplified model, so that it cannot handle a great number of the things (such as color, depth, and even many of the linear transformations) that the human visual system can handle, but we think we know how to build these in, in an organic way. On the other hand, the model is quite general within its domain, and predicts a good deal in the way of fine details of behavior that we would want to compare with human behavior. It also shows a certain tendency to do better than human beings. This is a tendency that we haven't taken too seriously, at least until very recently. For we assumed that once we had fit this quite broad model to the specifics of the human particular, and, more important, began to insist that this model serve as a subpart of a coordinated cognitive system, its abilities would be sufficiently reduced and limited in "natural" ways, that is, limited as a natural and inevitable function of the larger network of variables now involved in the total system.

We had always hoped that a model of perceptual learning would serve as a basis for a more complete model of cognitive processes, since the categories and concepts learned as a function of the organism's experiences in perceiving and coming to know the world would seem to be the inevitable, necessary, and possibly sufficient structure onto which even "higher" cognitive processes are subsequently built. But we appear to have found that, merely in the generalizing and strengthening of the perceptual-learning model alone, we can construct an organism that appears to be capable of the complete gamut of what have been called "cognitive processes" or "intelligent behavior."

From the standpoint of psychology, we suddenly find ourselves with a model for a whole encyclopedia of data that doesn't exist. This is a true embarrassment of riches, for the following reasons. First, this model appears to be a relatively efficient solution to the problem: given a completely unknown universe, one that continues indefinitely over all directions (in our instance this means, apparently, physical space and time), how can an organism that begins by knowing nothing come to knowledge (upon which it can act appropriately) about this universe through the particular experiences available to it? The model structures itself into as direct and efficient a function of the reality whose purpose it is to process as it is capable of finding. Thus, we take it to be serving the same set of functions as nature's living organisms. That is, evolution and learning in living organisms is a search for better functional systems, given the problem of coping with the universe as it manifests itself to the particular organism. Our model does the same. If, as we suspect, the model does this job more efficiently than the human brain, we take this to mean that the model is closer to the upper limit, closer to the most efficient possible system, that is, closer to the brain of tomorrow than to the brain of today. But this also makes it closer to the model that we really desire—the completely abstracted physical model of the perfect system, as opposed to the engineering model of a buildable, necessarily defective, system. We assume again that the study of such a model, with specific particularities—leading to defects—abstracted out, is the way to go about theory building and testing in psychology. That is, it should be relatively easy to spot the particular defects, particularities, and contingencies in specific human embodiments of general principles of information discovery, induction, organization, and utilization. We typically find the course of science one of painful gathering and abstracting of pertinent information about empirical particulars, painfully leading toward the essential underlying theory. We suggest that the computer may give psychology a shorter path to theory. This is because living organisms are "alive" in that they are searching to satisfy their purposes. The organism's problem, then, and his data (experience) are both clearly defined and accessible to the computer. The computer can now compute for us the efficient functions, simulating both built-in structure and learning.

We are asserting, thus, that the present model may be, in fact, a general model of what the human brain is nature's best approximation toward, as of 1961 on earth. This, by the way, seems to lead to the conclusion that the best way to study the brain is to study the structure of the world with which it must cope. This is *not* saying the best method is to study perception. It is rather saying that the best way would be to study the meaningful (that is, meaningful in the sense of information-carrying with respect to the organism in question) aspects of the external world. Thus, we may also be suggesting that psychology becomes the study of structure of the universe, in the sense of specific organisms learning about what can be done about this structure that appears functional to them. It thus falls on a continuum with physics, which studies the structure of the universe and its repercussions on specific entities (to the extent that these entities do not become modified in the sense that if they were put in the same situation once again they would behave differently). Psychology studies those things that have a purpose, that of fitting in better with the brute world around them, or, to use what we think is a more appropriate term, that of "knowing."

The problem that is posed in visual perception is the following: Given a set of two-dimensional matrices, design a computer that will *learn* to partition this set into the subsets denoted by a smaller set of proper names. Here we want to give the computer basic abilities that are plausible from the point of view of living visual systems, and ask it to give proper names across variants that are again plausibly related one to another. That is, we want this computer to be a model of the human visual system as it performs the many-to-one operation of mapping specific instances of patterns into general classes. For example, we *don't* want the computer to do an exhaustive "best" statistical analysis on some exhaustively large set of "all possible" independent measures. This would be completely implausible as a model for living organisms. For example, it would ask for far too much memory, computational ability, and precision, and would, in any case, take far too much time to do something that the living eye does quite quickly. We *don't* want the computer to learn names for arbitrary unrelated classes, e.g., some set of randomly generated patterns to which we assign the same name. We want a model that will do the same combining—form the same perceptual and conceptual classes—as the living brain.

The basic problem method that is suggested for processing any patterns is as follows. Assume there is some sequence of bits that the program should learn to associate with some other sequence of bits. Normally, this will be some name that the program must learn to associate with some pattern of bits. So, for the present we will use the words "name" and "pattern," although we will really be talking about two sequences of bits in some association one to another. Later we will suggest how these sequences might well be given interpretations that are rather different-looking on the surface. For example, the sequence of bits that we have called "name" might be interpreted as a future action, or sequence of actions. That is, as a string of numbers upon which the program's subsequent behavior depends. The sequence of bits that we called "pattern" might be a spoken sound, or a sentence of words, or the description (which some subroutine of the program, itself a built-up pattern of bits, will follow at some appropriate point) of a set of transformations that might map a sentence from one language to another, or might symbolize a sequence of interrelated patterns (describe an event, or a scene).

Thus, we are really treating "name" and "pattern" themselves in exactly the same way. What we have is a string of bits that has somehow been partitioned from the continuing stream of bits. There is some reason for this particular string to have been specified, and this reason is known to the program through the other strings of bits to which this string is related. Thus, for example, a "name" string is known by the "pattern" string to which it refers, an "action-producing string" is "known" by the sequence of events that it produces. We have, then, strings or structures of bits that characterize one another.

In the visual pattern-recognition problem, the interrelations between these structures are fixed. A pattern is a set of wholes over their unknown, but admissable, transformations. A characteristic is some subpart of wholes that carries some sufficiently useful piece of information about the patterns that it characterizes. The pattern-recognition problem is the problem of finding some suitably small, or suitably cheap, or suitably simple, or suitably plausible set of characteristics.

We are talking, then, about characterizing strings of bits by other strings of bits. All of these strings come from the stream of experience. This stream of its own experiences includes all of the data available to any organism. The organism must itself learn what strings of bits are the patterns.

Results with a Specific Pattern-Recognition Program

We have tested a pattern-recognition program that is a very weak simulation of a computer of this sort. This program has a method for discovery of redundancies within arbitrarily preprogrammed limitations. (These limitations were in the direction of modeling living visual systems. We conjectured that sufficiently powerful information about patterns—information that could later be used effectively to characterize unknown patterns—could be discovered by simulations of local neural nets, nets of the sort that appear to be present in iterated form throughout the retina.) The program has no method for interrelating these characteristics, but rather treats them as separate parallel measures. It is also very limited in its inductive abilities to build up general concepts of patterns in its memory, or to accumulate information as to the value and relevance of a measure. For example, it can make only a 1-bit weighting of a characteristic. Thus, this program has been rather grossly simplified in order to make it run efficiently on a sequential computer, when in fact it is a simulation of a relatively simple parallel computer of a different sort. Thus, the appropriate computer should work appreciably better.

Despite these simplifications the program appears to give surprisingly good results. Since it has no preanalyzed and preprogrammed characterizers or measures, it is capable of at least attempting to learn to recognize any set of patterns presented to it.

A typical experiment with the program consists of making a number of passes through a given array of patterns. Some of these patterns are "known" patterns which provide the training experience for the program by giving the program the correct name of the pattern after each attempted identification, allowing it to then make appropriate adjustments. Others are "unknown" patterns, which the program attempts to identify. These do not contain the pattern name as feedback to the program and are used simply to test the program's ability.

Runs were made using 5-, 10-, and 26-letter arrays of hand-printed characters. In each of these runs, the program obtained 100% recognition of the known patterns. For the 10-letter array, the program also achieved 100% recognition of an unknown set of the 10 letters after three passes through the training patterns, and for the 26-letter array it obtained 96% recognition of an unknown set of 26 after six training passes.

Using four known sets and one unknown set of five separate handwritten, instead of hand-printed, characters written by five different people, the program reached 100% recognition of the known patterns and 60% recognition of the unknown patterns in four passes. In this case it would appear that the four examples of known patterns did not provide enough information on the possible variations of handwritten characters to allow the program to recognize all characters in the unknown set, and that training with more known examples would improve the recognition rate on the unknown patterns.

To test the program with pictorial information, five different examples of each of five cartoon strip characters and pictures of five simple objects (trees, pliers, shoes, pots and pans, and brushes) were transferred into the 20 by 20 input-matrix format. With these degraded pictures the program reached 95% success on the four known sets and 70% on the unknown set on the fifth pass.

We have also coded a first version of a segmentation procedure that allows the program to attempt to handle continuous inputs. Here our first tests gave 100% success in learning to identify the individual letters in a single example of the words "pattern one" after several passes through the input. When tested on two examples each of the words "pattern one," "pattern two," and "pattern three," the program did rather poorly, although it still identified the individual letters with considerably better than chance accuracy. It seems that in recognition tasks such as this, context becomes of increasing importance. That is, the program should learn such things as the fact that what occurs in "patt—n" is more likely to be "er" than "w," things which to us are quite "obvious." But this is simply pattern recognition on a different level.

It is difficult to evaluate results such as these, since there are no good standards for comparison with anything. That is, we don't really know what some percent-success rate means until we know what our test is, or what our measuring stick is, or what our standard is.

More interesting, then, are results we have gotten with sets of "meaningless" patterns that we have used to test both the program and groups of human subjects. Here we have tried a number of conditions on our own, and we have replicated three experiments reported in the psychological literature. In all cases the program has done appreciably better than have human subjects. Of similar relevance, we tested the program on some speech inputs (the spoken numbers "zero" through "nine"), which we were able to get into our input format only by severly degrading the original spectrograms (we had to recode speech into an 18 by 20 matrix, in which each sample of the intensity of the sound wave could take on only one of two intensities, either zero or one). The program learned the "known" sets to 100% correct responses. It learned the "unknowns" to 100% for a five-word alphabet, and to 90% for a ten-word alphabet. The most interesting aspect of this test is that when we asked one of the country's outstanding experts at reading spectrograms to identify these patterns, he made seven mistakes; the program had made two. Finally, the program achieved 100% success in segmenting and recognizing continuous speech inputs consisting of four different words, as spoken by different speakers.

It is still necessary to subject programs of this sort to well-designed experimental tests in which the various aspects of their abilities and defects are clearly spotlighted. For the present, however, we would argue that the results of our comparisons of program and human in both meaningless pattern and speech recognition suggest that programs of this sort may already be performing their basic task—recognizing underlying patterns across variants, an extremely important type of concept formation—at a level that surpasses that of the human being.

Pattern Recognition in Language

The name "pattern recognition" has typically been used for sensory patterns of the sort the program we have just described handles. A program we have just finished planning, and expect to have running on the computer in the next week or so, is, essentially, another oversimplified embodiment of the same general discovery and induction computer. This, however, is a program whose inputs are languages. We wanted to get a feeling for what we took to be the opposite extreme of the general problem we have been attacking, the building of an organism that would begin to learn the way a human being learns: first sensing patterns; later organizing these into regularities of the sort we might call "concepts" and "objects"; and then learning symbols that refer to, and through which we can communicate about and manipulate, those things symbolized. However, we soon came to the conclusion that the problem of the learning of language was essentially the same as the problem of pattern recognition. In fact, the chief and rather inconsequential difference appears to lie in the differences in the format of presentation; that is, in the differences in the ways that these patterns are strung out. Sensory patterns are typically self-contained, so that all of the pertinent information lies within the individual letter; therefore, the measures or characteristics that should be noted by a recognizing computer should obviously come from within the pattern. On the contrary, much of the information about words, syntax, and meanings is contained outside the word itself, but the basic situation is identical. There must always be a network of structures, patterns (the symbols or strings we have discussed above), and interrelations between these patterns. Each of these structures is characterized by those other structures that are related to it. In the case of letters, the convention is to say that the letter "A" is characterized by its measures or properties, but we might just as well say that the patterns that characterize the letter A are themselves characterized by the pattern "A." That is, we arbitrarily designate some set of these structures as the set of patterns in which we are interested, and then the structure of these patterns' relation determines the structure of information that might fruitfully be collected in order to make cogent inferences as to the likelihood of the presence of the structure (designated pattern) in which we are especially interested. It turns out that as soon as we begin to define the basic unit in the language program as a single bit, rather than a letter (the six-bit hollerith character), we have a sensory-pattern-recognition program that should be appreciably more powerful than the program we have already written. It will, in fact, be quite similar in over-all method, but it will be able to make a much more powerful search for measures, will build up equivalence sets of measures, and will retain important topological information as to the interrelations between measures information that the original program threw away.

Thus, the general pattern-discovery and self-construction method builds an internal structure into the computer that is the computer's best induction as to what the structure of reality, or of those aspects of reality in which it is interested, seems to be.

The language program will take strings of symbols (which might be words in some natural language, or symbols in some mathematical or other artificial language) and try to predict what will come next on the string. This means, for example, that it will try to finish an as yet unfinished sentence, it will try to give the next sentence (so that, in the special case where the first sentence is a question it will try to give the answer), and it will try to give the equivalent sentence in another language. For this language translation task, we merely give it two strings of symbols in what should be considered a two-dimensional matrix, two rows high. The program's problem then becomes that of predicting both along the same row (along the string of the same language) and also predicting the *other* row in the matrix (translating).

In all of these modes of operation, the program must learn everything from its experiences with the external world. That is, it receives only strings of words in sentences, and pairs of sentences, in any two languages the experimenter can find or cook up.

Several very interesting pairs of languages, other than pairs of natural languages like French and English, or Chinese and German, present themselves. One is the string of words in some natural language such as English paired with the string of pictures in some sensory-input sequence such as vision.

A second is a set of objects as characterized by one pattern-recognition program and the same set of symbols as characterized by a second pattern-recognition program. We can now think of the first program as the eye, and the second as the ear or the hand. We can further think of the first program as the perceiver and the second program as the responder (that is, the program that draws out symbols that will be suitable inputs for some perceiver program, including the responder's own perceiver program). Here we have given our original pattern-recognition program some simple abilities to respond, in this case to draw the patterns and logical combinations of patterns in its memory. This was a very easy thing to ask the program to do, since we merely have it use its perceiver—the characterization lists it has built up in order to correctly identify new examples of patterns—as its responder, simply drawing characteristics back into its own input matrix. It can now try to recognize what it has just drawn, and, on the basis of its own musings over the situation, improve upon its own drawing abilities. Here, then, we make a translation from one pattern-recognition program to itself, but ask the program to now start learning an additional set of skills that will retain information that the program could safely throw away when it was confronted with only the recognition problem, as opposed to the reconstruction problem. This should become a quite realistic and nontrivial sensory-response system as soon as we ask it to act with a different set of operators. For example, to model a living organism we want it to do something like move a muscle that is holding a pencil. Essentially, though, all we would be asking is that it translate the information that one set of characterizers (for example, our 5 by 5 nerve nets, or some other program's n-tuple or templates) uses to describe and, hence, infer a pattern into a description that is couched in the basic symbols of some second set of characterizers (in the case of muscle-movers, something more like the geometric characterizations that would be given by a curve following program).

Finally, we can already see what are commonly named the "central" or "cognitive" processes building up, in a rather natural way, between sensory input and response mechanisms, given such a program. When strings of words connected in sentences are being learned in association with strings of objects connected in action sequences, the complex structures of symbol interrelations and transformations are being learned. When a program senses, recognizes, recognizes across a next-higher general class (as, for example, a symbol denoting some transformation, say an arrow or a plus sign), combines several recognized entities (thus giving either a string of pencil strokes, or a pair of words, or a transformation on a pattern, e.g., a rotation of a straight line or an addition of the letter s to the end of a word, changing it to the plural form), makes the resulting response, and then performs the same pattern-recognition sequence on the feedback input, which is itself a pattern, such a program is doing a great variety of things indeed, all elaborating on the basic theme of relating structures. We can think of this roughly as sensory pattern recognition exemplifying the problem in its most compact form. Strings of symbols like languages extend the pattern over some space. Transformations of symbols similarly string the symbols, but usually with a more explicit sequential structure. However, this emphasis on a new aspect of pattern, the patterning across sequentially ordered structures, would seem to be the only difference between the program and what we commonly call "problem solving." Games would seem to present an especially well-ordered abstraction from the real-life sequence of action and reaction in a well-defined domain. In a game, the pattern and the problem are made unusually clear. The rules for transformation and for moments in time are simplified to their extremes. Long sequences of action must be learned, and complex concepts of interrelated patterns must be built up. However, the basic unit of action-reaction would seem to be identical to the basic unit of the pattern-recognition program drawing, a second program recognizing and drawing its response, and so on in this circle.

Conclusion

We have tried to outline, and to discuss very briefly, a method whereby a suitable computer could discover patterns and build itself inductively into an efficient structure for storing these patterns and the important information about them. This appears to be a generally applicable method. Thus, the visual and auditory pattern-recognition program we have tested on a digital computer is one grossly simplified embodiment of the computer. A language-learning program that we are now coding to see how well it develops grammatical structures, predicts sentences, answers questions, and translates between two foreign languages is another. The language-learning program is, in fact, exactly like the pattern-recognition program, except that it has a few more abilities.

We conjecture that such a computer is the necessary and sufficient requirement for intelligent behavior. We further think it may be possible to say something relatively precise as to the likelihood of such a computer arising in a physical universe. We also suggest that living brains are more or less imperfect embodiments of organisms that follow general principles of the sort that we have outlined, principles that follow directly from the structure of the physical universe in which such computers find themselves.

REFERENCES

Uhr, L. and Vossler, C. 1961. Computer simulations of a model for form perception. SP-472. System Develop. Corp.

Uhr, L. and Vossler, C. 1961. A pattern-recognition program that generates, evaluates, and adjusts its own operators. Proc. Western Joint Computer Conf. 19, 555-569.

Uhr, L. and Vossler, C. 1961. Recognition of speech by a computer program that was written to simulate a model for human visual recognition. J. Acoust. Soc. Am. (in press).

Uhr, L. and Vossler, C. 1961. Suggestions for self-adapting computer models of brain functions. Behav. Sci. 6, 91-97.

Uhr, L. 1962. Pattern recognition computers as models for form perception. Psychol. Bull. (in press).

AN ASSOCIATIVE MACHINE FOR DEALING WITH THE VISUAL FIELD AND SOME OF ITS BIOLOGICAL IMPLICATIONS

Harry Blum

Electronics Research Directorate
Air Force Cambridge Research Laboratories
Bedford, Massachusetts

The present state of the field dealing with the understanding and performing of mental activity is largely the outgrowth of the mathematical insights produced by a century or so of developments in formalistic logic and probability theory. Their success in dealing with certain aspects of mental activity, and the ability of the neuron to implement the required mathematics, has given a tremendous impetus to investigation in this field. Yet, our ability to understand and perform artificially the intuitive, associative, and related processes has not passed beyond the elementary level. Therefore, the work described went back to the biological system to see whether alternative mechanisms could not be derived—mechanisms which would simulate these aspects of mental activity better than the classical methods. A specific mechanism for the processing of line visual data was derived. It has broad implications to the whole field of bionics.

The process uses a space with the point properties of a rudimentary neuron. It simplifies visual pattern recognition by transforming a line spatial pattern into a temporal one. The transformation has important invariances and pattern properties. The temporal pattern is then transmitted through a volume of association elements which are conceptually optimum filters. These filters, when excited, also transmit in the time domain. A highly parallel access to a large volume of association elements is thus facilitated. A system results with a stronger basic operation than that of classical systems since information that is gathered anywhere in the system is available everywhere. Problems introduced by such systems and their possible solutions are discussed. Biological implication and possible implementations conclude the paper.

INTRODUCTION

There is a considerable body of work aimed at understanding and performing recognition and related associative aspects of intelligent activity. This work straddles a broad set of scientific and philosophical disciplines. By and large, however, it bears the stamp of the insights of the last century or two of work in formalistic logic and probability theory. The ability of these fields to shed light on some aspects of mental activity and the ease with which neurons and neuron nets can implement the necessary mathematics have given tremendous impetus to the application of these tools to the associative problems. Yet neither our understanding of recognition, nor our ability to perform recognition artificially, has progressed beyond elementary levels. While these mathematical tools are strong ones, they might not, in their present state, supply the needed insight.

The approach, of which this paper is the result, comes from going back to a primitive machine symbology in order to avoid being limited by the mathematical tools of today. It attempts, with physical components, to build a system that would solve the fundamental problem in a way that is tractable. Since the field of biology gives examples of such systems, the elements of the machine were chosen from idealizations of the components available there. The question asked was, "Are there any machine organizations and/or architectures whose resemblances to biological systems at the most fundamental level are better than the computer and logical nets?" These resemblances should be judged by our experience with the biological system through all the fields that illuminate that system. Clearly, in outlining the architecture of such a system, the details of the structural technique have had to be eliminated, except for the verification that they were feasible. This lack represents an obvious failure of the work. It would have been impossible, however, to consider the structure as a whole, while at the same time trying to fill in all the details. The paper, therefore, weaves a thread between a variety of disciplines, trying to come to a model whose fundamental properties would be capable of satisfying criteria which appear to be primary to a reasonable degree from all these viewpoints. Such criteria include things like basic reliability, ability to deal with complex environment, and ability to recognize events. These will be discussed in the following sections. This machine is the result of a truly bionic approach, and it will be apparent in the paper.

It is indeed surprising, in the light of the complexity that must be added to presently fashionable mechanisms, that a naive approach which stressed simplicity could produce any capability. Yet this one has some surprising capabilities for breaking down the recognition and association process, and should serve at least as a parable. The concepts were formed before the author knew of the new graded-response neuron concepts (Bullock, 1959). There was something that appeared very potent about the proposed mechanism, and the appearance of the new neuron concepts gave support to its possible relevance to the biology of the central nervous system. It should be stated emphatically that this paper describes what may be a, rather than the, relevant mechanism. It would indeed be foolhardy to propose the latter in the light of the host of interacting mechanisms that in all probability exists there.

APPROACH

The key to an unresolved problem often exists in changing the questions asked. To do this one must look anew at the problem. Since the model is the result of such a process and the questions and viewpoint raised may be as important as the model, a review of this viewpoint is indicated. The existing biological knowledge is exceedingly complex and it will be necessary to simplify the problem drastically if any insights into processes are to be gathered. This must be done mercilessly and carefully to arrive at manipulatable concepts and to assure that crucial parts of the problem are not removed. This section gives the specific rationale by which the concept was arrived at. The machine does not depend on it, however, and this section can be scanned by readers not concerned with the rationale.

It is clear that cognitive systems start with sensory data. We will consequently start there and see whether progress can be made toward what is probably the more crucial problem—the nature of the central associative mechanism. The vast amount of incoming sensory data and the large number of effectors that exist in higher biological systems require a mechanism that by its make-up can deal with the complexity associated with processing and comparing the incoming information with a large memory. Different sensors assemble information in entirely different places, yet relevant information, when simultaneous, gets together. Some mechanism is likely to exist that by its basic make-up could deal with this problem. Since this capability exists in animals lower than man, and exists in man at the preconscious level, the formal logical methods which man displays, albeit ploddingly, in his conscious activity well may not apply. Therefore, other methods have been sought. These must not, however, rule out a role for the conscious activity (Hebb, 1949) which also exists and, consequently, serves a purpose. Strictly statistical mechanisms (i.e., without inherent pattern invariances), such as random nets whose connectivity is modified by experience, were avoided as sources of insight because they become weak when the dimensionality of incoming data becomes large. Their process may be too general, and there are stronger mechanisms which have value in the world we are actually imbedded in. Further, human learning has characteristics which are not understood in statistical terms.

The formal logical methods of today, without pattern properties that simplify recognition, were also avoided as sources of insight because it was felt that they can deal with the complexity of recognition only in the mathematician's world, since the numbers encountered from the combinatorial problems they introduce are even higher than astronomical. These methods can work in the real world only by sequential operations. Such "tree" methods serve only in a highly ordered world that can be broken down into ordered sequential decisions. What is needed is a machine whose basic character will develop "heuristic" methods.

What a priori assumptions may be assumed about the problem such a machine must deal with? Drastic simplifying assumptions must be made if any insight is to be gained. The major human senses, visual, auditory, and tactile, concern themselves with spatially distributed patterns. Except for the auditory sense, the spatial patterns are clearly two-dimensional. Even there, however, quantized time-frequency processes can lead to two-dimensional patterns. Because the visual system is our most complex one in terms of numbers of sensors, and its input is relatively clearly seen, it is a good sense to deal with. Even with this "single" sense, however, there are four separate sensor types consisting of both rods and cones. The rods and cones have considerably different properties and even go to the central system via different channels. Consequently, the problem of sensor integration exists even in vision alone. This is further brought home by the doubling of the problem through the requirement for binocular integration. An ability to do sensory integration appears basic. Can we make simplifications about patterns that maintain the central problem of recognition, yet sharpen our insights? Much biological evidence exists (Lettvin et al., 1959) for the preprocessing of data by the peripheral visual system. Our ability to recognize line outline, whether black on white or white on black, suggests line patterns as a reasonable simplification. Such a suggestion is reinforced by the human ability to perceive watercolor sketches easily, even where the black outline fails to coincide with the brush colors, since registration between the outline and the fill-in color is not required. Line patterns will, therefore, be assumed. Further, the patterns we deal with may be "noisy," i.e., corrupted, but in themselves they are not noise. Random patterns of dots such as might appear on a blank television screen are meaningless to us. The ability to recognize them appears to be of little value to survival in a macroscopic world (Kalin). Further, this viewpoint is consistent with what we know about biological systems and evolution. This eliminates statistical jumbling mechanisms which randomize the data. Recognition should have some invariance to translation and to rotation. Association and bunching of similar patterns is also likely to occur, otherwise the template-matching problem would become greater by orders of magnitude. An artist can give us a wide variety of distortion and still have us recognize the objects. He can also abstract out of reality a bare minimum of the highly redundant data of the world and yet have us recognize it. In a world as highly redundant in data as ours, a mechanism may collapse a considerable amount of information, if it will serve the end of giving us invariances that easily allow us to identify and at the same time allow for recognition of position and distortion. Absolute uniqueness of identification is not considered essential, since our conscious attention could sort from a few alternatives.

The above assumptions seem adequate enough, yet there is another assumption even more fundamental—reliability, primarily against death of neural and other cells, and of sensor elements themselves. Small dead spots should not have a perceptible effect on recognition. Whatever mechanism is used must also have a capability for highly parallel action that does not require the servoing of the eye, since in our single intake of a visual field we identify many things at once.

PROPAGATING SPACES

The key to the proposed mechanism lies in wave propagation. This has been considered by others (Beurle, 1956; Farley and Clark), but with a different approach. That work attempted to deal with the neuron net in as much complexity as mathematical or computer simulation would allow in order to study stability and related questions. The attempt here was to simplify as much as possible and stability was assumed. Propagation was chosen because it has an innate reliability against dead spots, due to a Huygen's-principle action which causes circumfusion of the wave around dead spots. The proposed mechanism is a double one, involving propagation in two physical spaces with distinctly different properties (Fig. 7). For the purpose of distinguishing them, they have been termed "Transformation Space" and "Association Space" in accordance with their functions. The first performs a transformation on two-dimensional spatial data, which makes it a time function. The second provides a vehicle for the parallel interchange of these time functions and also for interchange of secondary time functions which are in turn generated. These spaces are physical rather than mathematical. The functions they perform, however, can be viewed by considering them as mathematical spaces. Where the term "space" is used by itself, it should be understood that the meaning is that of the physical space. These two spaces will be discussed in sequence.

TRANSFORMATION SPACE

A space is defined with the point property of an idealized neuron net. Each differential element of the space normally has a value of 0. When excited it rises to 1 for some arbitrarily small interval of time, after which it returns to 0. An element on the face of the volume can be excited by an external input and all elements can be excited by adjacent elements with a delay that is equal to the distance between them, divided by the space propagation velocity. In order to simulate the refractory time property, it is also hypothesized that the exciting of an element during its fired state will not delay the return to 0. Such a model uses the excitation, delay, and refractory time properties of a neuron net in only the most rudimentary way. Since a wider class of propagating mechanisms is possible, this particular transformation space will be called a "neurospace." Figure 1 shows the effect of a one- and two-point input propagating in both a plane and a volume (a "neuro shell," consisting of a finite depth, could also be defined). A single-point input expands into circles or spheres of increasing radius with constant energy density in the wavefront giving amplification to the initial energy. This wavefront extent is a measure of the number of neurons firing at a given time. Such a space is not energy-conservative in the normal sense, energy being supplied locally by another action. A two-point input expands similarly until such time as the wavefronts start to intersect. Overlap propagation is prevented by the refractory time property since, for some arbitrarily small displacement from the intersection point, the second wavefront will arrive within the excited interval. This property has been termed an "intersection block." A complex shaped input will give rise to a complex expanding wavefront. Professor McCulloch had suggested the analogy of this process in a plane with a grass fire. The area of this expanding wavefront (arc length in the case of a plane) is a measure of the number of neurons firing in the neural net that the space is approximating, and, consequently, of the power being radiated at each instant of time. If this wavefront area is considered the output, then the neurospace performs a nonlinear transformation of a 0, 1-valued input function of x, y into an amplitude function of time. That is

$$B(x, y) \rightarrow A(t)$$

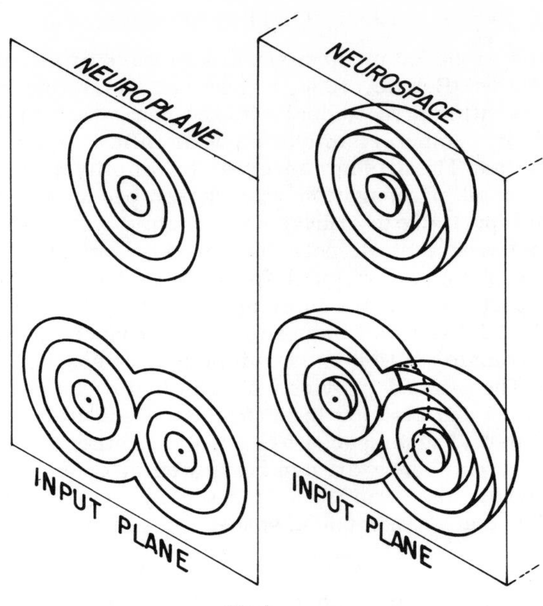

Fig. 1

by performing the following integral

$$A(t) = \iint_{\text{const } t} P(x, y, z, t)\, dS$$

where $P(x, y, z, t)$ is the propagation function whose input is $P(x, y, 0, 0)$. This function can be generalized so that the output is $f[A(t)]$. While there are reasons to study both the volume and shell case, it is much easier to visualize the process in the plane, so this case will be discussed. It should be pointed out that the shell and volume cases are simply related to the plane, at least in principle. A little reflection will show that with uniform propagation velocity the radial symmetry is such that the expanding pattern at a plane of distance z_1 from the input, $P_{z_1}(x, y, z_1, t)$, consists of all patterns that occur in the input plane at a time later given by

$$\sqrt{t^2 + \left(\frac{z_1}{t}\right)^2}$$

Consequently, the wavefront at depth z_1 is given by the relationship

$$P_{z_1}\left[x, y, z, \sqrt{t^2 + \left(\frac{z_1}{v}\right)^2}\right] = P(x, y, 0, t)$$

or stated inversely

$$P_{z_1}(x, y, z_1, t) = P\left[x, y, 0, \sqrt{t^2 - \left(\frac{z_1}{v}\right)^2}\right]$$

The wavefront area for a neuroshell of depth d in terms of the arc length of the neuroplane is gotten by integrating successive planes and can be reduced to:

$$A_d(t) = \int_0^{\substack{d \text{ for } z < vt \\ vt \text{ for } z > vt}} A_0\left[\sqrt{t^2 - \left(\frac{z}{v}\right)^2}\right]\left[\frac{t}{\sqrt{t^2 - (z/v)^2}}\right] dz$$

This has the form of an integral transformation from $A_0(t)$ to $A_d(t)$. (Notice that $A_0\sqrt{t^2 - (z/v)^2}$ represents a function of an argument and cannot be treated algebraically with the remaining integrand.)

Consider this transformation in the plane. An input pattern generates waves that flow through the space at constant velocity, except at points where the waves intersect. The space is stable for the inputs considered in that each point fires only once for each pattern input. The time of firing for any point is precisely its distance to the nearest point on the input pattern. A scalar field $t(x, y)$ can be defined which is continuous at each point. Because of the constant velocity, $t(x,y)$ obeys the eikonal equation $(dt/dx)^2 + (dt/dy)^2 = 1$ at all of the regular points (that is, points which are not wavefront intersection points) when the propagation velocity is normalized to unity. It resembles the scalar potential fields of mathematical physics, except that the value at a point is not dependent on the distribution of mass points of the input pattern, but only on the nearest point. Such a field can, of course, be generalized in a variety of ways while still maintaining the essential desired properties, e.g., by using the distance to other points or combination of points, or some function of these distances in place of using the distance to the nearest point. Notice that the output of the transformation space is not $t(x,y)$, but the integral of the arc length along constant t as a function of t, i.e.,

$$A(t) = \int_{\text{const } t} t(x,y)\, dl$$

More generally, the output is $f[A(t)]$. It will be apparent later that $d^n A(t)/dt^n$ is a particularly interesting subclass of $f[A(t)]$.

Further generalizations could include a different component of velocity in the z direction or a more complex logic and/or connectivity. Any transformation performed by a process which does not depend on an external coordinate system will be invariant to both rotation and translation. Since the above space (1) has an isotropic point property with respect to the input coordinates x and y, and (2) since this property is not a function of the coordinates, and (3) since the output measure is based solely on the input pattern, only the intrinsic properties of the input pattern are important. Hence, it is invariant to rotation, translation, and also right-left. Because the measure that is being used (arc length of constant distance to nearest pattern point) is of the most simple sort, its insights are likely to be incisive.

Let us try to get a feel for the pattern properties of such a transformation. Unfortunately, all that can be done in the allotted time is to present some select samples and state some general properties which can be proven and which appear reasonable from the examples. Figure 2 gives some examples of the transformation for a series of simple patterns. The left side shows the neurospace expansion and the right side the transformation output. A point expands into concentric circles so that the transformation is a line through the origin with a slope of 2π. A line expands into parallel lines with circular ends, thus giving a transformation which is a line of 2π slope with an initial value of twice the arc length. Two points transform as a line of 4π slope until such time as the wavefronts start to intersect. It then reduces its slope and becomes asymptotic to the line which connects these points, this line being the smallest convex figure (convex hull) that can be drawn through the pattern of two points. A circle expands with a decreasing inside wavefront and an increasing outside wavefront, the sum being constant. The transformation of the circle is a constant until the center wavefront disappears. It then increases with slope 2π. An "X" and the box, which is its convex hull, are also shown. Some general properties of this transformation are stated below. These hold for patterns consisting of lines and points of a finite number of pieces, each defined on a closed set, such as we associate with the ordinary recognition world.

$$\frac{dA(t)}{dt} \begin{cases} \to 2\pi \text{ as } t \to \infty \text{ for nonconvex figure} \\ = 2\pi \text{ for } t > 1/2 \text{ narrowest dimension for a convex figure} \end{cases}$$

$$A(0)^- = 0$$
$$A(0) = \text{input-pattern arc length}$$
$$A(0)^+ = 2\,(\text{input-pattern arc length})$$

where $A(0)^-$, $A(0)$, and $A(0)^+$ are the values of $A\,(t)$ in the region of $t = 0$ when approached from the left, at 0, and approached from the right, respectively.

$$A_\infty(0) = \text{arc length of convex hull}$$

where $A_\infty(t)$ is the function defined by the asymptote or "far-field" function.

$$B\,(kx,\ ky) = kA\,(kt)$$

that is, the function is linear with respect to size of input pattern and both amplitude and time scale of output. It can be normalized with respect to A and t, giving a function invariant to the size of the input pattern.

$$\frac{dA\,(0)}{dt} = 2\pi P + \pi E + \sum^{i} G\,(a_i)$$

where P is the number of points, E is the number of line ends, and $G\,(a)$ is the following function of all the angles existing in the pattern (a broken line contains two angles):

$$G(a) = \begin{cases} -2\tan\left(\frac{\pi - a}{2}\right) & \text{for } 0 < a \leq \pi \\ a - \pi & \text{for } \pi \leq a < 2\pi \end{cases}$$

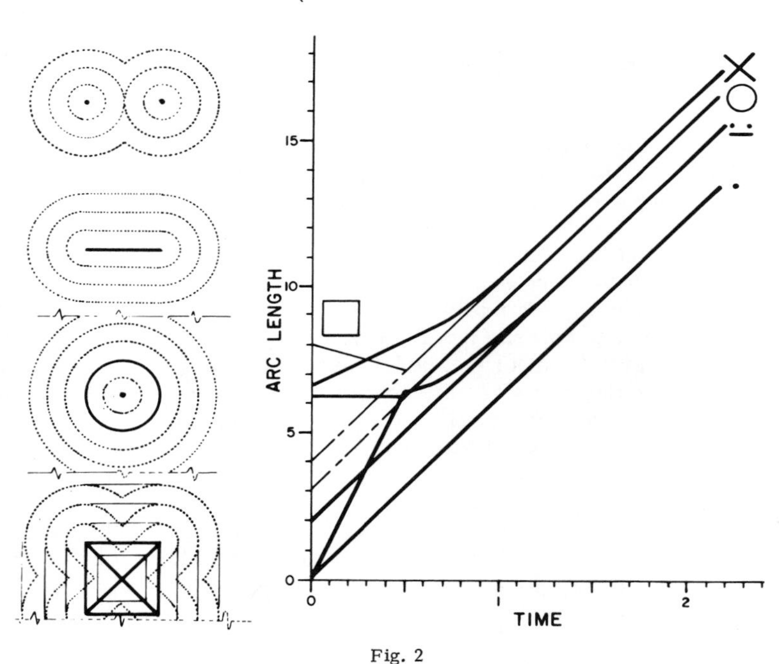

Fig. 2

$G(a)$ is shown in Fig. 3 and the geometry of the situation in Fig. 4. It can be seen that an arc propagates from the "outside" and a line segment is being removed from an "inside" angle leading to an unsymmetric situation; consequently, there is a sensitivity to line bends.

If a pattern of several disjoint parts has no angles in it, the contribution of all parts closed on themselves is 0; of parts not closed on themselves (that is, lines and points), the contribution is 2π times the number of lines and points. The original slope of $A(t)$ is constant until the minimum radius of curvature is reached or the expanding pattern starts intersecting with itself. Where angles and intersections do exist, this minimum curvature is immediately reached. The contribution, then, to $d^2A(0)/dt^2$ is positive for a cusp, negative for a bowed intersection, and 0 for intersecting lines.

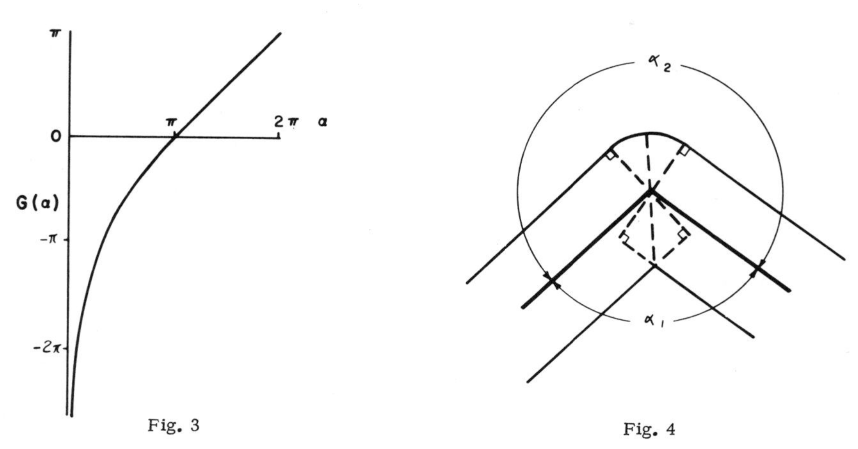

Fig. 3

Fig. 4

The transformation is continuous in important ways, although an exact statement of the conditions under which this prevails has not yet been formulated. Figure 5 shows how the transformation deals fundamentally with some of the pattern properties. It shows a handwritten input of 1, 0, and X, and the different outputs they generate. The initial slope of dA/dt at some time displaced from 0 is enough to distinguish these characters. Figure 6 shows (not to scale) what happens to a variety of handwritten 0's. The propagation property tends to fuse together the figure made of dots or eliminates the surplus of one made of a wiggly line.

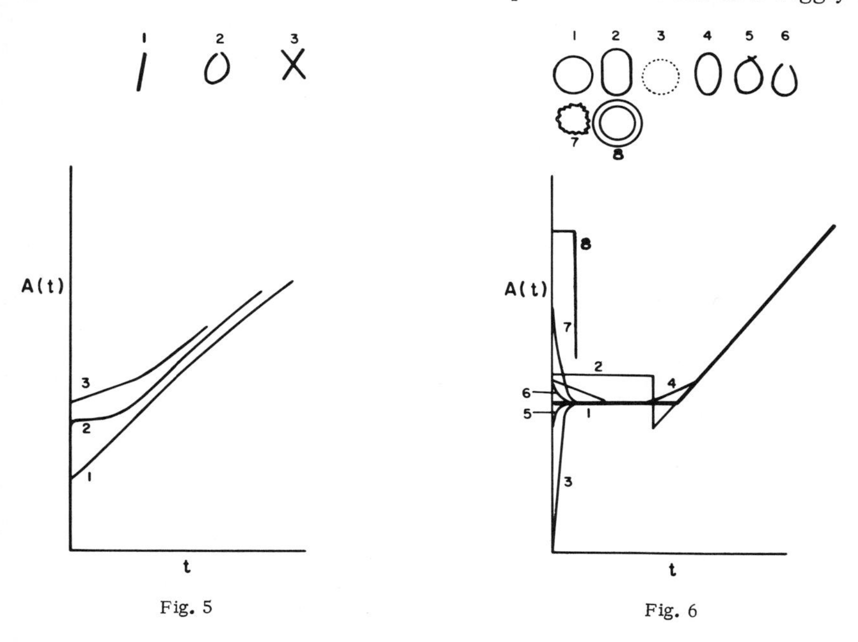

Fig. 5

Fig. 6

Crossed or unclosed 0's do not drastically affect the output. The property whereby precise geometric forms (patterns 1, 2, 3, and 8) have pronounced effects should be noticed since it will be of importance later. Another property of interest can be seen by comparing the 0 consisting of dots and that consisting of an ellipse. Properties which entail relationships of close points of the pattern affect the early time of the transformation, while properties far apart affect the later time of the transformation. Thus, tolerances can be separately set for these conditions.

The transformation is not unique, and this leads to a number of problems. This lack of uniqueness is shown in the following example. All polygons of equal perimeter and circumscribed about the same circle (equal area) have the same transformations. In order to separate these patterns it is necessary to define a special operation in the second stage of the process, which will be discussed later. This operation also has the advantage of obtaining a translation, rotation, and inversion sensitivity when desired.

Before leaving the neurospace, a word about this general transformation in shells and volumes is in order. While the volume consists of all space on one side of the input plane, the shell allows propagation only to some second plane parallel to the input one. (Again, this could be generalized by introducing attenuation as a function of distance from the input plane.) The far-field effect in the volume is considerably more explosive since $A(t)$ rises at t^2 rate. To control it and compare it with the plane case, it is necessary to use its derivative. The intersection effects are more pronounced because the frontal intersections of surfaces are essentially parallel when they start meeting. A volume intersection therefore is more sensitive to initial intersection of surfaces. The shell, as would be expected, is an "in between" case, acting like the volume for very early times and the plane for very late times. All initial intersections are strong, however, since they take place close to the input plane.

ASSOCIATION SPACE

The configuration shown in Fig. 7 has been hypothesized as a mechanism for realizing the output $A(t)$ of the neurospace. As each point of the neurospace or net fires, it generates a signal in the association space where the propagating mechanism is effectively linear. Consequently, the intersection block property does not exist here. This space has a velocity of propagation much higher than that of the neurospace. An association element samples the propagated wave in its vicinity. If it is of a bandwidth such that the difference in propagation time through this space from all the firing points of the neurospace is negligible, it integrates all the points firing at one instant in the transformation space. Yet, because of the slower neurospace propagation, it is sensitive to successive values of the expanding contour. This sees the $A(t)$ function. The association element is a matched filter, conceptually, responding by transmitting its own signal when a waveform or some property of a waveform that passes it, excites it. The angular response of the association element and each firing point in the neurospace is assumed to be uniform for all directions from which energy is interchanged. It is clear, then, that the element responds to the same input pattern, independent of location or orientation of the pattern or location of the element itself. The objects shown at the left in Fig. 7 would be identified by the value of the $dA(t)/dt$ at, or shortly after, the start of propagation, or by the appearance of and character of a positive $d^2A(t)/dt^2$ at a time displaced from zero. The excitation of a single element with a complex response or of many simple elements at once would signify a more complex pattern. If many patterns are put on at one time, they would all be recognized, providing that the interference problem could be overcome. This is an important and difficult problem and will have to be dealt with in a variety of ways. These will be discussed when the appropriate mechanisms are introduced.

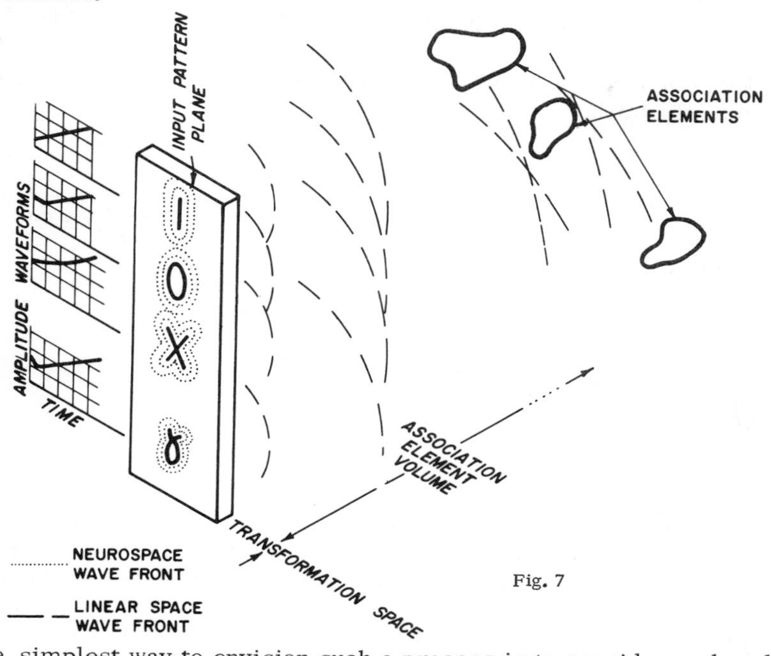

Fig. 7

The simplest way to envision such a process is to consider a phosphor, or a plane net of neon tubes with suitable delay lines, in which wavefronts propagate in the manner of a neuroplane. Then as each point is energized it emits light. An association element would be at some distance from this plane and have a photoreceptor for its input. This would, at one instant of time, measure the total length of emitting arc. The output voltage of this receptor would be processed by circuitry attached to it in order to determine conformance with some required property of the time waveform. If the wave conformed, the element would itself emit a signal. The mechanization of such a system is simple. However, to be able to stack the association elements in depth and/or to realize fully the potentialities of the system as later envisioned, it is necessary to have the association elements transparent to the energy propagating in the association space. Further, if a neuroshell or neurospace is used, it too must be transparent to this energy. The implementation using light or any very short wavelength phenomenon makes this difficult to achieve unless local reinforcement and/or retransmission of the energy in the association space is performed by active elements in it.

Suppose two filters have the same response function and are connected together so that the difference of arrival time is measured (Fig. 8). Such an arrangement measures the angle of arrival of the energy to the bisector plane of these two elements. The time difference of arrival is, then, the sine of the arrival angle to the plane divided by the velocity of propagation. A minimum of three noncolinear elements would determine the position of the pattern in the input plane. More are undoubtedly desirable from the point of view of combating interference and making the operation of the process independent of the death of any particular cell. The notion of identical filters (filters with the same response function) enriches the possibilities of this process considerably. The single-filter response is invariant to position and orientation, since it makes no reference to an external coordinate system. The use of similar response filters, however, introduces a coordinate system which d o e s depend on their relative location and, consequently, allows for the positioning of the objects that have been detected. Thus, the detection process includes the positioning of the patterns as well. This can be taken a step further.

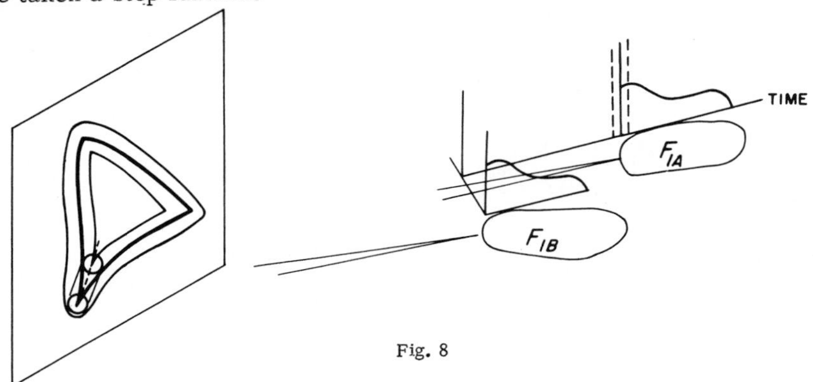

Fig. 8

The similar response elements have a resolution on the time of arrival of relevant signals, as shown in Fig. 8. This time resolution is equivalent to a spatial resolution on the input plane. For example, a tolerance which is a constant fraction of the time difference will have a relatively constant size resolution for angles up to about one radian. Since such a process can isolate small details of patterns, it is now possible to have transformations which depend on the fine details of an input pattern and its subsequent expansion in the neurospace. Such a process is sensitive to both space and time discontinuities of the expanding pattern. A triangle might fire elements which respond to its particular angles, the time discontinuity caused by the disappearing center, and the response element for the triangle taken as a whole. If the number and/or values of these angles as time progressed (i.e., as the figure expanded) were simply counted or just distances taken relative to each other, one would still get a rotation and translation invariant measurement. The location of the angles or similar coordinate-related data of the expanding figure would not have this invariance. Consequently, it would be able to separate rotated, translated, or right-left inverted patterns. Both large and small resolution elements can be made by using differing time tolerances and/or distances between the similar elements. Since these can also be used simultaneously, a selection is made primarily on those elements and combinations which best serve the recognition purpose. Figure 8 also shows a more intricate pattern. The initial value of $d^2 A/dt^2$ would identify cusps, bows, etc., and the character of the disappearing inner-propagating figure gives still further information on the pattern. The primary point is that a wide class of recognition characteristics depending both on detail and over-all character can be synthesized out of such an operation. A definitive study of this is beyond the scope of this paper; here it is only desired to show the strength of the proposed machine concepts.

ASSOCIATION SPACE ORGANIZATION

The association space has an extremely strong ability to integrate and synthesize information. This occurs because of the use of independent elements and the imbedding of these in a space transparent to the interelement communication energy. It is, therefore, possible to address the elements from the outside, in parallel or individually. Parallel address, for example, might consist of a particular frequency signal which would tell the system to modify to detect a particular incoming pattern, along with a reward or punishment signal. Or it could also announce that a motor action is or is not to accompany it. Individual address occurs, as described heretofore, by use of the signal to which the element is responsive. It could also occur by a designated code name that might be different, or by the location of the particular element through electronic navigation system techniques, such as range or angle systems which build up a propagated field at a particular place in space. It should be pointed out that when using particular address techniques, the read-in address is the time inverse of the readout address. Such a process is natural for a matched filter when its action is changed from detection to transmission. Association elements could be designed or taught by a "higher" capability such as sensory-motor tracking that consciously takes place during early learning. Much of present learning theory and adaptive filter technique would be applicable here. For example, multistage perceptrons could be built by reinforcing the wavefront response. This would also allow feedback between stages. It is not the object of this paper to investigate how this is best done.

A memory space which is time-quantized and which propagates its information in an effectively continuous linear space has a different character from a series or parallel "wired" space. It provides a mechanism for getting in and out of a large memory volume which does not limit as the volume gets bigger. It provides a high degree of potential connectivity or dimensionality for each element in the space, since physical distance to other elements has become unimportant. This connectivity also does not limit as the system increases in size. Whenever recognition takes place anywhere, a firing of that element makes this known everywhere. For example, visual and auditory events which take place simultaneously can know about each other without any prestructuring of the system. (Such a process has not been found physiologically. The ability of organisms to build events from separate senses shows that some strong associative process as this is taking place.) In this way a highly associative connectivity is obtained. A high density of wires at each element is not required.

What then is the price of this capability? It is the inability to assess independently the state of all the association elements. If a large fraction of them were to respond at once, they would interfere with each other and gibberish would result. A small amount of interference could be dealt with in many ways, using redundant information or recognition elements, as is done in a variety of military antijamming techniques. Is such a limitation severe? I believe not. In a real recognizer one might require a great many association elements to be stacked. Yet it is unlikely that in any single recognition more than a relatively small number would respond. Consider, for example, only 1000 elements. In a wired parallel system, it would be possible to ascertain 2^{1000} or about 10^{300} (over a gogol) states, most of which represent a response of about 50% of the elements. If in a propagating system no more than 10, for example, were tolerable, about 1000^{10} states would be identifiable. This is, in all probability, an adequately large number for the real world of a 1000-element system. A directly connected system has a connectivity with the memory that is badly matched in that it is too dense. The proposed system appears to be a far better matched communication system with an associative memory.

Thus far we have discussed the problem of individual association elements. When patterns get more complex, it is necessary to associate many elements. For some purposes, especially when the elements are close, directly wired logical chains could represent various combinations of these. Of much more interest, however, is what happens for elements connected via propagation in the association space. Simultaneity of firing of two elements generates a reinforced field in the bisector plane of these elements, three elements along a line as well as three planes, four elements giving six planes and four lines, and so forth. Simultaneity is represented by physical points in space, and physical forces are available at these places to structure the space (for example, breaking down synapses or threshold elements). This suggests a mapping of thought onto geometry, rather than onto arithmetic as done by Gödel. Learning in such a system would have to be divided into at least two types: one for the basic association elements, which might be compared to nonsense syllables; and a second for combinations of trained elements, which might be compared to combinations of known syllables. Geometric structuring and staging could give preparation for new experiences, especially when they consist of new combinations of known elements, since these points would have been identified beforehand. A system results which has an inherent capability for dealing with complexity per se, making this a sort of "gestalt" machine.

The problems of binaural, binocular, and color integration can be visualized by direct physical processes. In the color case, for example, three interwoven nets can independently connect the three color sensors. If each color fired with a different carrier frequency and particular association elements were to be separately responsive to each of these, then the proportion of these would determine color. Recognition could then be arranged to deal with color at the same time as form. Psychological color could be obtained by comparing the color proportions with the color proportion of known objects in the field since this information can be interchanged in the association space. Compensation for ambient light could then be obtained. Consider binaural or binocular integration. Association elements of similar response for right and left organs can be tied together by a communications method using propagation in the association space. Simultaneity of forms appearing in both organs would dictate it. They could also be tied together by a carrier-frequency method similar to the visual system described for color. Or the same association element could identify whether it is the right or left organ by the location of emission. Parallax effects would show themselves by both small location differences and by differences in the intersection of the expanding pattern with its immediate environment.

The problem of interference associated with propagation through the association volume has been mentioned. It is an extremely important one. Further, the system proposed has no address in the normal computer sense. While this is a virtue generally, it can be an extreme drawback. When the eye sees a coin, it should not have to fire the concepts, ellipse, dish, coin, etc., and then sort these. Some address is necessary to tell it not to bother with all the irrelevant identifications. For such purposes, an inhibition address mechanism (one which prevents irrelevant elements from responding) appears very useful. Confusion is thus kept to tolerable levels. It could be the mechanism through which the psychological notions of "context" or "set" are implemented. From a survival standpoint, inhibition address has the virtue of being better able to deal with the unexpected than a direct address. The reason for this is, of course, that all things that are not specifically ruled out are searched. The extensive preconscious inhibition mechanisms that are evident from the clinical experience with the human mind lead one to suspect that inhibition has an important central function in the activity of the central nervous system.

The machine proposed here has an entirely different feel from classical machines. This is characterized by its lack of point logic which, either by address and instruction or by wiring and switching, limits connectivity at each point to a small predecessor-successor class. Its basic universal connectivity is not geared to the problem of computation or optimization of a known problem, but rather to the comparison of inputs with a large class of stored items. Such a mechanism has a character much closer to that demanded by the survival problem. To survive, an animal must be able, at each instant of time, to recognize and avoid the large multiplicity of things which can lead to trouble. He is not liable to encounter many of these at once, but he must know about them immediately. Therefore, the machine is probably best characterized as a multiple property-matching processor. As such, it resembles biological activity, including a major part of human activity, much closer than the large variety of classical machines, even though those machines may be capable of subsuming these within the mathematical world.

IMPLEMENTATION

In considering the building of such systems, two questions are raised: (1) How does one implement a machine for performing this process artificially? (2) How could these or related processes take place in biological systems? In addition, the separate stages of this process require different mechanisms whose only requirement of each other is that they be able to interact. A general indication of implementation can be made in relatively short order and it will be clear what is entailed in the process. This is all that will be done because of the still formative state of the work. It will be clear, however, that filling in the details does not fall into the class of problems for the student to do for himself. Extremely deep technological, design, theoretical, and even conceptual problems will be raised in the details because the process involves new concepts. I feel they are all solvable, although the best way is certainly not clear at this moment. Intuitive feelings about the best way will vary with the experience and background of the constructor.

The neurospace might be implemented by a variety of techniques, using discrete active elements or continuous active media. Ordinary diodes, glow tubes, or magnetic elements with suitable delay elements (which could be simple RC circuits) and nets of natural or artificial neurons are a few of the lumped components that could be connected to perform the transformation. Continuous active materials with a domain that propagates and quenches itself by some dead-time property (or other equivalent of refractory time) may also be used—magnetic domain, magnetostrictive, phosphor, photoluminescent, and ionizing gas methods, to name a few. Even mechanical-optical schemes, such as tying a defocusing imaging system to an emission-limited photocell, are possible. It should be noted that the process in active, continuous materials is not an unnatural one. Propagation of a boundary which switches state emits a second form of energy in its switching and often has some inactive time following switching.

The association space can also be implemented in a variety of ways. The energy medium in a continuous implementation can be electromagnetic or acoustic. What is demanded is that the transformation space generate energy in this medium and that the association elements can receive this energy and also be adequately transparent to it. This can be arranged by choice of association element size with respect to energy wavelength and/or an impedance match to the medium. The use of an active element to make up the space could facilitate propagation around opaque association elements. For an artificial system, the use of electromagnetic waves in an electrolyte has some particular advantages because it can supply power locally; it aids the transfer of energy by its propagation impedance, and it can act as a heat-dissipation medium, solving a problem which may crop up severely with extreme microminiaturization. Impurities for structuring can be injected during a learning stage and removed during an operation stage. The major drawback to electromagnetic schemes is due to the large velocity of propagation, which makes time differential measurements extremely sensitive. An association space of active elements could conceivably get around this.

The question of biological significance is a much deeper one. Clearly, one does not design such a system. On the other hand, the arrangement of the biological elements which can perform the observed associative and recognition capabilities remains a mystery. All hypotheses are highly speculative. Unfortunately, they are based on a very restricted class of machine models, which class this machine avoids. It is worthwhile, therefore, to speculate on how the central nervous system components could be arranged to form such a machine. Again, it is necessary to insert a word of caution against taking this model too literally. Indeed, physiological evidence cited at the end of this chapter certainly precludes any naive identification of this model with the visual cortex. It is intended that the implementations proposed be taken in the spirit of broadening the type of action that might be anticipated and/or found useful. The most obvious biological implementations consist of a combined neural net with neurospace characteristics near the surface and association space characteristics beyond this. A less obvious but more exciting possibility exists in a "biospace" implementation. The neural net is imbedded in non-neural tissue, primarily glia cells. It is known that this plays some direct function in the central nervous system. Further, the whole field of electroencephalography gives evidence of sizeable amounts of energy existing in the non-neural tissue. While this energy is presently considered a by-product of the neuron process, it could just as well, and perhaps better, be considered as part of the functioning mechanism. The glia cells or the glia cells reinforced by the neuron firing constitute the implied vehicle of transmission. The delay property of the neuron makes it an ideal element for constructing matched filters. This over-all process has some very satisfying properties with respect to its physiological counterpart: it has a distinct surface and depth property; storage is a passive process; circular loops of neurons are used as matched filters; EEG energy is utilized; it requires multivelocity propagation processes; it combines some of the properties of "field theory" and point memory; and a host of other properties also exist. Its main defect is in reconciling it with some of the work on sectioning of the brain (Sperry, Miner, and Myers, 1958). This reconciliation might lead to further insights into the process.

SOME FURTHER PROPERTIES

The worth of such a machine concept cannot be proven in the normal deductive sense of the word. What remains, then, is to summon evidence on its value and relevance. While it is true that selection of evidence to fit the model is a rigged procedure, the way in which the model can fit in with the broad set of fields that concern the problem is of some importance. It might be compared to a Tchebycheff rather than a Taylor series approach to the problem since it attempts a goodness of fit over the interval rather than a close match for the criteria of one particular discipline. Let us consider some of these properties.

The Huygen's principle associated with propagation gives the mechanism an intrinsic reliability against both dead spots in the spaces and in the sensors. In addition, it can be combined with an inhibition mechanism to separate compound patterns. For example, if a line or a pattern of dots interfering with another figure is inhibited on the input space, then the resulting output will be close to that of the remaining pattern. This permits the elimination of any recognized object from interfering with remaining recognition. This suggests a function for efferent energy from the central nervous system to retinal cells and ganglia.

The mechanism compares a large amount of input data with a large memory in a fathomable manner. All actions depend only on what is happening in the local environment of the object performing the action. Local action of an extremely subtle nature by simple objects is not required.

The pattern properties of the transformation space reduce the "template-matching" problem drastically; that is, the comparison of the association space field with memory has a much smaller dimensionality of search.

The lack of address of the system allows it to deal with an unordered set of events, abstracting what is useful in identification and making a combined event of this.

The system has the property of seeing only what it recognizes, and ordering this geometrically. It does not have to compute and throw out information that is not relevant—it simply does not see it.

The transformations discussed have a particular sensitivity to geometric figures, that is, figures with constant-distance properties and/or symmetries. This is due to large wavefront intersections or changes of intersection character taking place over short intervals of time, or because intersections at several places give a reinforced output. This can be seen from cases 1, 2, and 8 of Fig. 6. It is interesting to note that man has such a capability, although there is no apparent evolutionary reason for its development since survival is not likely to have depended on that property before the advent of the civilization. This capability must result as a by-product mechanism, a situation which also exists in this machine.

The model has certain discriminatory capabilities and incapabilities which parallel the human. The above paragraph indicates its sensitivity to geometric and symmetric figures. The model indicates that arbitrary ordering is a process that may well be more difficult under most circumstances than recognition, and we should make such mistakes more frequently. Various optical illusions and learning problems can be explained in terms of this model.

The machine appears to fulfill some of the evolutionary requirements for development of larger and larger systems. It does not require new programing as it gets bigger. Size is its own reward as far as the association space goes. Further, none of the mechanisms proposed are unnatural ones.

The distinctly different properties of the surface and the depth resemble the situation in the cerebral cortex. The distinct learning mechanisms associated with the association elements and the combination of elements can give the distinct types of actions envisioned by both behaviorist and Gestalt psychology. The association space forms the vehicle by which the intra- and intersense data interact.

The amplitude sensitivity to the $A(t)$ function requires the nonthreshold mechanisms observed in the recent neuron concepts.

The propagation mechanism is in accord with the data whereby slices in the brain have little effect on performance. If these were to fill up with a fluid whose association space properties were adequately similar to those of the tissue, then the slices would not be noticed. There is a conflict between this model and slices in the transformation spaces when the slices are filled with dielectrics or metals. Consequently, no simple literal transfer to the central nervous system can be made. What modifications these experiments demand on the model and to what degree these experiments, which were not performed with this model directly in mind, are applicable is not known. This is clearly an important matter if the model has biological applicability.

The model implies a time quantification and a shutter mechanism since the whole pattern must start propagation simultaneously. Its propagation gives a "raison d'etre" for the rhythm characteristics and frequency sensitivity of the human brain. The EEG phenomena become the result of an integral working mechanism.

The model gives a "raison d'etre" for the intimate interplay of highly associative and inhibitive mechanisms that are our psychoanalytic facts of life.

Let me repeat again that the process demands no new hypotheses concerning the action of the brain components. It is merely the synthesis of a new system using these processes. Further, it uses a wide variety of the processes that the biological system is capable of performing.

CONCLUSIONS

A new class of machine is proposed which differs in its basic concept from the present mathematical machines and logical nets. Its basic concept uses a time-domain signal propagation to memory and gets from this a very powerful primitive associative mechanism. The force of such a time memory, even for spatial inputs, has also been shown. It presents an existence theorem (by presenting one example) showing the inadequacy of our present theoretical foundations of cognitive and associative machines. As such, it raises a host of questions in all fields concerned with such machines, both biologically and synthetically. A small sample follows. Is the neural or logical net an adequate model? Is the point logic of present mathematical machines adequate or must some new universal logic be introduced? Is inhibition logic an important concept? I feel that this model can generate studies and experiments in neurophysiology, psychology, and/or mathematical theories. Can this machine give insight into our clinical experience with the human mind? Engineering development is also indicated. At the least, the model is a parable which indicates the ripeness of the field for a new set of questions and a new viewpoint. Exploring this model may be extremely useful to that end, although the model may have much wrong with it as a final answer.

The model raises more questions than it answers. Unfortunately this short paper and the early state of the work cannot hope to do more than whet the appetite. Even here, however, the listener may have to think about these problems from this viewpoint for some time before the strength of these concepts becomes apparent. I urge that he try to interpret his actions from the viewpoint of such a model. I feel that these viewpoints can do both less and more than propose a solution. They can open up a new world of insights.

REFERENCES

Beurle. 1956. Properties of masses of cells capable of regenerating pulses. Phil. Trans. of the Royal Soc. 240, 55.

Bullock. 1959. Neuron doctrine and electrophysiology. Science 129, No. 3355.

Farley and Clark. Activity in networks of neuronlike elements. 4th London Symp. on Information Theory (to be published).

Hebb. 1949. The organization of behavior. John Wiley and Sons, New York.

Kalin. Some metric problems in pattern recognition. AFCRL 327.

Lettvin, Maturana, McCullough, and Pitts. 1959. What the frog's eye tells the frog's brain. Proc. IRE 47, 11, 1940.

Sperry, Miner, and Myers. 1958. Visual pattern perception following subpial slicing and tantalum wire implantations in the visual cortex. J. Comp. Physiol. Psychol. 48, 50-58.

EVALUATION OF A CLASS OF PATTERN-RECOGNITION NETWORKS

Laveen Kanal

General Dynamics/Electronics, Rochester, New York

INTRODUCTION

The realization of devices to perform a given pattern-recognition task can be considered in terms of the problem of providing the following specifications.

A. The observables (measurements or tests) x_i, $i = 1,2,\ldots,N$, by which patterns are to be characterized.

B. The form of the classification function, i.e., the manner in which observables are to be used in assigning a pattern to one of K known groups.

C. The procedures for determining the classification function from samples of patterns from the K different groups.

In any given instance the results of the measurements may be represented by $x = (x_1, x_2, \ldots, x_n)$. Then the universe of patterns can be thought of as being an N-dimensional space and the recognition task becomes one of dividing this N-dimensional space into mutually exclusive regions R_j, $j = 1,2,\ldots,K$, such that when x falls in R_j, the pattern is listed under group j.

Unless an especially auspicious choice has been made of the N characteristics which define the observation space, the x_i will, in general, have to be treated as stochastic variables. The recognition task then becomes the application of statistical inference to the classification of a pattern to one of the K known groups to which it can possibly belong. Information on the probability distributions of observables for the various groups can range from complete ignorance of the functional form of the distribution, to the case where the functional form and all parameters are known.

1. A CLASS OF PATTERN-RECOGNITION NETWORKS

In some recent articles (see, for example, Hawkins, 1961), work on the application of a class of networks to pattern recognition has been reported. Figures 1 and 2 show two networks typical of this class. The measurements x_i which

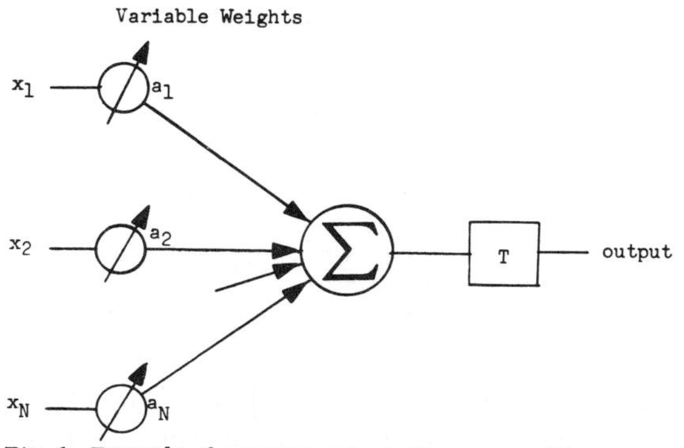

Fig. 1. Example of a neuron-type pattern-recognition network; see equation (1).

characterize the pattern are obtained, for instance, by placing the pattern on an "artificial retina" with the outputs of the retina elements being quantized such that the x_i are either 0 or 1.

In Fig. 1 the classification function takes the form of a weighted sum of the x_i, viz.,

$$\sum_{i=1}^{N} a_{ij} x_i > T_j \qquad j = 1,2,\ldots,K \tag{1}$$

where the set of coefficients a_{ij} which is desired is the one which permits the threshold T_j to be exceeded whenever a pattern from group j is present and not otherwise.

In the network of Fig. 2, subsets of the x_i, selected perhaps in a random manner, are connected through fixed weights (+1, −1) to summation units with thresholds. Let b_{im} be the fixed weights between the retina elements and the summation units, where b_{im} can be 0. Let T_m be the thresholds for the summation

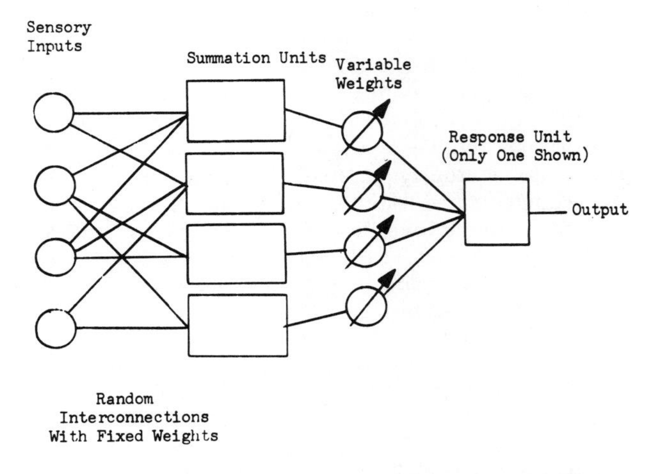

Fig. 2. Perceptron-type pattern-recognition network (after Hawkins); see equation (2).

units, and y_m be the outputs from the summation units, with y_m being 0 when the thresholds T_m are not exceeded, and 1 otherwise. Further, let a_{mj} be weighting coefficients (variable) between summation units and response units and let T_j be the thresholds for the response units. Then the classification function used by the network of Fig. 2 is

$$\sum_{m=1}^{M} a_{mj} y_m > T_j \qquad j = 1,2,\ldots,K \qquad M < N \tag{2}$$

with

$$y_m = \begin{cases} 1 \text{ if } \sum_{i=1}^{N} b_{im} x_i > T_m \\ 0 \text{ otherwise} \end{cases}$$

Although the network of Fig. 2 uses the derived variables y_m to characterize the patterns, the form of the classification function is the same as that for the network of Fig. 1. An evaluation of this class of networks can be considered in the context of comparable classification functions which can be derived from some more or less formal principles proposed in classification theory and practice.

2. A REPRESENTATION OF THE JOINT DISTRIBUTION

Let X denote the set of all points $x = (x_1, x_2, \ldots, x_N)$ with each $x_i = 0$ or 1, and let $p(x) = p(x_1, x_2, \ldots, x_N)$ denote the joint probability of the x_i in a given group. Since there are 2^N points in X, any parametric description of an arbitrary probability distribution will, in general, require $(2^N - 1)$ independent parameters. A particular parametric representation due to Bahadur (1959b) is used here.

Using E_p to denote the expected value when the underlying distribution is $p(x)$, define for each $i = 1,2,\ldots,N$,

$$m_i = p(x_i = 1) = E_p(x_i) \qquad 0 < m_i < 1$$

$$z_i = \frac{x_i - m_i}{\sqrt{m_i(1 - m_i)}}$$

$$r_{ij} = E_p(z_i z_j) \qquad i < j \tag{3}$$

$$r_{ijk} = E_p(z_i z_j z_k) \qquad i < j < k$$

$$r_{12\ldots N} = E_p(z_1 z_2, \ldots, z_N)$$

Further define

$$p_1(x_1, x_2, \ldots, x_N) = \prod_{i=1}^{N} m_i^{x_i} (1 - m_i)^{1 - x_i} \tag{4}$$

so that $p_1(x_1, x_2, \ldots, x_N) = p_1(x)$ denotes the probability distribution of the x_i when (1) the x_i's are independently distributed and (2) they have the same marginal distributions as under the distribution $p(x)$. It is shown by Bahadur that for every $x = (x_1, x_2, \ldots, x_N)$ in X

$$p(x) = p_1(x) f(x) \tag{5}$$

where

$$f(x) = 1 + \sum_{i<j} r_{ij} z_i z_j + \sum_{i<j<k} r_{ijk} z_i z_j z_k + \ldots + r_{12\ldots N} z_1 z_2 \ldots z_N \tag{6}$$

The $2^N - N - 1$ correlations and the N marginal frequencies m_i are the parameters which determine the probability distribution $p(x)$. In order that an arbitrary set of $2^N - N - 1$ real numbers $r_{ij}, r_{ijk}, \ldots,$ serve as the correlation parameters of a probability distribution $p(x)$ for any set of numbers m_i, $0 < m_i < 1$, it is necessary and sufficient that $f(x)$ be non-negative for each x.

The distribution $p(x)$ can now be approximated by distributions of lower order. Thus $p_1(x)$ is a first-order approximation to $p(x)$,

$$p_2(x) = p_1(x) \left[1 + \sum_{i<j} r_{ij} z_i z_j\right] \tag{7}$$

is a second-order approximation to $p(x)$, and so on. For $1 \leq m < N$, the approximation $p_m(x)$ is the only distribution of order not exceeding m under which any set $\{x_{j1}, x_{j2}, \ldots, x_{jm}\}$ of m variables has the same joint distribution as under the given $p(x)$. Of course, approximations to $p(x)$ may also be obtained by retaining various selected terms in the expansion for $f(x)$ and dropping the remaining terms. Because any approximation to $p(x)$ is obtained by dropping terms of $f(x)$, a classification procedure based on it will not do as well as the same procedure when $p(x)$ is used.

3. A CLASS OF CLASSIFICATION FUNCTIONS

A well-known theoretical solution to the problem of classifying an unknown pattern into one of two known groups in such a way as to minimize the probability of making an error in the assignment of inputs to the two groups, or in a manner which equalizes the errors for the two groups, minimizes the expected loss, or is best according to some other criterion, is in terms of the likelihood ratio (see, for example, Anderson, 1958, Chap. 6).

In the present case, the problem is to classify an unknown pattern into one of the several groups to which it can possibly belong. One way to proceed would be to set up likelihood ratios for each pair of the K groups (Anderson, 1958) which would require $K(K-1)/2$ classification functions. For the construction of networks, it is desirable to have only a small number of classification functions and by representing the K groups by, for example, a binary code, much less than K classification functions can be considered; each classification function pools patterns from all K groups into just two groups: those which should produce a 1 and those which should produce a 0. Denote these two groups by group 1 and group 2 respectively and let $p(x/i)$, $i = 1, 2 \ldots$, denote respectively the probability distribution for x under group 1 and group 2. Then the likelihood-ratio regions for classification are defined by

$$R_1 : L(x) = \frac{p(x/1)}{p(x/2)} > t \qquad\qquad (8)$$
$$R_2 : L(x) \leq t$$

Thus, if the function $L(x)$ exceeds the threshold t, the pattern is classified as belonging to group 1, otherwise the pattern is classified into group 2. [One way of deriving such a rule is to consider the conditional probabilities that, given a pattern having a certain $x = (x_1, x_2, \ldots, x_N)$, the pattern belongs to group 1 or group 2. The boundary of the two regions for classification can be defined by the equation $p(1/x) - p(2/x) = 0$, which gives the expression $p(x/1)/p(x/2) = p(2)/p(1)$.]

The classification functions and corresponding networks which result when various approximations to $p(x)$ are used in a likelihood-ratio procedure can now be derived. If a first-order approximation is used, $p(x)$ is replaced by $p_1(x)$. This implies an assumption of independence of the x_i. Letting m_i and n_i represent the means of the x_i in groups 1 and 2 respectively, the likelihood ratio is

$$L(x) = \frac{\prod_{i=1}^{N} m_i^{x_i}(1-m_i)^{1-x_i}}{\prod_{i=1}^{N} n_i^{x_i}(1-n_i)^{1-x_i}} \qquad (9)$$

taking the logarithm gives

$$\sum_{i=1}^{N} (a_i x_i + c_i)$$

where

$$a_i = \log \frac{m_i}{n_i} \frac{(1-n_i)}{(1-m_i)} \qquad (10)$$

and

$$c_i = \log \frac{(1 - m_i)}{(1 - n_i)}$$

The summation over c_i can be absorbed in the threshold and a particular weighted sum is obtained for the classification function. The resulting network is that of Fig. 1, with the coefficients as defined in equation (10). Let

$$z_i = \frac{x_i - m_i}{\sqrt{m_i(1 - m_i)}} \qquad y_i = \frac{x_i - n_i}{\sqrt{n_i(1 - n_i)}}$$

and let $r_{ij}, r_{ijk} \ldots$, and $s_{ij}, s_{ijk} \ldots$, be the correlation parameters for group 1 and group 2 respectively. Then for a second-order approximation to the joint distributions, the logarithm of the likelihood ratio is

$$\sum_{i=1}^{N} a_i x_i + \log\left(1 + \sum_{i<j} r_{ij} z_i z_j\right) - \log\left(1 + \sum_{i<j} s_{ij} y_i y_j\right) \tag{11}$$

plus a constant term. Using the approximation $\log(1 + \theta) \approx \theta$, and letting

$$u_{ij} = \frac{r_{ij}}{\sqrt{m_i(1 - m_i)\, m_j(1 - m_j)}} \quad \text{and} \quad v_{ij} = \frac{s_{ij}}{\sqrt{n_i(1 - n_i)\, n_j(1 - n_j)}} \tag{12}$$

expression (11) can be written as

$$\sum_{i=1}^{N} \left[a_i + \sum_{j \neq i} (-m_j u_{ij} + n_j v_{ij})\right] x_i + \sum_{i<j} (u_{ij} - v_{ij})\, x_i x_j \tag{13}$$

Similarly, if third-order correlations are retained, the above derivation gives

$$\begin{aligned} &\sum_{i=1}^{N} \left[a_i + \sum_{j \neq i} (-m_j u_{ij} + n_j v_{ij}) + \sum_{\substack{j \neq i \\ k \neq i \\ j<k}} (m_j m_k u_{ijk} - n_j n_k v_{ijk})\right] x_i \\ &+ \sum_{i<j} \left[(u_{ij} - v_{ij}) + \sum_{\substack{k \neq i \\ k \neq j}} (-m_k u_{ijk} + n_k v_{ijk})\right] x_i x_j + \sum_{i<j<k} (u_{ijk} - v_{ijk})\, x_i x_j x_k \end{aligned} \tag{14}$$

The above expressions come from Bahadur (1959a). Here we note that second-, third-, and higher order approximations give rise to expressions linear in the x_i, under certain conditions. In (13), if $u_{ij} = v_{ij}$, the resulting classification function is represented by a network such as that of Fig. 1, in which the coefficients are given by

$$a_i^{(2)} = a_i + \sum_{j \neq i} (-m_j + n_j)\, v_{ij} \tag{15}$$

Similarly, (14) will lead to a classification function, linear in the x_i, if $u_{ijk} = v_{ijk}$, and

$$u_{ij} = v_{ij} + \sum_{\substack{k \neq i \\ k \neq j}} (m_k - n_k)\, v_{ijk}$$

the coefficients of the classification function being

$$a_i^{(3)} = a_i + \sum_{j \neq i} (-m_j u_{ij} + n_j v_{ij}) + \sum_{\substack{j \neq i \\ k \neq i \\ j < k}} (m_j m_k - n_j n_k) v_{ijk} \qquad (16)$$

In this manner, a set of classification functions

$$\sum_{i=1}^{N} a_i x_i, \sum_{i=1}^{N} a_i^{(2)} x_i, \ldots, \sum_{i=1}^{N} a_i^{(N)} x_i$$

corresponding to increasing orders of approximation to the joint distributions of the x_i in the two groups, are obtained when specific assumptions are made about the relationships between correlation parameters. The network corresponding to each of these classification functions has the form of Fig. 1; a network which attempted to classify correctly eight groups of patterns could be constructed from three classification functions of the type used in Fig. 1. The performance of such networks relative to corresponding networks based on classification functions of the form (13), (14), and higher order approximations will be determined by the extent to which assumptions about relationships between correlation parameters, necessary to obtain the above linear classification functions, are true for a given experimental situation.

In addition to the above derivation, one can consider various intuitive procedures for deriving linear classification functions. An arbitrary linear combination of the measurements $(x_1, x_2, \ldots, x_N)$ is the function $\sum_{i=1}^{N} a_i x_i$, in which the coefficients a_i are to be chosen to provide maximum discrimination (in some sense) between the two groups. An example of such a procedure is that due to Fisher (1936). Let m_i and n_i represent the means of the x_i for group 1 and group 2 respectively, and let $d_i = m_i - n_i$. The difference in mean values of the linear function for the two groups is $\sum_{i=1}^{N} a_i d_i$. Furthermore, the function $\sum_{i=1}^{N} a_i x_i$ has the variance $\sum_{i=1}^{N} \sum_{j=1}^{N} a_i a_j v_{ij}$ where v_{ij} are elements of the covariance matrix, assumed equal for the two groups. The sense in which maximum discrimination between the two groups is provided by Fisher's discriminant function is to choose the coefficients a_i such as to maximize the ratio

$$\frac{(\Sigma a_i d_i)^2}{\sum_{i=1}^{N} \sum_{j=1}^{N} a_i a_j v_{ij}}$$

Introducing a Lagrangian multiplier λ and differentiating the expression

$$\Sigma \Sigma a_i a_j d_i d_j - \lambda \Sigma \Sigma a_i a_j v_{ij}$$

one obtains a set of linear equations which have the solutions

$$a_i = v^{1i} d_1 + \cdots + v^{Ni} d_N \qquad i = 1, 2, \ldots, N$$

where v^{ji} are elements of the inverse of the common covariance matrix. This same function results from a likelihood-ratio procedure for the case of continuous variables with multivariate normal distributions and equal covariance matrices for the two groups, and so it is the optimum discriminant function only when these specific conditions hold; without the assumption of equal covariance matrices, a quadratic function would result from the likelihood ratio (Rao, 1952,

Chap. 8; Anderson, 1958, Chap. 6). For the latter case, intuitive procedures which lead to linear discriminant functions can be considered. Examples are the Anderson-Bahadur method (1960) which for the case of arbitrary distributions, maximizes the ratio

$$\frac{\sum_{i=1}^{N} a_i d_i}{\left(\sum_{i=1}^{N}\sum_{j=1}^{N} a_i a_j v_{ij1}\right)^{1/2} + \left(\sum_{i=1}^{N}\sum_{j=1}^{N} a_i a_j v_{ij2}\right)^{1/2}}$$

i.e., the ratio of the difference between means to the sum of the standard deviations and the linear discriminant functions presented by Kullback (1959, Chaps. 9 and 13) obtained by maximizing three measures of information.

4. DETERMINATION OF COEFFICIENTS FROM SAMPLES

From the discussion up to this point it is apparent that, for the most part, the class of pattern-recognition networks considered in section 1 continue to be excursions in the realm of linear discriminant functions. It is also clear that the use of a weighted sum of the x_i as the classification function does not, as some have suggested, limit the x_i to being independent, but may imply a variety of relationships among correlations and covariances of the type present in the examples of linear discriminant functions given in the last section.

The major departure of the pattern-recognition efforts being discussed from the work in linear discriminant functions is the manner in which samples are used. Rather than obtain the coefficients of the classification function from assumptions concerning the functional form of the probability distributions or from a program of estimation, interest has shifted to starting from an arbitrary initial state $(a_1', a_2', \ldots, a_N')$ and using iteration based on experience with one or more samples on each trial, to go from the initial state to a final state $(a_1, a_2, \ldots, a_N)$ which will produce a desired result.

The problem of using experience to go from some arbitrary initial state of coefficients to a final desired state can be approached in many ways; one way is to use completely random perturbation of the coefficients and some of the adaptive systems presented at this symposium report using this method. One would generally desire somewhat more systematic methods which, at least conceptually, have a better chance of producing a sequence of adjustments which converge in some meaningful sense. The problem may then be stated as one of finding a set of transition operators T to apply to the state vector. In this form, varying degrees of complexity can be introduced into the formulation of the problem, as is discussed by Bellman (1961). However, complexity in formulation which introduces complexity in computation is not very helpful; the procedures which are desirable are those which involve simple calculations after each trial and do not require the storage of old data for use in future computations. Useful iteration procedures can be derived from the point of view provided by the techniques used in stochastic models for learning (Bush and Mosteller, 1955; Bush and Estes, 1959; Luce, 1959; Kanal, 1961; Kanal, 1962) and from the point of view provided by stochastic approximation methods (Dvoretsky, 1956; Sakrison, 1961; Kushner, 1960; Magee, 1960). Typical of a number of other efforts is the approach of minimizing a mean-square error criterion (Widrow, 1960; Widrow and Hoff, 1960; Gabor et al., 1961).

5. SOME COMMENTS ON COMPARING DESIGN PROCEDURES

The embodiment of adaptive procedures in a real-time pattern-recognition system is most desirable when the environment in which the system operates can undergo unsuspected changes. However, when the environment is stationary, the design of a pattern-recognition network corresponding to a given form for the classification function can be carried out on a computer. In this case the coefficients can be obtained either by using the data directly in an iterative procedure, or using statistical estimation of parameters to obtain classification functions such as outlined in section 3. Computer programs for obtaining discriminant functions and other classification functions for application in a variety of fields have been used for a number of years. Typical of some recent applications to speech and character recognition is the work reported in Marill and Green (1960), Welch and Wimpress (1961), and Keith-Smith and Klem (1961), from which an idea of the computation involved can be obtained. One point of comparison between the various methods one may consider is, of course, the relative complexity of the computation.

The error curve corresponding to a classification function can be obtained by computing the probabilities of misclassification for different choices of the threshold. An evaluation of the worth of the classification functions resulting when iteration based on experience is used to obtain the coefficients from samples can be provided by comparing their error curves with error curves obtained from the linear functions corresponding to the different orders of approximations as discussed in section 3, and with the error curves obtained from intuitive procedures such as those of Fisher (1936), Anderson and Bahadur (1960), and Kullback (1959).

6. SOME COMMENTS ON THE CHOICE OF OBSERVABLES, AND ON INVARIANCE PROPERTIES

It has been long recognized that a central problem is the choice of a suitable set of observables and, for the most part, an arbitrary choice has been made, as for example, the choice of dichotomous variables obtained from the elements of an "artificial retina."

Experience indicates that when using procedures which are not optimum, a classification procedure based on dividing the x_i into mutually exclusive subsets s_j, deriving classification functions f_j based separately on the s_j, and using f_j to obtain a final classification function F can, in some situations, do better than a similar function based directly on all the x_i. (In most of the work reported on the type of network represented by Fig. 2, subsets of dichotomous variables have been chosen in a random manner and arbitrary fixed weights have been used to form the first set of classification functions f_j.)

A discussion of the problem of selecting a small number of dichotomous variables from an available large set is presented in the paper by Raiffa (1957).

Some comments on the invariance of two measures of information to nonsingular transformations of the observables, and on the connection between the invariant properties and linear discriminant functions are presented in Kullback (1959). The paper by Ming-kuei Hu (1961) presents a set of moment-invariants. It should be noted that for most situations these moments will themselves be random variables.

ACKNOWLEDGMENT

The author is indebted to C. F. Fey for the computer simulation of various pattern-recognition procedures and to D. F. Smith for his contribution to a comparative study of a number of pattern-recognition devices. He wishes to thank J. Owen for helpful comments made at the presentation of this paper. He also wishes to thank K. K. Maitra for many helpful discussions related to the author's work, and N. F. Finkelstein for his encouragement and support.

REFERENCES

Anderson, T.W. 1958. An introduction to multivariate statistical analysis. John Wiley & Sons, New York.
Anderson, T.W. and Bahadur, R.R. 1960. Classification into multivariate normal distributions with unequal covariance matrices. Paper presented at Inst. Math. Stat. Meeting, Wash., D.C., Jan.
Bahadur, R.R. 1959a. On classification based on responses to n dichotomous items. USAF SAM series in Statistics, Randolph AFB, Texas.
Bahadur, R.R. 1959b. A representation of the joint distribution of responses to n dichotomous items. USAF SAM series in Statistics Rept. 59-42, Randolph AFB, Texas.
Bellman, R. 1961. Adaptive control: a guided tour. Princeton Univ. Press, Princeton, N.J.
Bush, R.R. and Estes, W.K. (ed.) 1959. Studies in mathematical learning theory. Stanford Univ. Press.
Bush, R.R. and Mosteller, F. 1955. Stochastic models for learning. John Wiley & Sons, New York.
Dvoretsky, A. 1956. On stochastic approximation. In: Third Berkeley symposium on mathematical statistics and probability. Univ. Calif. Press.
Fisher, R.A. 1936. The use of multiple measurements in taxonomic problems. In: Contributions to mathematical statistics, John Wiley & Sons, New York.
Gabor, D., Wilby, W., and Woodcock, R. 1961. A universal nonlinear filter, predictor and simulator which optimizes itself by a learning process. Proc. Inst. Elec. Engrs. 108, Part B.
Hawkins, J.K. 1961. Self-organizing systems—a review and commentary. Proc. IRE, Jan., 31-48.
Hu, Ming-kuei. 1961. Pattern recognition by moment invariants. Letter to the Editor, Proc. IRE, Sept.
Kanal, L. 1961. On a random walk related to a nonlinear learning model. IRE Internat. Convention Record, Part 2, Mar.
Kanal, L. 1962. A functional equation analysis of two learning models. Psychometrika, Vol. 27, Mar.
Keith-Smith, J.E. and Klem, L. 1961. Vowel recognition using a multiple discriminant function. Letter to the editor. J. Acoust. Soc. Am., p. 358, Mar.
Kullback, S. 1959. Information theory and statistics. John Wiley & Sons, New York.
Kushner, H. Efficient iterative methods for optimizing the performance of multiparameter noisy systems. M.I.T. Lincoln Lab. Rept. No. 22G-0043, Oct.
Luce, R.D. 1959. Individual choice behaviour. John Wiley & Sons, New York.
Magee, E.J. 1960. An empirical investigation of procedures for locating the maximum peak regression function. M.I.T. Lincoln Lab. Rept. 22G-0046, Oct.
Marill, T. and Green, D.M. 1960. Statistical recognition functions and the design of pattern recognizers. IRE PGEC Trans., Dec.
Raiffa, H. 1957. Statistical decision theory approach to item selection for dichotomous test and criterion variables. Rept. 56-139. SAM Series in Statistics. Randolph AFB, Texas.
Rao, C.R. 1952. Advanced statistical methods in biometric research. John Wiley & Sons, New York.
Sakrison, D. 1961. Application of stochastic approximation methods to optimum filter design. IRE Internat. Convention Record, Part 4.
Welch, P.D. and Wimpress, R.S. 1961. Two multivariate statistical computer programs and their application to the vowel recognition problem. J. Acoust. Soc. Am., Apr.
Widrow, B. 1960. Adaptive sampled-data systems. IFAC Moscow Congress Record. Butterworth Publications, London.
Widrow, B. and Hoff, M.E. 1960. Adaptive switching circuits. Tech. Rept. 1553-1. Stanford Electronics Lab., Stanford Univ., Calif., June.

A SEQUENTIAL DECISION MODEL FOR OPTIMUM RECOGNITION

K. S. Fu

School of Electrical Engineering, Purdue University
Lafayette, Indiana

INTRODUCTION

It has been recognized in recent years that the problem of pattern recognition can be viewed as a test of statistical hypotheses. A concise explanation of this theoretical approach to the recognition problem may be obtained by considering the statistical decision process as a zero-sum two-person statistical game. The two players will be referred to as nature and the decision maker, i.e., the recognition system. A non-negative weighting function measures the loss incurred by the decision maker as a consequence of each possible decision. The aim of the decision maker is to minimize the expectation of the loss in recognition.

If it is important to speed up the recognition process, one usually is led to consider sequential tests. The process of recognition may be considered as a multivalued, sequential test which proceeds in successive stages. The trading relationship that commonly exists in perceptual tasks between time and error has been examined. In this process, the observer decides after each observation whether to make a terminal decision or to request another observation before making a terminal decision. The physical model which performs the test is called a sequential decision model. The major feature of the model is that it requires less average recognition time as compared with that of a nonsequential decision model.

RECOGNITION AS A STATISTICAL DECISION PROBLEM

The statistical decision problem has been formulated in a form broad enough to include (1) the state of a priori knowledge, (2) losses associated with a false outcome, and (3) costs of experimentation. The problem is considered in relation to a sequence of random variables, say $x_1, x_2, \ldots, x_n$, denoted by $\{x\}$ which may represent, e.g., the results of a set of property measurements of the object to be recognized. Let Ω be a parameter space. It is divided into zones $w_1, w_2, \ldots, w_m$ such that w_i corresponds to the class of true signal associated with the ith object, where m is the number of possible objects to be recognized. To each point in the parameter space there corresponds a set of values of parameters $\{\theta\}$. Let H_i denote the hypothesis that $\{\theta\}$ lies in w_i. To each set of possible values of $\{x\}$ there corresponds a point in the n-dimensional sample space Δ. The space Δ is in turn subdivided into zones $\delta_1, \delta_2, \ldots, \delta_m$ such that hypothesis H_i is to be accepted if, and only if, $\{x\}$ fall in δ_i. A statistical decision problem can now be defined as the problem of selecting the zones $\delta_1, \delta_2, \ldots, \delta_m$ in the sample space Δ, given the zones $w_1, w_2, \ldots, w_m$ in the parameter space Ω.

Let $P = (P_1, P_2, \ldots, P_m)$ be the a priori distributions defined over the space Ω. P_i is the a priori probability that an object belongs to w_i. The space of decision D available to the recognition system consists of m possible decisions $d_1, d_2, \ldots, d_m$, where d_i is the decision that the hypothesis H_i is accepted. The weighting function $L(w_i, d_j)$ is the loss incurred by the recognition system if the decision d_j is made when the ith object actually occurs. A recognition system based on a statistical decision process is a machine that will automatically indicate the optimum decision rule for each set of measurements presented to the machine.

In the case of a nonsequential decision process, for any decision rule, d, the conditional risk in recognition of the objects belonging to class w_i may be written

$$r(w_i, d) = \int_{\Delta} L(w_i, d)\, p_{w_i}(x)\, dx \tag{1}$$

with integration over the entire space Δ. $p_{w_i}(x)$ is the conditional probability of x if w_i is the true class of the measured object. For given P, the average risk is

$$R(P, d) = \sum_{i=1}^{m} P_i\, r(w_i, d) \tag{2}$$

or

$$R(P,d) = \int_{\Delta} p(x)\, r_x(P, d)\, dx \tag{3}$$

where

$$r_x(P, d) = \frac{\sum_{i=1}^{m} L(w_i, d)\, P_i p_{w_i}(x)}{p(x)} \tag{4}$$

is defined as a posteriori conditional risk of the decision rule d for the given measurement x.

The problem is then to choose a decision rule to minimize the average risk $R(P, d)$, or to minimize the maximum of the conditional risk $r(w_i, d)$ (minimax). The decision rule which minimizes the average risk is called Bayes' rule. From (3) it is sufficient to consider each x separately and to minimize $r_x(P, d)$. If d' is Bayes' rule,

$$r_x(P, d') \leq r_x(P, d) \tag{5}$$

That is,

$$\sum_{i=1}^{m} L(w_i, d')\, P_i p_{w_i}(x) \leq \sum_{i=1}^{m} L(w_i, d)\, P_i p_{w_i}(x) \tag{6}$$

For the loss function

$$L(w_i, d_j) = \begin{cases} 0 & i = j \\ v & i \neq j \end{cases} \tag{7}$$

and, without loss of generality, let $v = 1$; it is easily shown that the risk function is essentially the probability of misrecognition. In order to minimize the probability of misrecognition, d_i must be chosen if

$$P_i p_{w_i}(x) \geq P_j p_{w_j}(x) \text{ for all } i \neq j \tag{8}$$

Define

$$\lambda_{ij} = \frac{p_{w_i}(x)}{p_{w_j}(x)} \tag{9}$$

as the likelihood ratio; the Bayes decision becomes d_i, i.e., H_i is accepted, if

$$\lambda_{ij} \geq \frac{P_j}{P_i} \text{ for all } i \neq j$$

The functional diagram of the Bayes' rule model is shown in Fig. 1.

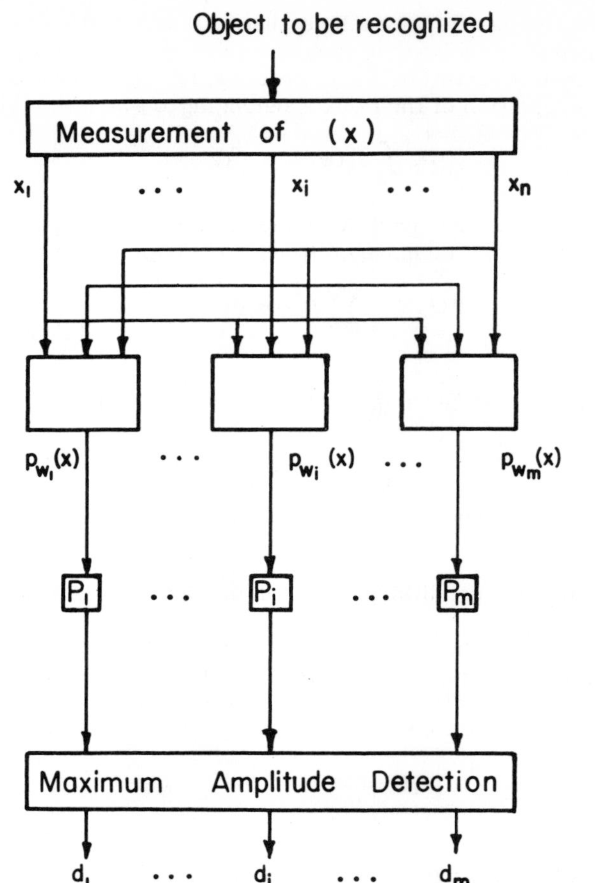

Fig. 1

If the number of possible objects to be recognized is very large, a "sequential tree" scheme may be used instead of the "parallel processing" scheme in Fig. 1. The concept of the "sequential tree" scheme is to reduce a multiple-decision problem to a multiple-stage binary classification problem. Consider an object in which we observe the characteristics $\{x\}$, which is known to come from one of two groups Δ_1 and Δ_2, but it is not known from which. In this case, the space Ω consists of only two subspaces, Ω_1 and Ω_2. The probability distribution of $\{x\}$ is given by $p_{\Omega_1}(x)$ if the individual belongs to Ω_1, and $p_{\Omega_2}(x)$ if the individual belongs to Ω_2. Bayes' rule can be directly applied to reach the optimum decision. After it has been decided to which group the object belongs, say Δ_1, the group Δ_1 is again divided into two subgroups, Δ_{11} and Δ_{12}. A second experiment is performed to decide to which of the subgroups the object belongs. Continuing this process (it is also known as discriminant analysis) until the subspace in Ω which corresponds to each of the two subgroups contains only one single class, w_i, the object will then be recognized by performing one additional experiment. The test procedure is illustrated in Fig. 2. Only a binary decision problem needs to be treated at each stage. Sometimes an optimum system may prove to be too expensive for mechanization. The "sequential tree" scheme may need a lesser number of computations, but the time required for recognition may be more as compared with "parallel processing" scheme.

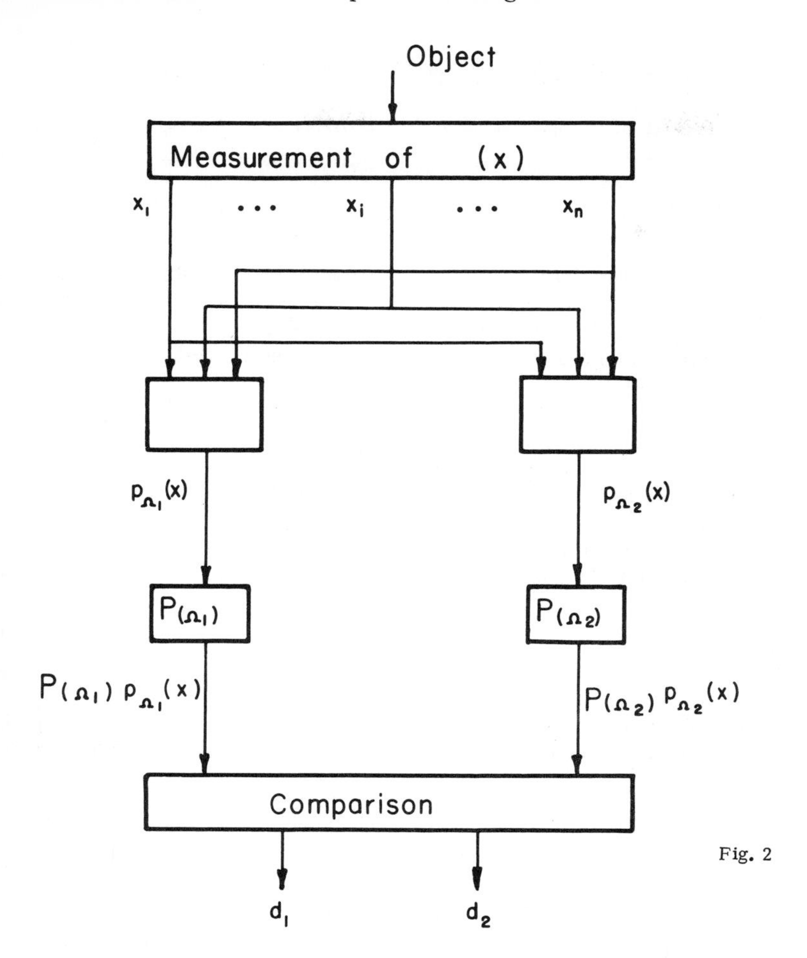

Fig. 2

RECOGNITION AS A SEQUENTIAL TEST PROBLEM

In the nonsequential decision model described above, the number of observations, i.e., the size of the sample n on which the test is based, is fixed. The test is carried out exactly in one experiment. Instead of exhausting all n observations in one stage, the recognition system might take observations in sequence, and at each stage decide on the basis of the information thus far collected whether to stop experimenting or to take another observation. The sequential method of testing a hypothesis H may be described as follows. A rule is given for making one of the following three decisions at each stage of the test: (1) to accept the hypothesis H, (2) to reject the hypothesis H, and (3) to continue the experiment by making an additional observation. Corresponding to these three decisions, the sample space Δ is divided into three zones: the zone of preference for acceptance, the zone of preference for rejection, and the zone of indifference. Thus, such a test is carried out sequentially. The process is continued until either the first or the second decision is made. The number of observations n required by such a test procedure is a random variable since the value of n depends on the outcome of the observations.

The sequential risk function for any sampling plan S and decision rule d is defined as

$$r(w_i, S, d) = \sum_{k=0}^{N} \sum_{x \in S_k} \left\{ c_k(x) + L[w_i; d(k, x)] \right\} p_{w_i}(x) \tag{10}$$

where $c(x)$ is the cost of observation. N is the total number of stages. The average risk is

$$R(P,S,d) = \sum_{k=0}^{N} \sum_{x \in S_k} \sum_{i=1}^{m} \left\{ c_k(x) + L[w_i; d(k,x)] \right\} P_i p_{w_i}(x) \tag{11}$$

For testing a simple hypothesis H_1 against a single alternative H_0, the sequential test procedure is defined as follows. At the kth stage of the experiment, let $p_{1k}(x)$ be the probability distribution of x when H_1 is true, and $p_{0k}(x)$ be the probability distribution of x when H_0 is true. The sequential probability ratio is computed.

$$\lambda_k = \frac{p_{1k}(x)}{p_{0k}(x)} \tag{12}$$

If $\lambda_k \geq A$, the process is terminated with the acceptance of H_1. If $\lambda_k \leq B$, the process is terminated with the rejection of H_1 (acceptance of H_0). If $B < \lambda_k < A$ the experiment is continued by taking an additional observation. The constants A and $B \, (B < A)$ are related with the specified error (α, β) by the following relations

$$A \leq \frac{1-\beta}{\alpha} \tag{13}$$

$$B \geq \frac{\beta}{1-\alpha} \tag{14}$$

where α = probability of accepting H_1 when H_0 is true, and β = probability of accepting H_0 when H_1 is true. For independently and identically distributed observations

$$\lambda_k = \frac{\prod_{j=1}^{k} f_1(x_j)}{\prod_{j=1}^{k} f_0(x_j)} \tag{15}$$

Wald and Wolfowitz have shown that: (1) The sequential probability ratio test is optimal in the sense that for given a priori probabilities, it minimizes the average risk; (2) for assigned (α, β), this test minimizes the average number of observations. It is also noted that the operation of the sequential ratio test is essentially independent of a priori information P, although the average risk or cost of recognition necessarily depends on the a priori data.

In recognition problems it is seldom the case that the number of possible objects to be recognized is only two. For the case of more than two objects, the sequential ratio test may be applied through several modifications. In testing a simple hypothesis H_i against a set of alternatives, the zone of preference for acceptance consists of the single parameter point $\{\theta\} = \theta^i$. Denote the zone of preference for rejection by Ω_r. This will usually be the set of all points θ whose "distance" from θ^i is greater than or equal to some given positive value. For any θ in Ω_r, let $\beta(\theta)$ denote the probability that H_i will be accepted when H_r is true. A weighting function $W(\theta) \geq 0$, for all θ in Ω_r, is chosen such that

$$\int_{\Omega_r} \beta(\theta) W(\theta) \, d\theta = \beta \tag{16}$$

and

$$\int_{\Omega_r} W(\theta) \, d\theta = 1$$

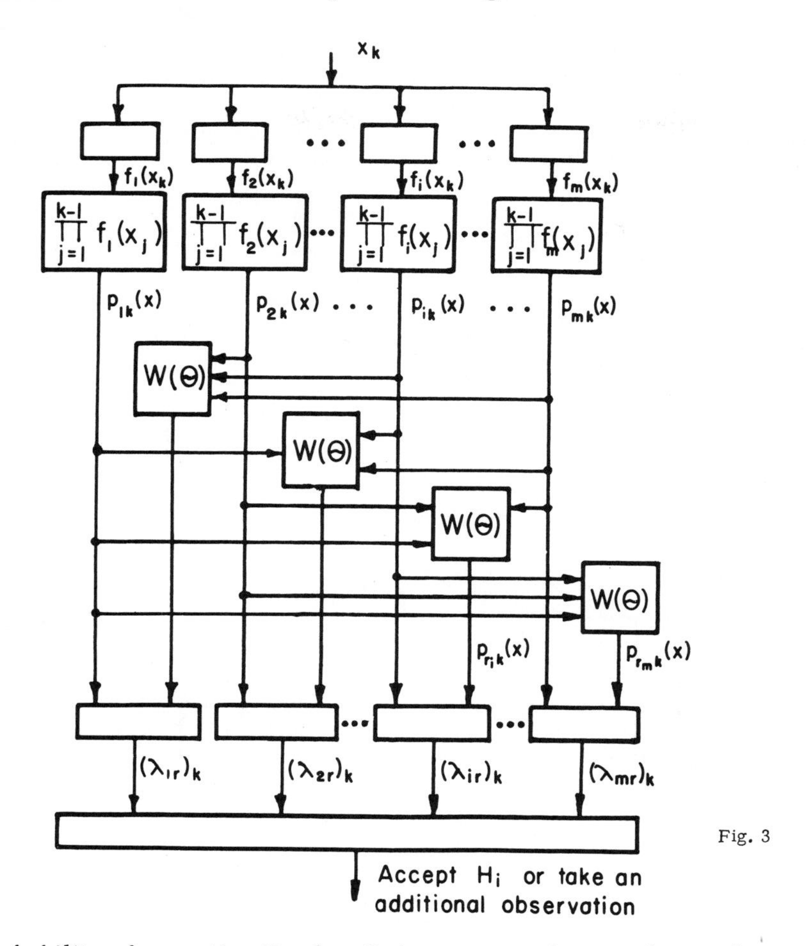

Fig. 3

The probability of accepting H_r when H_i is true remains equal to α. Let

$$p_{ik}(x) = f_i(x_1)\, f_i(x_2) \ldots f_i(x_k) \tag{17}$$

be the probability distribution of x when H_i is true, and

$$p_{rk}(x) = \int_{\Omega_r} f_\theta(x_1)\, f_\theta(x_2) \ldots f_\theta(x_k)\, W(\theta)\, d\theta \tag{18}$$

be the probability distribution of x when H_r is true.* Thus, the test procedure is given as follows. Reject H_i if

$$\lambda_k = \frac{p_{rk}(x)}{p_{ik}(x)} \geq A$$

accept H_i if $\lambda_k \leq B$, and take an additional observation if $B < \lambda_k < A$. For given values of A and B, a reasonable choice of $W(\theta)$ is to select a $W(\theta)$ for which the maximum of $\beta(\theta)$ with respect to θ in Ω_r takes its smallest values. The functional diagram for such a sequential decision model is shown in Fig. 3.

Note that the system shown in Fig. 3 belongs to the "parallel processing" scheme. Parallel to the system in Fig. 2, a "sequential tree" scheme can also

*Instead of defining p_{rk} by equation (18), p_{rk} may also be defined more conservatively as the maximum of $f_\theta(x_1)\, f_\theta(x_2) \ldots f_\theta(x_k)$ with respect to $\theta \in \Omega_r$.

be formulated in sequential analysis. This corresponds to the case of testing composite hypotheses. In testing a composite hypothesis H that the parameter point θ lies in a subset of the parameter space, the zone of preference for acceptance Ω_a will now consist of more than one parameter point. Two weighting functions $W_a(\theta)$ and $W_r(\theta)$ will be chosen such that

$$\int_{\Omega_a} \alpha(\theta)\, W_a(\theta)\, d\theta = \alpha \tag{19}$$

$$\int_{\Omega_r} \beta(\theta)\, W_r(\theta)\, d\theta = \beta \tag{20}$$

A proper sequential test satisfying these modified requirements can be constructed as follows. Let p_{0k} and p_{1k} be defined by

$$p_{0k} = \int_{\Omega_a} f_\theta(x_1)\, f_\theta(x_2) \ldots f_\theta(x_k)\, W_a(\theta)\, d\theta \tag{21}$$

and

$$p_{1k} = \int_{\Omega_r} f_\theta(x_1)\, f_\theta(x_2) \ldots f_\theta(x_k)\, W_r(\theta)\, d\theta \tag{22}$$

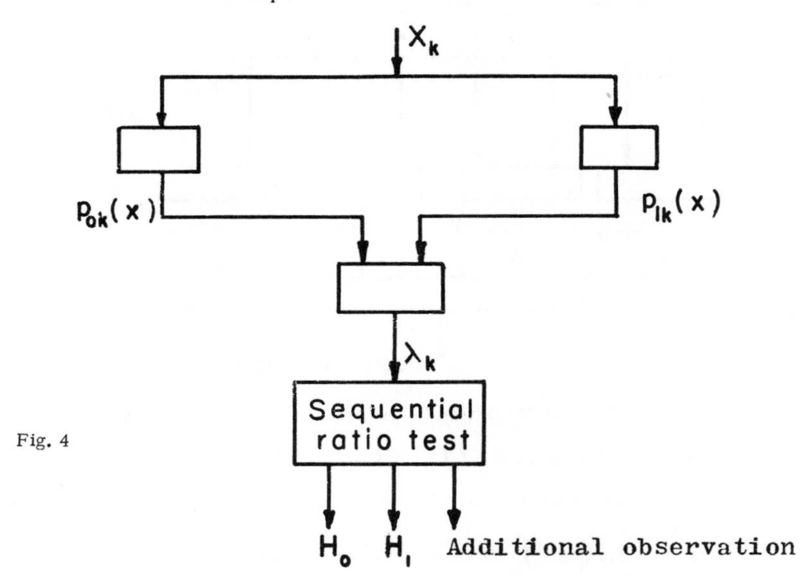

Fig. 4

Denote by H_0 the hypothesis that the distribution of the sample $(x_1, x_2, \ldots, x_k)$ is given by (21), and by H_1 the hypothesis that the distribution of $(x_1, x_2, \ldots, x_k)$ is given by (22). The sequential probability ratio test for testing H_0 against H_1 provides a solution which indicates whether the object required to be recognized belongs to the class Ω_a or not (i.e., belongs to Ω_r). For given values A and B, the weighting functions $W_a(\theta)$ and $W_r(\theta)$ may be regarded as more desirable the smaller they make the maximum values of $\alpha(\theta)$ and $\beta(\theta)$. Repeat this classification process successively and at each stage of the classification discriminate the class to which the object does not belong. A smaller subclass which the object still belongs to will be formed until the object is recognized. The operation is illustrated in Fig. 4.

TRUNCATED SEQUENTIAL TESTS

A standard sequential test procedure may be unsatisfactory because: (1) an individual test may last longer than can be tolerated, and (2) the average length of the test becomes extremely large if α and β are chosen to be very small. In some situations it may become virtually necessary to interrupt the standard procedure and resolve between the alternative courses of action. This can be achieved by truncating the sequential process at $n = N$. The new rules of decision procedure will be the following. Carry out the regular sequential test until either a decision is made or stage N of the test is reached. If no decision has been reached at stage N, accept the hypothesis H_0 if $\lambda_N \leq 1$, or accept the hypothesis H_1 if $\lambda_N \geq 1$. Under the new rule the test must terminate in, at most, N stages. Truncation is a compromise between an entirely sequential test and a classical, fixed-sample test. It is an attempt to reconcile the good features of both of them: the sequential feature of examining observations as they accumulate and the classical feature of guaranteeing that the tolerances will be met with a specified sample size.

* * *

Part of this work was done by the author during the summer of 1961 at IBM Thomas J. Watson Research Center, Yorktown Heights, N.Y.

REFERENCES

Blackwell, D. and Girshick, M. A. 1954. Theory of games and statistical decisions. John Wiley & Sons, New York.

Bussgang, J. J. and Middleton, D. 1955. Optimum sequential detection of signals in noise. Trans. IRE on Inf. Theory. Dec., 5-18.

Chow, C. K. 1957. An optimum character recognition system using decision functions. Trans. IRE on Electronic Computers. Dec., 247-253.

Hawkins, J. K. 1961. Self-organizing systems—a review and commentary. Proc. IRE. Jan., 31-48.

Highleyman, W. H. 1961. A note on optimum pattern recognition systems. Trans. IRE on Electronic Computers. June, 287-288.

Middleton, D. 1960. Introduction to statistical communication theory. Part 4. McGraw-Hill, New York.

Minsky, M. 1961. Steps toward artificial intelligence. Proc. IRE. Jan., 8-30.

Swets, J. A. 1961. Detection theory and psychophysics. Psychometrika 26, 1, 49-63.

Tanner, W. P., Jr. Mathematical models in sensory perception. Proc. First Bionics Symposium. 263-286. WADD Tech. Rept. 60-600.

Wald, A. 1947. Sequential analysis. John Wiley & Sons, New York.

Wald, A. 1950. Statistical decision functions. John Wiley & Sons, New York.

Wald, A. and Wolfowitz, J. 1948. Optimum character of the sequential probability ratio test. Ann. Math. Stat. 19, 326-339.

MACHINE INTERPRETATION OF RADAR DISPLAYS

A. J. Cote, Jr.

The Johns Hopkins University
Applied Physics Laboratory
Silver Spring, Maryland

The development of radar systems is being hampered by a continually increasing conflict between complexity, reliability, size, and cost on one hand, and more sophisticated performance requirements on the other hand. Yet many of the data-processing operations which must be carried out by these man-made systems are also carried out by the living biological systems found throughout the natural world. These living systems operate reliably with unreliable components; they are self-adjusting; and they are capable of altering their operation to cope with unforeseen conditions. Thus, it is not surprising that man is beginning to look more closely at nature for possible solutions to his data-processing problems. A portion of the initial activity in this effort is reported in this volume and in previous publications (Yovitts and Cameron, 1960; Bionics Symposium, 1960), and this paper discuss some aspects of an attempt to apply such a design philosophy to the development of a specific radar subsystem.

It should be noted at the outset that the subsystem was not realized and is not likely to be in the near future. The purpose of this paper is to stimulate interest in the general approach which was proposed to solve the problem, since it is the writer's contention that the major obstacle to implementation is the lack of suitable components, rather than the lack of a satisfactory approach. One might also argue that the approach is unsatisfactory if it cannot be implemented with presently available components, and the writer is only "passing the buck" in requesting the device designer to provide a suitable component. However, employing available components may result in a more complex systems approach than is necessary or practical. In any event, having read the paper, the reader is invited to draw his own conclusions as to the merit in the proposed approach.

The problem to be treated is basically one of pattern recognition. Much of the material published in this field reflects a heavy emphasis on digital-computer techniques, apparently because of the ready availability of both analytical methods and hardware. Yet, there is no basis for concluding that digital approaches are more applicable to the problem than the few analog methods which are occasionally proposed. It is the writer's opinion that the analog approach will lead to the more versatile general-purpose pattern-recognition device, but the components required to implement the device do not presently exist and, unfortunately, nobody is trying to develop them.

Having thus clearly positioned myself far out on the wrong end of a weak limb in a high tree, I shall proceed to arm the saw.

THE MAN AND THE FROG

A man can view a radar display cluttered with noise and recognize those signals corresponding to aircraft. By noting the direction in which they move, their speeds and positions relative to each other, he can make an approximate estimate as to which aircraft will be the first to reach a critical location on the display. In attempting to design a machine which will emulate the man's ability to interpret the radar display, it will be assumed that he carries out his task by using a process of visual pattern recognition. The machine design philosophy will be to try and process the visual data in the same way that man does; hence, it is appropriate to consider his wiring in some detail. Unfortunately, the complexity of the human and animal nervous systems is such that only crude data are available concerning their properties. Hence, the system design for the machine proposed in this paper is the result of a precarious extrapolation of available data and should not necessarily be construed as a valid explanation for the operation of the nervous system. However, it is of interest to review briefly the biological data which are the basis for the proposed system. But before this is done, consider in more detail the nature of the man's problem.

Figure 1 illustrates a B-scan radar display on which spots of light are positioned at the present range and bearing of all targets. For our reference purposes, each of the three targets is numbered and their respective directions of motion are indicated. It is the radar operator's function to monitor the motion of the spots and perhaps continually evaluate which target is apt to be the first to

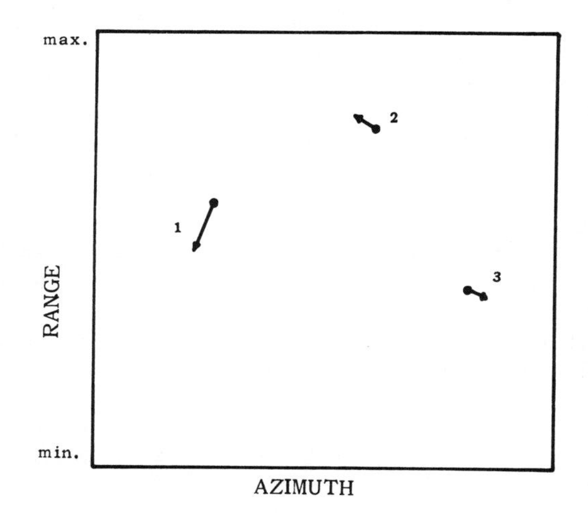

Fig. 1. A B-scan radar display.

reach a critical area on the display, e.g., zero range. In arriving at a solution to this latter problem, he is influenced by the target's present position, its recent speed, and its heading. Thus, in the case of Fig. 1, he will eliminate target 2 from consideration (although he will continue to monitor it in case it should change course and speed), and compare the paths of targets 1 and 3. If both have about the same speeds, he may not be able to clearly decide between the two. However, if 1 is moving much faster than 3, it is clear that it will probably reach zero range first and the operator will so estimate.

Note that in arriving at his decision he makes no complex computations, and his choice is only a rough estimate. In addition, his observations are frequently made using a display cluttered with additional randomly occurring spots of noise, referred to as "false alarms." At any given time, the false alarms and targets are very similar in appearance, and only the time history of the return serves to help the operator distinguish the two.

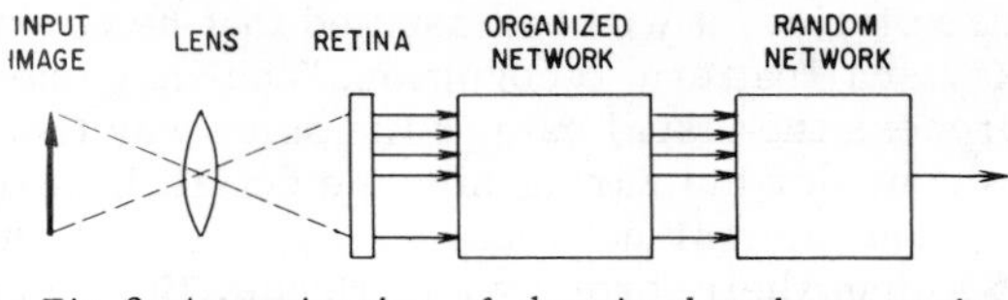

Fig. 2. Approximation of the visual pathway to the brain.

Our purpose here is to consider how this task might be carried out by a machine whose wiring, if possible, is patterned after that of the man.

The eye sends visual data to the brain via the path shown in Fig. 2. The input image is focused by the lens of the eye onto the retina, which is an array of over 10^8 sensing elements. These elements, and the following several layers of cells to which they are connected, appear to be topologically oriented in a purposeful pattern. It has been suggested that this portion of the system serves to filter and classify the visual images presented to the eye; hence, we should try to copy its wiring in any machine we design. However, since there is little information concerning the transfer function of this portion of the human nervous system, we must employ our knowledge of the retinal networks in the lower forms of life. Fortunately, recent experiments carried out on frogs (Lettvin et al., 1959) are particularly applicable to our problem.

These experiments indicate that the frog's eye and its associated optic nerve network are particularly suited to the observation of objects the size of flies, a not-surprising property considering his diet. To be successful at fly catching, it would seem that he should first be able to distinguish the moving fly from a diverse, essentially stationary background and then obtain information concerning its present position, speed, heading, and estimated time of arrival within range of his tongue. Thus, with a little imagination, we can see the similarity between the frog's pattern-recognition problem and that which confronts the radar observer. Knowledge of the properties of neurons in the frog's data-processing net might be of use in the design of a display interpretation machine. The specific properties (McCullough et al., 1959) which have led to the approach proposed in this paper are as follows:

a. "Some neurons have a moderately low sensitivity but a wide receptive field... The magnitude of the response also depends on a factor with a long time constant...."
b. "A second group is much like the first except for having narrow fields and high sensitivity."
c. Both groups respond with a frequency which is related to a direction of motion of the object in the field.
d. A third group is much like the other two except that "...the field has a large hole in the center." Neurons in this group were always found "...paired with their complementary fibers–that is, those responding to the hole."
e. It was also observed that "...the response of a fiber to an appropriate stimulus occasionally seems to be dependent, in part, upon the history of the stimulus before it arrives at the receptive field."

It would appear that both items c and e would be of value in the pattern-recognition device for either recognizing aircraft within noise or comparing the characteristics of several aircraft flight paths. Although the other properties do not seem useful, they are not ignored. Instead, it is assumed that they may represent the characteristics of neurons which are at some intermediate stage in the data processing which leads to properties c and e. Then, be executing the most primitive form of synthesis (i.e., trial and error and a large amount of luck!), the organization of a useful data-processing system can be obtained.

The approach to be employed is as follows. Items a and b, above, suggest that the retina should contain two basic types of sensing units. Beginning with this premise, and postulating properties not unlike those of the frog, it will be shown that by properly combining their outputs, a speed-and-direction-sensitive property filter can be obtained. The filter's properties are related to the relative positions of the two basic types of units. An additional weighting can be superimposed upon these to modify the result according to position on the retina. Then the manner in which this result could be employed to interpret a B-scan radar display will be considered. Since the results do not yield a clear-cut indication of the ability of the filter to operate in a false-alarm environment, a simulation in which a target was selected from a noisy display will be described. Finally, the components problem, which prevents an immediate practical realization of the subsystem, will be discussed.

THE BASIC PROPERTY FILTER

Consider the one-dimensional array of basic elements shown in Fig. 3. Assume that each element is sequentially energized by a moving triggering

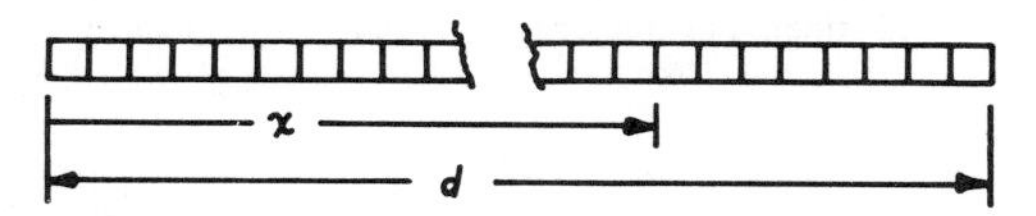

Fig. 3. Linear array of sensing elements; see equation (1).

mechanism which is traveling toward the right with a speed v. The response of each element, all of which are Δ units wide, is postulated to be

$$\phi = Be^{-t/\tau}\Delta \tag{1}$$

where B is the peak output of the array per linear length, assuming all elements were simultaneously energized. Assume that the output of all elements located in the interval from zero to d supply their outputs to a common summing unit. The output of this summing unit as a function of time is of interest.

As the triggering mechanism passes point x, since $t = x/v$, the total output from all basic units is

$$\phi_t = Be^{-x/v\tau}\,\Delta y + Be^{-(x-\Delta)/v\tau}\,\Delta y + \cdots + Be^{-(x-n\Delta)/v\tau}\,\Delta y = \sum_{k=0}^{n} Be^{-(x-k\Delta)/v\tau}\,\Delta y \tag{2}$$

where $n\,\Delta y = x$. This result can be approximated with the integral

$$\phi_t \approx B\int_0^x e^{-(x-k\Delta)/v\tau}\,dy \tag{3}$$

from which

$$\phi_t = Bv\tau\,[1 - e^{-x/v\tau}] \qquad x < d \tag{4a}$$

$$\phi_t = Bv\tau e^{-x/v\tau}\,[e^{-d/v\tau} - 1] \qquad x > d \tag{4b}$$

Expressing x as a fractional portion of d, and defining the parameter ρ,

$$x \equiv kd \tag{5}$$

$$\rho \equiv \frac{v\tau}{d} \tag{6}$$

equation (4) can be rearranged to

$$\frac{\phi_t}{Bd} = \rho\,[1 - e^{-k/\rho}] \qquad x < d \tag{7a}$$

$$\frac{\phi_t}{Bd} = \rho e^{-k/\rho}\,[e^{1/\rho} - 1] \qquad x > d \tag{7b}$$

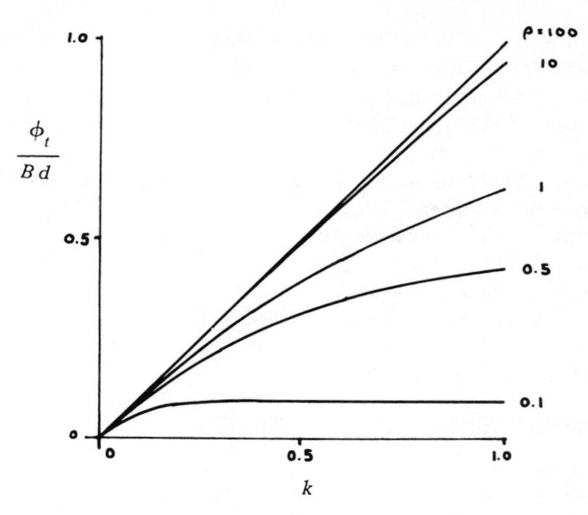

Fig. 4. Total signal from all elements in sensing array as a function of the pertinent parameters; see equations (5) and (6).

Equation (7a) is plotted in Fig. 4 and some comments concerning its significance are in order.

First, it is the output of the summing unit only at the time the trigger is passing the element located at x. Second, if the time constant of the element and the distance d is fixed, then at any point x, the output is a function only of the speed. Hence, we have a mechanism which is sensitive to speed. However, for any given speed, the output is also a function of x.

This second feature can be exploited to obtain a sensitivity to direction of motion. Consider the two-dimensional circular array of the same units, as shown in Fig. 5, and examine the summed output when the trigger source reaches point R. Assume that R is not centered within the circle and the trigger mechanism travels in a straight line as it passes through the circle and reaches point R.

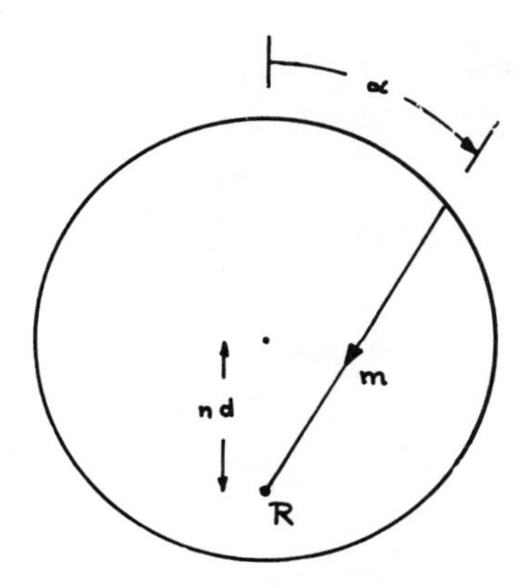

Fig. 5. Important parameters in circular array of sensing elements; see equation (8).

The angle through which the trigger path approaches R is defined as shown. The geometry of the situation is such that

$$\frac{m}{d} = n\left[\cos\alpha + \sqrt{\frac{1}{4n^2} + \cos^2\alpha - 1}\right] \tag{8}$$

Since m/d is the same as k in Fig. 4, for any given off-centering of the point R in Fig. 5 (the amount of offset being represented by the value of n), equation (8) and Fig. 4 can be employed to determine ϕ_t/Bd for each value of α and ρ. An example of the resulting series of curves (for $n = 0.4$) is shown in Fig. 6. The curves are plotted in polar coordinates. The curves are symmetrical about the vertical axis, the radial scale is linear, and α is measured clockwise from the 12 o'clock position. The actual magnitudes of ϕ_t/Bd (i.e., the radial distance) are of secondary importance to the discussion; hence, they have been omitted to keep from cluttering the figure.

The significance of Fig. 6 is as follows. First, these are the values of ϕ_t/Bd at the time the trigger mechanism reaches point R in Fig. 5. Second, the maximum value of ϕ_t/Bd for this point occurs when the trigger approaches R from an angle $\alpha = 0°$, and the minimum value occurs when the approach is from $\alpha = 180°$. Intermediate values result for all other angles. Thus, the output when the trigger reaches point R is clearly a function of the direction of motion.

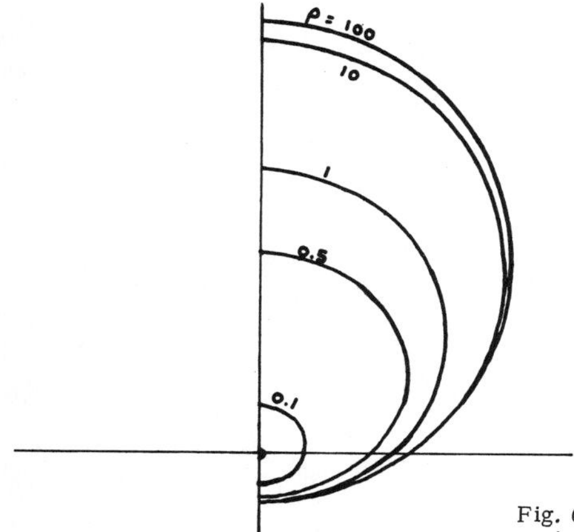

Fig. 6. Total signal from circular array as function of direction of motion; see equation (6).

How can these properties be exploited to solve the problem being considered? Consider Fig. 7. Here we have a retina which has two classes of sensors. When triggered by a moving object, the output from each of the white sensors has the form given by (1) and the black sensors exhibit an "on-off" response, i.e., they go on when the object is at their location and immediately turn off when it leaves. The outputs of the white sensors are summed by the B unit, hence its output is ϕ_t. The A unit sums the black-sensor outputs and generates a uniform level output which exists only during the time the triggering object passes across the black sensors. The C unit sums the outputs of the A and B units. The resulting response to a moving object can be clarified with the aid of Figs. 8 and 9.

In Fig. 8, the sensors which serve as sources of signals for the B unit are represented by the large circle, while the A-unit sources are located within the

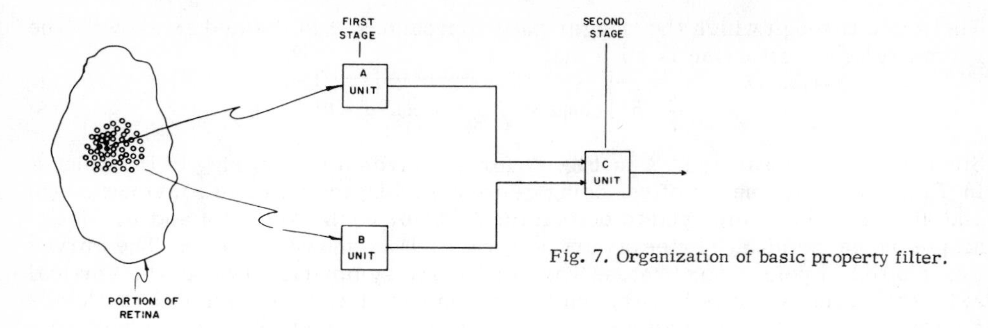

Fig. 7. Organization of basic property filter.

small circle. As a triggering object moves across this area of the retina, the *C* unit sums the output of the *A* and *B* units, as is shown.

Notice that the peak output of the *C* unit occurs as the trigger passes across the *A* sensors. Since the output of the *A* unit is standardized, the amplitude of its contribution will be independent of speed. However, the output of the *B* unit as

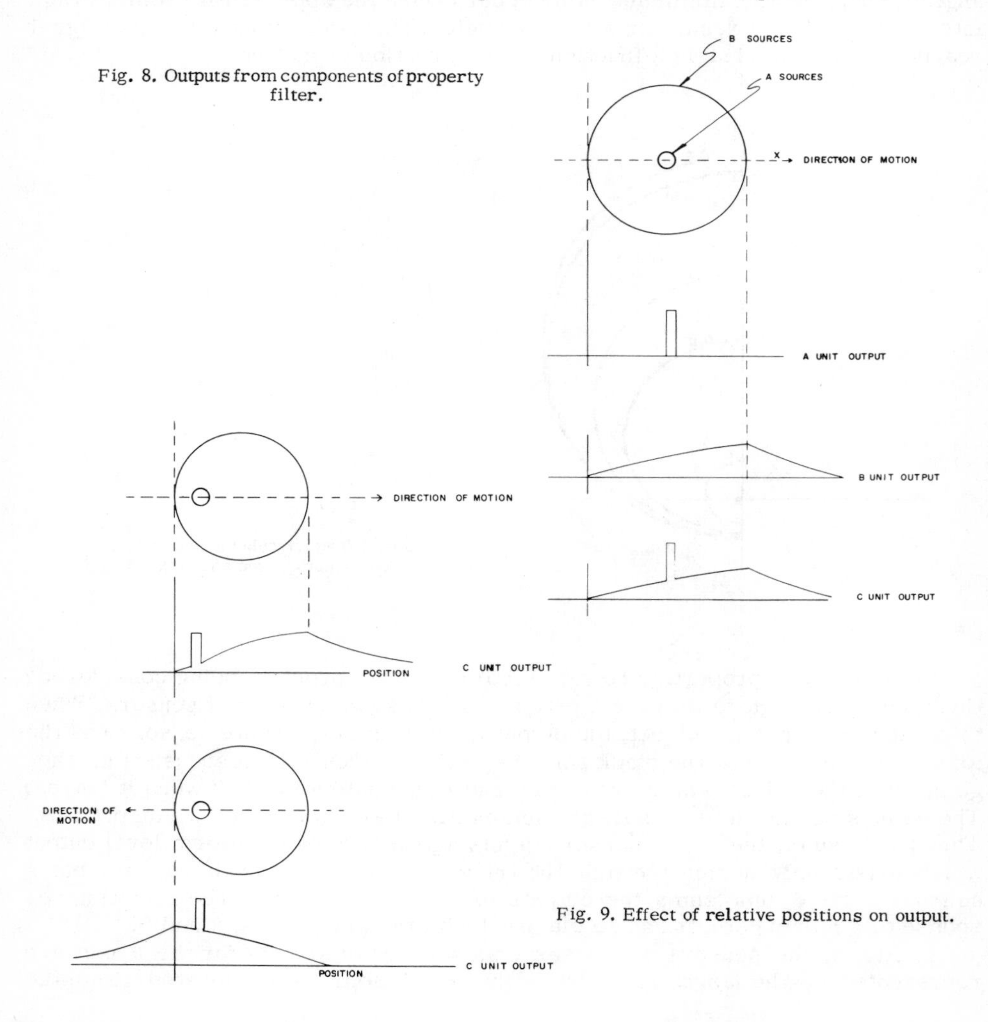

Fig. 8. Outputs from components of property filter.

Fig. 9. Effect of relative positions on output.

the triggering object passes the *A* sensors will be a function of the object's speed. If, in addition, the location of the *A* sensors is off-centered with the group of *B* sensors, the peak output at that time will also be related to the direction of motion of the triggering device, as shown in Fig. 9, because of the relations given by Fig. 6. Thus, the combination serves as a basic property filter, but before considering how to apply it to the display problem, let us compare the results thus far with the five properties previously attributed to the frog's nerve fibers.

a. This property is exhibited by the output of the *B* unit.
b. This property is exhibited by the *A* unit, but in e, below, we will find another point in the processing where this property is also encountered.
c. If the *C* unit were monitored only at the time of its peak output, it would have an output related to the direction of motion.
d. The fiber with the hole would correspond to the *B* unit and the complementary fiber would correspond to the *A* unit.
e. If the *C* units were followed by a *D* unit which transmitted a signal only during the time of the *C* unit's peak, the *D* unit would appear to have a narrow field (property b), an output related to the direction of motion (property c), and an output which would be dependent upon the history of the stimulus before it arrives at the receptive field. We shall see shortly that, in the complete system, it will be necessary to employ a *D* unit.

Therefore, with the proper interpretation, we can see a distinct similarity between the fibers in the frog's eye and the processing units proposed here. Whether or not such an interpretation would be acceptable as a valid explanation of the frog's operation is of minor interest in the light of the major objective, which is the synthesis of a useful man-made data-processing system, not the analysis of an existing biological one.

PANDEMONIUM

At this point we have a property filtering network and it is now appropriate to consider how large numbers of these units can be combined to realize the system objectives, i.e., the interpretation of the B-scan display. The basic system philosophy to be used here has previously been employed elsewhere in other pattern-recognition problems and is termed Pandemonium for reasons which may become clear in the following brief review of the approach (Selfridge, 1959).

A Pandemonium system operates on the incoming data with a large number of parallel channels which simultaneously subject the data to the three-level processing sequence shown in Fig. 10. The first level consists of a large number of basic units which serve only to gather the data and to perhaps convert the format of the incoming data to one which is more suitable for transmission to the interior of the system. (An example might be a device which converts light intensity to a train of pulses.) The units of this level are referred to as the "data demons."

The outputs of this first level are examined by a second level of units for significant properties. (In the case considered here, speed, range, and direction of motion of targets are the properties of interest.) Since these units can recognize particular features in the input set of data, they are referred to as "cognitive demons." These demons are all operating simultaneously and transmitting their information at different levels of intensity, depending upon the nature of the input. Thus, all are "shouting" at once; hence, the term "Pandemonium."

The third level listens for the loudest shout and lets that signal pass; thus, the units in this level are the "decision demons." In this problem the decision demons must decide which target will be the first to reach zero range on the radar display.

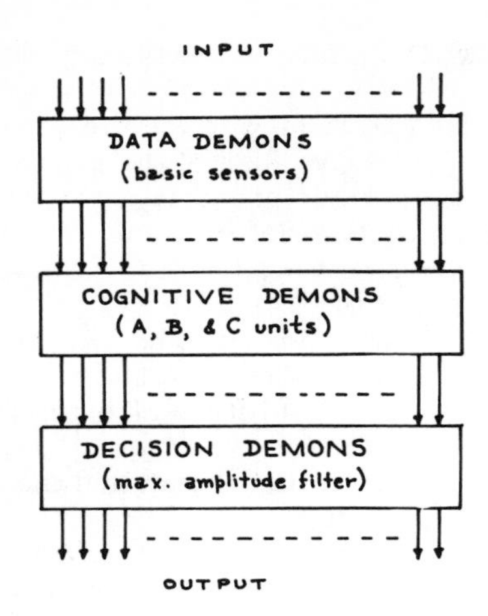

Fig. 10. Organization of Pandemonium system.

To solve the display interpretation problem, let the input B-scan radar display be optically imaged on a retina of optical sensing units. Let each one of these sensing units correspond to the *A*-unit sources of Figs. 7, 8, and 9. Assume further that each sensing unit receives signals from neighboring units within an off-centered circular area, as represented by the large circles in Fig. 11. The contribution of these neighboring units must correspond to those of the *B*-source sets and, hence, each neighboring elements contribution must obey equation (1). The total must then be summed to obtain a net signal comparable to that of Fig. 9. Just how such properties may be most practically realized in terms of physical components has not been examined in detail; however, a neuron-like element

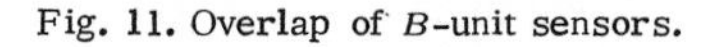

Fig. 11. Overlap of *B*-unit sensors.

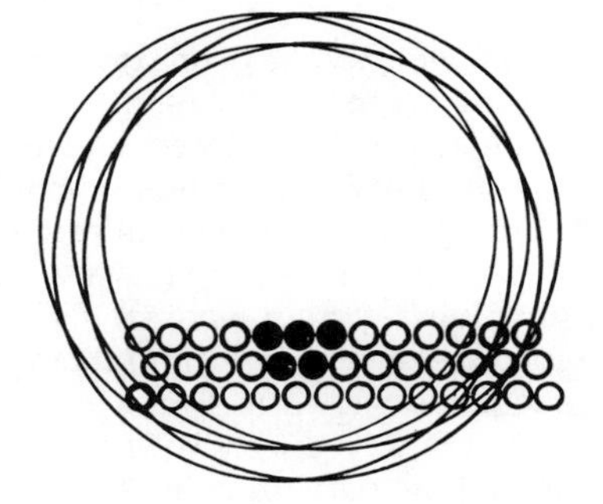

might be useful. In such a device, a direct path from the input sensors to the cell body would provide the *A*-unit behavior, while the dendrites would provide synaptic connections to neighboring cells in order to yield *B*-type behavior. The cell body would perform the necessary integration and combining of *A* and *B* signals with the resulting output from the axon driving the next layer of the system.

This array of elements constitutes the field on which the radar display is imaged. If the individual circular areas which define the neighboring connections are all off-centered in the same direction (i.e., specifically, that which yields maximum output for a flight path perpendicular to the zero-range line), a useful output will be obtained. To elaborate, a spot of light moving on the display will always cause an *A* unit to be energized. The magnitude of the *B* contributions will be dependent upon speed and heading. If we simultaneously monitor all *C* units, the peak signal will occur only at the location of the spot's present position.

Reconsider Fig. 1, in which more than one spot is displayed. The largest *C*-unit signals will occur for those *C* units located at the present positions of the three light spots. However, the signals from these three *C* units will have different magnitudes because of the *B* units' contributions. Thus, spot 1 will have the greatest output, while spot 2 will have the least.

To this point, the peak *C*-unit signals are functions of present position, speed, and heading. To include range, the magnitude of the *A*-unit outputs can be altered so that those *A* units closer to minimum range will contribute a larger signal to the *C* units. Thus, in Fig. 1, if spots 1 and 3 were moving with the same speed and heading, the output of the *C* unit at 3's position would be greater than that at 1's.

If the complete array of *A*, *B*, and *C* units exhibits the above properties, and the *C* units drive a maximum amplitude filter array (Taylor, 1956), then the output of the array will be located at the position of the aircraft which is most apt to be the first to reach minimum range. In short, the complete Pandemonium array is "interpreting" the radar display.

FALSE ALARMS

The above discussion does not consider the case in which the input display is also cluttered with those randomly occurring spots of light referred to as "false alarms." However, the randomness of these spots provides a basis for discriminating between them and the spots corresponding to targets. This is because the build-up of signals in the *B* unit occurs because a spot corresponding to aircraft will successively energize sensors within the circle corresponding to the *B* sensors for that *B* unit. Because of the decaying action of the individual *B* sensors, a large number of successive and/or simultaneous false alarms must occur within the *B*-sensor circle in order to cause the same level of *B*-unit output as that caused by an aircraft. Upon reflection, it would seem that such events would be unlikely because of the random nature of the false alarms. However, an analytical confirmation of this postulate is not readily obtainable because the *B*-source sensor overlaps make such an analysis formidable. Therefore, a simulation was undertaken in order to verify this aspect of the proposed machine's performance.

The number of *A* units required in the proposed machine would be approximately the same as the number of rods and cones in a man's retina; hence, one million is not an unrealistic figure to consider. Similar quantities of *B* and *C* units are needed. Hence, conventional components pulse generators, etc., cannot be wired together in order to stimulate the final network, even if a reduced-size retina is employed. Similar considerations rule out a digital computer simulation. The simulation which was carried out employs a conbination of distributed arrays of elements connected via optical and electronic "wiring."

To illustrate how this was accomplished, consider Fig. 12a. The array of *A* sensors in Fig. 11 was simulated by the planar light-sensitive input surface of a vidicon TV camera; i.e., the individual *A* sensors were simulated by the individual photosensitive particles on the camera's light-sensitive element. (This array of sensors is referred to as the receiver plane in Fig. 12.) The "wiring" between the radar display and the *A*-sensor array was carried out optically with a sharply focused lens, the same way the radar display is coupled to the radar observer's retina. Thus, any point *A* on the receiver is "wired" to a corresponding point on the input display, because it will receive light only from that point.

Now, if the lens is defocused, as in Fig. 12b, the point *A* now receives light from a circular area on the input display concentric with the original point.

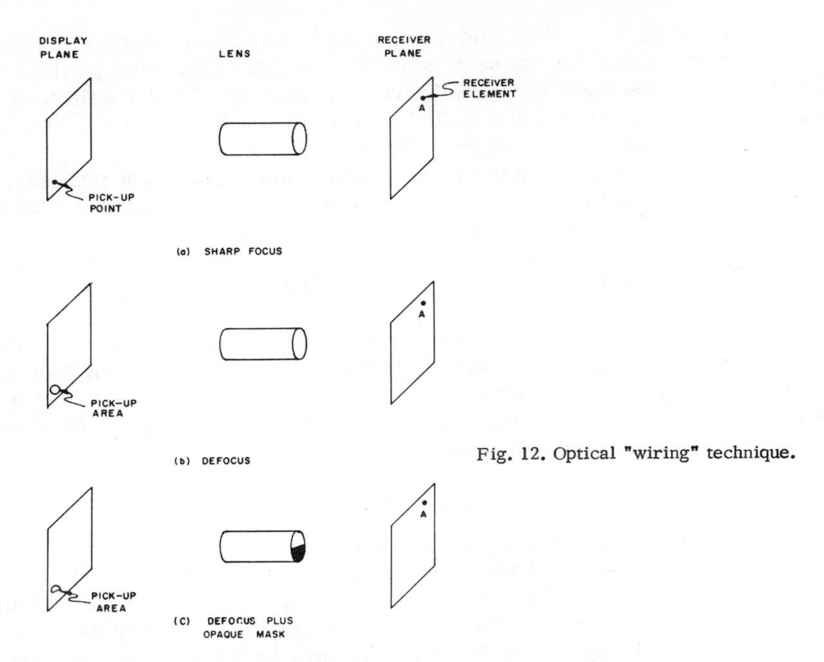

Fig. 12. Optical "wiring" technique.

Hence, this whole circular area is now "wired" to point A. By making the lens as shown in (c) we could even be more selective in choosing the area to which A is wired. Therefore, to obtain the wiring required between the B units and the B sensors, a second TV camera was employed and the radar image was simultaneously coupled to the sensitive surface of this camera via a defocused lens. The second TV camera was a Permachon (Nicholsen, 1959) rather than a vidicon. The Permachon is similar to a vidicon, except that it stores the input optical image. This storage capability provided an approximation to the slow decay required by the B sensors; thus, the combination of the Permachon and defocused lens served to approximate B sensors and their B units.

The two cameras were operated with synchronized sweep circuits and their outputs were combined in a resistive summing network, as shown in Fig. 13. In a television camera, each point on the photosensitive input surface is sequentially sampled by the moving electron beam. Therefore, if the camera lens systems are properly aligned on the input display, at each instant of time, as the camera electron beams sweep the camera sensing surfaces, (since the beams are synchronized) the vidicon is sampling an A unit and the Permachon is sampling the corresponding B unit. Therefore, the summation block is acting as a C unit. The circuitry following the summation block operated as a maximum amplitude

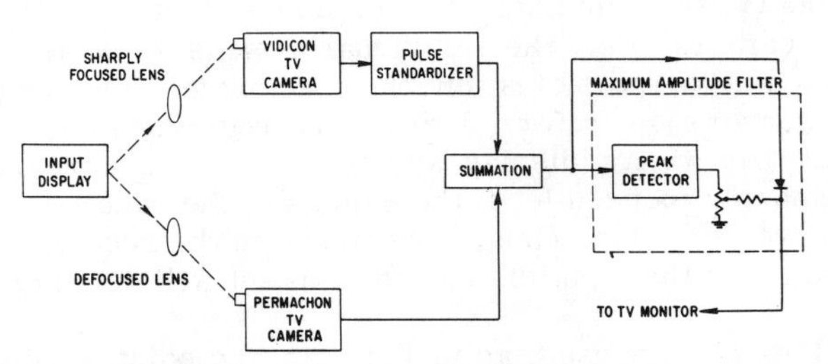

Fig. 13. Simulation to evaluate ability of system to discriminate aircraft from false alarms.

filter and its output was displayed on a monitor. Thus, the system of Fig. 13 operated as a partially sequential, rather than parallel, Pandemonium system.

The system differed from that required, however, in a couple of respects. First, the *B* sensor-unit combination was not accurately simulated due to properties of the Permachon–in particular, its long storage time and its integration properties. (The latter property serves to eliminate the ability to discriminate between stationary and moving targets.) Second, it was difficult to maintain alignment of the rasters on the two cameras. (If perfect raster alignment were possible, the first defect could be overcome by: (a) sharply focusing the Permachon and (b) inserting between the Permachon and the summing block a limiter, monitor, and defocused vidicon, in that order. Then, if the Permachon camera would also exhibit an automatic erase feature, the proposed system could be realized.)

However, the available behavior was sufficient to demonstrate the ability of the proposed system to discriminate between aircraft light spots and false alarms. An aircraft simulator was employed to illuminate the input display and random noise was also inserted. The resulting input display was so heavily cluttered with false alarms that it was not readily apparent to human observers which spot of light was due to the simulated aircraft.

When the display was presented to the system of Fig. 13, the output monitor initially contained both false alarms and the aircraft. However, after several seconds the false alarms faded and only the moving aircraft spot remained. Thus, the proposed machine is capable of discriminating between aircraft and false alarms.

DISCUSSION

I believe the above material constitutes sufficient evidence that the proposed machine would provide a satisfactory interpretation of the B-scan; however, it is apparent that it will be some time before such a machine could be realized. The present state of the art is such that the required million or so components cannot be practically assembled and wired in a reasonably sized package. Although progress in the field of microelectronics would indicate that the required capability might someday be available, current efforts are directed toward a different type of component than that required here. Efforts are currently directed towards components for digital computers, since there are indications that there exists a demand for such components. This would not be an undesirable situation if there were a parallel effort to realize the type of components needed for the type of system proposed here. However, such an effort will not be forthcoming until the device manufacturer sees a need for this type of device.

Unfortunately, it appears that such a need will be rather slow in coming. In this writer's opinion, it is because the people who are working in the research area (i.e., bionics) most likely to generate the need for the new components are, in the great majority of cases, barking up the wrong tree! The digital computer has become a Pied Piper to the extent that researchers are confusing its role as a simulating medium with its usefulness (in the bionics application) as a vehicle for implementation. Several of the more publicized activities in the field suffer from a digital-Boolean bias and lead to proposals which are completely unrealistic from the standpoint of eventual practical fabrication. There is too great a tendency to demonstrate a technique which solves a simple problem and imply that the extension required to solve the *real* problem is simply a matter of engineering details. It seems to this writer that the engineering details are a major aspect of the problems in the bionics area and until this is recognized and taken into account, progress in this field will be very slow.

At this point it would seem to be appropriate for the writer to defend the machine just proposed in terms of the above arguments. To do so properly, however, would require space equivalent to a separate paper. It will be sufficient to note that the principles upon which the machine is based are compatible with an over-all approach which embodies some of the ideas of Tinbergen (1951), Selfridge (1959), Neisser (1960), and Taylor (1956). With such an approach, some of the engineering problems, such as inaccurate wiring, are not only tolerated, but employed to advantage; "learning" in such a system is necessary and the network that learns cannot be replaced with a fixed wiring network after the learning is completed! The basic components for such a system are more likely to take the form of a device such as Crane's meuristor (Crane, 1960; Cote, 1961), rather than the form of an AND gate.

ACKNOWLEDGMENT

Several people contributed encouragement, stimulating comments, and suggestions at various stages of this work and I would particularly like to thank M. Davidson and F. Nathanson for their comments. In addition, it should be noted that the television simulation was implemented largely through the efforts of Mr. Nathanson.

This work was supported by the Bureau of Naval Weapons, Department of the Navy, under contract NOrd 7386.

REFERENCES

Bionics Symposium. 1960. Wright Air Development Div., WADD Tech. Rep. 60-600.

Cote, A. J., Jr. 1961. A neuristor prototype. Proc. IRE 49, 1430-1431.

Crane, H. D. 1960. Neuristor studies. Stanford Electronics Lab., Tech. Rep. 1506-2.

Lettvin, J. Y., Maturana, H. R., McCullough, W. S., and Pitts, W. H. 1959. What the frog's eye tells the frog's brain. Proc. IRE 47, 1940-1951.

McCullough et al. 1959. Optic nerve. MIT Research Laboratory of Electronics, QPR 52, 176-178.

Neisser, U. 1960. A theory of cognitive processes. Lincoln Laboratory, Group Report, 54-19.

Nicholsen, J. F. 1959. Permachon—a storage pickup tube. Electron Devices Conference, Washington, D. C.

Selfridge, O. G. 1959. Pandemonium: a paradigm for learning. Proceedings Symposium on Mechanization of Thought Processes. Her Majesty's Stationary Office, London.

Taylor, W. K. 1956. Pattern recognition by means of automatic analog apparatus. Proc. IEE (Part B) 106, 198-209.

Tinbergen, N. 1951. The study of instinct. Oxford Univ. Press.

Yovitts, M. C., and Cameron, S. (ed.). 1960. Self-organizing systems. Pergamon Press.

SOME MODELS FOR PULSE-INTERVAL MODULATION SYSTEMS

H. J. Hunt

Polytechnic Institute of Brooklyn, Brooklyn, New York

INTRODUCTION

One of the common approaches taken by researchers in bionics interested in translating biological functions into electronic systems is the development of models which simulate various types of biological phenomena. The development of models which simulate biological functions is important, as many of the input-output relationships that are observable are complex and inherently nonlinear. These factors tend to complicate the problem of characterizing the system under study.

The most typical example of problems of this class is the characterization of functions performed by sensory receptors and neurons. D. and K. Stanley-Jones, in an excellent review of numerous examples of encoding and decoding by the nervous systems of biological organisms at all levels of organization, have indicated the complexity involved in the performance of these functions. Although this author has been primarily concerned with an analog model to simulate relationships based upon physiological data, it is felt that some forms of hybrid models must be developed in order to describe various functions performed by sensory receptors and neurons.

In this paper, we shall describe our version of a "neuromime" and some of the results that have been obtained with it. Although the particular elements used in the model may not have their biological counterparts, the approach used in developing the model has been based upon the philosophy typified by Harman and others, namely, that of simulating some of the functions of sensory receptors as closely as possible with an electronic device.

DESCRIPTION OF THE MODEL

The language of the nervous system is a form of pulse-interval or pulse-rate modulation. The types of pulse trains that are observable are numerous and vary considerably in their structure.

For example, the various types of receptors can be classified into two categories, depending upon the type of response exhibited upon application of a stimulus.

The first type of receptor responds to a stimulus with an output of a finite train of pulses of pulse width T_1 and interval spacing T_2, where T_1 is a constant and T_2 is a function of time that generally tends to increase. This type of receptor is one which exhibits the property of "fatigue" under the application of a constant stimulus.

Outputs from the second type of sensory receptor are generally continuous trains of pulses, the average frequency of which is a function of the logarithm of the input variable. To simulate these functional relationships as well as other types of neural phenomena, a model was constructed (Fig. 1).

The model consists of a pulse generator, a sweep-generator feedback element which is triggered from output pulses, and a summer. The sweep generator is utilized in most of the simulations, although it may be replaced by other types of function generators, depending upon the type of nonlinear function desired.

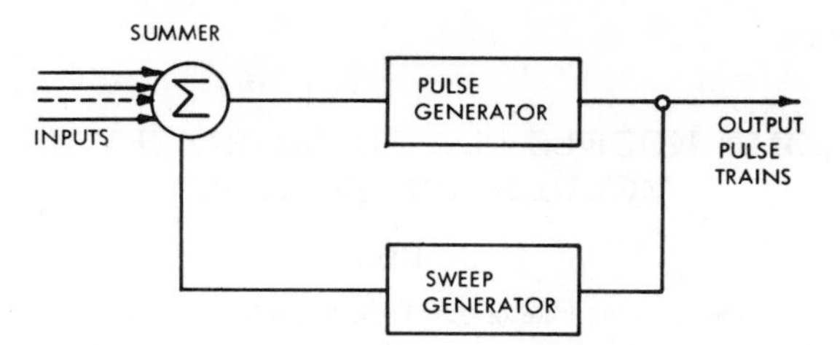

Fig. 1. Model for simulation of pulse-interval modulation.

For a pulse generator, a simple monostable multivibrator is employed to produce an output pulse of fixed amplitude and time duration. The summer is a simple summing amplifier which linearly sums the inputs (which may be continuous or discrete) and the feedback signal from the sweep generator.

The operation of the model is fairly basic. Linear summation of the inputs with the periodic feedback from the sweep generator produces a switching function at the output which controls the operation of the multivibrator. A typical sequence for a single input is illustrated in Fig. 2.

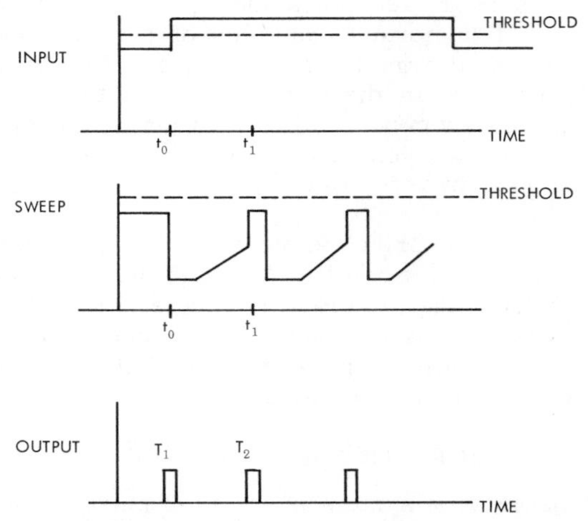

Fig. 2. A typical sequence of operation.

In the absence of an input signal, the output of the summing amplifier is maintained slightly below the threshold of the pulse generator by the steady-state output of the sweep generator. Consequently, both generators are off and the model is in the inactive state. Upon application of a stimulus at t_0, the output of the summer triggers the multivibrator, which in turn triggers the sweep generator. The output of the summer is now a time-varying voltage which periodically recycles the model whenever it exceeds the threshold. When the stimulus returns to zero, the model automatically returns to the inactive state.

The model is characterized by two relationships, one governing the average frequency of the output pulse train when a single constant dc voltage is applied to the input, and the second controlling the triggering of the multivibrator. The time constant of the sweep is adjusted to give a logarithmic relationship between the average frequency of the output and the dc input voltage. To produce an output pulse, the following equation must be satisfied:

$$\Sigma X_j - X_f = V_t \tag{1}$$

where ΣX_j is the sum of all inputs, X_f is the feedback from the sweep generator, and V_t is the threshold voltage.

RESULTS OF SOME SIMULATION EXPERIMENTS

From equation (1), it is readily seen that a wide variety of output pulse trains is possible, particularly in the cases where the inputs are allowed to vary with time.

To simulate a spontaneously operating neuron or receptor, all that is required is to apply a single constant dc input sufficient to raise the output of the summer above the threshold. The model then acts as a simple relaxation oscillator. It will be noted, however, that the phase of the oscillations may be reset from an external trigger.

To simulate an adapting type of receptor, decaying exponentials are used as inputs. These inputs tend to cause the interval between successive pulses to increase with time.

Some fairly interesting results are obtained with a sinusoidal input if the sine wave is allowed to vary about the threshold. For a fixed frequency and low amplitudes, the pulses in the output train will tend to be randomly spaced. As the amplitude is slowly increased, a critical amplitude is found at which the output pulls into synchronization with the positive peaks of the sine wave. This behavior is remarkably similar to flicker fusion. A similar result has been noted by Harman. Harman has also demonstrated that a similar result can be obtained with a human subject by controlling the amplitude of a sine wave driving a flashing light.

To simulate neural functions, multiple pulse inputs are used. Various arbitrary conditions of excitation and inhibition can be established and readily simulated. The results are generally in agreement with those predicted by equation (1). In general, to simulate almost any neural output pattern that has been observed, it usually is sufficient to calculate beforehand the required input that will give rise to the desired response.

CONCLUSIONS

From the results that have been obtained by this experimenter, it appears that a good deal of insight into nervous system phenomena can be obtained through simulations with "neuromimes." Whether or not the same mechanisms are responsible for the behavior of the biological systems is a matter for speculation only. Simulation does, however, give some insight into the problem of abstracting the pertinent data from physiological observations. The basic idea of constructing a simulator from a set of input-output relationships appears to have considerable merit.

Although the model described in this paper is only a crude approximation to actual biological systems, the results that have been obtained seem to justify the assumptions and certainly suggest some modifications.

The fairly complex amplitude, phase, and frequency requirements used in the simulations are typical of most nervous system activity. Of particular interest is the fact that some agreement with biological data was obtained with as simple a model as described.

ACKNOWLEDGMENT

This work was supported in part by the U. S. Army Signal Research and Development Laboratory, the Office of Naval Research, and the Air Force Office of Scientific Research, under Contract AF-18(600)-1505.

REFERENCES

Hawkins, J. S. 1961. Self-organizing systems—a review and commentary. Proc. IRE 49, 31-47.
Van Bergeijk, W. A. and Harman, L. D. 1960. What good are artificial neurons? WADD Tech. Rept. 60-600, 395-406.

QUANTITATIVE ASPECTS OF THE PROBLEM OF SHAPE IN BIOLOGY

W. R. Baum

Department of Mathematics
Syracuse University, Syracuse, New York

ABSTRACT

In studies on the interrelationships of form and function in biology, an important role is played by the notion of shape and its determination. Although several notions of shape are used in mathematics, it is not a trivial problem to find a shape concept, expressed in mathematical language, which could serve as a base for a quantitative treatment of biological questions involving structures and patterns.

One can introduce a relative shape concept (like relative motion in mechanics) which allows one to compare two sets (or "figures") to each other. It is based on elementary classical geometrical ideas, like that of a parallel domain of a given domain and a certain measure of deviation between two figures. Congruent figures have the deviation zero. A fundamental task of a quantitative shape theory is to study the dependence of the underlying shape concept upon suitable functionals defined on figures. Specifically: can one find a number of parameters associated with a figure such that if for two figures the values of corresponding parameters differ only a little then the shapes of the figures deviate not too much? For the shape concept proposed here the suitable parameters are of intrinsic geometric meaning with respect to the given figures (volume, surface area, total mean curvature, total Gaussian curvature, diameter, thickness, etc.). Their computability does not present principal difficulties. Applicability of this approach to biological phenomena is discussed.

DESIGN STUDIES OF CONDITIONAL PROBABILITY COMPUTERS*

Kenneth H. Reid

Computer and Control Systems Laboratory
Departments of Electrical and Mechanical Engineering
University of Saskatchewan, Saskatoon, Saskatchewan

INTRODUCTION

This paper is intended to show that large conditional probability computers, capable of dealing with many hundreds of binary inputs, can be constructed. This possibility is due to one fundamental fact: if a computer is dealing with a time-varying environment, only recent history is relevant to the present task. Data from the remote past must be discounted as irrelevant and misleading. Consequently, the maximum amount of information that can usefully be stored is just that amount of information that enters the system during the segment of time relevant to the present task. This storage requirement increases linearly with the input capacity of the system.

Learning machines, and conditional probability computers in particular, perform inductive operations on samples of data from the immediate past. Input combinations that have occurred only rarely during the relevant past cannot be used with confidence. This is also a fundamental limitation—the size of the relevant sample is just too small. For computers with many inputs, nearly all of the 2^n possible combinations of binary inputs can be ruled out on this basis alone. Only those which have occurred during the relevant past need be considered at all, and of this tiny fraction, only those which have occurred often enough to build up a reasonable statistical sample can be used with confidence for predicting the approaching future. Consequently, it is unnecessary to provide storage space for all possible combinations.

BACKGROUND: CONDITIONAL PROBABILITY COMPUTERS

A conditional probability computer is one of the simpler forms of a large class of networks known as semilinear nets (Papart, 1960). Perceptron-type networks also belong to this general class. Conditional probability computers were developed by Dr. A. M. Uttley (1956) as possible analogs of certain functions of the nervous system. In his original design (Uttley, 1958), the computer is organized as an array of interconnected boxes, as shown in Fig. 1. Each box is a memory unit. It has an input line on which, at unit intervals of time, binary pulses may or may not appear. These pulses are accumulated by the box so its contents grow with time. In addition, the box leaks. In our work we have assumed, following Uttley, that the box leaks exponentially, like a leaky capacitor. In doing this we implicitly assume that the relevance of the past history of the pulse train diminishes in the same manner. This assumption may or may not be true. Later we shall show that for the purpose of memory requirements it doesn't matter how the relevance is distributed over the past history, as long as it covers only a finite time interval.

The contents of our leaky box represent the probability of a pulse arriving. It is simply a smoothing device. For conditional probability computation, at

*The work reported in this paper was supported by the Defence Research Board of Canada under grant No. 2804-05.

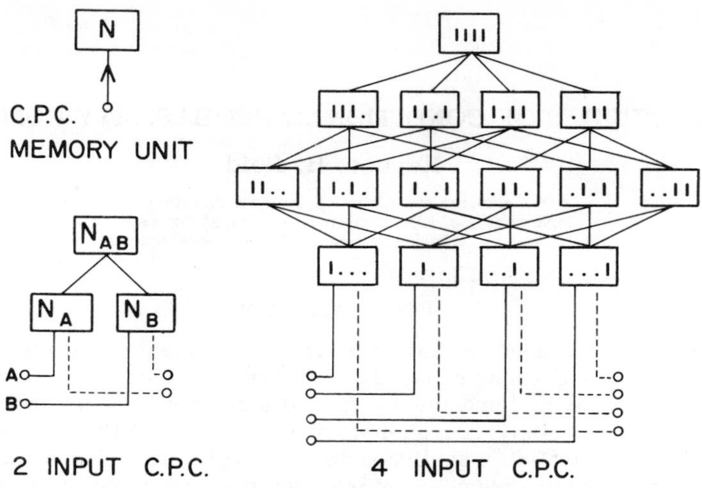

Fig. 1. Conditional probability computers.

least two boxes are needed. In the lower left corner of Fig. 1, a 2-input computer is shown. It has three boxes. The lower left box accumulates pulses arriving on channel A, the lower right box accumulates pulses arriving on channel B, while the top box accumulates coincidences—pulses on both A and B. From this it is not hard to show that the ratios of the contents of appropriate boxes represent conditional probabilities. N_{AB}/N_A represents the probability of a pulse arriving at B, given that one is due to arrive at A. N_{AB}/N_B represents the probability of a pulse appearing at A, given one at B. Now we can do some prediction. If line B is intermittent, and N_{AB}/N_A is close to 1 when a pulse arrives at A, we are almost certain that a pulse was on line B but didn't arrive due to some fault on the line.

That's all this little machine will do for us. We have gone into its behavior in some detail since it is the basis of the statistical results to be described later. More elaborate computers, such as the one on the right of Fig. 1, can be constructed. These will fill in missing probable pulses on the basis of past history and the pattern of coincident pulses present. The behavior of such devices has been described at length in Uttley's papers (Uttley, 1956, 1958). We will point out, at this time, only one alarming fact: the number of boxes rises as 2^n where n is the number of inputs. This amounts to a great many boxes once n passes four or five. If one wishes to use 50 or 100 channels, the number of boxes required soars into the billions.

How can we cut down the number of boxes? The method to be used depends on one's point of view. We approached conditional probability computers with the idea of using them in a control system. This meant we were primarily interested in dynamic responses to changing situations. We were relatively uninterested in elaborate classificatory abilities.

PRELIMINARY EXPERIMENTS

We began our study (Reid, 1961a) by simulating a typical computer on an LGP-30 digital computer and measuring transient behavior directly. We simulated both biased and unbiased* computers.

*A biased computer, Uttley's original form, is one which regards the presence of a pulse as definitive evidence of a real pulse on the line while considering the possibility of error only when a pulse fails to appear; it disregards the possibility of noise pulses. An unbiased computer regards both pulses and no-pulses with an equally jaundiced eye.

This preliminary study yielded four useful results:

1. The unbiased computer was twice as effective as the biased one in handling a problem involving unbiased errors, i.e., equally likely false pulses and missing pulses.
2. The biased computer could be used as an unbiased computer by running the input sequence twice, with 1 and 0 bits interchanged on the second run.
3. Variable leakage rate, a plausible modification alleged to improve the transient response, was found to be extremely noise-sensitive and dropped as ineffective.
4. The whole concept of direct transient response study was dropped since it was inefficient.

This preliminary skirmish gave us sufficient confidence to go ahead and build a 5-input computer (Buhr, 1961). This is currently being used, in both biased and unbiased modes of operation, in an experimental process control loop. Little can be said about this here, as this work is still in progress. It is going well, and we expect to have some of the results published within the next few months.

The problem of transient response and memory requirements remains. Our approach to this (Reid, 1961b) has been statistical in nature, and forms the main subject of this paper.

STATISTICAL ANALYSIS OF CPC

The concept of "relevant past," introduced earlier, is a central one in the adaptive system designer's frame of reference. Conditions change and the adaptive system must change as well. Data which refer to a different set of conditions are irrelevant.

In the conditional probability computer the parameter governed by the length of the relevant past is the leakage rate of the memory unit. The only other im-

BASIC EQUATIONS GOVERNING THE N DISTRIBUTION

$$N(t_m) = \sum_{n=0}^{-\infty} \psi_{m+n} \Delta^{-n} \qquad \psi = 1 \text{ with prob. } p; \quad = 0 \text{ with prob. } 1-p$$

$$= \sum_{n=0}^{\infty} \phi_{m+n} \qquad \phi_n = \Delta^n \text{ with prob. } p; \quad = 0 \text{ with prob. } 1-p$$

$$\bar{N} = p \sum_{0}^{\infty} \Delta^n = p/(1-\Delta)$$

$$\sigma_N^2 = p(1-p) \sum_{0}^{\infty} \Delta^{2n} = p(1-p)/(1-\Delta^2)$$

$$\frac{\sigma_N}{\bar{N}} = \left[\frac{1-p}{p} \cdot \frac{1-\Delta}{1+\Delta}\right]^{\frac{1}{2}}$$

Fig. 2. Equations governing the behavior of the contents of a single CPC memory unit subjected to a stationary random input sequence.

portant independent parameter is the rate of arrival of pulses at the input, which determines how full the memory units are and, more importantly, how much they fluctuate. These two parameters determine the accuracy with which conditional probabilities can be measured.

To obtain quantitative information on the relationship between decay rate, input frequency, and measurement accuracy, we assumed a statistically stationary uncorrelated input. The essential results for a single memory unit are shown in Fig. 2.

The current value of N is the sum of the series shown, from a long time ago to the present. This can be rewritten in a simpler form by substituting the weighted random variables ϕ_n for the $\psi\Delta^{-n}$ products. The mean value and standard deviation follow by straightforward summation, noting that the successive terms are independent, so that the sum variance is just the sum of the variances of the terms. The percentage variability σ/N follows directly from the preceding two results.

Figure 3 shows how this variability varies with input probability and decay rate. The factor (1-Δ) is the reciprocal of the time constant of the memory unit; this must be very small if low probability signals are to be followed with any accuracy. In other words, if the relevant past, which determines the selection of the maximum time constant, provides few samples of an interesting pattern, little can be said about its likelihood in the future. The important point is that the accuracy of prediction depends on the environment, not the computer. Variability is an inherent consequence of limited relevant data.

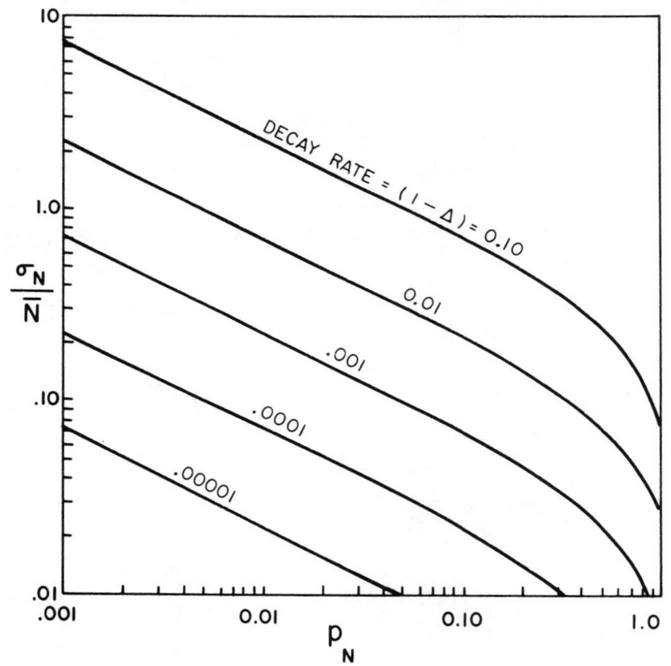

Fig. 3. Fluctuations in the contents of a single CPC memory unit as a function of input pulse probability.

On closer examination it appears that most of the variability arises from fluctuations caused by the most recent pulses. We express this idea in quantitative form in Fig. 4. Here the contents of a memory unit are split into two portions, those from the most recent M time periods, and those due to previous

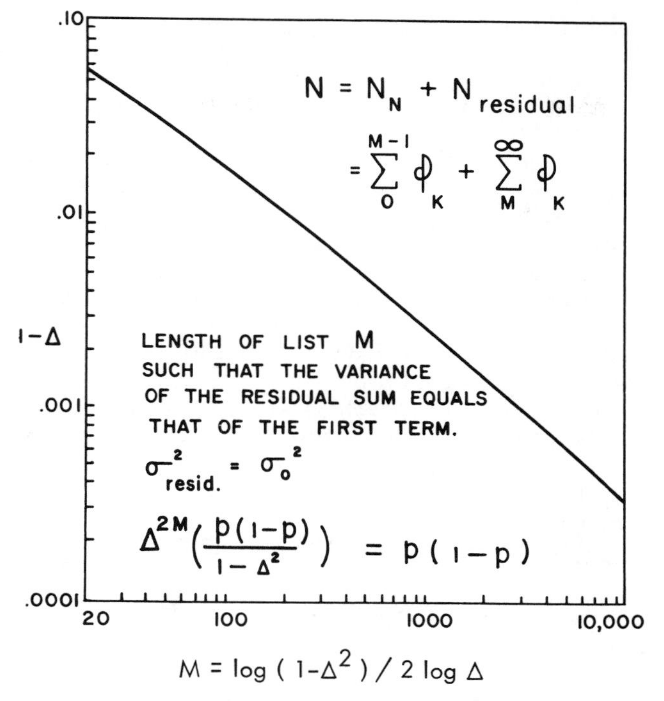

Fig. 4. Cutoff criterion for list memory.

arrivals. If the effects of the residual component are submerged in the noise of the recent one, there is no justification for keeping more than the M most recent terms in memory. The number of terms to be kept is given by the formula shown here; it is plotted against $(1-\Delta)$ immediately above. The criterion used here, not

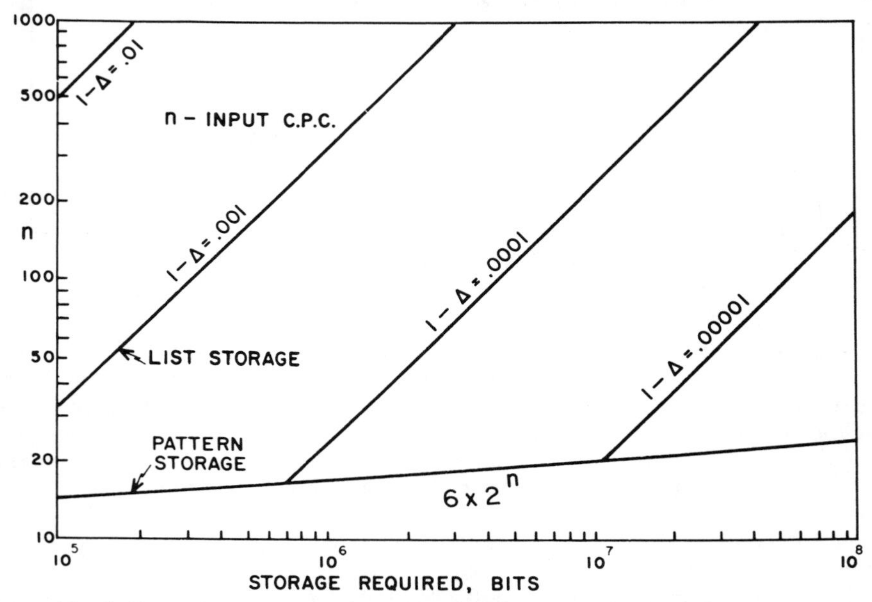

Fig. 5. Comparison of storage requirements for list and pattern storage procedures.

perhaps intuitively obvious, states simply that once the signal : noise ratio drops below one, the signal isn't much use and might as well be dropped. A more obvious criterion—comparing the mean value of the residual with the variance of the total sum—can also be used, with almost identical results. The one given here is easier to calculate.

In Fig. 5 the results of storing a truncated list of past inputs are compared with the practice of having one storage unit for each possible input pattern. The lower line is drawn on the assumption that each analog N unit can contain six bits of information—one part in 64. As mentioned above, this method requires 2^n units. The lines above it represent list storage requirements for various time constants. The lower the time constant, the shorter the relevant past, and hence the less the storage space required to record it.

So far all the analysis presented has dealt with the statistical behavior of a single memory unit. Conditional probabilities are estimated by comparing two units. Consequently, we must check to see if there are circumstances under which the variability of the ratio of two units could greatly exceed that of the units themselves. The equations governing the behavior of the conditional probability estimates are presented in Fig. 6.

BASIC EQUATIONS GOVERNING THE R DISTRIBUTION

$$R_{AB} = N_{AB} / N_A \qquad R_{BA} = N_{AB} / N_B$$

$$R_{AB} = \sum_{K=0}^{\infty} \Phi_{AK} \Psi_{BK} \Big/ \sum_{K=0}^{\infty} \Phi_{AK}$$

$$\bar{R}_{AB} = \bar{N}_{AB} / \bar{N}_A = \bar{\Psi}_{BK} = P_B$$

$$\frac{\sigma_R}{\bar{R}} \approx \sqrt{1-\bar{R}} \left[\left(\frac{\sigma_A}{\bar{N}_A} \right)^2 + \left(\frac{\sigma_{AB}}{\bar{N}_{AB}} \right)^2 \right]^{\frac{1}{2}}$$

$$1 - \bar{R} = (\bar{N}_A - \bar{N}_{AB}) / \bar{N}_A$$

Fig. 6. Equations governing the behavior of the conditional probability estimate $P_{B|A} = N_{AB}/N_A$, for a CPC with stationary random input.

The estimate R is the ratio of two related stochastic series. It is not easy to evaluate and an exact formulation has eluded us. The formula for the variability of R is a straightforward engineer's math job. The quantity inside the bracket is the standard formula for calculating the variance of the product or quotient of two independent variables for small variations. Here the variables are not independent, and the variations are not small, hence the correction factor out front. This correction factor is based on the assumption that the degree of dependence of N_{AB} on N_A is proportional to R, and is, hence, a first-order (linear) approximation to the true correlation.

To check this approximate formula we used a well-known trick—Monte Carlo—and fed a long string of random numbers into a 2-input CPC simulated on our

LGP-30 digital computer. We repeated this for several different input probability combinations and decay rates; the results are compared with those of this formula in Fig. 7.

The formula tends to be slightly pessimistic. Most of the theoretical values are about 10% above their Monte Carlo counterparts. One point is not. Either the formula is better in this area, or the Monte Carlo run was biased. Since this particular run involved 2000 samples, we think the latter unlikely, but one never can tell. In any case, the lack of drastic deviations from the expected justifies our concentration on the statistics of a single memory unit, and the conclusions we have drawn from it.

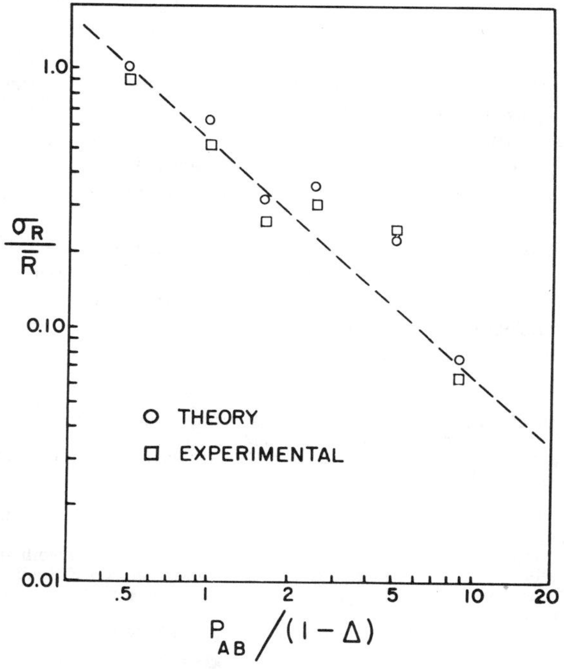

Fig. 7. Ratio variability vs effective sample size—a comparison of the equation of Fig. 6 with Monte Carlo calculations from a simulated CPC.

MECHANIZATION OF THE CPC MEMORY

Let us look at this memory problem once again. The bit scale shown in Fig. 5 goes from 10^5 to 10^8 bits. This is a rather large memory—3000 to 3,000,000 words. How are we to mechanize this?

Let us take a special case: a 10^5-bit (3000 word) magnetic drum for a 100-channel CPC. The space available dictates a maximum list length M of 1000, and, hence, from Fig. 4, a minimum $(1-\Delta)$ of 0.0026. This gives a maximum time constant of 384 input cycles. Suppose an input arrives containing 47 1's and 53 questionable blanks. (We assume a biased unitary CPC.) The input is used first as a mask to scan the 1000 previous inputs for those containing the same pattern of 1's. Since all tracks of the drum can be scanned at once, this can be a very rapid operation. Suppose 120 such patterns are found. These patterns are listed in a separate storage area together with their locations in the sequence. They are then sorted on the contents of the blank spaces in the input, and a count, weighted appropriately according to their distance back in time, of the occurrence of each pattern is computed. This count is divided by a similarly weighted count of the entire 120 relevant patterns, to give the conditional probabilities of the various possible additions to the input pattern. Finally, those combinations whose conditional probabilities exceed a preassigned threshold are added into the input pattern.*

There is nothing here that is not well within the scope of present-day digital technology. In the applications we are interested in, high speed is not of the essence; high information capacity is. For our purpose, the best system would seem to be a flexible magnetic belt, wide enough to hold all the inputs side by side, and long enough to contain a record of the entire relevant past. The actual computation and auxiliary storage would be done by a conventional digital computer. One complete run of the tape would be necessary at each input; if inputs are minutes apart, as is typical of chemical process work, this is easily feasible, even for quite long tapes.

Consequently, we can say now with confidence that large conditional probability computers, capable of handling several hundred inputs, can be constructed with present-day technology.

We are presently studying these computers as possible controllers of complex chemical processes. Although many problems remain, we have made encouraging progress towards this goal, and hope to achieve useful results within the not-too-distant future.

REFERENCES

Buhr, R. J. 1961. The development of a conditional probability computer. Rept. No. 2, Computer and Control Systems Lab., Univ. Sask., Saskatoon, Saskatchewan.

Papart, S. 1960. Redundancy and linear logical nets. Bionics Symposium, pp. 181-195. WADD Tech. Rept. 60-600.

Penfield, W. 1958. The excitable cortex in conscious man, pp. 24-37. Charles C. Thomas, Springfield, Ill.

Reid, K. H. 1961a. Simulation studies of conditional probability computers. Rept. No. 3. Computer and Control Systems Lab., Univ. Sask., Saskatoon, Saskatchewan.

Reid, K. H. 1961b. Statistical analysis of a conditional probability computer with stationary random input. Rept. No. 7. Computer and Control Systems Lab., Univ. Sask., Saskatoon, Saskatchewan.

Uttley, A. M. 1956. Conditional probability machines and conditioned reflexes. Automata Studies, pp. 253-275. Princeton Univ. Press.

Uttley, A. M. 1958. The design of conditional probability computers. Natl. Phys. Lab. Rept. Sept.

*It is interesting to note that there is evidence indicating that human memory is also organized in this fashion. Observations by Dr. W. Penfield (1958) indicate that the human brain contains a continuous record of the consciously perceived past—our "list memory." Coordination and comparison are performed elsewhere in the brain—our "separate computer and auxiliary storage area."

BAYES STRATEGIES AS ADAPTIVE BEHAVIOR*

Raymond A. Wiesen and Emir H. Shuford

Psychometric Laboratory, University of North Carolina
Chapel Hill, North Carolina

The central tendency or regression effect is one of the most commonly observed phenomena in psychophysical judgment tasks. By regression effect we refer to the fact that the subject tends to overestimate the low values in the stimulus distribution and underestimate the high values. One interpretation, which is unsatisfactory if one poses as a goal an understanding of such behavior, is that this and other observed phenomena represent biases and errors on the part of the subject. If, on the other hand, we assume that the individual is an adaptive organism who behaves optimally in such situations, then we are faced with the problem of showing in what terms the observed effects represent optimal behavior.

Let us consider the analysis of a specific judgment task (Fig. 1). On each trial of an experiment the subject sees a 3 by 3 matrix such as the one shown

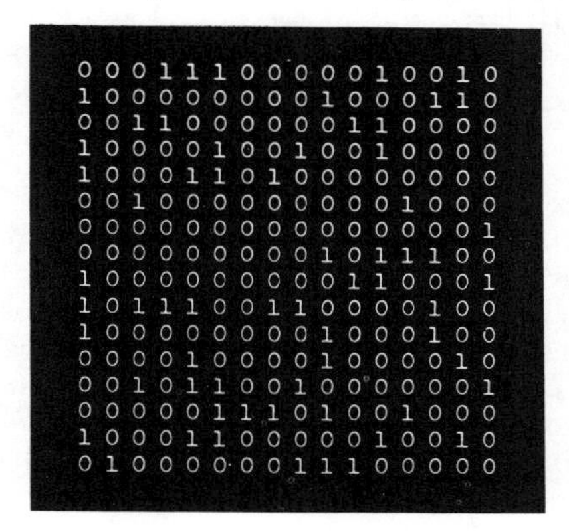

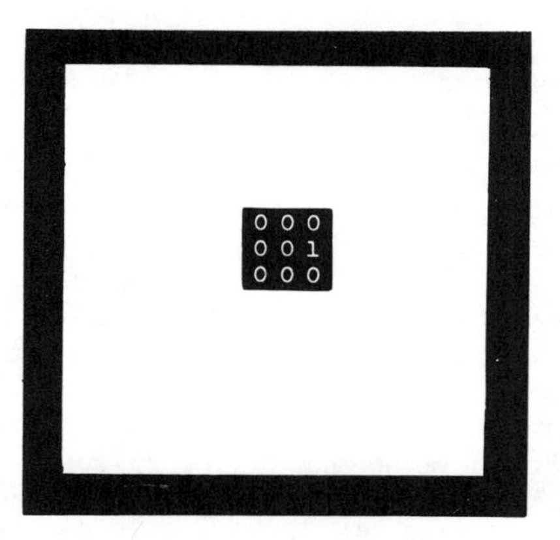

Fig. 1.

*This research was supported by a United States Air Force Research Contract AF-49(638)-729 with the Air Force Office of Scientific Research.

in the lower portion of Fig. 1. His task is to estimate the percentage of 1's in the large 16 by 16 matrix shown in the upper portion of the figure. The subject does not see this larger matrix. He sees only the small 3 by 3 matrix which contains the nine elements near the center of the larger matrix. After the subject records his estimate, he is told the actual proportion of 1's in the 16 by 16 matrix and is paid a fixed amount of money for each estimate which is correct to the nearest percentage point. The 3 by 3 matrices are presented in a random sequence.

On each trial the subject's task is analogous to estimating the parameter p of a binomial process, where p is the proportion of 1's in the large matrix. One such estimate is the maximum likelihood estimate which gives $\delta = x/n$, where δ is the estimate, x is the number of 1's in the 3 by 3 matrix, and n is the number of elements in the 3 by 3 matrix. Notice that this estimate is unbiased. A model proposing such an estimate would not be an adequate description of behavior if performance in this task exhibits the effects previously mentioned. Such a model would view behavior as rather static and unaffected by the context of the situation.

Many investigations have shown that the distribution of stimuli over a series of trials affects the relation between stimulus and response. Let us consider a statistical estimation procedure which takes into account this distribution, namely, a Bayes procedure. A Bayes strategy is optimal in the sense that it maximizes average payoff over the trials of the experiment. In our analysis, the stimulus distribution is the prior distribution, the observation is the sample, and the posterior distribution is defined as usual.

Since we wish to present a wide variety of distributions of stimuli to the subject, we must select a continuous distribution which can take on many forms on the interval (0, 1). The beta distribution with parameters α and β is such a distribution. It is also the conjugate of the binomial and, hence, affords mathematical ease in obtaining a solution. Using a beta distribution as a prior distribution and a binomial data-generating process, the posterior distribution is a beta distribution with parameters $x + \alpha$ and $n - x + \beta$, where all terms are as previously defined. In order to obtain a solution, we must further specify a loss function or a utility function. We mentioned earlier that the subject is paid an amount of money if his estimate is correct to the nearest percentage point. That is, the gain to the subject is, say, 1 if his estimate is correct and 0 if his estimate is incorrect by as much as one percentage point. Hence the proper function is an all or none, which may be paraphrased as "a miss is as good as a mile." Studies in the area of probability learning indicate that subjects adopt such a utility function even when the situation is not purposely structured to reinforce adopting such a utility function.

Using an all-or-none loss function, the estimate is

$$\delta' = \frac{x + \alpha - 1}{n + \alpha + \beta - 2}$$

This is the mode of the posterior distribution. The derivation of this estimate is explained in the appendix.

The Bayes estimate is a linear function of the sample proportion. The slope of this line is determined by the parameters α and β of the prior distribution. When the prior distribution is uniform, the slope is one. For other prior distributions, the estimates are regressed about the mode of the prior distribution.

In order to approximate the Bayes strategy, the subject must know the stimulus distribution, which can be learned during the course of the experiment. Let us refer to the prior distribution adopted by the subject at any particular time as his subjective distribution. We assume that the subjective distribution is approximately uniform at the beginning of an experimental session; that is, the mean of this distribution is close to one half and the variance is rather large. This subjective distribution is modified during the course of the experiment, and as it approaches the true distribution of stimuli used in the experiment, the subject's behavior approaches optimal performance as represented by the Bayes strategy.

Let us now turn to the empirical evidence for the Bayes model and also take a closer look at the learning of the stimulus distribution. We shall discuss the results of two experiments.

In the first experiment, 22 college students were shown a series of 150 3 by 3 matrices. The exposure time was long enough to allow the subject to get an accurate count of the elements in the matrix. The subject recorded his estimate, was told the correct proportion, recorded this, and was immediately paid 50 cents for each correct estimate. The 16 by 16 matrices were chosen to approximate a beta distribution with $\alpha = 6$ and $\beta = 3$, a negatively skewed distribution with a mean of 0.67.

Each subject's estimates for the last 15 trials were analyzed and compared with the Bayes model and the maximum likelihood model.

In general, the Bayes model, as represented by the equation in the appendix with $\alpha = 6$, $\beta = 3$, and $n = 9$, predicted the final 15 estimates of most subjects.

Estimates of the mean and variance of the subjective distribution for the ten successive 15-trial blocks were also obtained. The ten inferred means and variances were plotted for each subject. Inspection of these graphs indicated that most subjects were learning the stimulus distribution, although at somewhat different rates (Fig. 2). A rapid learner, such as the one shown in this figure,

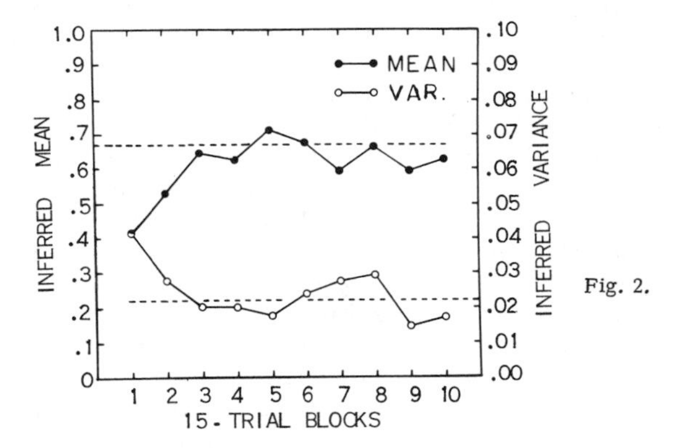

Fig. 2.

typically began with a broad, unimodal subjective distribution centered around 0.50. With experience, the mean and variance of the subjective distribution quickly reached the theoretical asymptotic values, 0.67 and 0.022, of the stimulus distribution. The graphs of only a few subjects, however, were as regular or indicated such rapid learning as did this one (Fig. 3). Some subjects, such as the one shown in this figure, gave no evidence of learning. Remember that these graphs are estimates of the mean and variance of the subjective distribution.

This experiment supports the Bayes model which predicts asymptotic behavior. However, an adequate model must also be able to account for the trial-to-trial changes in behavior.

One model which deserves attention is an association model; that is, on each trial of the experiment an association is reinforced between correct proportion and sample proportion. A model of this type was tested and found to be consistent with the data of the first experiment if we assumed that the model described the changes in the subjective posterior distribution and that the subject responded

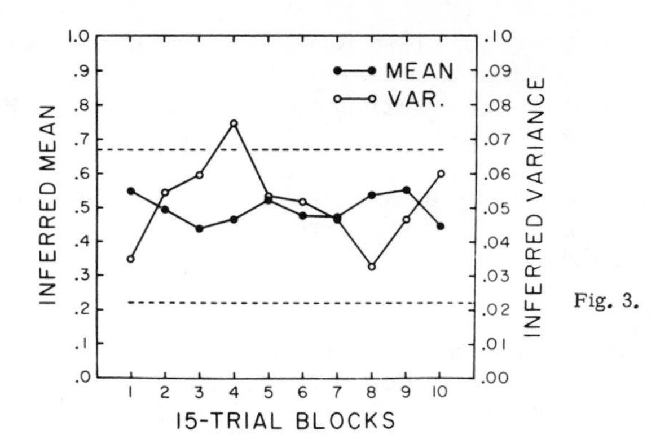

Fig. 3.

with the mode of this distribution. Without going into more detail about this model, let us look at the second experiment. The second experiment was designed to test the adequacy of an association model. A model of this type would be inadequate if subjects in this experiment behaved in accordance with the Bayes model.

Thirty-nine college students participated in the second experiment. All subjects were tested on two different occasions a week apart. Each subject became a member of one of four experimental groups, depending on his time of arrival for the first session.

On the first day all groups were shown 77 small matrices based on proportions chosen at random from a positively skewed beta distribution. The conditions for groups I and II were the same as those for the first experiment in that the correct proportions were given at the end of each trial. This condition will be referred to as one of complete feedback. The subjects in groups III and IV, however, were not told the correct proportions until the end of the session. This condition will be referred to as one of partial feedback. In the second session all groups were shown a series of 122 small matrices based on proportions randomly drawn from a negatively skewed beta distribution. Groups I and III received complete feedback while groups II and IV received partial feedback. At the end of the session, each subject received 50 cents per estimate correct to the nearest percentage point. The recording of estimates and actual proportions, when given, was identical to the first session.

With complete feedback there are two sources of information available to the subject. First, there is the information provided by the sample proportion obtained from the 3 by 3 matrix. Second, there is the information provided by the distribution of actual proportions. It is quite feasible for the subject to estimate this distribution by looking back at the distribution of actual proportions. With partial feedback the subject can use the information provided by the sample proportion to estimate the distribution of actual proportions.

A subject following the maximum likelihood model does not use the information about the stimulus distribution and gives the sample proportion as his estimate of the actual proportion. A subject using the Bayes strategy uses both sources of information under conditions of complete feedback. Under conditions of partial feedback, a subject following the Bayes model uses the information contained in the sample proportion to reconstruct the distribution of actual proportions, as well as in making his estimate.

The Bayes model and the maximum likelihood model yield predictions for each sample proportion. The estimates of each subject for the last 15 trials of the first session and the corresponding trials of the second session were compared with these predictions. For each subject an F statistic was computed for each of the models. The F statistic is the ratio of the variance about the predicted values to the error variance. The ordinate of each F was found and used in a likelihood ratio to compare the likelihood of the data given the one model with the likelihood of the data given the other model.

There are two main effects indicated by these results. First, there is a stronger tendency for subjects to adopt the Bayes strategy with complete feedback than with partial feedback (Table I). Table I shows the distribution of likelihood ratios under complete and partial feedback for each session. The like-

Table I. Likelihood Ratios for Trials 63-77 of Each Session

First Session		Second Session	
Partial feedback	Complete feedback	Partial feedback	Complete feedback
15.0	250.0	172.0	1,628,000.0
1.2	28.0	28.2	22,590.0
1.0	15.0	4.7	4,935.0
1.1	9.2	2.5	596.3
1.4	6.9	2.3	376.8
1.6	4.2	1.2	55.6
2.2	3.2	1.2	49.7
4.6	3.0	1.2	49.4
7.2	2.4	1.2	34.8
8.5	2.5	1.1	19.1
11.0	3.8	1.1	13.1
12.0	4.2	1.2	12.5
16.0	7.6	1.4	5.4
23.0	9.9	2.6	5.2
26.0	14.0	11.5	4.4
26.0	68.0		3.9
250.0			2.2
300.0			1.8
560.0			1.3
670.0			1.2
2,500.0			1.2
4,900.0			1.1
56,000,000,000.0			2.4
			336.9

lihood ratios above the line represent odds favoring the Bayes model, while those below the line favor the maximum likelihood model. In the first session, the subjects under the partial feedback condition tended to follow the maximum likelihood strategy, while the subjects under the complete feedback condition tended to divide evenly between the Bayes and the maximum likelihood strategies. In the second session, the subjects under the partial feedback condition tended to divide evenly between the Bayes and the maximum likelihood strategies, while the subjects under the complete feedback condition tended to follow the Bayes strategy.

The preponderance of Bayesian subjects in the second session suggests that experience with the experimental task leads to an increased tendency for subjects to follow the Bayes strategy. Table II shows the likelihood ratios for the subjects in group I, who had complete feedback in both sessions, and for the subjects in group IV, who had partial feedback in both sessions. The tendency to follow the

Table II. Likelihood Ratios for Each Session (Groups I and IV)

Group I		Group IV	
First session (complete feedback)	Second session (complete feedback)	First session (partial feedback)	Second session (partial feedback)
28.0	4,935.0	1.0	28.2
15.0	596.0	1.6	2.5
3.2	55.6	2.2	2.3
2.4	49.4	4.6	1.2
2.5	19.1	7.2	1.2
3.8	5.2	12.0	1.2
4.2	3.9	250.0	1.2
9.9	1.3	300.0	1.1
14.0	1.2	560.0	1.4
68.0	1.2		

Bayes strategy is very strong in group I during the second session. In group IV the case is not so clear since there are no very large odds in favor of the Bayes strategy. However, the large odds in favor of the maximum likelihood strategy present in the first session have disappeared by the second session. Thus, the tendency to follow the Bayes strategy increases with repeated experience in the experiment, whether under conditions of complete or partial feedback.

We have shown, on the basis of two experiments, that subjects tend to follow the Bayes strategy under conditions of complete feedback. Even under conditions of partial feedback there is a tendency to adopt the Bayes strategy with experience in the situation. The Bayes strategy is optimal in terms of maximizing average payoff and the model predicts the regression effect found in many psychophysical judgment tasks.

Since with partial feedback there are no correct proportions available for association, an association model offers an inadequate description of the observed behavior. The Bayes model is also presently deficient in that it says nothing about the trial-to-trial changes. It only predicts the asymptotic result. The task of giving a complete description of the situation still remains. Let us examine a few models which show some promise.

One model suggests that the subject begins the experiment with a distribution over the set of possible prior distributions. This distribution is a function of previous experience. It is mathematically expressible as a prior distribution over the parameters α and β of the beta distribution. Since the beta distribution is the prior distribution over p, the distribution over α and β is a *prior* prior distribution. Given the form of this distribution, it would seem possible to specify some criterion of optimality which would tell how the information obtained from the sample proportions or the actual proportions is to be used to modify this distribution. Such specification presents a problem. Another problem is that of specifying the form of the *prior* prior distribution. What we need is a distribution that produces a beta distribution as a posterior distribution. Such a distribution has not been worked out, and, unfortunately, no progress can be reported on this model.

Another model assumes that at the beginning of the experimental session the subjective distribution is approximately uniform. This initial distribution represents a sort of averaging of past experience. In effect, it is based upon a certain number k of complete observations which are similar to those trials of the experiments just discussed in which the actual proportion is given at the end of each trial. After the first trial, the initial distribution is adjusted by assigning a weight λ to the mean of the posterior distribution and a weight $(k - \lambda)$ to the mean of the initial subjective distribution to obtain a subjective distribution for the second trial.

A similar adjustment in the variance of the subjective distribution is also effected. In general, the subjective distribution on the $(i+1)$st trial is a weighted average of the subjective distribution used on the ith trial and the posterior distribution given the observation of the ith trial.

This model specifies two parameters, k and λ. The weight given to the initial subjective distribution is defined by k, which is an individual difference parameter whose need has been amply demonstrated. In a series of experiments k is not necessarily a constant from one experiment to the next. In fact, the results of the second experiment suggest that k decreases from session to session, provided that the feedback condition is constant.

Reference to the previous model shows that this need not necessarily be the case. If the same distribution of stimuli is presented in a series of experiments, the variance of the *prior* prior distribution will be decreased. This might lead to an increase in k. If, on the other hand, the distribution of stimuli changes from experiment to experiment, the variance of the *prior* prior increases and would seem to lead to a decrease in k.

The other parameter, λ, specifies the weight given to the posterior distribution. λ is a decreasing function of the variance of the posterior distribution. With partial feedback, this variance is larger than zero. With complete feedback, the posterior distribution becomes a point distribution with variance zero.

Since λ is a decreasing function of the posterior variance, the weight given to the stimulus distribution is larger in the case of complete feedback than in that of partial feedback. It follows that the subjective distribution of a subject with complete feedback would, in general, more rapidly approach the actual stimulus distribution.

We have specified a normative model for a very specific situation and have indicated that this model constitutes a partial description of the situation. We are currently working on a more complete model.

What have we implied about behavior in general? We have shown that behavior in a psychophysical judgment task is adaptive and optimal. Similar analyses of other situations may well lead to the same conclusions. The general class of Bayes strategies provides a very broad and powerful set of potential models for the analysis of behavior and for the development of adaptive automata.

APPENDIX

Data generating model:

$$f(x|p) = \binom{n}{x} p^x (1-p)^{n-x} \qquad 0 \le x \le n \qquad 0 < p < 1 \tag{1}$$

Maximum likelihood estimate, δ of p:

$$\delta = \frac{x}{n} \tag{2}$$

Define a prior distribution $g(p)$ over p. Then the posterior distribution, $g(p|x)$, is

$$g(p|x) = \frac{f(x|p)\,g(p)}{\int_\Omega f(x|p)\,g(p)} \tag{3}$$

Then, in particular, if the prior distribution is a beta distribution

$$g(p) = [B(\alpha,\beta)]^{-1} p^{\alpha-1}(1-p)^{\beta-1} \qquad 0 < p < 1 \qquad \alpha,\beta > 0 \tag{4}$$

The posterior distribution over p is:

$$g(p|x) = [B(x+\alpha,\ n-x+\beta)]^{-1} p^{x+\alpha-1}(1-p)^{n-x+\beta-1} \tag{5}$$

Define a loss function L:

$$L[p, \delta'(x)] = \begin{cases} 1 \text{ if } |p - \delta'(x)| > \epsilon \\ 0 \text{ if } |p - \delta'(x)| \leq \epsilon \end{cases} \tag{6}$$

where ϵ is a small positive number and δ' is the decision function. Then $\delta'(x)$, the mode of the posterior distribution, is the estimate which minimizes average risk.

The mode of $g(p|x)$ is obtained by differentiating (5) and setting it equal to zero. Doing this we obtain the Bayes estimate

$$\delta' = \frac{x + \alpha - 1}{n + \alpha + \beta - 2} \tag{7}$$

For a more complete discussion of this estimate and other Bayesian procedures, see Raiffa and Schlaifer (1961).

REFERENCES

Raiffa, H. and Schlaifer, R. 1961. Applied statistical decision theory. Harvard Univ., Cambridge, Mass.

Shuford, E.H. 1961. Percentage estimation of proportion as a function of element type, exposure time, and task. J. Exp. Psychol. 61, 430-436.

Shuford, E.H. and Hall, W.J. 1959. A decision theory approach to psychophysics. UNC Psychom. Lab. Rept. No. 22.

Shuford, E.H. and Wiesen, R.A. 1959. Bayes estimation of proportion: the effect of stimulus distribution and exposure time. UNC Psychom. Lab. Report No. 23.

A SELF-ORGANIZING BINARY LOGICAL ELEMENT

E. B. Carne, E. M. Connelly, P. H. Halpern, and B. A. Logan

Advanced Computer Laboratory, Computer Department
Melpar, Inc., Falls Church, Virginia

INTRODUCTION

Many adaptive, or learning, systems have been developed in direct imitation of some concept of a neurological system. Once the system is built, attempts are then made to analyze its behavior and to build suitable mathematical models and techniques. This paper describes a simple mathematical model which applies to most learning systems and shows how it leads directly to the self-organizing binary logical network.

Historically, a special case of the self-organizing binary logical network was developed some time ago (Corneretto, 1960, 1961). Called the ARTRON (ARTificial neuRON), this unit represents the special case of a two-input—one-output device which can be trained to form any general Boolean connective. It is shown that the general network should behave considerably better than the ARTRON and the results of computer simulations which confirm these results are included.

In general, the optimum self-organizing binary logical network requires statistically dependent switches. However, this condition implies too much complexity for any general n-input—one-output function and it is shown that an acceptable optimization can be achieved using statistically independent switches.

A concept for the distance between logical functions is introduced and applied to the problems of error correction and approximation of functions by "insufficient" hardware. An adaptive system is capable of better performance than the standard techniques for error correction and detection. Given a device for error detection (the goal circuit), the problem of error correction is simplified where these errors are due to failure of components.

A MATHEMATICAL MODEL OF A LEARNING SYSTEM

Information Concept

Figure 1 shows a typical learning or adaptive system. It consists of a device which must be "organized" to perform some connective between inputs and outputs, and an "organizer" or goal circuit which measures "how well" the device is doing according to some criterion. Based on these measurements, the goal circuit provides instructions (information) to the device. These instructions are generally called reward or punishment signals. The description can be formalized in the following manner. Suppose there is a finite number of states which can be assumed by the device or network, and suppose that for each state k, there is a probability p_k that the network will be organized under random training to perform connective (k). Then the information required to organize the network to perform connective (k) may be defined as

$$I_k = -\log_2 p_k \text{ (bits)} \tag{1}$$

To show that this is a reasonable definition of the amount of information to organize a network to perform a given connective (k), consider the following:

1. $I_k \geq 0$; i.e., information is always positive.

2. If the network can only perform connective (k), then $p_k = 1$, $I_k = 0$; i.e., no information is required to organize an already organized network.

3. Intuitively, the amount of information necessary to organize the network should increase as the a priori probability of finding the network in the proper state decreases.

4. If two independent networks are to be organized, one to perform connective (j), the other (k), the information required to do this should be the sum of the separate information. This follows from the definition since $p_{jk} = p_j \cdot p_k$ and $-\log_2 (p_j \cdot p_k) = -\log p_j - \log p_k$.

From 4 it can be shown that $I(p)$ must be a logarithmic function. Consider the functional equation

$$I(p_j \cdot p_k) = I(p_j) + I(p_k) \tag{2}$$

Taking partial derivatives of both sides of the equation with respect to p_j and with respect to p_k gives

$$p_k I'(p_j \cdot p_k) = I'(p_j) \tag{3}$$

$$p_j I'(p_j \cdot p_k) = I'(p_k)$$

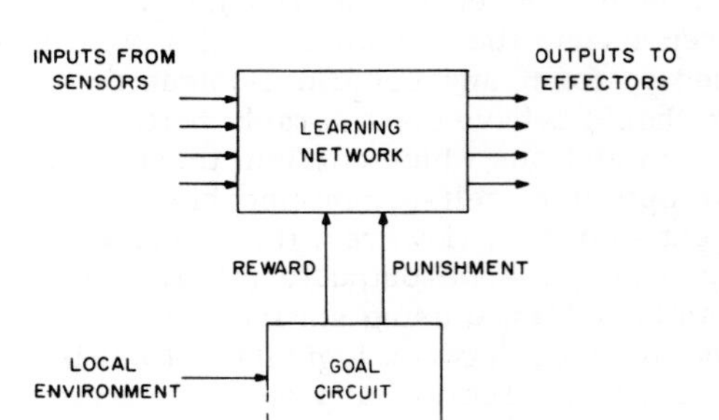

Fig. 1. Block diagram of learning system.

Eliminating $I'(p_j \cdot p_k)$ in either equation gives

$$p_k I'(p_k) = p_j I'(p_j) \tag{4}$$

which is an identity for all p_k and all p_j. The only way this can be an identity is if each is equal to a constant. Hence, solving the differential equation

$$I(p) = c \log(p) \tag{5}$$

and choosing $-\log_2 e$ as the constant gives the definition

$$I(p) = -\log_2 p \text{ (bits)}$$

Entropy

An efficient learning system should conform to the following general criteria:

1. The learning network should require the least amount of information (on the average) to organize it to the proper connective.

2. The goal circuit should provide the greatest amount of information (on the average) about the proper connective for each measurement of the environment, or per unit time.

Each of these criteria may be subject to hardware or other types of constraints. To compute the average amount of information required to organize the network requires a knowledge of the a priori probability q_k that the system will be required to perform connective (k). Hence, to compute the average information, the information required to organize the network to perform function (k) must be weighted by q_k. This average information will be called the entropy.

$$H = -\sum_{\text{all } k} q_k \log_2 p_k \tag{6}$$

Some Minimization Problems

The probability p_k that the network will be predisposed to perform connective (k) under random training can be specified by the designer. Ideally, this probability should be chosen to minimize the entropy according to the aforementioned criteria. This is under the obvious constraint

$$\Sigma p_k = 1 \tag{7}$$

Using the standard calculus of variations, this corresponds to minimizing

$$J = H + \lambda \Sigma p_k \tag{8}$$

where λ is the Lagrangian multiplier. That is

$$\frac{dJ}{dp_k} = \frac{d}{dp_k}(-\Sigma\, q_k \log_2 p_k + \lambda\, \Sigma p_k) = 0 \tag{9}$$

Remembering that $\Sigma p_k = \Sigma q_k = 1$, this reduces to

$$p_k = q_k \tag{10}$$

that is, the probability of the network being predisposed to perform connective (k) should be equal to the probability that connective (k) will be required by the system, which is not a surprising result.

Consider, as an example, a network which can be organized to perform any function of n variables, and suppose that all the functions are equally likely; then it requires 2^n bits of information to organize the network to any one of these functions. Figure 2 shows a realization of this, a three input—two-output self-organizing binary logical network. It consists of an alternation of canonical

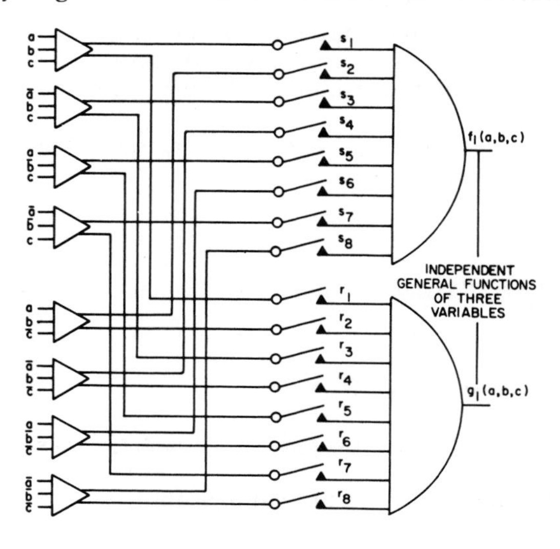

Fig. 2. Three-input—two-output self-organizing binary logical network.

products, each connected to an "or" gate through a "statistical switch." It requires one bit of information about the proper logical function for each of the statistical switches to organize the network.

A special case of this, the ARTRON, was considered by Mr. R. J. Lee and others. The ARTRON is a two-input—one-output device, or four canonical products and four statistical switches. For systems requiring more than two inputs, it was proposed that the ARTRONs be interconnected to provide the desired capacity. This proved not to be an optimum system. The limitations of this concept are discussed in detail later.

Consider another simple example. Suppose it is known a priori that the correct connective is a function of the number of inputs which are true; in other words, any input may be interchanged with any other, leaving the connective invariant. The correct function can then be written as some alternation of the basic function j/n, where j runs from 0 to n (j/n is one if, and only if, exactly j inputs are one). There are, therefore, $(n+1)$ basic functions and 2^{n+1} such symmetric functions. If no other functions are possible, and these are equally likely, it would require $(n+1)$ bits of information to organize the $(n+1)$ switches.

Consider now the problem of optimizing the learning system for any set of q's. Suppose that only 2^m functions are required, and that each has a different probability of being required. Further, suppose that these functions can be coded with m two-position switches (the switches may be multiple throw and may be statistical) so that each combination of switches corresponds to one of the functions. The probability of any switch combination being present will be the probability that the corresponding function is present. For minimum entropy, $p_k = q_k$, i.e.,

$$q_1 = P(s_1 s_2 \ldots s_m) \qquad (11)$$

$$q_2 = P(\bar{s}_1 s_2 \ldots s_m)$$

. . all binary combinations . .

$$q_{2m} = P(\bar{s}_1 \bar{s}_2 \ldots \bar{s}_m)$$

If the switches are all independent, this set corresponds to 2^m equations in m unknowns. It is obviously impossible to satisfy these equations for arbitrary q's. Hence, in general, to satisfy the minimum-entropy criterion, dependent switches are required.

There are several ways to construct dependencies so that the equations have solutions. One way is to write

$$\begin{aligned} q_1 &= P(s_1 s_2 s_3 \ldots s_{m-1} s_m) \\ &= P(s_1) P(s_2|s_1) P(s_3|s_2 s_1) \ldots P(s_m|s_1 s_2 s_3 \ldots s_{m-1}) \end{aligned} \qquad (12)$$

. . . .

$$\begin{aligned} q_4 &= P(\bar{s}_1 \bar{s}_2 s_3 \ldots s_{m-1} s_m) \\ &= P(\bar{s}_1) P(\bar{s}_2|\bar{s}_1) P(s_3|\bar{s}_2 \bar{s}_1) \ldots P(s_m|\bar{s}_1 \bar{s}_2 s_3 \ldots s_{m-1}) \end{aligned}$$

etc., and to solve for any of the conditional probabilities

$$P(s_j|x) = \frac{\sum_{s_j x} q_i}{\sum_{x} q_i} \qquad (13)$$

where x is any binary combination of any subset of the switches, $P(s_j|x)$ is the probability that switch s_j is closed, given that the binary combination x of switches is true, and $\sum_x q_i$ is the sum of all the q's associated with the functions which have binary combination x in their formation. A typical construction of the composite switches $s_1 s_2 \ldots$ is shown in Fig. 3. This construction is impractical for any large number of functions since it requires the same number of switches as functions.

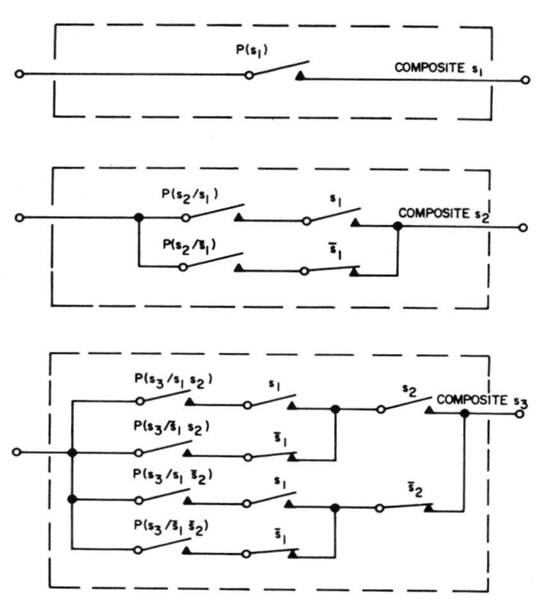

Fig. 3. Typical construction for dependent switches satisfying minimum entropy requirement.

Consider now the problem of minimizing entropy under the constraint that the switches be independent. In this case

$$\log_2 P(x \cdot y) = \log_2 P(x) + \log_2 P(y) \tag{14}$$

and

$$H = -\sum_{s_j} q_i \log_2 P(s_j) - \sum_{\bar{s}_j} q_i \log_2 [1 - P(s_j)] \tag{15}$$

plus other terms not involving s_j. Minimizing H with respect to s_j gives,

$$\frac{dH}{ds_j} = \log_2 e \left[-\frac{\sum_{s_j} q_i}{P(s_j)} + \frac{\sum_{\bar{s}_j} q_i}{1 - P(s_j)} \right] = 0 \tag{16}$$

Now

$$\Sigma q_i = 1$$

so that

$$\sum_{s_j} q_i = 1 - \sum_{\bar{s}_j} q_i \tag{17}$$

Hence,

$$P(s_j) = \sum_{s_j} q_i \tag{18}$$

or the probability that any switch be closed should equal the sum of the probabilities of requiring those functions which need switch s_j closed in their formation. In this case, the minimum entropy becomes

$$H = -\sum_{j=1}^{m} P(s_j) \log_2 P(s_j) + [1 - P(s_j)] \log_2 [1 - P(s_j)] \tag{19}$$

Amount of Information Obtained by the "Goal" Circuits

The amount of information gained about the connective to which the network must be organized by making observation x is

$$I_x = -\log_2 \frac{P_x}{P_{ox}} \tag{20}$$

where P_x is the probability that x is true prior to the observation, and P_{ox} is the probability that x is true after the observation.

The self-organizing binary logical network can be organized to perform any function of n variables with 2^n (independent) bits of information, when all functions are equally likely. The circuit requires one bit of information about each statistical switch associated with each minterm (canonical product). If the goal circuits can be designed to provide a comparison (reward or punishment signal) for each switch independent of any other switch, then the network can be organized with 2^n comparisons. If, however, it is only possible to provide a reward or punishment signal after the occurrence of a sequence of input combinations (more than one statistical switch is involved), then, in general, it will require more than 2^n comparisons to provide 2^n independent bits to organize the network.

It is possible to determine how much information can be obtained (on the average) from a goal circuit which provides a comparison signal after a sequence of k canonical products. If the amount of information obtained by observing that the k sequence is correct is $-\log_2 P_k$, where P_k is the a priori probability that the sequence was correct, then the amount of information obtained by observing that the k sequence is incorrect is $-\log_2 (1 - P_k)$. The average amount of information (entropy) obtained by the observation of each k sequence will be weighted by the probability of the outcome of the observation; i.e.,

$$H_k = -P_k \log_2 P_k - (1 - P_k) \log_2 (1 - P_k) \tag{21}$$

Now P_k can be computed by observing that the fraction of the total functions which contain a certain k canonical product is 2^{-k}. If all functions are equally likely, $P_k = 2^{-k}$ so that

$$H_k = \frac{k}{2^k} - (1 - 2^{-k}) \log_2 (1 - 2^{-k}) \tag{22}$$

If k is large, this reduces to

$$H_k = \frac{k + \log_2 e}{2^k} \tag{23}$$

If 2^n bits of information are required to organize the network, then the number of comparisons, on the average, would be $N = 2^n/H_k$. It is interesting to compute a short table of values of $1/H_k$ for various values of k. $1/H_k$ represents the multiplying factor by which the minimum number of comparisons must be multiplied to organize the network by observing any length sequences k.

k	H_k	$1/H_k = N/2^n$
1	1.0	1.0
2	0.812	1.23
4	0.306	3.27
6	0.115	8.7
10	0.0111	90.0

These values are plotted in Fig. 4.

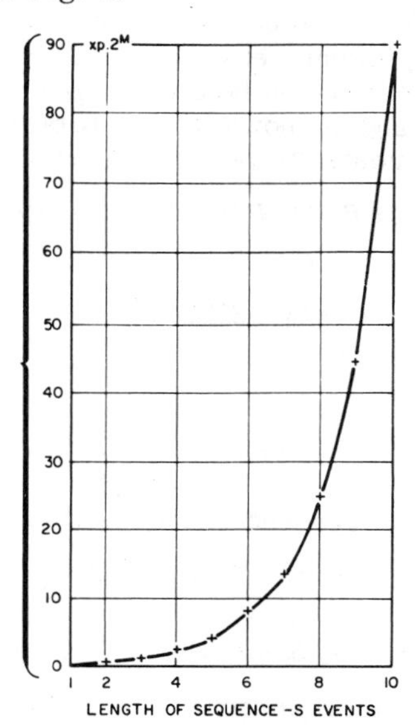

Fig. 4. Variation of number of comparisons required to organize network with the number of events which must be observed before the truth of one event can be determined.

Design of the Statistical Switch in the Presence of Noisy Goal Circuits

The term "noisy goal circuits" is intended to imply that there exists a probability that the goal circuits may give an incorrect signal. Let

N_{00} be the number of times the goal circuit gives a signal which says open the switch when it should be open,

N_{01} be the number of times the signal says close the switch when it should be open,

N_{10} be the number of times the signal says open the switch when it should be closed, and

N_{11} be the number of times the signal says close the switch when it should be closed. Then the probability that the switch should be closed, given a single measurement y that says it should be closed, is

$$P(s|y) = \frac{N_{11}}{N_{11} + N_{01}} \tag{24}$$

and the probability of generating a signal that says the switch should be closed when it should be is

$$P(y|s) = \frac{N_{11}}{N_{11} + N_{10}} \tag{25}$$

Similarly

$$P(s|\bar{y}) = \frac{N_{10}}{N_{00} + N_{10}} = 1 - P(\bar{s}|\bar{y}) \tag{26}$$

If $P(s) = P(\bar{s})$, then

$$P(\bar{s}) = \frac{N_{00} + N_{01}}{N_{00} + N_{11} + N_{01} + N_{10}} = \frac{N_{11} + N_{10}}{N_{00} + N_{11} + N_{01} + N_{10}} = P(s) \tag{27}$$

If the goal signal lies just as often when it says the switch should be open as it does when it says the switch should be closed, then $N_{01} = N_{10}$ or $P(s|y) = P(y|s)$.

Consider now two independent sets of measurements x, y on the switch. If the probability that the switch should be closed, given that each of the measurements separately $P(s|x)$, $P(s|y)$ is known, the probability that the switch should be closed, given both measurements $P(s|xy)$, can be computed. Using Bayes' formula

$$P(AB) = P(A) \cdot P(B|A) = P(B) \cdot P(A|B) \tag{28}$$

gives

$$P(B|A) = \frac{P(B) \cdot P(A|B)}{P(A)}$$

or

$$P(s|xy) = \frac{P(xy|s) \cdot P(s)}{P(xy)} \tag{29}$$

In this case, the independence of x and y implies that

$$P(xy|s) = P(x|s) \cdot P(y|s) \tag{30}$$

and

$$P(xy|\bar{s}) = P(x|\bar{s}) \cdot P(y|\bar{s})$$

but not $P(xy) = P(x) \cdot P(y)$ since there is an obvious correlation between two measurements of the same thing. Now

$$P(xy) = P(xy|s) \cdot P(s) + P(xy|\bar{s}) \cdot P(\bar{s}) \tag{31}$$

so that, from equation (29),

$$P(s|xy) = \frac{1}{1 + \dfrac{P(x|\bar{s}) \cdot P(y|\bar{s}) \cdot P(\bar{s})}{P(x|s) \cdot P(y|s) \cdot P(s)}} \tag{32}$$

Using Bayes' formula twice

$$P(s|xy) = \frac{1}{1 + \dfrac{[1 - P(s|x)]\,[1 - P(s|y)]\,P(s)}{P(s|x)\,P(s|y)\,P(\bar{s})}} \tag{33}$$

Without loss of generality, the statistical switch can be assumed initially unbiased, i.e., $P(s) = P(\bar{s})$. Using this as the origin, a recursion formula for the state of the statistical switch can be developed to give

$$P_n = \frac{1}{1 + \dfrac{(1 - P_{n-1})\,[1 - P(s|y_n)]}{P_{n-1} \cdot P(s|y_n)}} = \frac{P_{n-1} \cdot P(s|y_n)}{1 - P_{n-1} - P(s|y_n) + 2P_{n-1} \cdot P(s|y_n)} \tag{34}$$

where $P_n = P(s|xy) =$ the state of the switch after the nth reward (punishment).

It will be observed that the probability is adiabatic, i.e., if two successive signals are received, one of which says the switch should be closed with probability $P(s|x)$, and the other says it should be open with the same probability [which is the same as it should be closed with probability $1 - P(s|x)$], the switch returns to its probability state prior to these signals. The adiabatic property is important because it means that the difference between the number of signals to open and the number of signals to close can be used to determine the probability that the switch should be closed. It will also be observed that $0 \leq P_n \leq 1$ and is equal to one if, and only if, some reward signal has 100% probability of being correct.

Now consider the case when all reward and punishment signals are equally reliable; then $P(s|R) = Z$ and $P(s|P) = 1 - Z$. The probability that the switch should be closed in terms of the numbers of signals that say it should be closed can be determined as follows. Suppose any sequence Q has k signals that say the switch should be closed and l signals that say the switch should be open, then

$$P(Q|s) = P(x|s)^k [1 - P(x|s)]^l \tag{35}$$

and

$$P(Q|\bar{s}) = P(x|\bar{s})^k [1 - P(x|\bar{s})]^l \tag{36}$$

but

$$\begin{aligned} P(s|Q) &= \frac{P(Q|s)P(s)}{P(Q)} \\ &= \frac{P(Q|s)P(s)}{P(Q|s)P(s) + P(Q|\bar{s})P(\bar{s})} \\ &= \frac{1}{1 + \dfrac{P(Q|\bar{s})P(\bar{s})}{P(Q|s)P(s)}} \end{aligned} \tag{37}$$

This can be written

$$P(s|Q) = \frac{1}{1 + \dfrac{P(x|\bar{s})^k [1 - P(x|\bar{s})]^l P(\bar{s})}{P(x|s)^k [1 - P(x|s)]^l P(s)}} \tag{38}$$

If $P(x|s) = P(s|x) = z$, this reduces to

$$P(s|Q) = \frac{1}{1 + \left(\dfrac{1 - z}{z}\right)^{k - l}} \tag{39}$$

and, if $P(s|Q) = P(s)$ is plotted against $(k - l)$, theoretical learning curves for an ideal statistical switch result, as shown in Fig. 5. A model which can be made to approximate any shape has been built and is described later.

It will be observed that the learning curve for the statistical switch in the presence of noisy data is not greatly different from the shape that the switch

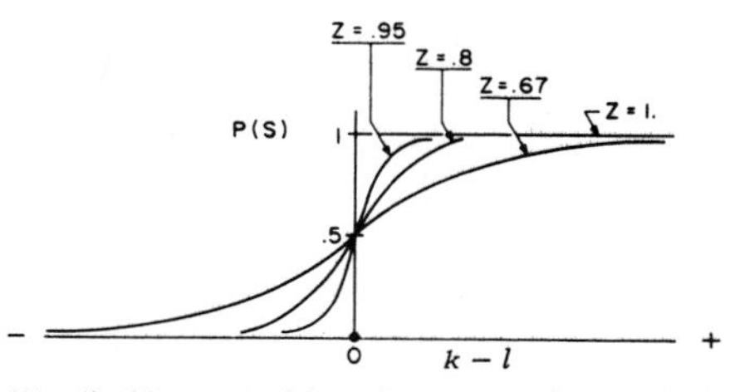

Fig. 5. Theoretical learning curves for an ideal statistical switch.

should have for minimizing entropy under the constraint that the switches are statistically independent. In fact, if all functions are equally likely, then

$$P(s_j) = \frac{1}{1 + n/m} \tag{40}$$

where m is the number of functions that require the switch closed, and n is the number that require the switch open. As information is obtained on sequences of inputs, the numbers m and n change.

Definition of Length and Distance for Logical Functions

The length N of a logical function is defined as the number of canonical products in its minterm expansion. The following laws governing the quantity N follow directly from the Boolean algebra.

$$N(A \cup B) = N(A) + N(B) - N(A \cdot B) \tag{41}$$

$$N(A \cdot B) \leq N(A)$$
$$N(A \cdot B) \leq N(B) \tag{42}$$

If $X_i \cdot X_j = 0$, $i \neq j$, then

$$N(X_1 \cup X_2 \cup X_3 \ldots \cup X_n) = N(X_1) + N(X_2) + N(X_3) + \cdots + N(X_n) \tag{43}$$

Consider two logical functions of n variables, $Y(a_1 \ldots a_n)$ and $Z(a_1 \ldots a_n)$, applied successively to a self-organizing binary logical element with X output functions. The number N of statistical switches that must be changed to accommodate Y and Z successively will be called the distance between the two functions. That is,

$$D(Y,Z) = N(Y \uplus Z) = \text{number of canonical products of the exclusive or combination } Y \uplus Z \tag{44}$$

It can be shown that this definition has the standard metric properties, namely,

$$D(Y,Z) = D(Z,Y) \tag{45}$$

$$D(Y,Z) \geq 0 \tag{46}$$

$$D(Y,Z) = 0 \text{ implies } Y = Z \tag{47}$$

$$D(Y,Z) + D(Y,W) \geq D(Z,W) \qquad \text{(triangle law)} \tag{48}$$

Redundancy Without Other Means of Error Detection

Consider the particular case of a set of n statistical switches (pseudocanonical products), k of which may fail to a zero or one. The maximum possible number of different functions which can be coded without confusion can be determined. This is the largest set of binary combinations of switches such that if there are k or less changes of switches in any two members of the set, the resulting pair will still be coded differently. This can be seen to be the same problem as finding the largest number of points which are distance $(2k+1)$ apart coded with n canonical products. This problem has been considered in one form or another by Hamming (1950), Slepian (1956), Plotkin (1960), and others. The problem has not been solved in the general case. It is much easier to correct for errors in the case where other means for detecting errors are provided (such as goal circuits).

Approximation of Functions

It has already been shown that the number of statistical switches required for the synthesis of a general function of n variables increases exponentially with n. While a priori information may limit the number of canonical products required and an increase in packing density and/or a decrease in cost may make the synthesis of many statistical switches more attractive, the synthesis of general functions of many variables soon gets out of hand. For example, an increase in problem complexity of 20 variables multiplies the hardware requirement by more than a million. In the practical case, the fine structure of a large problem contains many "don't care" situations which can be well satisfied by a smaller set of logical functions which span the total space within distance d. In this way, the effects of rapid exponential growth can be avoided. The problem is to find the smallest set of functions in any space such that every function in the entire space will be within distance d of some member of the set.

All functions in the space can be represented as binary combinations of the m switches (canonical products) which span the space, and, hence, can be represented as binary numbers. Thus, if four canonical products span the space, typical functions would be 0101, 1010, 1110, etc.

Let the symbol $*$ define a connective between two functions (numbers) such that

$$01010 * 11100 = 10110$$

i.e., an exclusive-or-combination term by term. Using this definition, the number of ones that appear in $A * B$ is the distance between A and B; also, if $A * B = C$, then $A = B * C$ and $A * A = O$. Again, if $B * O = B$ for all B, it is also clear that $A * B = B * A$ and $(A * B) * C = A * (B * C)$. Thus, the associative and commutative laws apply to this connective. Now, any function that is exactly distance d from A can be written $A * B$ where B has exactly d ones in it. The total number of functions in an m-space (m statistical switches) which are distance d from A is the combination of m things taken d at a time

$$C_d^m = \frac{m!}{(m - d)!\,d!} \tag{49}$$

and the total number of functions within distance d from any function is then

$$\sum_{j=0}^{d} C_j^m$$

Therefore, k functions can span a maximum of

$$k \sum_{j=0}^{d} C_j^m$$

functions within distance d, provided there is no overlap, i.e., none of the k functions span the same functions twice. Equating this number to the total number of functions gives

$$k = \frac{2^m}{\sum_{j=1}^{d} C_j^m} \tag{50}$$

and the smallest number of statistical switches (possibly multiple throw) required is then

$$n = \log_2 k = m - \log_2 \sum_{j=0}^{d} C_j^m \tag{51}$$

The adequacy of this lower bound has not been fully proven, however, no cases which violate this rule have been found. Hence, it is tentatively assumed that such a rule holds.

The quantity $\log_2 \sum_{j=0}^{d} C_j^m$ is the possible savings in switches achieved by the approximation. Writing

$$\log_2 \sum_{j=0}^{d} C_j^m = \log_2 C_d^m + \log_2 \left[1 + \frac{\sum_{j=1}^{d} C_{d-j}^m}{C_d^m}\right]^{\log_2 c} \tag{52}$$

it can be shown that the last member is less than 2 provided $m > 3d - 1$. Hence, the savings may be estimated by evaluating the term $\log_2 C_d^m$. Using Stirling's formula

$$n! \doteqdot \sqrt{2n\pi} \left(\frac{n}{e}\right)^n \tag{53}$$

C_d^m can be written

$$\begin{aligned} C_d^m &\doteqdot \sqrt{\frac{m}{2\pi d\,(m-d)}} \cdot \frac{m^m}{(m-d)^{m-d}\,d^d} \\ &\doteqdot \sqrt{\frac{1}{2\pi d\,(1-d/m)}} \cdot \frac{(m/d)^d}{(1-d/m)^{m-d}} \end{aligned} \tag{54}$$

$\log_2 C_d^m$ then becomes

$$\log_2 C_d^m \doteqdot d \log_2 \frac{m}{d} - \left(m - d + \frac{1}{2}\right) \log_2 \left(1 - \frac{d}{m}\right) - \frac{1}{2} \log_2 d - \frac{1}{2} \log_2 2\pi \tag{55}$$

The last term is approximately -1 and will tend to cancel the previous approximation. The fractional saving as m grows large can be written

$$\frac{d}{m} \log_2 \frac{m}{d} - \left(1 - \frac{d}{m}\right) \log_2 \left(1 - \frac{d}{m}\right) \tag{56}$$

The term d/m can be regarded as the worst case value for the fractional number of times the output is incorrect. Numerical values for the fractional savings for a few values of d/m are

$\frac{d}{m}$	$\frac{\log_2 k}{m}$
0.001	0.011
0.002	0.038
0.01	0.076
0.04	0.244
0.1	0.463
0.2	0.720
0.3	0.884

An alternative interpretation of these values is shown in Fig. 6. It shows the performance which can be obtained from a failing system if optimum reorganization can be achieved after each failure.

Another class of problems under present consideration is to find the best set of functions which span the space within distance d and which can be coded according to some restricted code. For example, a simple code but a poor one in regards to optimizing the number of switches is: restrict the functions that span the space within distance d to be expressible as all possible unions of non-intersecting functions with the condition that $\bigcup_{\text{all}} x = 1$. In this case it can be shown

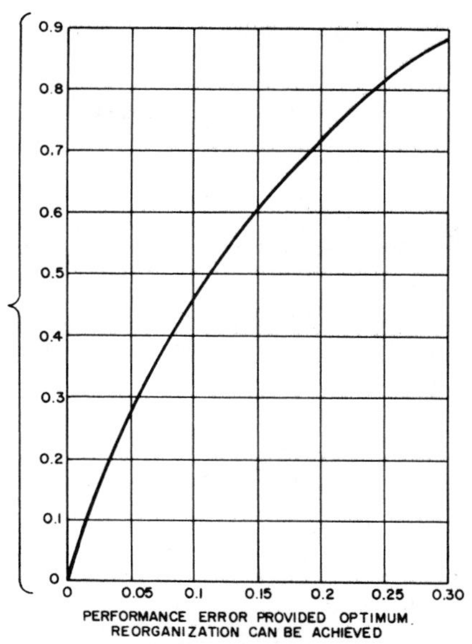

Fig. 6. Variation of performance with fraction of hardware failing under optimum reorganizing conditions.

that the optimum number of x's (switches) is $(m - 2d)$ where m is the number of canonical products in the whole space and d is the allowable distance. This can be seen by writing z as the union of nonintersecting z's, $z = z_1 \cup z_2 \ldots \cup z_k$, where is a function of some of the same canonical products as are contained in x_i. The distance between z and $\cup x_i$ is

$$Z \uplus \cup x_i = \sum_{i=1}^{k} z_i \uplus x_i \quad = \text{the sum of the distances between the } z\text{'s and } x\text{'s} \tag{57}$$

Thus, if x_i contains b canonical products, where b is odd, then the worst z_i that can be chosen to maximize the distance would contain $(b - 1)/2$ of the canonical products.

If x_i contains b canonical products and x_j contains c, then the worst z_1 and z_2 that can be chosen would make the distance be $(b + c)/2 - 1$ if b and c are odd. If $(b + c)$ is a constant, the individual values of b and c can be chosen odd to fulfill the constraint. Reapplying this argument, the x's can be defined to have one canonical product each, except the last, which must contain the remaining canonical products. If this last contains an even number of products, the function can be simulated as well with one less switch. The distance for the worst case z given kx's will be determined by the number of canonical products in the last switch, or

$$d = \frac{m - (k - 1) - 1}{2} = \frac{m - k}{2} \tag{58}$$

Hence, the number of switches required is $(m - 2d)$.

LIMITATIONS OF THE ARTRON

Consider two ARTRONs connected in series, as shown in Fig. 7. For every connective c_1 which gives an output z, there is a corresponding connective $\bar{c}_1$ which yields the complement $\bar{z}$, and, for every connective c_2 which is a nontrivial function of z, there exists another connective c_2' which yields the same output if

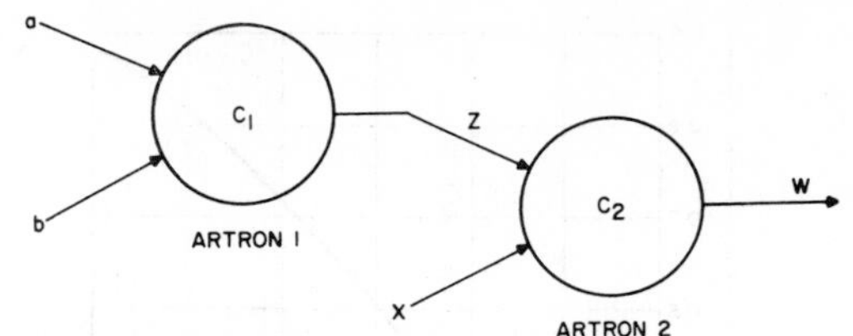

Fig. 7. Interconnection of two ARTRONs to form three-input—one-output net.

z is replaced by $\bar{z}$. Hence, the output of the combination remains the same if both interchanges are made. If c_2 is one of the four trivial functions which do not involve z, c_1 can be replaced by any connective without changing the function w, so that the total number of unique functions that can be realized is

$$\frac{16 \cdot 12}{2} + 4, \text{i.e., } 100$$

Now there are 2^{2^n} ways in which n binary inputs can be connected to give a single binary output, i.e., assuming a, b, x distinct, 256 connectives are possible. Direct interconnection of ARTRONs, therefore, restricts the total number of unique connectives which can be formed.

The minimum number of ARTRONs required to perform any general function can be determined as follows: each ARTRON can assume any one of 16 states so that m ARTRONs can assume a maximum of $(16)^m$ states. For m ARTRONs to perform any n-input—one-output function

$$(16)^m \geq 2^{2^n} \tag{59}$$

i.e.,

$$m \geq 2^{n-2} \tag{60}$$

or at least 2^{n-2} ARTRONs are necessary to perform such a function.

To show that 2^{n-2} ARTRONs are sufficient, remember that any function of n variables can be expressed in terms of two functions of $(n-1)$ variables and a variable x as follows

$$f_n = xg_{n-1} + \bar{x}h_{n-1} \tag{61}$$

The synthesis of an arbitrary function of n variables can, therefore, be accomplished by the connection of a variable x to two functions of $(n-1)$ variables by fixed logical elements. In turn, the two functions of $(n-1)$ variables can be reduced to four functions of $(n-2)$ variables, etc., so that a general function of n variables can be reduced to 2^{n-2} functions of two variables, or 2^{n-2} ARTRONs, with $(n-2)$ variables connected by fixed elements. As an elementary extension of these arguments, it can be shown that $k(2^{n-2})$ ARTRONs are necessary and sufficient to implement an n-input—k-output function, provided the outputs are independent.

The number of fixed three-input connectives of the form $fx \cup g\bar{x}$ can be seen to be one for the first reduction, two for the second, four for the third, etc., until f_n has been reduced to the sum of N functions of two variables, where

$$N = \sum_{j=1}^{n-2} 2^{j-1} = 2^{n-2} - 1 \tag{62}$$

Each of the three-input fixed connectives can be replaced by three two-input connectives directly. However, it is also possible to perform the reduction with two two-input connectives, namely

$$(f_{n-1} \cup X) \equiv g_{n-1}$$

i.e., (f_{n-1} or x) quantity if-and-only-if g_{n-1}. This is equivalent to

$$(g_{n-1})x \cup \bar{x}(f_{n-1} \equiv g_{n-1})$$

which is perfectly general.

A diagram of the minimum representation of an n-input—one-output network is shown in Fig. 8.

Referring to equation (61), each different function for either g_{n-1} or h_{n-1} gives a new f_n. These functions are, therefore, independent. Depending on whether x or $\bar{x}$ is a logical "one," reward (or punishment) should only be applied to that

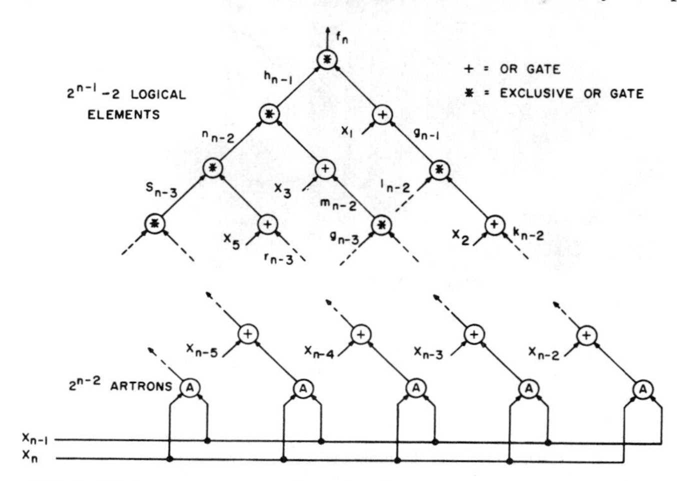

Fig. 8. Minimum representation of n-input—one-output ARTRON network.

part of the network which contributes to the construction of either g_{n-1} or h_{n-1}. Specifically, if $x = 0$, $\bar{x} = 1$ no information can be obtained from the output as to the truth or falsehood of the states of the group of ARTRONs contributing to g_{n-1}. In this case only those contributing to h_{n-1} should be rewarded (or punished). But both g_{n-1} and h_{n-1} can be expanded into separate functions of $(n-2)$ variables as before, and the same remarks apply. Repetition of this argument leads to the result that in the minimum synthesis with the ternary connective, only one ARTRON is effective in determining the output for any particular combination of variables, and this is the only ARTRON which should be rewarded (punished).

In the minimum synthesis using fixed two-input building blocks the switches can no longer be trained independently; however, the fixed two-input building blocks may be replaced by ARTRONs. While this does not provide the most efficient use of hardware, it allows the network to be constructed from a single basic unit. In this case $(3 \cdot 2^{n-2} - 2)$ ARTRONs will be required and the learning time will increase because it will be necessary to organize the desired connectives. The minimum synthesis with respect to both hardware and learning time, using ARTRONs, comprises (2^{n-2}) ARTRONs and $(2^{n-2} - 1)$ fixed ternary logical elements.

HARDWARE

A bench breadboard of a simple decision element has been built based on the principles enumerated in the first section. Figure 9 is a photograph of the unit and Fig. 10 shows learning and relearning characteristics. In this experiment the maximum average learning permitted by the statistical switch characteristic curve was 95%. It will be observed that this level was achieved in approximately eight attempts for initial learning and 16 attempts for complete relearning.

Fig. 9. Bench breadboard of decision element.

On the basis of present circuit designs, it is possible to compute the volume required by a network capable of organizing to any general connective of n variables. Figure 11 shows the variation of size with number of input variables and component packing density. The size increases very rapidly as the number of input variables increases and it soon becomes prohibitive even for component packing densities compatible with modern molecularization techniques. A reduction in size can be achieved by time-sharing hardware. Referring to Fig. 2, only those statistical switches which connect the input AND gate to the output OR gates are contributing to the performance of the network for a specific input.

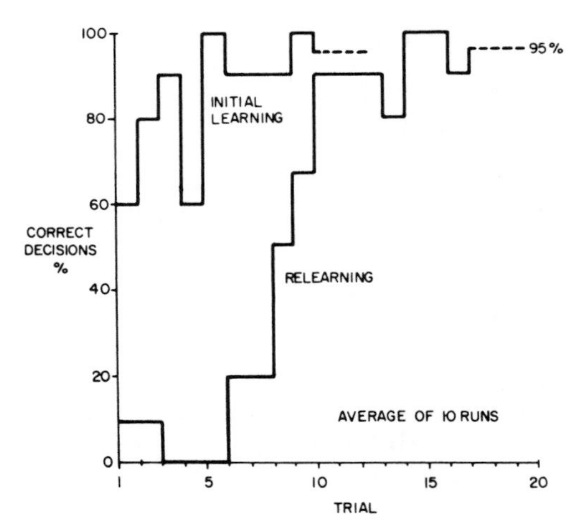

Fig. 10. Learning curves for decision element.

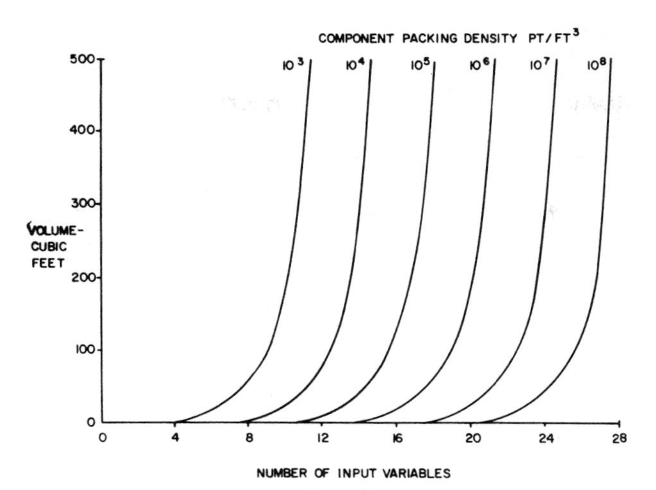

Fig. 11. Volume necessary to realize an n-input—one-output self-organizing binary logical element.

The other switches stand idle until an input is received which corresponds to the minterm to which they are connected. If the state of each of these switches is stored in a central memory rather than in individual counter circuits, a considerable reduction in hardware will be achieved. Figure 12 shows a block diagram of such a system. The statistical state of the switches is stored as a 4-bit binary number and is read-out to the output generator on command. The output

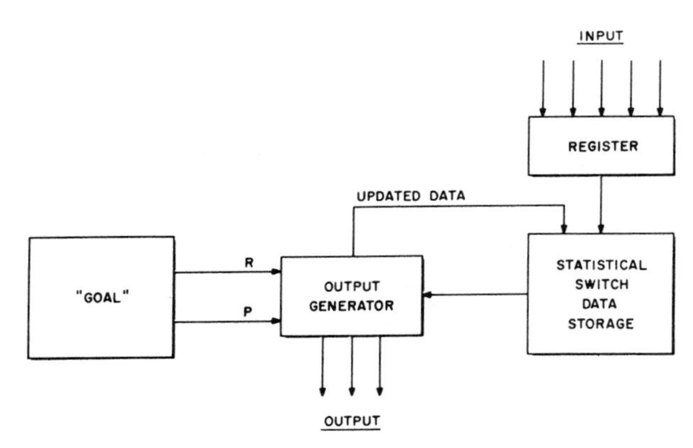

Fig. 12. Physical realization of a self-organizing binary learning element for a large number of input-output functions.

generator comprises as many statistical switches as required outputs. Upon generation of the output function, reward or punishment signals are applied to the statistical switches in the output generator. The updated statistical states are then returned to central storage. If time is available and the outputs are independent of one another, a further reduction can be made by implementing only one statistical switch. This would be shared between the output generator stations. Using this technique, a ten-input—four-output learning element can be constructed in a standard relay rack. Such a unit would be the equivalent of 1024 ten-input AND gates, 4096 statistical switches, and 4×1024-input OR gates with a capability of organizing to any one of approximately 10^{1200} connectives.

COMPUTER STUDIES

Studies of the characteristics of the self-organizing binary logical network and other networks have been made by simulating their characteristics on a digital computer. Comparisons were made of the ability to form one function of three input variables using five ARTRONs in a symmetrical network, four ARTRONs in a minimal network, two ARTRONs and two fixed connectives in a minimal network, and the self-organizing binary logical network. Learning curves for the simulated networks are shown in Fig. 13. The circuits simulated are shown

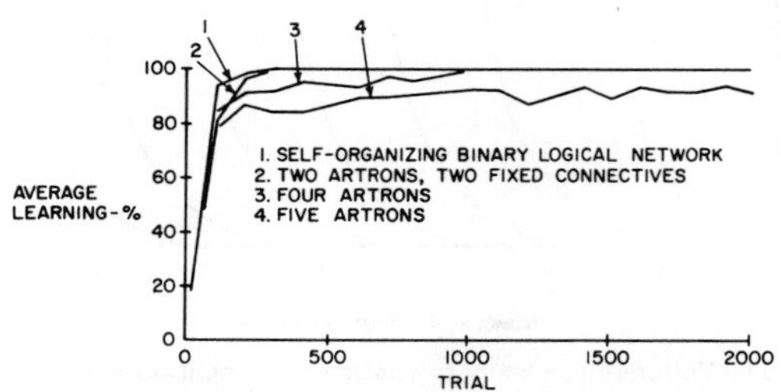

Fig. 13. Comparison of learning times for various networks learning to perform one function of three variables.

in Fig. 14. In addition, a comparison was made of the ability to form five functions of four input variables using the following networks: 65 ARTRONs in a symmetrical network with both selective and nonselective reward and punishment;* 205 ARTRONs in a semi-randomly connected network; 20 ARTRONs and 30 fixed connectives in a minimal network; and the self-organizing binary logical network. Learning curves are shown in Fig. 15.

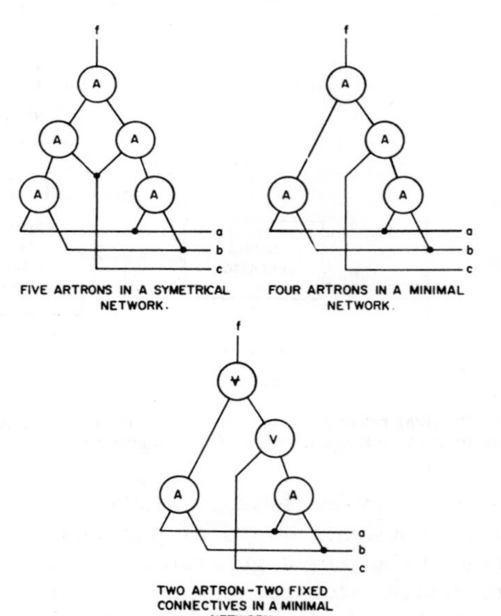

Fig. 14. Three of the networks used in forming one function of three variables.

*Selective reward and punishment implies that groups of statistical switches directly associated with separate portions of the output are rewarded or punished according to the correctness of that portion and not according to the correctness of the total output. Nonselective reward and punishment implies that the learning network is only rewarded when the total output is correct.

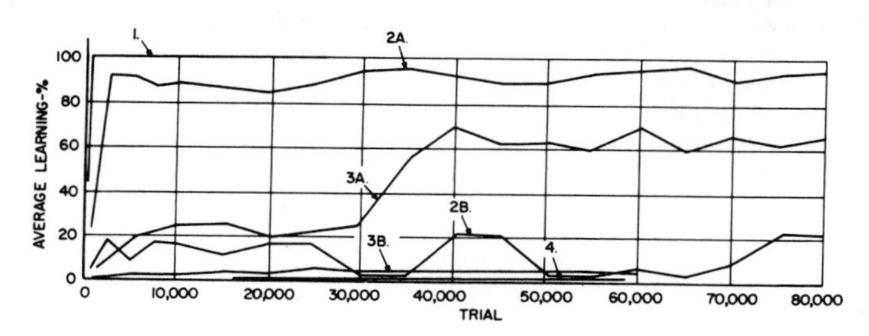

Fig. 15. Comparison of learning curves for various networks learning to perform five functions of four variables.

In all of the experiments it can be seen that the self-organizing binary logical network has a shorter learning time than the other networks. This is due to the fact that complete learning is dependent only upon the number of trials required for each different input combination to be presented enough times to cause the statistical switch to change from initial unbiased state to the maximum or minimum count which represents a closed or open switch, respectively.

CONCLUSIONS

The self-organizing binary logical network described is capable of being trained to perform any general logical function. It makes maximum use of hardware and is so constructed that learning time is a minimum. From an engineering viewpoint, therefore, it is an ideal device for inclusion in adaptive systems. It is, in fact, the lower bound of a large set of networks with varying degrees of redundancy and organization. The original ARTRON is probably somewhere close to the upper bound in this analogy.

Much work remains to be done to exploit the unique properties of the self-organizing binary logical network and of other less organized, more redundant networks. This is particularly true if useful engineering models of higher thought processes and human decisions are to be made. It is anticipated that more sophisticated hardware will be developed in the near future and that further significant results will be achieved in the application of information theory to the organization of these networks, particularly in the areas of teaching strategies. Further attention will also be given to the concept of distance between logical functions and its application to the approximation of functional tasks. Improvement of reliability by the provision of redundant elements will also be investigated.

ACKNOWLEDGMENTS

The authors would like to take the opportunity to acknowledge the considerable assistance of their colleagues, Messrs. J. J. Turtora, J. A. Rodgers, R. S. Flanders, and C. Friis-Baastad.

The basic research reported in this document has been made possible through support and sponsorship extended by the Electronic Technology Laboratory of the Aeronautical Systems Division, Air Force Systems Command, under Contracts No. AF33(616)-7682 and AF33(616)-7834. It is published for technical information only, and does not necessarily represent recommendations or conclusions of the sponsoring agency.

REFERENCES

Corneretto, A. 1960. Electronics learns from biology. Electronic Design., Sept. 14, p. 44.
Corneretto, A. 1961. Bionics Efforts Center on Learning Machines, Electronic Design, Sept. 13, p. 30.
Hamming. 1950. Error detecting and error correcting codes. Bell Syst. Tech. J., Apr.
Plotkin, M. 1960. Binary codes with specified minimum distance. IRE Trans. on Information Theory. Sept.
Slepian, D. 1956. A class of binary signal alphabets. Bell Syst. Tech. J., Jan.

FIRST-ORDER EXPERIENTIAL CONCEPT FORMATION

Robert D. Turner

General Electric Advanced Electronics Center
Ithaca, New York

INTRODUCTION

The author takes the standpoint that *concepts* are the results of direct or indirect structuring (or organizing) of experience. The objective of such structuring is to simplify and facilitate the description, interpretation, or memorization of that experience. Concept formation is assumed to be a functional element of a larger, self-organizing *system*; the system itself will remain substantially undefined in this discussion. For the moment, it will suffice to say that the system is capable of sensing a portion of its experiences in the form of fragmentary *images*; it is further capable of recalling some portion of those images. Finally, it is assumed that the system has a *goal* (or set of goals).

In general, concepts may take many forms, depending on the complexity of the concept-forming mechanism. The most obvious examples are apparent cause-and-effect relationships, where the effects are directly pertinent to the system goal. At a higher level are more abstruse image-association phenomena, such as the association of words and phrases in a foreign language with corresponding words and phrases in a known language. In the sense that they lend structure and pattern to the images sensed by the system, concepts may be said to be images of images.

The concern of this paper is with experiential concept formation, which involves the direct association of events (as experienced by the system) at the most elementary level. The simple observation that two classes of events (or, rather the images attributed to these classes of events) occur simultaneously more often than can be ascribed to chance coincidence alone is a simple form of experiential concept formation. Once a concept is formed, the system may become more *perceptive* to those events which the concept serves to structure. The system may then be better able to detect the occurrence of such events in a variety of situations by exploiting the selectivity afforded by the concept structuring. In so doing, the system gains additional experience regarding the structured events, and may employ such experience to refine and add additional structure to the concept. There is evidence that in natural systems the images provided are deliberately defocused at the outset, thereby reducing the volume of image processing necessary until preliminary concepts have been formed. Once the preliminary concepts have been formed, the detail included in the images can be increased since the system is then able to make use of the detail. For example, certain tactile elements of the image provided to the infant human brain appear to be suppressed until some degree of maturation has ensued. The visual images provided are blurred, and are only refined gradually as the eyeball changes shape with growth. The observations made above would indicate that these changes are not merely accidents of growth, but are the consequence of deliberate suppression of input data until the brain is capable of using such data. The suggestion is made that if the full gamut of sensed data provided to the adult human were made available to the infant, preliminary concept formation would be severely arrested, if not absolutely inhibited. A corollary to this conjecture would be that once maturation (and sensory refinement) has taken place, the system is stuck with whatever preliminary concepts it has formed; revision of the basic or primitive concepts could only be accomplished by suppression of the input data for a period sufficient for the system to revert to its immature state.

It is not difficult to define levels of concept formation above the experiential level. The first example that comes to mind is the structuring of a class of concepts (which may be experiential or of a higher level) into a concept. Another example is extension, or generalization, of a structuring scheme to include lower-level concepts or portions of experiential images not previously included. While of great interest, these higher levels of concept formation are beyond the scope of this paper. The essential difference between the higher levels and the experiential level is that the higher levels require some means for the synthesis of candidate structures; at the experiential level, the candidate, or *hypothesized* concepts can be drawn directly from the experienced images. This, of course, does not imply that synthetic concepts cannot be applied directly at the experiential level.

INTERNAL STRUCTURE OF THE CONCEPT-FORMING MECHANISM

As has already been noted, the concept-forming mechanism must possess the capability for hypothesizing trial concepts or structures applicable to experience. In addition, the concept-forming mechanism must be able to evaluate the candidate structures; at the experiential level, the evaluation involves a correlation (in the broadest possible sense) of the candidate structure with experience. Whatever the evaluation criteria may be, they should ultimately lead to rejection of candidate concepts which experience shows are erroneous or irrelevent to the system goal. The latter requirement is essential, since the capacity of the system for storing concepts, and for processing experienced images in the light of those concepts, is necessarily finite. An example of an erroneous concept is the baseless *superstition*, which arises from the erroneous association of a collection of events (or their images), some of which had a bearing on the system goal.

A hypothesized concept, once tested, may be rejected, accepted, or subjected to further evaluation. In the simple scheme to be described later, the last alternative will be ignored for purposes of simplification; it should be noted, however, that the three alternatives presented constitute a natural and logical extension of the sequential procedures of statistical decision theory. The act of accepting a concept may have one of several implications. It may mean that the system begins using the concept in forming the responses to its environment in striving for its goal, but continues to evaluate the concept against experience. Alternatively, the concept may become *fixed*, that is, no longer subject to evaluation. This, of course, relieves the system of the burden of further evaluation, but subjects it to the danger that the fixed concept may be erroneous. Fixation of an erroneous concept may inhibit the system from even attaining, or even approaching, its goal. Finally, a higher level of evaluation may be undertaken once a concept is accepted; rather than evaluation via direct comparison with experience, the system may measure the validity and relevancy of its aggregate of concepts in terms of goal performance, reverting to experiential evaluation only when the goal performance appears to indicate that the concept aggregate is unsatisfactory.

In some instances the system may be capable of discarding a concept because it is no longer useful; in other words, if a concept is not used sufficiently often, it may be forgotten.

Finally, the concept-forming mechanism should have the capability of refining its concepts; in general, it is from the fine structure of experiential concepts that higher-level concepts will be formed.

The concern of this paper is with first-order experiential concept formation. In the present context, the term "first-order" is taken to mean that the rules and procedures for evaluating and refining a concept are independent of the concept itself. That is, no inference is drawn from the nature of a candidate structure as to the "best" techniques for evaluating that concept, or for refining it, should it be accepted.

CONCEPT HYPOTHESIZATION AND EVALUATION

Prior to the commencement of experiential concept formation, the experience of the system is assumed to consist of a sequence of (apparently) randomly occurring, uncorrelated sensations of events. One of the major objectives of the concept-forming mechanism is to permit the classification of these sensations or images into those which relate to events pertinent to the system goal, and those which relate to apparently irrelevant events. This implies that the scheme for hypothesizing trial concepts should be intimately related to the system goal. Figure 1 shows the functional structure of a scheme for selection of trial concepts for the first-order experiential concept-forming mechanism. The entire system is considered to be imbedded in an environment. Images of the events occurring in that environment are provided to the system (in particular, to the trial concept selection device) by the experience sensors. The images are then tentatively evaluated as to their pertinence to the system goal; if found to be meaningless or insignificant, they are discarded. If found to be relevant, an image is stored in the trial concept memory.

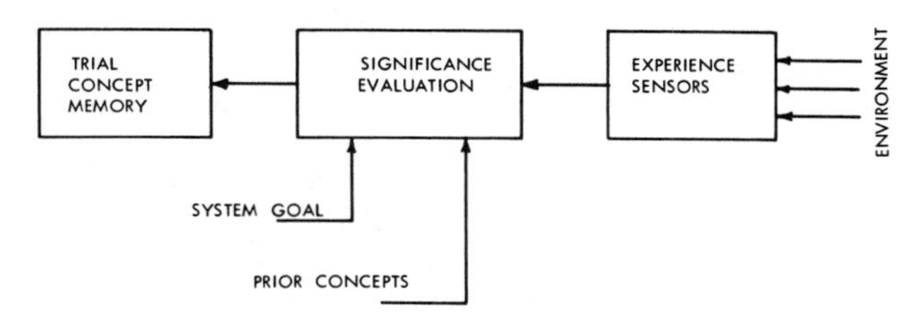

Fig. 1. Experiential concept formation: trial concept selection.

The structure of the significant-evaluation function will remain substantially unspecified. A few examples may serve to clarify its role, however. First, the image provided at any instant may contain many elements. One or more of these elements may pertain directly to goal performance: pain, relief of sensations of hunger, detection of a signal, and so forth. The objective of the concept-forming mechanism may be to establish the existence of concomitant elements of the image whose occurrence is correlated with the occurrence of the goal-performance elements. These concomitant elements may be precursors (which would aid in the anticipation of certain events), or antecedents (which would aid in the interpretation of certain images), or may occur simultaneously (in which case, they would aid in the detection of certain events). Whether the significance-evaluation function seeks precursors, antecedents, or simultaneously occurring concomitant elements depends on the system goal and the relation of previously established concepts to that goal. Indeed, the significance-evaluation criteria may depend entirely on the previously established concepts, and only indirectly on the system goal. For example, it may have been found that a certain image element is generally a precursor to some image element pertaining directly to goal performance. To aid in detection of the precursor, the concept-forming mechanism is assigned the task of establishing the existence and nature of concomitant elements which occur simultaneously with the precursor. If this can be accomplished, the concept-forming mechanism will have extended the concept of the precursor, and will have better equipped the system to anticipate the image element (or, rather, the event which gives rise to that element) which bears directly on achievement of the goal.

When a concept is accepted, the system is committed to using that concept in selecting future responses to its environment. The question to be raised (and partially answered) here deals with the maximum rate at which concepts can be accepted. In its broadest sense, the answer to this question requires the specification of a value measure of the consequences of acceptance of a useful concept, versus acceptance of an irrelevant (inapplicable) concept or acceptance of an erroneous concept. This value measure is, in effect, a generalization of the payoff matrix of game theory, or the loss matrix of statistical decision theory, for the case where the experiences and responses can be made discrete, and it is the corresponding kernel or function in the continuous cases. It is clear that the value measure, whatever it might be, must depend on the nature of the concept being formed, and, in particular, on the nature of the responses made by the system once it accepts the concept. It is also apparent that the system will never be completely knowledgeable, insofar as the value measure is concerned, since specification of the value measure requires a complete knowledge of the total structure of the environment in which the system is imbedded. Thus, the system, at the outset, will be forced to develop an approximation to the value measure, based on its goal, the past history of the consequences of its responses, and previously established concepts. Given this level of sophistication, the system can then proceed to develop its estimate of the "true" value measure, and to apply that measure to the evaluation of trial concepts. It is perhaps apparent that the value measure estimate is itself a concept and, therefore, subject to the rules of concept formation.

From the foregoing discussion, it can be seen that establishing bounds on the rate of acceptance of trial concepts is a very difficult task in any but the most trivial situations, e.g., those instances in which the system is provided with inputs from some omniscient source of intelligence. To avoid these difficulties, the concept-forming mechanism will be disjoined from its system and considered in isolation. The applicable value measure is now one to be specified in terms of the operation of the concept-forming mechanism, and can be taken as independent of the trial concept itself and of the over-all consequences of accepting that concept. Since the resulting bound is specified in terms of the information-handling capabilities of the concept-forming mechanism, it will be information-theoretic in character, rather than reflecting the value aspects of the system goal performance.

Figure 2 shows the functional structure of a scheme for evaluating and accepting (or rejecting) trial concepts. The elements of the input image, as provided by the experience sensors, are delivered to the comparator through an optional preliminary screening mechanism. The function of the preliminary screening mechanism (shown within the dashed-line box) is to permit application of a significance test prior to comparing the experienced image with the trial concept. The configuration shown is appropriate for establishing the existence and nature of a precursory image element which may precede an image of direct pertinence to goal performance. Thus, the input images are stored in the temporary storage and discarded at once unless followed (at some preselected interval) by a "significant" image. When a significant image does occur, the image preceding it is delivered to the evaluator proper. As already noted, the preliminary screening mechanism may take any of several forms, depending on the type of concept to be formed. In some instances, it may take the form of a preliminary "inhibitor," excluding well-understood images from consideration by the evaluator.

At any rate, input images eventually reach the comparator, where they are compared with the trial concept. The precise mechanism for determining the

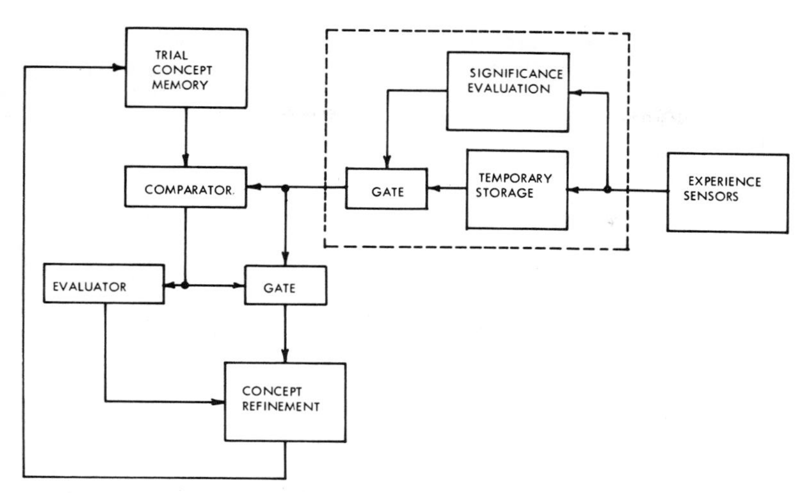

Fig. 2. Experiential concept formation: trial concept evaluation and refinement.

degree of agreement between the trial concept and the experienced images will not be specified in detail. In certain elementary configurations (e.g., the adaptive filter) a simple cross-correlation technique has been found adequate. In other cases, a more powerful statistical decision procedure may be required. In the simple scheme shown in Fig. 2, the comparator has a binary output: either the experience agrees with the concept (i.e., the concept appears to structure the experience satisfactorily), or it does not agree with the experience. If the trial concept and the experienced image agree, the comparator so notifies the evaluator and actuates a gate which allows the agreeing image to pass on to the concept refinement function. The concept refinement function takes those input images which appear to agree with the trial concept and attempts to establish a more refined version of that concept, e.g., elimination of irrelevant image elements, greater detail, and suppression of background interference effects present in the outputs of the experience sensors. The refined concept obtained in this fashion may or may not be used to modify the original trial concept stored in the trial concept memory.

The essential element of the trial concept evaluation process is contained within the evaluator of Fig. 2. The evaluator makes the decisions as to whether the trial concept should be accepted or disregarded. It must base this decision on the accumulated results of comparing the trial concept with experience and, in so doing, must surmount two intrinsic difficulties. First, not every set of experienced images need agree with the trial concept for the trial concept to be useful; that is, the nature of the concept may be such that it is useful in some situations and not in others. Second, it is possible for accidental (or coincidental) occurrences to give rise to an apparent agreement with an erroneous concept. Thus, the evaluator must be tolerant of the occurrence of experienced images which do not agree with the trial concept (in spite of preliminary screening), yet must be prepared to discriminate against accidental coincidences which might give rise to a spurious indication that an erroneous concept should be accepted. These two difficulties act together to limit the rate at which concepts can be accepted. To indicate the nature of this limitation, a simple evaluation decision procedure has been constructed. While not an optimum procedure in the statistical decision-theoretic sense, it is sufficiently heuristic to warrant discussion.

At the beginning of the trial concept evaluation process (i.e., as soon as a trial concept has been selected) the evaluator is provided with a predetermined time period T_1. The comparator is simultaneously provided with a comparison threshold B_1. In order to generate an output from the comparator, the incoming image must agree (according to the test made by the comparator) to a degree greater than or equal to B_1. That is, if the result of an instantaneous comparison of the image and the trial concept is denoted by $B(t)$, then

$$B(t) \geq B_1$$

is the necessary and sufficient condition for the comparator to generate an output. Now if this event does not occur within the period T_1, i.e., if the evaluator does not receive an output from the comparator during T_1, the evaluator causes the trial concept stored in the trial concept memory to be discarded, and the concept-forming mechanism reverts to the trial concept selection mode. However, if the event does occur within T_1, the threshold in the comparator is immediately reset to a new value B_2 and the "holding period" in the evaluator is reset to a new interval T_2. The process then beings again. To generalize: during the kth holding period, the comparator determines the degree of agreement between the incoming images and the trial concept (which may be highly refined by this point) for a period not exceeding the holding period T_k. If the degree of agreement does not reach or exceed B_k during this period, the trial concept is discarded. If $B(t)$ equals or exceeds B_k during T_k, the trial concept is then compared with the incoming images, using the comparison criterion B_{k+1}, for a period T_{k+1}. Finally, after k_0 "successful" holding periods have elapsed, the trial concept is accepted. If the concept then becomes fixed, evaluation ceases. Alternatively, the concept may be accepted for purposes of selecting system responses, but may continue to be evaluated in the manner described. The latter alternative makes provision for discarding concepts which become obsolete or outdated (i.e., concepts which, while originally correct and applicable, become erroneous or irrelevant because of a nonstationary environment).

It is apparent that the duration of the kth holding period T_k, and the comparison criterion used during the kth holding period B_k, reflect in some way the confidence the concept-forming mechanism places in the trial concept. It is to be expected that a long history of satisfactory and recurrent comparisons of experience with the trial concept should be reflected in increasing holding periods and (perhaps) reduced comparison criteria. Such confidence should not be permitted to increase too rapidly, however, since overconfidence may significantly increase the probability of accepting and retaining an erroneous concept.

To render the notion of confidence into more quantitative form, consider the following model of the input and the comparison procedure. The input consists of a randomly evolving image. Over a time period inversely related to the collective bandwidth of the input data, the image will be statistically independent of its previous version. Now suppose that one such image, or a finite history of such images, has been selected (either at random or according to the trial concept selection criteria discussed earlier) and placed in the trial concept memory. If it is assumed that the environment is *without structure*, then the postulated situation may be taken as typifying the situation that arises when an erroneous concept is selected. In such a situation, the trial concept evaluation scheme should ultimately reject any and all trial concepts, with probability one.

With the setting just postulated, let q_k represent the probability that a randomly selected experience confirms the trial concept. That is, let

$$q_k = \text{Prob}\,[B(t) \geq B_k \text{ for a single value of } t]$$

Next, let WT_k represent the effective number of independent values of $B(t)$ obtained during the holding period T_k. Finally, let Q_k represent the probability that $B(t)$ is greater than or equal to B_k at least once during an interval of duration T_k. If (as will usually be the case) T_k spans a large number of independent images, then Q_k will be given by

$$Q_k = 1 - (1 - q_k)^{WT_k}$$

The requirement that an erroneous concept be ultimately rejected with probability one is equivalent to a requirement that it be accepted for an indefinitely large number of holding periods with probability zero:

$$\lim_{k \to \infty} \prod_{j=1}^{k} Q_j = 0$$

which, in turn, is equivalent to the requirement that

$$\lim_{k \to \infty} \sum_{j=1}^{k} \log Q_j = -\infty$$

Now

$$\log Q_j = \log [1 - (1 - q_j)^{WT_j}]$$

The sum will diverge to $-\infty$ if the arguments of any one (or more) of the logarithms vanishes. But this would imply that either $WT_k = 0$ (an infinitesimally short holding period) or $q_k = 0$ (B_k chosen so that it is impossible for $B(t)$ to exceed B_k). Either of these alternatives amounts to rejection of the trial concept by fiat, and they are therefore not of interest in the present context. The remaining alternative is that the sum diverges to $-\infty$ simply because it fails to converge. Suppose, for example, that the q_j's are all constant, or approach an equilibrium value q_∞, $0 < q_\infty < 1$. This situation arises in many cases of interest. Then, if the evaluation procedure is such that $T_j \to \infty$ as $j \to \infty$, reflecting increased confidence that the trial concept is valid, then the quantity

$$(1 - q_j)^{WT_j}$$

will become very small. In this case, it becomes appropriate to use the first term in the series expansion of $\log(1 - x)$ about $x = 0$. As $j \to \infty$, then

$$\log Q_j = -(1 - q_j)\, WT_j$$

approximately, and the divergence requirement becomes

$$\lim_{k \to \infty} \sum_{j=1}^{k} (1 - q_j)^{WT_j} = +\infty$$

Now a sufficient condition that the sum of a sequence of positive numbers

$$\sum_{j=1}^{k} a_j$$

should diverge to infinity is that

$$a_k = 0(1/k)$$

as $k \to \infty$. [The author does not know of a necessary condition. The sufficient condition could be refined further by requiring that $a_k = 0\,(1/k \log k)$, or $a_k = 0\,(1/k \log k \log\log k)$, etc., but use of these more refined conditions does not modify the result to be obtained.]

Thus, the requirement that an erroneous concept ultimately be rejected with probability one leads to the requirement that

$$(1 - q_k)^{WT_k} = 0(1/k)$$

as $k \to \infty$. Taking logarithms of both sides yields, finally

$$-WT_k \log(1 - q_k) = \log k + o(\log k) \tag{1}$$

as $k \to \infty$. This condition, and no weaker one, insures that an erroneous concept will ultimately be rejected by the trial concept evaluation scheme, with probability one. It states that if the q_k's approach an equilibrium value, then the holding periods should grow no more rapidly than logarithmically with the number of satisfactory comparisons between the trial concept and experience. The alternative to meeting this condition is that the system will be forced to accept an erroneous concept with finite probability; in some settings, the system will be presented with one or more erroneous concepts with probability one. Condition (1) thus amounts to a consistency requirement for concept-forming mechanisms; regardless of the value measures assigned to the trial concept evaluation scheme in a realistic setting, (1) must be met if the system is to be assured that ultimately all erroneous concepts will be rejected.

Condition (1) has a simple information-theoretic interpretation as well. The factor $-\log(1-q_k)$ is the information gained on a single trial when $B(t)$ does not exceed B_k. Accordingly, the left-hand side of (1) is the information gained if $B(t)$ does not exceed B_k during the kth holding period, i.e., the information gained from discarding the trial concept during the kth holding period. Condition (1) thus states that the information gained, should a trial concept be rejected, should not build up too rapidly. In the light of these observations, the left-hand side of condition (1), with the terms as defined previously, is proposed as an information-theoretic measure of the *confidence* that the concept-forming mechanism has in a trial concept after $k-1$ satisfactory comparisons between the concept and experience.

It would be most auspicious to be able to report the effect that incorporating condition (1) has on the probability of acceptance of a bona fide concept. It would be even better to be able to write a condition (2), indicating the *minimum* rate of growth of confidence to insure acceptance of a valid concept (if such a rate exists). Unfortunately, the author has been unable to establish any results of this sort, except an indication that if a concept does indeed serve to structure recurrent aspects of the experience, then eventually it will be accepted, provided certain fairly loose restrictions on recurrence statistics, trial concept selection rules, and trial concept evaluation rules are made, and that T_k does not diminish as $k \to \infty$.

CONCEPT REFINEMENT

The trial concepts selected for evaluation are obtained as images, or portions of images, drawn directly from experience. Under these conditions, a trial concept, even if it is valid and accepted, will contain extraneous elements which are not germane to the true concept and the fine structure will be degraded, in some instances, by background interference. The first source of degradation of the trial concept arises because, at the outset, the concept-forming mechanism does not know precisely which portions of an experienced image are structurable and must, therefore, include more than is absolutely necessary in the trial concept to be certain of obtaining all of the elements of the image that are structured by that concept. The second source of degradation arises from the natural interference processes which appear in the output of any physically realizable sensor, and which serve only to characterize the internal status of the sensor.

In order to obtain a true replication of a concept which serves to structure certain recurrent elements of the experienced images, it is necessary to refine the original trial concept. A general scheme for accomplishing this has already been described; in the broadest sense, it involves deducing the true form of the concept from those image elements which appear to be structured by the trial concept. There is, however, a limit to the extent that first-order refinement can improve a trial concept. This will be shown by constructing an artificial refinement situation, the performance in which bounds the performance of a realistic refinement scheme.

Let it be supposed that certain elements of the experienced images occurring at times not previously known to the concept-forming mechanism are structured by a vector function $f(\mathbf{X}, t)$, where $\mathbf{X}$ is a vector representing all of the nontemporal variables entering into the specification of f, and t is an independent variable corresponding to time. It is assumed, for simplicity, that f is nonzero over a finite region of the $\mathbf{X} - t$ space. For example, f might represent the appearance of a rectangle for a finite period in a visual space.

In the elementary setting postulated here, it is assumed that the images structured by f take the form of elementary transformations—rotations, changes in scale, affine transformations, etc.—of the original concept. By restricting the structured images to such transformations, the images can be regarded as replications of the basic concept which differ only in the choice of certain "free" parameters, which may change from one occurrence of a structurable image to the next. Again, to simplify the discussion, it will be assumed that the transformations are simple translations in space and time, so that the recurrent, structurable images take the form

$$f(\mathbf{X} - \mathbf{X}_n, t - t_n) + g_n(\mathbf{X}, t)$$

where $\mathbf{X}_n$ is the vector spatial displacement of the image on its nth occurrence, t_n defines the time of the nth occurrence, and $g(\mathbf{X}, t)$ represents extraneous data and background interference.

The objective of the refinement process is to remove the effects of $g(\mathbf{X}, t)$, thereby obtaining a true replication of the recurrent images, i.e., the concept. Now, if it were possible to store and combine the recurrent images so as to form the sum

$$\frac{1}{N} \sum_{n=1}^{N} f(\mathbf{X}, t) + g'_n(\mathbf{X}, t)$$

where g'_n is the result of translating g_n by $(\mathbf{X}_n, t_n)$, then the result would be the "best possible" estimator of $f(\mathbf{X}, t)$, in the sense that the variance of the estimate would (asymptotically) approach zero at least as rapidly as the variance of any other estimator. Unfortunately, this estimate is not realizable since in forming the estimate it is first necessary to estimate the unknown parameters $(\mathbf{X}_n, t_n)$. Because of the extraneous data and background interference, such estimates will always contain errors. Thus, the result of the translation operation (to align the meaningful portions of the images) will be the formation of the sum

$$\frac{1}{N} \sum_{n=1}^{N} f(\mathbf{X} - x_n, t - \tau_n) + g''_n(\mathbf{X}, t) \qquad (2)$$

where x_n represents the error in estimating X_n, τ_n represents the error in estimating t_n, and g''_n is the result of translating g_n. (It is assumed that g_n, g'_n and g''_n are statistically indistinguishable.)

It is now asserted that the sum (2) will not converge, in the stochastic sense or otherwise, to the true function $f(\mathbf{X}, t)$. The same remark holds for any nontrivial concept, that is, no matter how complex the transformations which relate the recurrent images (in their unperturbed forms) to the original concept may be. To illustrate the point just made, consider the further simplification of making f a function of t alone, and suppose that f and τ_n are such that $f(t - \tau_n)$ can be expanded in a power series. Denoting the sum (2) by F, there is obtained

$$F = f(t) + \frac{1}{N} \sum_{n=1}^{N} \tau_n f'(t) + \frac{\tau_n^2}{2} f''(t) + \ldots + \frac{1}{N} \sum_{n=1}^{N} g''_n(t)$$

where f' and f'' denote the first and second derivatives of $f(t)$, and g'' has the same significance as before. Now let it be supposed that the errors τ_n have zero means (this can usually be done without loss of generality) and that the g_n'' have zero mean. Then the sums involving f' and g_n'' will have zero means and will converge stochastically to zero, having variances proportional to $1/N$. The contribution of the remaining term (involving f'') can be assessed by taking the expected value; this yields

$$E[F] = f(t) + \frac{\sigma^2}{2} f''(t)$$

where σ^2 is the variance of τ_n. The discussion just given is purely of a heuristic nature in that it was assumed that $f(t)$ could be expanded in a power series. More generally

$$E[F] = \int_{-\infty}^{\infty} f(t-\tau) W(\tau) \, d\tau \tag{3}$$

where $W(\tau)$ is the probability density function of the errors τ_n. The variance of F can be shown to be given by

$$\text{Var } F = \frac{1}{N} \left\{ \int_{-\infty}^{\infty} f^2 (t-\tau) W(\tau) \, d\tau - \left[\int_{-\infty}^{\infty} f(t-\tau) W(\tau) \, d\tau \right]^2 + \sigma_g^2 \right\} \tag{4}$$

where σ_g^2 is the variance of the extraneous data and the background interference. Thus, equation (4) demonstrates that the variance of F goes to zero as $N \to \infty$. In short, F can be expected to converge stochastically to its expected value as $N \to \infty$, but this expected value (3) is not equal to $f(t)$; hence, F does not converge to $f(t)$.

The immediate implication of this result is that it is not possible for a first-order experiential concept-formation mechanism to structure the experience, or any portion of the experience, to an arbitrarily high degree simply by combining several experienced images which appear to be satisfactorily structured by the trial concept and averaging their transformed versions. The process of deducing the "true" concept (if this is possible) must involve a higher level of concept formation. One procedure, which leads to stochastically convergent estimators, is to hypothesize a functional form for the concept. It is then possible to determine whether the hypothesized form affords a satisfactory representation for the structurable image elements, provided that the setting is not too complicated. Once a satisfactory form is established, parameter estimation is fairly straightforward.

CONCLUSION

It has been demonstrated that there are intrinsic limitations on the rate at which a first-order experiential concept-forming mechanism can place confidence in a trial concept, and in the degree to which such a device can refine the trial concept. The interesting question is, of course, to what extent can these limitations be overcome by higher-order or higher-level concept-forming mechanisms. Answers to this question are inhibited by a lack of knowledge of the concept hypothesizing function. This difficulty was avoided in the discussion above by postulating that the trial concepts be drawn directly from experience. It would seem that understanding of the concept hypothesizing function requires understanding the very roots of human creativity. A great deal of work is being done in this area, but genuine understanding appears to be inhibited by the abilities of humans to verbalize their thought processes. The human mind did not, and does not, proceed from a finite or even denumerable set of hypothetical concepts for its higher-order formative processes; it appears to be able to synthesize trial concepts almost effortlessly, and to tailor the evaluation criteria almost as effortlessly. The "ultimate" approach to concept formation, problem solving, language translation, and related arts through automatic machines must eventually be able to duplicate these aspects of the human mentality.

The author wishes to thank R. S. Robins, M. Ascher, and R. E. Schwartz for enlightening discussion and constructive criticism.

KINEMATIC AND TESSELLATION MODELS OF SELF-REPAIR*

Lars Lofgren

University of Illinois, Urbana, Illinois

One of the causes of the great survival capability of some biological systems is the fact that they are systems of individuals such that the system behavior does not critically depend on any one individual. Such systems can be regarded as redundant systems with different kinds and levels of redundancy. For example, although each specimen of a biological society has a limited lifespan, the whole society can exist for a much longer time. This is primarily due to self-reproduction, one form of redundancy. On a lower level, the lifespan of a specimen can be larger than the lifespan of parts of the specimen. Again this is due to redundancy, but of another form if the specimen is required to have a definite internal structure.

The concept of self-repair is studied in terms of automata theory. Different classes of automata (systems), like well-localized and non-well-localized automata, are considered. The parts (components) of the automata are uniformly exposed to errors. It is shown that if an automaton of a certain class has a lifespan not exceeded by any other automaton of the class, then it must contain a "repairing" mechanism. Such automata can be said to be self-repairing with respect to the class. A definition of self-repair is suggested. It is found that a self-repairing system which is well-localized with respect to its inputs and outputs has a finite lifespan. This corresponds to the finite lifespan we observe in nature for any animal or for any well-localized machine. On the other hand, if we relax the condition that the automaton be well-localized, then infinite lifespans can be obtained. Such automata also have self-reproducing properties and we obtain here a connection between the concepts of self-repair and self-reproduction. These self-repairing automata are, in a way, similar to growing biological societies with loosely specified internal structures.

Automata have been studied by von Neumann and others with different kinds of models, namely kinematic models and tessellation (this name was suggested by Moore) models. We shall see that these two models can be traced back to the particle and wave aspects of matter. We will develop the concept of self-repair from both aspects.

1. INTRODUCTION

In automata theory we ask questions like: What can a computer compute? What can a constructive automaton construct? Both machine types are supposed to belong to well-defined classes, usually defined on a recursive basis. Both in the process of formulating the classes and in the process of asking questions as to the behavior of the automata, we are intuitively guided by our observations of our surrounding physical and biological world, including ourselves and other animals. Examples are Turing's formulation of the so-called Turing machines (Turing, 1936), von Neumann's study of self-reproducing automata (von Neumann, 1951), and Moore's study of Garden-of-Eden configurations (Moore, 1961), i.e., configurations which can be specified as initial configurations in certain tessellation structures, but which cannot be produced by any other configurations. Garden-of-Eden configurations thus throw light on the limitations of the ability of machines to reproduce themselves. The concept of self-repair, which we want to study here from an automata-behavior point of view, is a concept for which we have an intuitive feeling because of its biological manifestations. It is interesting because the immediate difficulties arise already on a finite level with respect to the largest possible lifespan of an ordinary (well-localized) automation. We are thus led to the question of whether infinite lifespans can be obtained if we relax some of the constraints usually placed on automata. This will lead us to non-well-localized self-repairing systems.

*Sponsored by Information Systems Branch, Mathematical Science Division, Office of Naval Research.

From the beginning it should be made clear that there are, in principle, limits for automatic error correction in a system with well-localized inputs and outputs, and with prescribed normal behavior. If there were no such limits, it would imply that we could completely isolate a deterministic event in nature, which is the prescribed normal behavior. We know, however, from quantum physics, that such a complete isolation is not possible.

An automaton with a finite lifespan, belonging to a certain class (for example the class of well-localized automata), will be said to be self-repairing with respect to the class if there is no other automaton of the class which has a larger lifespan. (A less restrictive definition is suggested in Sec. 8.) From a logical point of view, it would be desirable to use a notion like "restricted self-repair" for an automatic repairing machine with well-specified inputs and outputs and with a lifespan according to the finite bounds dictated by automata theory. The notion "self-repair" could then be reserved for the non-well-localized machines with infinite lifespan. However, judging from the use of the similar notion, "self-reproduction" (see Sec. 6), we will instead use the term "self-repair" unqualified, but qualify the machines for which it is used, e.g., a "self-repairing well-localized machine." (Compare a "self-reproducing configuration in a tessellation," and the discussion of "self-reproduction" in Sec. 6.)

The error concept over which "self-repair" will be developed is discussed in Sec. 2. An error is a deviation from "truth"; but "truth" is, in general, not known or knowable. It has to be hypothesized. We will make the hypothesis that "truth" is a deterministic behavior. Deterministic systems are defined in Sec. 2, and a classification of errors is obtained by denial of the definition.

In Sec. 3, where we will make a distinction between lifespan (measured in actuations) and lifetime (measured in hours), we will discuss our assumption concerning the statistical nature of errors. We will deal with stationary errors and permanent-state errors, i.e., errors which remain in the component after they have occurred.

Two kinds of automata models originally proposed by von Neumann (1952) are outlined in Sec. 4. One represents the tessellation model [compare Moore (1961)], the other the kinematic model. Relationships between these two models will be discussed, and similarities between these concepts and the wave and particle aspects of matter will be pointed out.

Kinematic self-repairing well-localized machines are discussed in Sec. 5. The essential problems for such a self-repairing machine are: (1) to freeze spare cells in order to prevent error growth, (2) to locate erroneous cells, and (3) to replace an erroneous cell with a spare cell. All three activities should be carried out inside the system, i.e., with parts uniformly exposed to errors upon actuation. It is shown that the maximum lifespan of a well-localized system working according to steps (1), (2), and (3) is larger than for a well-localized system with any other form of redundancy.

In Sec. 6 the von Neumann concept of self-reproduction is briefly presented and arguments which have recently developed are discussed.

Self-repair in non-well-localized tessellation systems and its connection with self-reproduction is treated in Sec. 7. Necessary conditions for the infinite lifespan of such systems are derived. These conditions refer to the error probabilities, the complexity of the self-reproducing elementary configurations, and the geometrical form of the whole self-repairing automaton. For a more detailed treatment of some of the sections, especially Sec. 2, the reader is referred to Lofgren (1962).

2. DETERMINISTIC SYSTEMS AND ERRORS

To Determine a Physical Quantity q Means: To specify the physical dimension of the quantity, to partition the set of all possible q's (real numbers) of the dimension in question into equivalence classes—states s_i—and to establish to which equivalence class q belongs. The quantity q cannot be thought of as a continuous quantity in the sense that any q (any real number) belongs to some state, for then there must be two q's in different states, although they may be infinitely close to each other. But then it is, in principle, impossible for us, or for a deterministic machine, to establish whether the two q's are equal or not in the sense that they belong to the same state or not. Hence, in order to be able to measure (determine) q under all circumstances, q must be thought of as quantized, i.e., as having stable states s_i well separated by unstable transition regions.

Deterministic System: A system with specified output states and input states such that the output states are determined by the input states.

Deterministic Behavior: The behavior of a deterministic system. A convenient representation of such a behavior is in terms of a mapping

$$F: \quad S_1 \times S_2 \times \ldots \times S_k \to S_m \times \ldots \times S_n \tag{1}$$

The domain and range of the mapping F are formed as Cartesian products of the state sets S_j. The elements of a state set are states s_i. The ordering of the state sets over the Cartesian products is with respect to the inputs and the outputs of the system.

If we pay no attention to the execution time—the time interval between a cause (an element of the domain) and the corresponding effect (an element of the range)—the mapping F can be thought of as the behavior of a switching net. If, on the other hand, we consider the deterministic behavior of a time-sequential machine—usually thought of as decomposed into switching nets and time delays—each finite behavior can again be represented with a mapping of equation (1), but with some of the state sets containing elements corresponding to a quantized time.

There are two and only two distinct structures of uniform switching nets, the c and the g structure. A proper gate net has a g structure. The state sets can here contain any finite number of elements, states. A contact net belongs to the class of nets which have c structure. The number of elements in a state set can here be two if the states have point structure, and three if the states have band structure (Lofgren, 1961).

We hypothesize that an error-free behavior of a machine is a deterministic behavior. By denial of the definition of a deterministic behavior, the following classification of component errors is obtained:

A_1: At a certain actuation, i.e., when stimulated with certain stable (error-free) input states, a component gives a stable output state that belongs to the set S_m of its output states, but which is different from the particular state which is prescribed by the deterministic behavior of the component at this actuation.

A_2: A component gives a stable output state which does not belong to the set S_m of its (deterministic) output states.

A_3: A component gives a continuously oscillating (unstable) output state not contained in some element of S_m.

Component errors of type A_2 and A_3 can be observed by measuring the output state alone. An error of type A_1, however, can only be observed (located) by measuring both the output state and the input states of the component and by a subsequent combinatorial decision. We will, in the following, be concerned with errors of type A_1. From the point of view of error location, errors of type A_2 and A_3 are easier to deal with because, in these cases, a component output contains within itself information about an eventual error.

3. LIFESPAN AND LIFETIME

Concerning the statistical nature of the errors, we will make the following distinctions:

Temporary Errors. An error appears at an elementary component at an actuation with probability p. The appearances of errors at different elementary components at an actuation are independent of each other. The appearances of errors at an elementary component at different actuations are independent of each other.

Stationary Errors. An error appears at an elementary component at an actuation with probability p, provided that no error has appeared at the component at a previous actuation. The first appearances of errors at different elementary components at an actuation are independent of each other. After a first appearance of an error at an elementary component, the component is in error at all following actuations.

Permanent-State Errors. A permanent state (right or wrong) appears at the output of an elementary component at an actuation with probability p, provided that no permanent state has appeared at the component at a previous actuation. The first appearances of permanent states at different elementary components at an actuation are independent of each other. After a first appearance of a permanent state at an elementary component, the output of the component remains in this permanent state at all forthcoming actuations.

We will assume that an error in an elementary component is either a stationary error or a permanent-state error. Temporary errors imply, in a sense, self-repairing components, and it is not too surprising that we can construct a self-repairing system by using self-repairing components. There are, however, many interesting questions in connection with temporary errors [compare Lofgren (1962)]. In the communication case we have the channel-capacity theorem of Shannon (Shannon, 1948). In the computation case we have the works of von Neumann (1956), Moore and Shannon (1956), McCulloch (1958), and Lofgren (1956, 1962). It can, however, be shown (Lofgren, 1962) that the ordinary redundancy techniques which give infinite lifespans to computers when they are exposed to temporary errors only, cannot increase the lifespan of a computer beyond the lifespan of its parts in the case of stationary errors or permanent-state errors.

Stationary errors and permanent-state errors which are defined with respect to actuations imply an average lifespan $\bar{\nu}$, measured in actuations of a component. The probability that an error-free component is error-free during an experiment of ν actuations is $(1-p)^{\nu}$. The length of an experiment which gives this probability the value $1/2$, we take as the average lifespan of the component. Hence

$$\bar{\nu} \approx \frac{\ln 2}{p} \tag{2}$$

We have evidence for such an assumption regarding lifespans measured in actuations in examples taken from biology. It has been observed that the total metabolism—measured in calories per pound of body weight—for an animal during its lifetime—measured in hours—is almost constant and independent of the species (Wachtmeister, 1961). Because of the different sizes of different animals, they can have different metabolic rates and, hence, different lifetimes, although they may have about the same lifespans, measured in terms of their total relative metabolism. Even among animals of about the same size and weight, we find species with very different metabolic rates and observe corresponding differences in their lifetimes. It has also been observed that it is possible to increase the lifetime of a species by an artificial decrease of its metabolic rate, as, for example, an artificial extension of the hibernation of the hedgehog.

However, what we really want to achieve with a self-repairing system is an extension of its lifespan, not an increase in the lifetime at the expense of its total number of actuations (total metabolism).

We could have made a stronger assumption as to the statical nature of the stationary component errors and the permanent-state errors. We have assumed that the probability of the occurrence of an error upon actuation in an error-free component is independent of the specific actuation. Of course, this restriction can be dropped by introducing, say, probabilities p_ν such that, for example, $p_{\nu+1} > p_\nu$, i.e., the probability of an error occurring at actuation $\nu+1$ is greater than the probability of one occurring at a previous actuation ν. However, this seems to be only a matter of decomposing the system into elementary components, and this will be covered by our treatment. If we partition our system into units such that each unit consists of several elementary components—for each of which the assumed independence is valid—then we can observe aging effects in these units, regarded as components. The units can be so designed that a single error in one of its elementary components does not result in an error in the behavior of the unit. However an error of a certain weight, greater than unity, can result in an error in the unit. Hence the probability of an error in an error-free unit will be larger for a later actuation than for an earlier.

4. TESSELLATION AND KINEMATIC AUTOMATA MODELS

Constructive automata were studied by von Neumann, who considered two different models, first a kinematic model, and later a tessellation model (von Neumann, 1952; Moore, 1961).

In the kinematic model, an automaton consists of physical components connected together so as to show a deterministic behavior. The automaton is assumed to be in a stockroom in which a sufficient amount of components are floating around. The behavior of the automaton is such that it can identify the components floating around and connect an appropriate component to a certain part of itself (the identification and connection processes are to be regarded as outputs of the automaton). In this way the automaton can establish connections between stockroom components, and at a certain state separate the construction, i.e., another automaton, from itself.

For the tessellation model, von Neumann considered a two-dimensional Euclidean space subdivided into square cells of equal size, like the squares of a checkerboard. Each square or cell of such a tessellation is able to assume states of a finite state set S. The states of the different cells interact in a synchronous way. At each integer-valued time $T > 0$, the state of each square depends on its own state at time $T-1$, and on the states of its neighboring cells at time $T-1$. The state set S is partitioned into subsets. One of these consists of the unexitable state U. A cell in state U can do nothing, but it can be converted by proper signals (proper states of its neighbors) into other states. [Concerning the different states and the transition rules for them, the reader is referred to von Neumann (1952).] Here it is sufficient to distinguish between U and the other states of S, which we call active states. At time $T = 0$, all but a finite number of cells of the tessellation are in state U. The configuration of the active cells constitutes an automaton. The cells of the automaton can compute and transmit signals so as also to direct construction and destruction in accordance with the transition rules. The conversion of a cell in state U to some active state is thought of as construction. The conversion of a cell into state U is thought of as a destruction.

In a study of self-repair (Lofgren, 1962) in connection with well-localized systems, we have used two automata models which are distinct in very much the same way as are the tessellation and the kinematic automata models of von Neumann. In one of them we started out from a sufficiently large structure of parts [components and connectors ("wires")] in which the activity, i.e., normal computation, error location, and bounding off the activity to a certain region of the structure, was concentrated to a certain region of the structure. Upon error, the activity of the defect region was switched over to another region of the structure, previously at rest. We did not require the activity to be switched over to a neighboring region, but to a region connected to the periphery of the faulty region over "wires." However, considering the finite speed of the propagation of a signal along a "wire," we have indeed, on another time and component scale, the same neighbor influence stipulated for the cell-interaction in the von Neumann tessellation model of an automaton. We will, therefore, refer to this model as a self-repairing, well-localized, tessellation model. For the other type of well-localized self-repairing system (Lofgren, 1962), we used an automata model of the kinematic type. We shall, in Sec. 5, give a more thorough treatment of this type of self-repairing system.

It seems that the tessellation and kinematic automata models are reflections of the wave and particle aspects of matter. The quantum-mechanical field theory (Bohm, 1957) describes all motion in the quantum-mechanical domain in terms of creation and destruction of elementary particles. If an electron is scattered from one direction of motion to another, this is described as the destruction of the original electron and the creation of another electron moving in the new direction. There is, in this theory, no particle which permanently retains a fixed identity as a particle. Moreover, the field representation of even the motion for a free particle is mathematically described as a destruction of the particle at a given point and its creation at a closely neighboring point. The motion is analyzed as a series of creations and destructions, whose net effect is to continually displace the particle in space. Bohm (1957) suggests, in connection with his proposal for a sub-quantum-mechanical theory, a Brownian-motion model of an orbit as the perpetual formation and disintegration of particles with somewhat random fluctuations. These fluctuations are assumed to be so rapid that in the large-scale level, or even in the atomic level, the tracks appear, essentially, as a continuously existing orbit. But in processes whose energies are very high, the associated frequencies will be of the order of the frequency of formation and disintegration. Here the track ceases to act like a continuous orbit. The process of formation and disintegration will then be affected systematically, and the pattern of motion will, in general, be changed, so as to lead to a tendency to create new types of particles. In this way high-energy transformations of particles could be explained.

The constructive and destructive processes of the tessellation model for an automaton are evidently similar to the creation and destruction processes of the quantum-mechanical field theory. The similarity between the kinematic model for an automaton and the classical particle aspect is evident. Concerning the first similarity, however, there are also some differences.

In the tessellation model we have assumed a perfect synchronization of all cells for which we find no correspondence in quantum mechanics, even if time sometimes is thought of as quantized here. Furthermore the transit time (the time during which a cell changes states) is assumed to be infinitely small, whereas the creation and destruction times are finite. This dissimilarity could be overcome by a more realistic time quantization for the tessellation model, as suggested elsewhere (Lofgren, 1962). There a finite transit time as well as a finite synchronization interval is taken into consideration. However, the synchronization assumption does not seem to be necessary [compare Muller and Bartky (1959)].

The dissimilarity concerning determinism (quantum mechanics is not strictly deterministic) is what we are trying to overcome with our statistical component errors.

An interesting difference is in the media in which the state transitions are implemented. In the tessellation model we can think of a cell as a kind of gate, whereas in quantum mechanics the tessellation corresponds to the empty space (compare, however, the classical ether concept). If we argue that the whole tessellation can be considered as an automaton, i.e., a configuration in an underlying, perhaps simpler, tessellation, then we are lead to the question: what is the tessellation that ends such a sequence; can it be the empty space? For gates of a g structure, the answer is definitely no because these gates are nonlinear [compare Lofgren (1961)], whereas the superposition principle holds for waves in empty space. On the other hand, the gates of a c structure [compare Lofgren (1961)] are linear and it is possible that this circumstance could be of importance for a deeper study of this question.

5. SELF-REPAIR IN WELL-LOCALIZED SYSTEMS

Both in kinematic and tessellation models of self-repairing well-localized systems (well-localized inputs and outputs for the normal computation), the following steps have to be considered: (1) freezing the spare cells (switching off the activity of the spare cells); (2) locating erroneous cells (error-location computability); and (3) replacing erroneous cells with spare cells (switching over the activity of a faulty region to a region, previously at rest). All three steps should be made within the system, i.e., so that all elementary cause-effect relations are exposed to errors.

Let us examine the relevance of the three steps. If step (1) were deleted, we would be back to an ordinary redundancy design (a redundancy design for temporary errors, where the redundant components are constantly actuated). Such a design cannot increase the lifespan of the system over the lifespan of its components in this case of stationary errors or permanent-state errors [compare Lofgren (1962)]. If step (2) were deleted, the alternative would be to have a systematic replacement of the active cells, independent of whether the cells are in error or not. This would call for a high replacement rate, such that the service span for each cell, say ν_0 actuations, is small compared with the average lifespan $\bar{\nu}$ of a component [equation (2)]. In addition there might, of course, be errors in such a systematic replacement mechanism. It should also be pointed out that if the systematic replacement is made on the component level such that a cell contains only one component, then a replacement of a cell which happens to be without error will do no good because the probability of error upon actuation is independent of the actuations in this case. In Sec. 5.4.3 and 5.4.4 we shall show, on a quantitative basis, the advantage of a procedure according to steps (1), (2), and (3) over a procedure with systematic replacement. For a non-well-localized system, however, the situation is changed (compare Sec. 7). Step (3), finally, is implied by step (1).

5.1 Freezing of the Spare Cells

The problem of how to freeze the spare cells, in order to give them a sufficiently long lifetime, is resolved by our assumption (Sec. 3) that the stationary errors and the permanent-state errors occur upon actuation.

In the tessellation model (Lofgren, 1961), the actuations of the cells outside the active region are switched off by active cells. In the kinematic model, also to be discussed in Sec. 5.4, the actuations of the spare cells are switched off by their presence in the reservoir. The reservoir cells are, however, allowed to move around, even though their switching actuations are switched off. Hence, the spare cells of the tessellation model can be said to have a lower "temperature" than those of the kinematic model. For both models, however, we will attribute no errors to the spare cells, even though we admit that the underlying assumptions are easier to defend in the tessellation model than in the kinematic model.

5.2 Error-Location Computability

Let the set of all n components (all components in the tessellation case, all active components in the kinematic case) be partitioned into μ disjoint subsets. The system has μ error-indication outputs besides the outputs for its normal behavior. Between the error-indication outputs and the subsets of components there shall be a correspondence such that an error in the ith subset gives state $s_2 = 1$ (an error indication) to the ith error-indication output. If there is no error in the ith subset, the ith error-indication output is in state $s_1 = 0$. It has been shown (Lofgren, 1962) that μ must be less than n in the case of a c structure. Obviously, μ must be less than n for a g structure also, for if $\mu = n$, the error-indication outputs must be the outputs of the n gates, and these outputs are not all in state $s_1 = 0$ in the case of a nontrivial normal behavior with no errors.

5.2.1 Error-Locating c Nets with Components of Transfer Type

As can be shown (Lofgren, 1962), it is necessary to impose some restrictions on the errors in a c net in order to obtain error-location computability. We can, for example, require that the locating net have components of transfer type such that an error in a left transfer is a right transfer, and vice versa. A locating net must contain at least two components correlated to each other in the case of no error. If their output states are equal in the case of no error, the error-locating function is the mod 2 sum of the states. The basic single-error-locating nets are shown in Fig. 1.

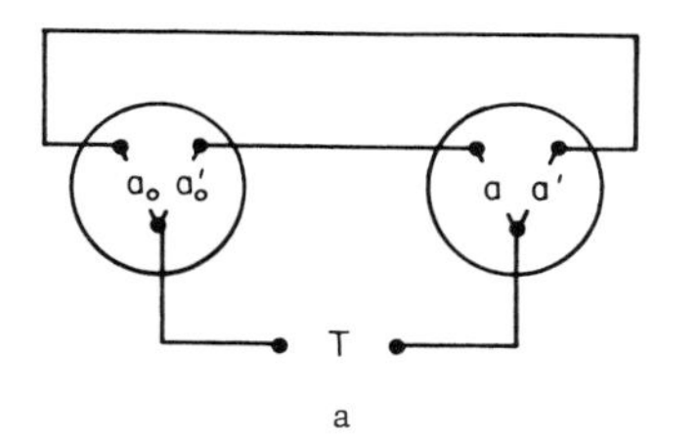

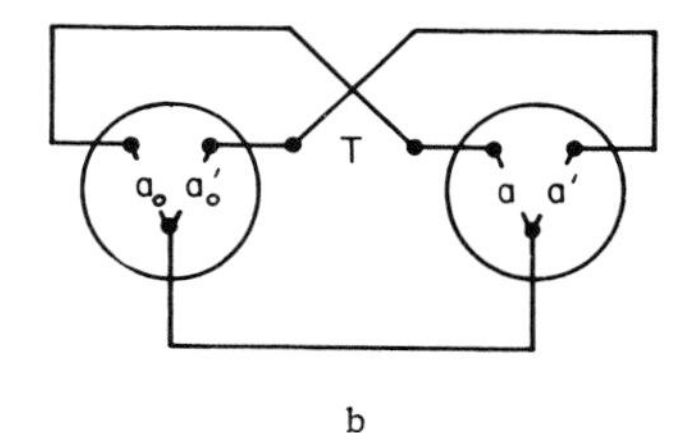

Fig. 1. Basic single-error-locating nets. An error in a left transfer is a right transfer and vice versa. Single errors are indicated at the T terminals, where the error function $E = a_0 + a$ mod 2 is generated.

Consider an ordinary c net for a given normal behavior. If each component of this net is replaced by an a_0 component, as embedded in the locating net of Fig. 1, then we get a net for the normal behavior which, in addition, locates all single errors (Lofgren, 1962). Each locating net consists of two transfer components, and an error is thus located to a set of two components.

If the right transfer component of the single-error-locating net (Fig. 1a or b) is replaced by the comparator net of Fig. 2, a locating net is obtained which indicates all errors in itself of weight up to w. The net will contain $w+1$ transfer components. The weight w can be made as large as we want. Again, if each ordinary component of a c net is replaced by an a_0 component, as embedded in such a w-error-indicating net, we obtain a net which, in addition, locates errors up to weight w.

For reasons to be explained in Sec. 5.4, we also want to consider an error-indicating net where the comparator net is insensitive against errors up to a certain weight. A single- and a double-error-insensitive comparator net is

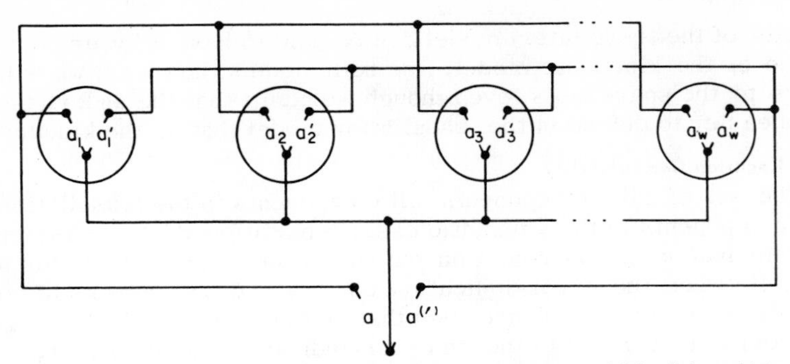

Fig. 2. Comparator net. If the right-transfer component of Fig. 1 (a or b) is replaced by this comparator net, the net of Fig. 1 will indicate all errors in it of weight up to w. The comparator function is $a = a_1 \cup a_2 \cup \ldots \cup a_w$, $a^{(')} = a_1' \cup a_2' \cup \ldots \cup a_w'$.

shown in Figs. 3a and 3b, respectively. The connectivity pattern is obviously generalized to a comparator net containing $(w_0 + 1)^2$ transfer components, insensitive against all w_0 errors. The output of the comparator net is, even for errors in the transfer components, always of transfer type $[a = (a')']$. Such a w_0-error-protected transfer component should be compared with an ordinary w_0-error-protected c net component (not of transfer type), again containing $(w_0 + 1)^2$ elementary components [compare Lofgren (1962)].

These error-locating c nets obviously work both for stationary errors and permanent-state errors.

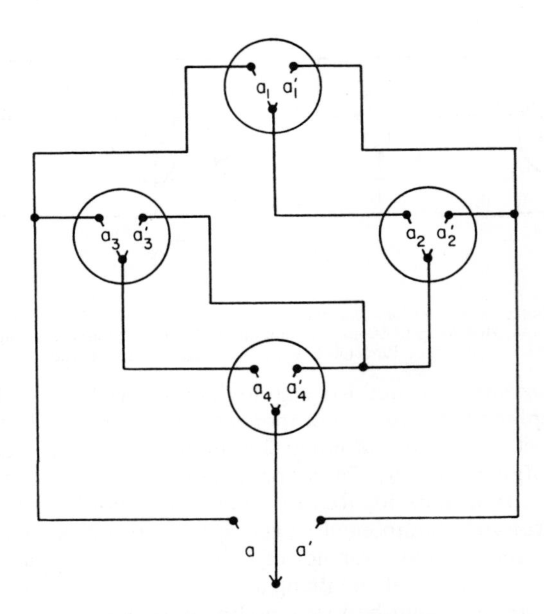

Fig. 3a. Single-error-insensitive comparator net. If the right-transfer component of Fig. 1 (a or b) is replaced by this comparator net, the net of Fig. 1 will indicate all errors of weight up to 2, provided that one error component is in the a_0 transfer. No error indication is obtained for single errors, provided that the a_0 transfer is correct. The comparator function is $a = a_1a_2 \cup a_3a_4$, $a' = (a_1a_2 \cup a_3a_4)'$.

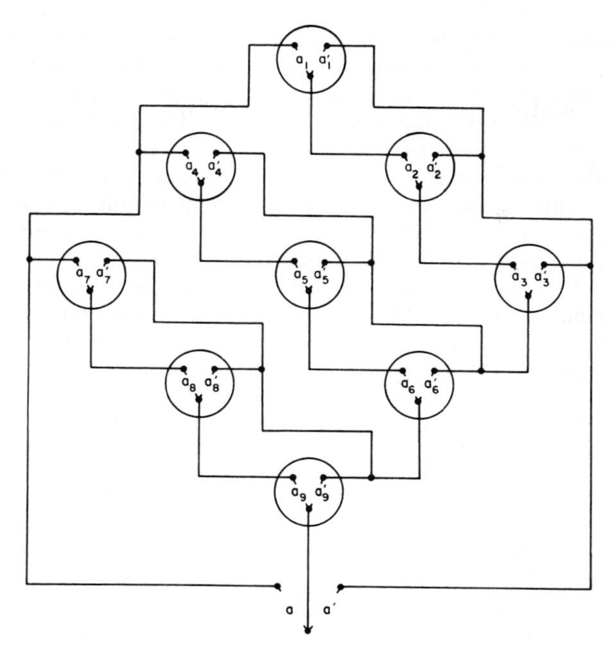

Fig. 3b. Double-error-insensitive comparator net. If the right-transfer component of Fig. 1 (a or b) is replaced by this comparator net, the net of Fig. 1 will indicate all errors of weight up to 3, provided that one error component is in the a_0 transfer. No error indication is obtained for single or double errors, provided that the a_0 transfer is correct. The comparator function is $a = a_1a_2a_3 \cup a_4a_5a_6 \cup a_7a_8a_9$, $a' = (a_1a_2a_3 \cup a_4a_5a_6 \cup a_7a_8a_9)'$.

5.2.2 *Error-Locating g Nets*

Let us first consider a subnet of g type which indicates all single stationary errors in itself (Fig. 4). It contains at least one gate g_0, which is also used for the normal behavior of the whole net. Further, it contains a gate g_1 (or an input to the whole net) whose output state s^* is correlated to the output state s of g_0 in the case of no error. Finally, the locating net contains a comparator gate g_2 with a binary output state s^{**}. If no errors, i.e., if $s = s^*$ (or s is some

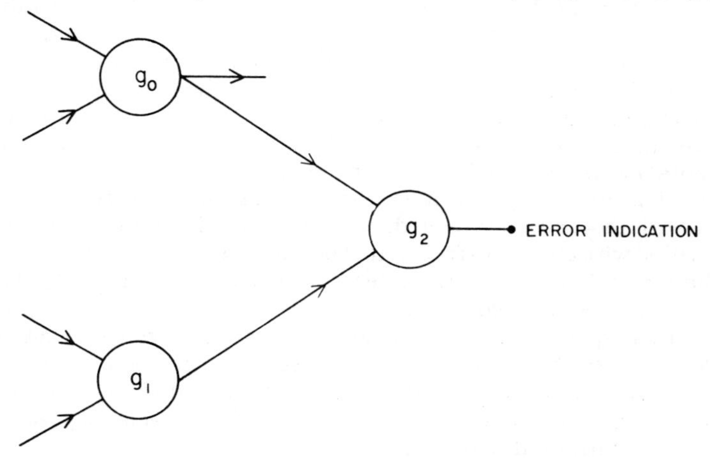

Fig. 4. Single-error-locating g net for stationary errors.

prescribed negation of s^*), s^{**} is 0, indicating no error. If there is an error in g_0 or g_1, i.e., if $s \neq s^*$ (or s deviates from the prescribed negation of s^*), s^{**} is 1, indicating an error. If the single error is in g_2, it will automatically be indicated. In the case where the states s and s^* are binary and such that $s = s^*$ if no error in g_0 or g_1, the comparator gate g_2 is a sum mod 2 gate.

It is obviously impossible to construct a locating g net which, at the single-error-indication output, indicates all errors up to weight w, except when $w = 1$. If the net indicates an error in gate g_0, a double error with its error components in g_0 and in the final gate (g_2) will be indicated as no error.

The net of Fig. 4 will not indicate all permanent-state errors. If, for example, the permanent state $s^{**} = 0$ occurs at g_2, no error indication is obtained. Locating nets for permanent-state errors will be dealt with in connection with the layout of the entire self-repairing g system in Sec. 5.4.3.

5.3 Cell Replacement

In a kinematic model of a well-localized self-repairing system, a cell consists of all the components of an error-locating subnet, together with their internal connections.

As an introduction to the cell replacement mechanism, let us consider a self-tightening automobile tire. The rubber particles (cells) have only one normal state. An error, a hole in the rubber, corresponds to a state which does not belong to the state set. We have, thus, no problem with error-location computation. The error automatically identifies its position, and the compressed air inside the tire streams through the hole, bringing with it rubber particles which fill the hole.

Consider, analogously, a lake in which a sufficiently large number of spare cells are floating around. In the bottom of the lake are a number of holes into which these cells fit. In position in a hole, a cell makes contact with a communication layer, consisting of connectors ("wires") only, built into the bottom of the lake. If no errors exist, each hole is filled with a cell and the normal behavior is obtained over the well-specified inputs and outputs of the wiring layer. If, after some actuations, one of the active cells makes an error, this is indicated as an error state at the output of the error-locating net built into the cell.

In the case of a g net, the error-indication state may be a physical across-or-through quantity [an (A or T) quantity (Lofgren, 1961)]. The error state may thus be identified with a length dimension of the cell (its diameter), so that the cell is smaller than the hole in the case of an error. If so, it flows through the bottom of the lake, and the hole is filled with one of the spare cells.

In the case of a c net, the error-indication state is an (A and T) quantity (Lofgren, 1961). The two states at the error-indication output may, in this instance, be identified with "the cell is resistant in the hole" and "the cell is non-resistant in the hole." In the latter state, which is the error state, the cell flows through the hole and is replaced by one of the spare cells.

It is convenient to distinguish among three states, the release state, which can be identified with the error state at the error-indication output, the empty hole, and the hole filled with an error-free cell. The release state causes the hole to be empty and the empty hole causes the hole to be filled with a new cell. The driving force for this cause-effect chain is the pressure in the streaming liquid (a more or less statistical quantity). We will not attribute errors to it, but consider a replacement to be strictly implied by a release state. In another model we have considered, the replacement mechanism is based on a diffusion process. There it is perhaps easier to defend the assumption that we can neglect statistical disturbances in a statistical process.

It is now important that we do not hide some of the error-location computation in the release-replacement relation. Instead, all parts of this computation should be exposed to errors according to our assumptions of how errors affect the components of a c or g net. Such a uniform exposure is secured by our requirement that the error indication is decoded (only one error-indication output for each cell).

It should be noted at this point that the form of the holes may be such that each of several states of a cell may be the cause of a replacement. The release state should then be defined as the disjunction of these states. The "computation" of this disjunction will then, according to our assumptions, be made without error. This is certainly without reproach if the release of a cell can be regarded as the behavior of a c net. The components of a c net (Lofgren, 1961), to all of which we associate errors, are 1-1 switches or transfer components. Hence, if the states, whose disjunction forms the release state, have the physical (A and T) dimensions which permit a c structure, then the disjunction is implemented by connectors only [compare Lofgren (1961)], to which we associate no errors. Errors are associated, however, to each of the states which form the release state over the disjunction.

On the other hand, if the whole system is regarded as a g net where the release state has the physical dimension of an (A or T) quantity, then we will not encounter the above situation. We must then require that the release state be decoded (a state at only one output).

5.4 Lifespan of a Well-Localized Kinematic Self-Repairing System

We want to determine the lifespan of a kinematic self-repairing system with error location and compare it with the lifespan of a system with systematic replacement. The self-repairing system has a cell-replacement mechanism according to Sec. 5.3. [For some details of such a system not treated here, the reader is referred to Lofgren (1962).]

We will use the following notation:

t_1—cell release time;
t_2—cell release-replacement time;
w—error weight for which the error-location computation is correct;
w_0—error weight for which the comparator net is insensitive;
W—error weight for which the normal behavior of the system is correct, i.e., the number of cells which can be in error at an actuation without giving an error in the output of the whole system.

We have assumed that the errors occur upon actuation, i.e., that the error events are synchronized with actuations. We will make the following further assumptions: (a) the time t_1 is large compared with the switching time, i.e., the transit time for a change between two states; (b) the time t_1 is small compared with t_2; (c) the time t_2 is of the same order as the actuation time.

5.4.1 Self-Repairing c System with w-Error Location

A cell consists here of $w+1$ transfer components (Figs. 1 and 2). If, upon actuation, it experiences an error of weight less than or equal to w, it is replaced during this actuation. However, if it experiences an error of weight $w+1$, it will be stuck in its hole and will, thereafter, give an irreparable state in that hole. The probability P_s of obtaining a stuck situation at a hole upon actuation is, thus

$$P_s = p^{w+1} \tag{3}$$

The probability $Q_s(\nu)$ that no stuck situation appears at a hole during ν actuations is

$$Q_s(\nu) = (1 - P_s)^{\nu} = (1 - p^{w+1})^{\nu} \tag{4}$$

If, at an actuation of a cell which has not previously been stuck, an error of weight up to w occurs, then the cell is replaced. The hole will be empty during this actuation and is filled after time t_2, i.e., at the next actuation. We will consider the empty hole as a temporary component error for the normal behavior of the system. Provided that a cell has not previously been stuck in a hole, the probability that such a temporary error will not occur, and that the cell will not be stuck, is $(1-p)^{w+1}$. At the νth actuation we thus have the probability $Q_{\nu,w}$ that a cell in a hole will give no error cause for the normal behavior of the system

$$Q_{\nu,w} = Q_s(\nu-1) \cdot (1-p)^{w+1} = (1-p^{w+1})^{\nu-1} \cdot (1-p)^{w+1} \tag{5}$$

As long as $Q_{\nu,w} \geq \frac{1}{2} + \epsilon$, where the positive number ϵ can be arbitrarily small, the normal behavior of the system can be made arbitrarily reliable if W is made large enough [compare Moore and Shannon (1956)]. If, however, $Q_{\nu,w} = \frac{1}{2}$, the normal behavior will be completely uncertain. For a fixed value of $p(<\frac{1}{2})$, the behavior of $Q_{\nu,w}$ is as follows. For small values of ν and w, $Q_{\nu,w}$ is larger than $\frac{1}{2}$. For all ν, $Q_{\nu,\infty} = 0$. For any fixed finite positive integer w, $Q_{\nu,w}$ is monotonic, decreasing towards zero with increasing values of ν. Hence the maximum lifespan L_1 of a system of this kind is the largest value of ν which satisfies $Q_{\nu,w} = \frac{1}{2}$. We will denote with w_{opt} the value of w for which L_1 is obtained. For p values small enough to justify the approximation $1-p=e^{-p}$, we obtain over some elementary steps

$$L_1 = 1 + \left[\frac{1}{p}\right]^{[(\ln 2)/p] - 1 - [\ln\ln(1/p) + 1]/\ln(1/p)} \tag{6}$$

$$w_{opt} = \frac{\ln 2}{p} - 1 - \frac{1}{\ln(1/p)} \tag{7}$$

Hence

$$L_1 \approx \left[\frac{\bar{\nu}}{\ln 2}\right]^{\bar{\nu}} \tag{8}$$

$$w_{opt} \approx \bar{\nu} \tag{9}$$

where $\bar{\nu}$ is the lifespan of a component of the system [equation (2)].

For large values of $\bar{\nu}$, the lifespan L_1 of the self-repairing system is very large. It is finite, however.

5.4.2 *A c System with w_0-Error-Insensitive Comparator Nets*

The lifespan L_1 is finite because w is finite. w must be limited, for otherwise the replacement rate will be so large that the probability of having a cell released upon actuation is larger than $\frac{1}{2}$.

We can obviously decrease the replacement rate if we construct the cells so that they do not indicate low-weight errors in the comparator net, but only low-weight errors with one error component in the a_0 transfer component (Fig. 1). This component is the only one of the cell components which takes part of the normal behavior of the system.

We want to determine the lifespan L_2 of such a system and compare it with L_1. We shall find that $L_2 < L_1$. A c system with w_0-error-insensitive comparator nets is the only possibility we have to decrease the replacement rate—the factor that limits L_1. Hence, no c system can have a larger lifespan than L_1, which motivates the name "self-repairing system" for the c system of Sec. 5.4.1.

A cell of the type we wish to consider is obtained from the net of Fig. 1 if the a_1 transfer is replaced by a w_0-error-insensitive comparator net of Fig. 3. The cell will contain $(w_0+1)^2+1$ transfer components. It indicates all errors of weight up to $w_0 + 1$, provided that one error component is in the a_0 transfer. It does not indicate errors of weight up to w_0, provided that no error component is in the a_0 transfer. If there is an error of weight larger than w_0 in the comparator net and, at the same actuation, an error in the a_0 transfer occurs, the cell will be considered stuck in the hole. From that actuation on the cell is irreparable.

We can represent the behavior of the cells in a hole with the probability graph of Fig. 5. Let $X_{w,\nu}$ be the probability that the hole is filled with a cell

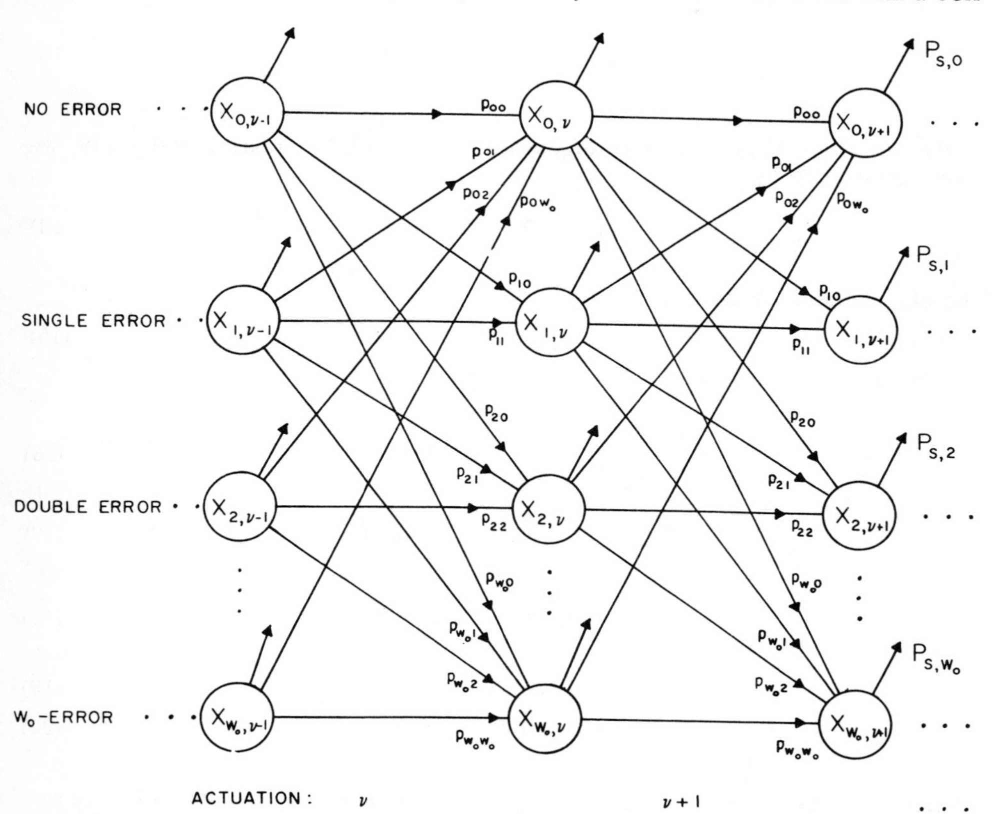

Fig. 5. Probability graph for the behavior of cells appearing in a hole of a system. The comparator net of each cell is w_0-error-insensitive. $X_{w,\nu}$ is the probability that the hole is filled with a cell with a w error after the νth actuation. p_{ij} is the probability that a cell in situation $X_{j,\nu}$ becomes a cell in situation $X_{i,\nu+1}$ after actuation. $P_{s,w}$ is the probability that a cell in situation $X_{w,\nu}$ becomes stuck upon actuation.

with a w error after the νth actuation. Let p_{ij} be the probability that a cell in situation $X_{j,\nu}$ becomes a cell in situation $X_{i,\nu+1}$ after actuation. We then have the following recursive relations:

$$
\begin{aligned}
X_{0,\nu+1} &= p_{00}X_{0,\nu} + p_{01}X_{1,\nu} + p_{02}X_{2,\nu} + p_{03}X_{3,\nu} + \dots + p_{0w_0}X_{w_0,\nu} \\
X_{1,\nu+1} &= p_{10}X_{0,\nu} + p_{11}X_{1,\nu} \\
X_{2,\nu+1} &= p_{20}X_{0,\nu} + p_{21}X_{1,\nu} + p_{22}X_{2,\nu} \\
X_{3,\nu+1} &= p_{30}X_{0,\nu} + p_{31}X_{1,\nu} + p_{32}X_{2,\nu} + p_{33}X_{3,\nu} \\
&\vdots \\
X_{w_0,\nu+1} &= p_{w_00}X_{0,\nu} + p_{w_01}X_{1,\nu} + p_{w_02}X_{2,\nu} + p_{w_03}X_{3,\nu} + \dots + p_{w_0w_0}X_{w_0,\nu}
\end{aligned}
\tag{10}
$$

or with matrix notation

$$X_{\nu+1} = \| p_{ij} \| X_\nu \tag{11}$$

Hence

$$\Delta X_\nu = X_{\nu+1} - X_\nu = \| p_{ij} - \delta_{ij} \| X_\nu = \| \overline{p}_{ij} \| X_\nu \tag{12}$$

If $\lambda_0, \lambda_1, \ldots, \lambda_{w_0}$ are the eigenvalues of the matrix $\| \overline{p}_{ij} \|$, we thus have

$$X_{i,\nu} = \sum_{k=0}^{w_0} c_{i,k} (1+\lambda_k)^\nu \tag{13}$$

If the absolute values of the eigenvalues are small compared with unity, we approximate (13) by

$$X_{i,\nu} = \sum_{k=0}^{w_0} c_{i,k}\, e^{\lambda_k \nu} \tag{14}$$

The eigenvalues are determined by

$$| \overline{p}_{ij} - \delta_{ij} \lambda | = 0 \tag{15}$$

The matrix $\| \overline{p}_{ij} \|$ has the following properties:

$$\sum_{i=0}^{w_0} \overline{p}_{ij} = -P_{s,j} = 0\,(p^{2+w_0-j}) \tag{16}$$

$$\sum_{i=0}^{w_0} \overline{p}_{iw_0} = -(w_0^2 + w_0 + 1)\, p^2 + 0\,(p^3) \tag{17}$$

$$\sum_{j=0}^{w_0} \overline{p}_{ij} = 0^*(p^2) \tag{18}$$

$$\overline{p}_{ii} = 0\,(p) \tag{19}$$

$$p_{ij} = 0^*(p) \qquad (i \neq j) \tag{20}$$

where $0\,(p^\mu)$ is a power series in p starting with power μ, and $0^*(p^\mu)$ is a power series in p starting with power μ or $\mu^* > \mu$.

The properties represented by equations (16-20) permit us to estimate the eigenvalues. If we replace the first row of the determinant of (15) with the sum of all rows, we get

$$\begin{vmatrix} -\lambda+0(p^{2+w_0}) & -\lambda+0(p^{1+w_0}) & -\lambda+0(p^{w_0}) & \cdots\cdots & -\lambda-(w_0^2+w_0+1)p^2+0(p^3) \\ p_{10} & \overline{p}_{11}-\lambda & 0 & 0 & 0 \\ p_{20} & p_{21} & \overline{p}_{22}-\lambda & 0 & 0 \\ p_{30} & p_{31} & p_{32} & \overline{p}_{33}-\lambda & 0 \\ \vdots & \vdots & \vdots & \vdots & \vdots \\ p_{w_0 0} & p_{w_0 1} & p_{w_0 2} & p_{w_0 3} & \overline{p}_{w_0 w_0}-\lambda \end{vmatrix} = 0 \tag{21}$$

If we replace the first column in the above determinant with the sum of all columns, we get

$$\begin{vmatrix} -(w_0+1)\lambda-(w_0^2+w_0+1)p^2+0(p^3) & -\lambda+0(p^{1+w_0}) & -\lambda+0(p^{w_0}) & & -\lambda-(w_0^2+w_0+1)p^2+0(p^3) \\ -\lambda+0^*(p^2) & \overline{p}_{11}-\lambda & 0 & & 0 \\ -\lambda+0^*(p^2) & p_{21} & \overline{p}_{22}-\lambda & \cdots & 0 \\ -\lambda+0^*(p^2) & p_{31} & p_{32} & & 0 \\ \vdots & \vdots & \vdots & & \vdots \\ -\lambda+0^*(p^2) & p_{w_0 1} & p_{w_0 2} & & \overline{p}_{w_0 w_0}-\lambda \end{vmatrix} = 0 \tag{22}$$

If we expand this determinant with respect to the top row, we get

$$[-(w_0+1)\lambda-(w_0^2+w_0+1)p^2+0(p^3)]\cdot\prod_{i=1}^{w_0}(\overline{p}_{ii}-\lambda)+\Sigma\,[-\lambda+0^*(p^2)][-\lambda+0^*(p^2)]\cdot 0_0(p^{w_0-1})=0$$

where

$$0_0(p^{w_0-1}) = 0^*(p^{w_0-1}) \qquad \text{if } \lambda = 0(p^2)$$

Hence

$$\lambda_0 = -\frac{w_0^2+w_0+1}{w_0+1}\,p^2+0(p^3) \tag{23}$$

The product of all eigenvalues is obtained directly from the determinants of (21) and (22)

$$\prod_{k=0}^{w_0}\lambda_k = -(w_0^2+w_0+1)\,p^2\prod_{i=1}^{w_0}\overline{p}_{ii} = 0(p^{w_0+2}) \tag{24}$$

Because of (19) and (20) we must have for all k: $\lambda_k = 0^*(p)$. It thus follows from (23) and (24) that

$$\lambda_k = 0(p) \qquad k = 1, 2, \ldots, w_0 \tag{25}$$

All λ_k must have negative real parts for the probabilities $X_{i,\nu}$ [equation (14)] must be bounded below unity for all positive ν.

We can now write for (14)

$$X_{i,\nu} = c_{i,0}\,e^{-p^2\nu(w_0^2+w_0+1)/(w_0+1)p^2\nu}+\sum_{k=1}^{w_0}c_{i,k}\,e^{-\kappa_k p\nu} \tag{26}$$

where the positive numbers κ_k are of the form $\kappa_k = 0(p^0)$. The sum in (26) represents transients which quickly die out—relative to the first term—after a number of actuations proportional to $1/p$. Thereafter the first term of (26) will dominate since p is assumed small. It is seen from (10), where the diagonal coefficients $p_{ii} = 1-0(p)$ and where the other coefficients $p_{ij} = 0^*(p)$, that the factors $c_{i,0}$ in (26) must all be equal for small p.

The smaller the absolute value of the exponent of the first term of (26), the larger is the lifespan L_2 of this system. The best choice of w_0 is, thus, $w_0 = 1$.

In this case we have

$$X_{0,\nu} = \frac{1}{2}\,e^{-(3/2)p^2\nu} + \frac{1}{2}\,e^{-8p\nu}$$
$$X_{1,\nu} = \frac{1}{2}\,e^{-(3/2)^2\nu} - \frac{1}{2}\,e^{-8p\nu} \tag{27}$$

corresponding to the initial condition $X_{0,0} = 1$, $X_{1,0} = 0$. The probability of having a correctly working a_0 component during the νth actuation is thus $e^{-(3/2)p^2\nu}$. The largest lifespan L_2 is the value of ν for which this probability is $1/2$. Hence

$$L_2 \approx \frac{2}{3}\;\frac{\ln 2}{p^2} = \frac{2}{3\ln 2}\cdot\bar{\nu}^2 \tag{28}$$

where $\bar{\nu}$ is the lifespan of a component of the system [equation (2)].

If, instead, we put $w_0 = 0$ in (26), we are back to the situation with a generating net of Fig. 1. Since the lifespan for $w_0 = 1$ is smaller than for $w_0 = 0$, it follows that any net generated by a net with $w_0 = 1$ must have a smaller lifespan than nets generated with $w_0 = 0$, i.e., the nets of Sec. 5.4.1 with lifespan L_1. We conclude that the most effective error-location computation is the one where all w_{opt} errors of a cell [all single errors, all double errors, and so forth, up to the optimum weight of equation (7)] are indicated.

5.4.3 Self-Repairing g Systems

For g systems we have to distinguish between stationary component errors and permanent-state errors.

In the case of stationary errors, we can at most indicate all single errors (Sec. 5.2.2). The largest possible lifespan is, thus, the largest value of ν which makes $Q_{\nu,1}$ [equation (5)] larger than η (a value of magnitude $1/2$). If the basic components (gates) are all alike, we have for η the value $5/6$ [compare von Neumann (1956)]. As long as $Q_{\nu,1}$, the probability that a cell will give no error at the νth actuation of a hole, is larger than η, we know that it is possible to construct a multiplexed system (von Neumann, 1956) with a normal behavior which is insensitive against the cell errors. The lifespan L_3 of a self-repairing g system exposed to stationary component errors is thus

$$L_3 = \frac{1}{p^2}\,\ln\left(\frac{1}{\eta}\right) = \bar{\nu}^2\cdot\frac{\ln(6/5)}{\ln^2 2} = 0.38\,\bar{\nu}^2 \tag{29}$$

where $\bar{\nu}$ [equation (2)] is the lifespan of a component of the system.

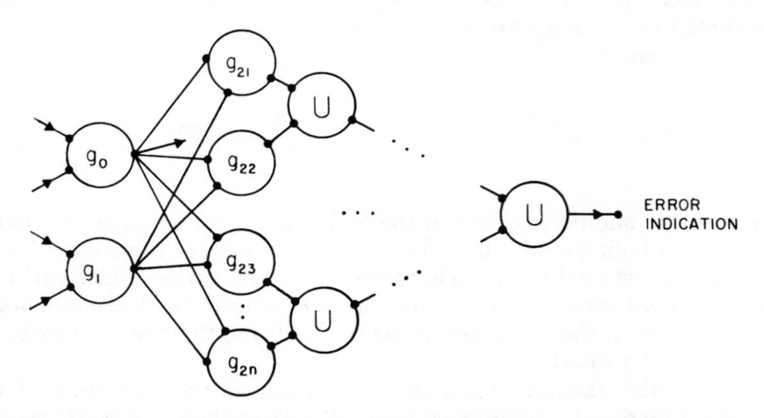

Fig. 6. Error-locating net (cell structure) for a g system with 0-state errors.

For permanent-state errors, let us distinguish among three cases. A 1-state error is an error which always results in a permanent state indicated by 1. A 0-state error always results in a permanent state 0. A 01-state error is an error which results in the permanent state 0 or in the permanent state 1.

For 1-state errors in the error-locating net of Fig. 4, the immediately preceding treatment applies, and the lifespan of the system is L_3 of equation (29).

For 0-state errors in the g_2 gate of Fig. 4, no error indication will be obtained. Hence, subsequent errors in g_0 or g_1 will not be indicated. The method of dealing with this case is to increase the number of g_2 gates to n, as shown in Fig. 6. The g_{2i} gates (mod 2 gates) are followed by OR gates, and the error-indication output is the output of the final OR gate. The OR gates are only actuated once in a replaceable cell, whereas the g_{2i} gates, the g_0 gate, and the g_1 gate are actuated with the normal actuation frequency. If n is increased, the probability that all g_{2i} gates will be in the 0-state error before an error occurs in g_0 or g_1 will be diminished. An increase in n does not change the replacement rate of the cells. For n being sufficiently large, the dominating causes for a stuck situation are an error in the final OR gate or a double error in g_0 and g_1. For ν normal actuations, we have the stuck probability

$$\nu \cdot (2p) \cdot p + \nu p^2$$

This indicates that the final gate is in error with probability p and is actuated with $\nu \cdot (2p)$ actuations; a double error in the two first gates occurs with probability p^2. The stuck probability can at most be allowed to approach the value $1-\eta = 1/6$. If it exceeds this value, the multiplexing will not be effective (von Neumann, 1956). Hence, the lifespan for a g system exposed to 0-state errors is

$$L_4 = \frac{1}{18p^2} = \frac{\bar{\nu}^2}{18 \ln^2 2} = 0.12\,\bar{\nu}^2 \tag{30}$$

where $\bar{\nu}$ is the lifespan of a component of the system [equation (2)].

If we had used three first gates instead of only two (g_0 and g_1), the stuck probability would still have been the same ($3\nu p^2$), because of an increase in the actuation rate of the final OR gate and decrease in the probability for errors occurring in all three first gates at the same actuation. However, with four or more first gates, the lifespan will be smaller than L_4 of equation (30).

If all n of the g_{2i} gates obtain 0-state errors before an error occurs in g_0 or g_1, the cell will be stuck in its hole. The probability of such an occurrence will be small compared to the above stuck probability $3\nu p^2$ if $n \approx 1/(3p)^{1/2}$. Hence, for small values of p, the cells have to be rather complex in order to give the lifespan L_4 to the system in the case of 0-state errors.

Finally, in the case of 01-state errors, let us specify the probabilities p_0 and p_1, respectively, for the occurrence of a 0-state error and a 1-state error in a component upon actuation. Let us assume that $p_0 = p_1 = 1/2\, p$. The net of Fig. 6 is, in this case, not an optimum error-locating net. Because of the 1-state errors, the final OR gate will be actuated $n \cdot p \cdot \nu \approx \nu\sqrt{p}$ times during ν normal actuations of g_0. The lifespan would thus be of the order

$$p^{-3/2}$$

If, however, the net of OR gates following the g_{2i} gates in Fig. 6 is replaced by a majority-indicating net (Fig. 7; compare the error-insensitive comparator net of Sec. 5.4.2), then we can increase n without increasing the replacement rate, thus diminishing the probability of a stuck situation. Hence, we can obtain the stuck probability

$$\nu \cdot (2p) \cdot p_0 + \nu p^2 = 2\nu p^2$$

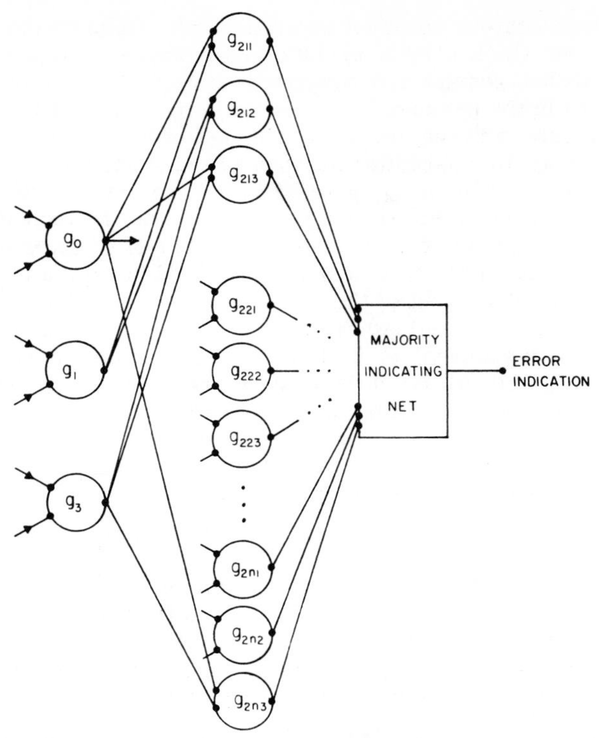

Fig. 7. Error-locating net (cell structure) for a g system with 01-state errors (with $p_0 = p_1$).

during ν normal actuations if each cell has two first gates, g_0 and g_1. If instead each cell contains three first gates, we can reach the lower stuck probability

$$\nu \cdot (3p) \cdot p_0 + \nu p^3 \approx \frac{3}{2} \nu \cdot p^2$$

A further increase in the number of first gates does not give any improvement. The stuck probability can at most be allowed to approach the value $1 - \eta = 1/6$. Hence the lifespan for a g system exposed to 01-state errors with $p_0 = p_1$ ($= 1/2\, p$) is

$$L_5 = \frac{1}{9p^2} = \frac{\bar{\nu}^2}{9 \ln^2 2} = 0.23\, \bar{\nu}^2 \qquad (31)$$

where $\bar{\nu}$ is again the lifespan of a component of the system.

5.4.4 g Nets with Systematic Replacement

If the replacements are not caused by the appearance of an error, but are instead performed at predetermined actuation intervals, we will speak of a "systematic replacement." We shall see that the largest lifespan which can be obtained with a systematic replacement is smaller than the lifespans of the g systems of Sec. 5.4.3.

We can look upon a system with systematic replacement in much the same way as we can upon systems which follow the previously outlined kinematic model, but with one distinction—that the cells do not contain error-locating nets. Instead, a cell contains a counter which brings it into the release state after a fixed number of actuations, say ν_0. There might be errors in the counter, of course, and, taking these into account, we want to estimate the largest possible lifespan.

If a cell contains only one counter, it will be stuck in its hole if a permanent-state error stops the counter before ν_0 actuations. The first stage of the counter is actuated with the normal actuation rate. Hence the stuck probability $(\nu_0 - 1)p$. This permits, at most, a lifespan of the order p^{-1} for the whole system.

If, however, each cell contains several counters, we can obtain a lower stuck probability. Each counter is set for a count to ν_0, and the outputs of the counters are fed to an OR gate network. The output state of the final gate of the OR net is to be identified with the release state of the cell. With a large enough number of counters, we can reach the value p_0 for the probability that a cell is stuck during a replacement interval. The probability of a 0-state error occurring in the final gate is p_0 (= $1/2\,p$).

The probability $P(\nu)$ that there will be a permanent-state error in the normal behavior of a cell precisely at the νth actuation of a replacement interval is

$$P(\nu) = (1 - p)^{\nu-1} \cdot p \tag{32}$$

The cell will also be in error during the $(\nu_0 - \nu)$ actuations which remain before it is released. The average number of errors Σ in a replacement interval is

$$\Sigma = \sum_{\nu=1}^{\nu_0} (\nu_0 - \nu + 1) \cdot P(\nu) = \nu_0 - \frac{1-p}{p}\,[1 - (1-p)^{\nu_0}] \tag{33}$$

Taking both the Σ errors and the stuck-situation errors into account, we obtain for $\sigma(\nu)$, the average number of erroneous cells per number of holes at the νth actuation

$$\sigma(\nu) = \frac{\Sigma}{\nu_0} + \frac{\nu}{\nu_0} \cdot \frac{p}{2} \tag{34}$$

(during ν actuations we have had ν/ν_0 replacement intervals, for each of which the stuck probability is $p_0 = 1/2\,p$). $\sigma(\nu)$ cannot be allowed to exceed $1-\eta = 1/6$ in order to make the multiplexing effective. The lifespan L_6 is the largest value of ν for which $\sigma(\nu)$ approaches $1/6$. From equations (33) and (34) we obtain

$$L_6 = \frac{1}{36\,p^2} = 0.058\,\bar{\nu}^2 \tag{35}$$

where $\bar{\nu}$ is again the lifespan of a component of the system. L_6 occurs for

$$\nu_0 = \frac{0.182}{p} = 0.26\bar{\nu} \tag{36}$$

L_6 is the smallest of all previously derived lifespans, although it is of the same order of magnitude as the lifespans for the self-repairing g systems (Sec. 5.4.3). The replacement rate ν_0^{-1} is higher with systematic replacement than in the self-repairing g systems [compare Sec. 5.4.3 and equation (36)].

6. SELF-REPRODUCTION

As an introduction to Sec. 7, let us briefly discuss the possibilities of self-reproduction.

The concept of self-reproduction has been shown to be meaningful within automata theory by von Neumann (1951). He demonstrates the existence of self-reproducing automata over an inference from Turing's result (Turing, 1936) that it is possible to give the description number of a single machine (the universal Turing machine) which can compute any computable number. The von Neumann existence proof also covers automata which, beside their self-reproductive behavior, also have a further normal behavior.

Simple models of self-reproducing automata have been demonstrated by Penrose (1959) and Jacobson (1958).

Rosen (1959) has recently criticized self-reproduction as a concept of automata theory. His argument is as follows. The behavior of an automaton can be represented by a mapping $F: A \to B$. If the elements of B should themselves be mappings, then the automaton represented by F is capable of synthesizing automata represented by the mappings of B. The automaton F would be self-reproducing if $F \in B$. However, a mapping F is not specified until both its domain and range are stipulated. Hence the range B of a self-reproducing automaton cannot be stipulated until the automaton itself (F) is given since the automaton is a member of its own range. Rosen concludes that a logical paradox is implicit in the notion of a self-reproducing automaton.

However, as Moore (1961) points out, with careful specification of what is meant by an automaton, we do not have to encounter the Rosen paradox. If, for example, an automaton is defined as a configuration in a tessellation, we have indeed simple examples of truly self-reproducing automata (configurations). Here the Rosen paradox does not apply because we have not included the tessellation in the automaton.

If we regard the tessellation as a configuration in an underlying tessellation, and so forth, we would eventually come to the situation where we have a configuration on a tessellation which consists of the empty space. Compare the propagation (a form of self-reproduction) of an electromagnetic wave in vacuum. It seems that the Rosen paradox would apply here. However, the class of automata on a vacuous tessellation may well contain self-reproducing automata, although there might not be an effective decision procedure for the identification of these. It thus seems that the Rosen paradox does not necessarily exclude the existence of self-reproducing automata in the case of a tessellation consisting of the empty space (compare the conceptual difficulties in connection with a wave propagating in the empty space which lead to the classical ether concept).

There are limitations in the behaviors of self-reproducing automata. Examples are the Garden-of-Eden configurations of Moore (1961). A Garden-of-Eden configuration cannot be produced by any other configuration, and no self-reproducing configuration can contain a copy of a Garden-of-Eden configuration. A Garden-of-Eden configuration can only occur at time zero, when somebody outside the system is allowed to interact with it.

It appears that another type of limitation for the behavior of self-reproducing configurations does occur in connection with redundant configurations. If a configuration contains subconfigurations which are truly redundant for the normal behavior, then, if this normal behavior is reproduction, the offsprings will not contain this redundancy.

7. A CONNECTION BETWEEN SELF-REPAIR AND SELF-REPRODUCTION FOR NON-WELL-LOCALIZED TESSELLATION SYSTEMS

We can think of the kinematic g system with systematic replacement (Sec. 5.4.4) as a bridge to the non-well-localized systems. A cell in a hole can evidently be said to be reproduced there, when it is systematically replaced after ν_0 actuations. The effect of replacement errors can obviously be diminished if a cell is "replaced" with more than one cell. This requires an increasing number of holes, such that each of the replacing cells (offsprings) can take part in the normal behavior of the system. This behavior can be said to be correct if the majority of the cells are correct at each actuation. We shall find that there are circumstances under which such systems can have infinite lifespans if the region from which the normal behavior is determined as a majority value does not have a fixed position.

We want to investigate the conditions for infinite lifespans in non-well-localized tessellation systems which contain elementary self-reproducing configurations and, in addition, have some normal behavior. We shall not require here that an elementary configuration contains redundancy which eventually permits it to start a correct reproduction process upon an error in itself. Instead, we shall deal with the case where the cause of a reproduction process is systematic; compare the systematic replacement for well-localized systems (Sec. 5.4.4). We shall, however, discuss how the normal behavior can be used to secure proper death of configurations with errors (compare error location and release in the well-localized systems).

Let us first point out that any finite population of automata with a fixed (average) number of individuals (automata) N at each actuation must have a finite lifespan if there is a nonzero probability of death for each automaton at an actuation. Consider actuation intervals σ_i. The number of actuations in an interval σ_i is somewhat smaller than the number required for a complete reproduction process of an individual. Let π be the probability of death for an individual during σ_i (π is either independent of index i or π is the smallest value of the death probability for any σ_i). The probability of a total death of the whole population at σ_i is (at least) π^N. The probability that a total death occurs during $\frac{1}{2}\pi^{-N}$ actuation intervals is thus larger than or equal to $\frac{1}{2}$. The lifespan, measured in σ_i intervals, is thus bounded upwards by the finite value $\frac{1}{2}\,\pi^{-N}$.

However, if N is growing so that $N(i)$, the average number of individuals at interval σ_i, is growing with index i, we obtain for the probability of a total death during ν intervals $\sum_{i=1}^{\nu} \pi^{N(i)}$. Hence, if $N(i)$ grows at least as rapidly as a logarithmic function of index i, we can have $\sum_{i=1}^{\infty} \pi^{N(i)}$ less than $\frac{1}{2}$, indicating a reasonable probability for an infinite lifespan. If we do not take a total death as a criterion for a population death, but instead say that the population will die if the number of individuals drops below a relative value $[\kappa \cdot N(i)]$, we again have the possibility for an infinite lifespan if the average growth is at least as rapid as a logarithmic growth.

Let ΔN be the average increase, during a σ^0 interval, in the number of error-free individuals (configurations) of a population of self-reproducing configurations on a tessellation. Each σ^0 interval contains a number of actuations μ_0 which permit a reproduction process of a configuration to be completed. Let the corresponding average increase of erroneous individuals during σ^0 be ΔN^*. We will specify that the population as a whole is correct if the majority of the individuals, at each σ^0 interval, are error-free. The conditions

$$\Delta N \geq \Delta N^* \tag{37}$$

$$\Delta N \geq \epsilon > 0 \tag{38}$$

fulfilled at each σ^0 interval, permit an infinite lifespan of the population. Equation (37) assures that the majority of the individuals will remain correct, on an average basis, and (38), where ϵ is a fixed positive number, assures that the growth of N will be at least linear with the number of actuations, i.e., larger than the critical logarithmic growth.

In order to determine under which circumstances the condition of (37) can be fulfilled, let us first consider a dense, packed configuration on an n-dimensional tessellation (Fig. 8). At a certain time (actuation), the configuration has the diameter D and contains N elementary self-reproducing configurations. Each elementary configuration has the complexity C, i.e., occupies C cells ("squares")

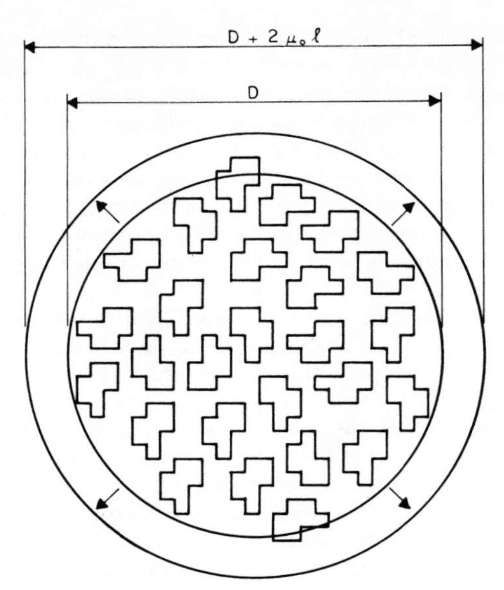

Fig. 8. An expanding but mortal configuration of elementary self-reproducing configurations on a two-dimensional tessellation.

of the tessellation. In the case of no errors, we can have, at most, an increase, $f(D)$, in the total number of elementary configurations during μ_0 actuations (μ_0 is the number of actuations in a σ^0 interval)

$$f(D) = c_n \frac{(2\mu_0 l + D)^n - D^n}{v \cdot C} \approx \frac{2 c_n n \mu_0 l D^{n-1}}{v \cdot C} \tag{39}$$

l and v are the length and volume, respectively, of a cell in the tessellation. c_n is a volume factor (the ratio between the volumes of an -dimensional sphere of diameter D and an n-dimensional cube of side D). The increase in N cannot be larger than $f(D)$, for there is no room for further elementary configurations. This method of reasoning is the same as that used by Moore to derive a bound for the fastest growth of a self-reproducing configuration (Moore, 1961).

Taking errors into account, we obtain for the fastest increase ΔN of the number of error-free elementary configurations, and for the increase ΔN^* of the number of erroneous configurations

$$\Delta N = f(D) - \frac{p \mu_0 a c_n D^n}{v} \tag{40}$$

$$\Delta N^* = \frac{p \mu_0 a c_n D^n}{v} \tag{41}$$

$a c_n D^n/v$ is the average number of cells which are being actuated. We count here both the actuations for the normal behavior and those for the reproduction. If a_0 is the average number of cells which are being actuated for the normal behavior, we have $a > a_0$ where a_0 can be assumed to be independent of D. Equations (40) and (41) are correct for small values of p, for we can then assume that the total number of errors is, on the average, distributed with, at most, one error per elementary configuration. Since $f(D)$ is proportional to D^{n-1}, it follows that there must come a time when $\Delta N < \Delta N^*$, and we conclude that a configuration with the form of a sphere cannot have an infinite lifespan.

If however, the whole configuration has the form of a surface region of an expanding sphere (Fig. 9), the condition of (37) can be fulfilled. At a certain instant, let the wave (the surface region) be bounded by the two diameters D and $(D + 2d)$. The quantity d is the depth of the wave. It is assumed to be constant during the propagation of the wave. At the next σ^0 interval, i.e., μ_0 actuations later, the wave can, at most, have propagated a distance $\mu_0 l$. It is then bounded by the diameters $(D + 2\mu_0 l)$ and $(D + 2d + 2\mu_0 l)$. The increase in the number of erroneous elementary configurations [the number of erroneous cells; compare (43) below] in the wave during these μ_0 actuation intervals is

$$\Delta N^* = c_{n-1} \frac{(D + 2\mu_0 l)^{n-1}(d-\mu_0 l)}{v} \cdot a_0 \mu_0 p - c_{n-1} \frac{D^{n-1} \mu_0 l}{v} \cdot \frac{d-\mu_0 l}{l} a_0 p$$

$$- c_{n-1} \frac{D^{n-1} \mu_0 l}{v} \cdot a_1 \mu_0 p + c_{n-1} \frac{(D + 2d)^{n-1} \mu_0 l}{v} \cdot a_1 \mu_0 p$$

$$= c_{n-1} \frac{(n-1) D^{n-2} 2dl}{v} \cdot \left[a_0 \cdot \frac{d-\mu_0 l}{d} + a_1\right] \cdot \mu_0^2 p \qquad (42)$$

The first term is the increase of errors due to normal actuations in the region of the tessellation (region B in Fig. 9) which is contained in the wave throughout the μ_0 actuation intervals. a_0 is the actuation density for the normal behavior. The second term corresponds to the errors which have been accumulated in the back region of the wave (region C in Fig. 9) due to normal actuations, and, thus,

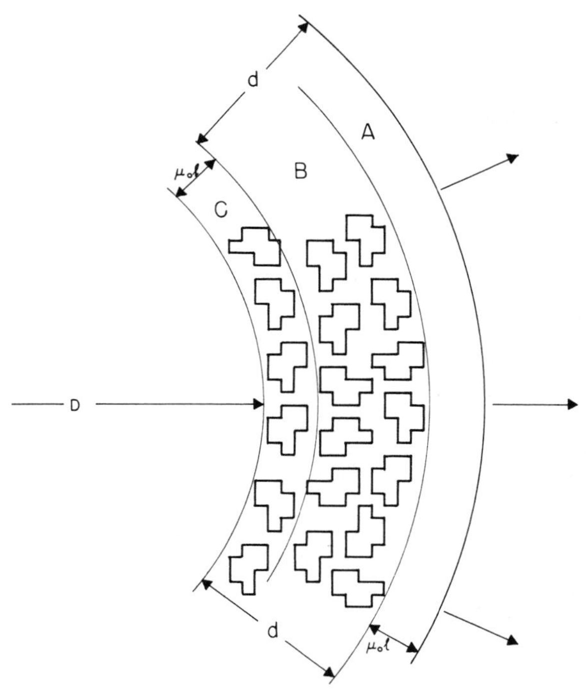

Fig. 9. An immortal automata wave of elementary self-reproducing configurations on a two-dimensional tessellation. The depth d is constant while the wave is propagating. The complexity C of each elementary configuration is bounded by equation (43).

are removed from the wave when it is propagating. The third term corresponds to the errors in the back region which came about when this region was created. a_1 is the actuation density for the self-reproducing behavior. The fourth term, finally, corresponds to the errors which come about at the creation of the front region of the wave (region A in Fig. 9).

The error density in the wave is highest in the back region where it is $p\, a_0\, (d-\mu_0 l)/l + p\, a_1\, \mu_0$. Evidently it is of no use to have the wave depth d so large that the majority of the elementary configurations in this region will be in error. We, therefore, require that

$$(\epsilon_0 =)\ C\left[p a_0 \frac{d-\mu_0 l}{l} + p a_1 \mu_0\right] < \frac{1}{2} \tag{43}$$

where C, as before, is the complexity of an elementary self-reproducing configuration. We have then, on the average, one error at most in an elementary self-reproducing configuration. The number of erroneous elementary configurations in the wave will, therefore, be equal to the number of erroneous cells in the wave [compare equation (42)].

The total increase in the number of elementary configurations during the σ^0 interval is

$$\Delta N + \Delta N^* = \frac{1}{C}\left[c_{n-1}\frac{(D+2\mu_0 l)^{n-1} d}{v} - c_{n-1}\frac{D^{n-1} d}{v}\right]$$

$$= \frac{1}{C} c_{n-1}(n-1)\, 2\mu_0 l\, d\, \frac{D^{n-2}}{v} \tag{44}$$

The condition of (37) is, over (42) and (44), equivalent to

$$C\left(a_0 \frac{d-\mu_0 l}{d} + a_1\right) \mu_0\, p \leq \frac{1}{2} \tag{45}$$

Since, obviously

$$d \geq \mu_0 l \tag{46}$$

we see that the condition of (45) is actually contained in the condition of (43).

In order to investigate the condition of (38), we can rewrite (44), using (42), (43), and (46), as

$$\Delta N \geq \frac{1-\epsilon_0}{C}\ \frac{(n-1)\, c_{n-1}\, 2\mu_0 l\, d\, D^{n-2}}{v} \tag{47}$$

The right member of (47) is nonzero and positive if $n \geq 2$, thus fulfilling the condition of (38). A one-dimensional automata wave, however, has $\Delta N = 0$ and is, thus, mortal.

In conclusion, an automata wave can be immortal if it is at least two-dimensional and if equation (43) is fulfilled. If the actuation densities a_0 and a_1 are of the same order of magnitude, and if $d >> \mu_0 l$, the condition of equation (43) becomes

$$(\epsilon_0 =)\ C\ \frac{d}{l}\ a_0\, p < \frac{1}{2} \tag{48}$$

For a given probability of error p, the complexity C of an elementary self-reproducing configuration is thus bounded, as is the depth d of the surface region over which the majority of the normal behaviors should be taken.

If the complexity of the self-reproducing elementary configurations is $C = 1$, we can explicitly demonstrate the existence of an immortal automata wave. Let the transition rule for the reproductive behavior be such that a cell, being in any of its active states, converts all of its neighbor cells, which are in the unexitable state U, into an active state. Let the transition rule for the active states be such that every cell not in the U state has one and the same normal behavior.

A single cell should, when $C = 1$, carry out the whole normal behavior. If the initial state of the tessellation is such that some neighboring cells are in active states, an expanding configuration of active cells will result. If there is an error in the reproductive behavior, i.e., a cell c remains in the U state although stimulated by neighbors, then a cell which should have been stimulated by c will instead be stimulated by another neighbor. Hence, equation (43) applies, and a front region of the configuration determined by this equation will give the correct answer for the normal computation on a majority basis.

Two questions immediately arise in connection with these non-well-localized automata. First, how do we know that we take the answers from the allowed automata in the wave region? Second, can the structure of the cells be simpler than to account for the whole prescribed normal behavior? Can't this behavior be obtained instead from an elementary configuration with $C > 1$?

Let us assume that $C > 1$. An automatic indication of the allowed wave region can, for example, be obtained if the cells behind the wave are converted into the U state, the state in which they were before the wave reached them. However, the most we can hope for is to have all cells but those in which permanent-state errors have occurred converted into the U state. The tessellation could then also be used for a new concentric immortal wave, for it is supposed that an elementary configuration can sense an area planned for an offspring before the reproduction takes place. Too many waves cannot be allowed, however, for the density of erroneous cells will increase, and sooner or later the condition of equation (37) will be violated.

An elementary configuration cannot convert itself into U states. It can kill itself, i.e., stop its own activities when it has, for example, reached a certain age, but it cannot bury itself, i.e., it cannot completely convert all of its cells into U states. One living configuration can, however, convert a neighboring configuration, say a dead one, into U states. The burying activity, thus, calls for a slight interaction between neighboring elementary configurations. We can, for example, require that part of the normal activity of an elementary configuration is to call out "I am alive" in different directions. Furthermore, a configuration should listen for such calls after it has been ν_0' actuations old, and start burying activity in a silent direction. Finally, a configuration should kill itself if it is over ν_0'' actuations old and is not occupied with the burial of one of its dead neighbors. The suicide age ν_0'' determines the depth d of the immortal wave. The interaction between the elementary configurations requires that there is a sufficient amount of free cells around each configuration. These free cells should be included in the complexity C.

There is, however, a difficulty in this case of $C > 1$. It can happen that an error in the reproductive behavior does not stop the reproduction (as it did in the case of $C = 1$). An offspring may inherit an error. We can diminish the probability of having affected offsprings reproduce if we require that the above-mentioned call be replaced with a more complicated one, such as "I am alive... and correct." The generation of just this call, which prevents a neighbor from starting a destruction process, should require that almost all cells in the configuration are behaving correctly.

By considerations of this kind we are led to consider elementary configurations which compete with each other. The most "powerful" will survive. For a given tessellation, the class of all self-reproducing elementary configurations fulfilling the requirement of equation (43), will eventually contain a configuration which is more "powerful" than the other. If this configuration is selected, we know that errors in it which give rise to affected but self-reproducing configurations will not be propagated in the long run. It is possible, however, that the most "powerful" configuration will have a normal behavior which perhaps does not meet with the requirements we have. We then have to investigate another tessellation with another set of transition rules.

Equation (43) is, in the case of $C > 1$, only a necessary condition for immortality.

8. CONCLUSIONS

We have found that the lifespan $L(\bar{\nu})$ of a well-localized self-repairing system increases at least as rapidly as a quadratic function of $\bar{\nu}$, the lifespan of a component of the system. For a finite $\bar{\nu}$, $L(\bar{\nu})$ is finite. This might suggest an iterative scheme, leading to a self-repairing system of components which are self-repairing systems of components which are self-repairing systems of components, etc. There are, however, principal difficulties with an iterative scheme.

In the case of c nets, we have required that the components in the error-locating nets are of transfer type such that an error in a left transfer is always a right transfer and vice versa. If an iteration becomes possible, we must also require that the normal behavior is always that of a transfer net. But this we cannot do, for during an actuation at which a cell is replaced, the corresponding error for the normal behavior may be "no transfer at all," i.e., an illegitimate type of error.

Also, in the case of g nets, we have a principal difference between a component and a system which prevents iteration. In a system, each output for the normal behavior is multiplexed, whereas the output of a component is required to be nonmultiplexed—at least the output of the final component in the error-locating net.

The obtainable lifespans $L(\bar{\nu})$ are, however, very large for reasonably large $\bar{\nu}$. Even the lifespans for self-repairing g systems—the quadratic functions—are large enough to meet with most practical requirements. It should be kept in mind that the larger lifespans we have devised for c systems represent an idealized situation. We have assumed here that an error in a left transfer is always a right transfer and vice versa. In a practical system we should also have a finite probability for no transfer at all and for a transfer in both directions.

We have seen that "unrestricted self-repair," corresponding to a well-localized system which repairs any kind of errors in itself, is not a meaningful concept, except when no normal behavior of the system is prescribed. We have, therefore, developed the idea of a self-repairing well-localized system, as a system with a lifespan which is maximum with respect to the lifespan of any other system belonging to the class under consideration. This seems to be a reasonable line of development for a theoretical analysis. Such a characterization would, however, imply that a self-repairing and a non-self-repairing system can have lifespans which are very much the same. This is not desirable from a practical point of view. We want to have a more pronounced distinction between self-repair and non-self-repair. We observe, therefore, that a system with a lifespan larger than the lifespan of its components must contain spare cells and a mechanism for the conversion of spare cells into active cells (replacement or "repair"). On the other hand, systems in which all cells are actuated with about the same actuation rate have lifespans which can be, at most, of the same order of magnitude as the lifespan of their components. We, therefore, suggest the following characterization: A self-repairing well-localized system is a closed system with a prescribed normal behavior, measured at well-localized outputs and inputs, such that its lifespan is larger than the lifespan of its components.

With this characterization, a system with systematic replacement can also be self-repairing (Sec. 5.4.4). Also, systems with error location such that w is somewhat less than w_{opt}—in which case the replacement rate can be held within practical limits—can be regarded as self-repairing [equation (7)].

The non-well-localized self-repairing systems are interesting because of the connection established here between the concepts of self-repair and self-reproduction. They permit, at least for very low complexities of the elementary self-reproducing configurations, infinite lifespans.

It is likely that the automata view of non-well-localized self-repairing systems developed here will find applications in other scientific areas—in biology, for example, in connection with the growth of bacteria and viruses, and how we protect ourselves from some of them. One answer to the question of why we reproduce is obviously obtained from this automata study.

If the ideas are at all applicable to configurations on a vacuous tessellation, we might get views on the question: why is our universe expanding?

ACKNOWLEDGMENT

Stimulating discussions on the subject with Professor H. Von Foerster and the members of the Biological Computer Laboratory at the University of Illinois are gratefully acknowledged.

The author wishes to express his thanks to G. Kjellberg of the University of Stockholm and of Telefonaktiebolaget L. M. Ericsson for some remarks on the subject.

REFERENCES

Bohm, D. 1957. A proposed explanation of quantum theory in terms of hidden variables at a sub-quantum-mechanical level. Observation and interpretation; a symposium of philosophers and physicists. Butterworths Publications Ltd., London.

Jacobson, H. 1958. On models of reproduction. Am. Sci. 46, 3, 255.

Lofgren, L. 1956. Automata of high complexity and methods of increasing their reliability by redundancy. Actes du Premier Congres International de Cybernetique, Namur, 26-29 June 1956, Gauthier-Villars, Paris, 1958, p. 493. Also published in Information and Control 1, 2, 127, 1958.

Lofgren, L. 1961. A theory of uniform switching nets. Tech. Report No. 2, National Science Foundation Grant 17414, Electrical Engineering Research Laboratory, University of Illinois, Urbana, Illinois. Also presented under the title "The structures of switching nets" at the Fifth Midwest Symposium on Circuit Theory, University of Illinois, May 1961.

Lofgren, L. 1962. Self-repair as the limit for automatic error correction. Proc. symposium on the principles of self-organization. University of Illinois, June 8-9, 1960. Pergamon Press, London.

McCulloch, W. 1958. Agathe Tyche of nervous nets—the lucky reckoners. National Physical Laboratory Symposium on the Mechanization of Thought Processes. Teddington, England, 2, 611.

Moore, E. 1961. Machine models of self-reproduction. Symposium on Mathematical Problems in the Biological Sciences, New York, 1961.

Moore, E. and Shannon, C. 1956. Reliable circuits using less reliable relays. J. Franklin Inst. 262, 191; Part II, 262, 281.

Muller, D. and Bartky, S. 1959. A theory of asynchronous circuits. Proc. International Symposium on the Theory of Switching. Harvard Univ. Press.

Penrose, L. 1959. Automatic mechanical self-reproduction. New Biology, No. 28 (January 1959), Harmondsworth, England: Penguin Books, p. 92.

Rosen, R. 1959. On a logical paradox implicit in the notion of a self-reproducing automaton. Bull. Math. Biophys. 21, 387.

Shannon, C. 1948. A mathematical theory of communication. Bell Syst. Tech. J. 27, 379.

Turing, A. 1936. On computable numbers with an application to the Entscheidungs-problem. Proc. London Math. Soc. 42, 230.

von Neumann, J. 1951. The general and logical theory of automata. In: Jeffress, L. [ed.], Cerebral mechanisms in behavior. John Wiley & Sons, Inc.

von Neumann, J. 1956. Probabilistic logics and the synthesis of reliable organisms from unreliable components. In: Shannon, C. and McCarthy, J. [ed.], Automata studies. Princeton Univ. Press, Princeton, New Jersey.

von Neumann, J. The theory of automata: construction, reproduction, and homogeneity. Uncompleted typescript of three chapters (n.d., circa 1952) to be edited by A. Burks for publication by Univ. of Illinois Press.

Wachtmeister, C. G. 1961. Tiden och Livsprocesserna (The time and the processes of life), Svenska Dagbladet, July 9, 1961 (understreckare).

THEORY OF STRUCTURALLY HOMOGENEOUS LOGIC NETS*

R. M. Stewart

Space-General Corporation
Glendale 1, California

INTRODUCTION

The purpose of this note is to present an elementary approach to a theory of the role of structure in logic nets and to give examples of some simple applications. We are primarily, although not exclusively, interested in "cellular" or "honeycomb" structures which have: (a) the approximate form of three-dimensional regular lattices; (b) a uniform type of elementary component in a single lattice; and (c) simply connected elementary components, i.e., components connected only to adjacent components, or possibly, if located on the periphery, to "system" inputs or outputs. Such structures are termed "peripheral access lattices" or simply PAL's.

The composite structure and its behavior, observed at the peripheral connections, are referred to as the macrostructure, while its constituent elementary components are referred to as microstructures or microcomponents. We are especially concerned with the range of possible macroscopic behavior for nets having a fixed basic structure but some variability in microscopic behavior. Such a concept includes, for example, fully connected machines of finite size in which cuts may be made in any connection.

VARIABILITY AND THE BASIC THEOREM OF COMPOSITE STRUCTURES

Let N represent the number of different possible modes of behavior of a multistable logic structure. Variations in behavior are presumed to correspond to different possible quasi-stable states in which the structure may exist, according to its past history, treatment, or conditioning.

If a macrostructure consists of an assembly of n microstructures, then the number of different system-states equals

$$\prod^{n} (N_{\text{micro}})_i$$

and, thus, obviously

$$N_{\text{macro}} \leq \prod^{n} (N_{\text{micro}})_i \tag{1}$$

The equality applies if for every different arrangement of microstates, the macrostructure responds differently as observed at its periphery. If we define

$$C = \log_2 N \tag{2}$$

then

$$C_{\text{macro}} \leq \sum^{n} (C_{\text{micro}})_i \tag{3}$$

C may properly be called the equivalent structural information content and is

*The first part of this paper appeared in condensed form in the Correspondence section of Proc. I.R.E. 49, 8, 1961.

numerically equal (if an integer) to the minimum number of binary digits required to specify, identify, or describe the behavior or response function of a structure. This definition and the associated theorem closely parallel Shannon's fundamental treatment of the capacity of a communication channel.

As a special case, if all C_i are equal (e.g., assembly of identical components)

$$C_{\text{macro}} = n\, C_{\text{micro}} \tag{4}$$

MAXIMUM CAPACITY OF BINARY DEVICES

For a unilateral device having n_i binary inputs and n_o binary outputs which are functionally dependent on the inputs,

$$C \leq 2^{n_i} n_o \tag{5}$$

The equality applies to a structural unit capable of assuming any describable functional dependence of the output pattern on the input pattern and is essentially the dimensionality of the associated "truth table" (Wittgenstein, 1921) or generalized Venn diagram (Venn, 1880). Such a device is termed a "universal" computer.

For example, a unit having two inputs and one output as shown

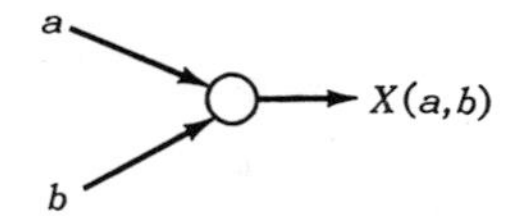

has a maximum structural capacity of 4 bits. If it has such capacity, it must be capable of performing as an "AND gate," "OR gate," "NOR gate," "exclusive-OR gate," and all such possibilities (16 in all), including such things, usually considered somewhat trivial in the logical design of computers, as $X \equiv 0$, $X \equiv 1$, $X \equiv a$, $X \equiv \bar{a}$, $X \equiv b$, or $X \equiv \bar{b}$. With $n_i = 1$ and $n_o = 2$

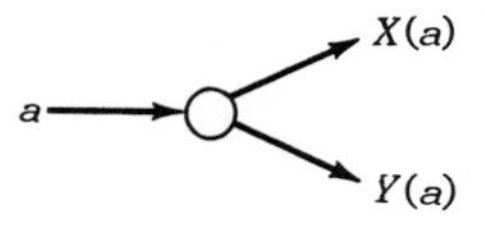

the maximum capacity is likewise 4 bits.

MINIMUM SIZE OF UNIVERSAL BINARY MACHINES

If a binary macromachine (N_i inputs and N_o outputs) consisting of a number of identical binary microcomponents is to be universal, then from (4) and (5)

$$2^{N_i} N_o \leq n 2^{n_i} n_o \tag{6}$$

or

$$n \geq 2^{N_i - n_i} \left(\frac{N_o}{n_o}\right)$$

As an example of the implications of this result, consider the structure shown in Fig. 1.

If the components are universal elements at each junction and split

$$(C_{\text{micro}})_i = 4 \text{ bits}$$

and hence,

$$\sum^{n=60} (C_{\text{micro}}) = 240 \text{ bits}$$

But

$$2^{N_i} N_o = 2^6 \cdot 6 = 384 \text{ bits}$$

Thus, it is fundamentally impossible for this macrostructure to be universal. In other words, there are apparently some response functions which can be described for $N_i = 6$ and $N_o = 6$, but which cannot be realized with this internal structure and connectivity regardless of how we may choose the behavior of the (binary) internal components.

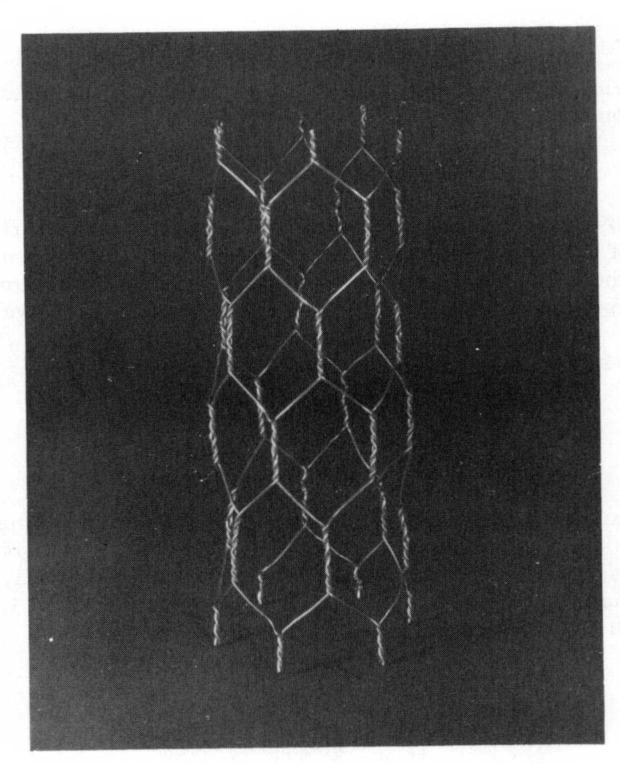

Fig. 1

THE CLOSURE RULE

A useful theorem in dealing with machines is based on the assumption that there are no loose ends, i.e., every input connection to a microcomponent is either a peripheral input to the macrosystem or the output of some microcomponent, and that every output of a microcomponent either terminates as an input to some microcomponent or as a peripheral output of the macrosystem. Then, by counting internal connections,

$$\sum^{n} n_i - N_i = \sum^{n} n_o - N_o \tag{7}$$

When N_i and N_o are much less than n_i and n_o (i.e., many more "internal" connections than peripheral connections)

$$\Sigma n_i \approx \Sigma n_o \tag{8}$$

and, therefore,

$$\langle n_i \rangle = \langle n_o \rangle \tag{9}$$

where

$$<n_i> = \frac{1}{n}\sum^{n} n_i \quad \text{and} \quad <n_o> = \frac{1}{n}\sum^{n} n_o$$

are, respectively, the average number of inputs and outputs per microcomponent. Under these conditions, this might suggest, for example, that a net partially composed of microcomponents for which $n_i = 2$ and $n_o = 1$ might be completed with an approximately equal number of components for which $n_i = 1$ and $n_o = 2$.

Another class of structures of interest is that corresponding to a simply connected lattice of closest-packed spheres. For such a lattice

$$n_i + n_o = 12 \tag{10}$$

for every component except those on the periphery. Therefore, from the modified closure rule [equation (9)]

$$<n_i> = <n_o> = 6 \tag{11}$$

If we let

$$n_i \equiv n_o \equiv 6$$

for every component,

$$C_{\text{micro}} \leq 2^6 \cdot 6 = 384 \text{ bits/component}$$

POSSIBILITIES AND PROBABILITIES

Various workers have concerned themselves with calculating and describing theoretical constraints on macrosystem behavior when the constituent microcomponents are constrained in certain special ways. As yet, there has appeared very little analysis involving structural constraints as well. As a simple example, it is probably well known that an assembly exclusively comprised of any number of "AND gates" and "OR gates" and having just two peripheral inputs (a, b) and one peripheral output $[X(a,b)]$ can behave macroscopically only in the trivial ways:

$$X \equiv 0, \; X \equiv a, \text{ or } X \equiv b$$

or else either as an "AND gate" or as an "OR gate." What may not have been demonstrated is that if the trivial responses are structurally impossible (or very unlikely) and if the microcomponent response functions are chosen at random with

$$p_{\text{AND}} = p_{\text{OR}} = \frac{1}{2}$$

then the macrosystem response probabilities are likewise

$$p_{\text{AND}} = p_{\text{OR}} = \frac{1}{2}$$

This result is a direct consequence of De Morgan's theorem.

The model shown in Fig. 2 represents a machine for which

$$N_i = 3$$

and

$$N_o = 3$$

Hence,

$$C \leq 2^3 \cdot 3 = 24 \text{ bits}$$

The machine represented actually achieves the theoretical maximum

$$C = 24 \text{ bits}$$

(corresponding to approximately 16 million different response functions) and contains just 24 switches or points (in addition to a fixed section of "NOR" elements) which may either be connected or not connected:

$$a \circ\!\!\!-\!\!\!-\!\!\!\dashv \;\; \vdash\!\!\!-\!\!\!-\!\!\!\circ \qquad X(a) = 0$$

or

$$a \circ\!\!\!-\!\!\!-\!\!\!-\!\!\!-\!\!\!\circ \qquad X(a) = a$$

and, hence, have a microcapacity of just 24 bits:

$$C_{\text{micro}} = \log_2 2 = 1 \text{ bit/component}$$

and

$$\sum^{24} C_{\text{micro}} = 24 \text{ bits}$$

Furthermore, if for each bistable component

$$p_o = \frac{1}{2}$$

and

$$p_a = \frac{1}{2}$$

i.e., switch positions are chosen at random, then the probability of occurrence of each possible response function is the same (about 1 : 16,000,000).

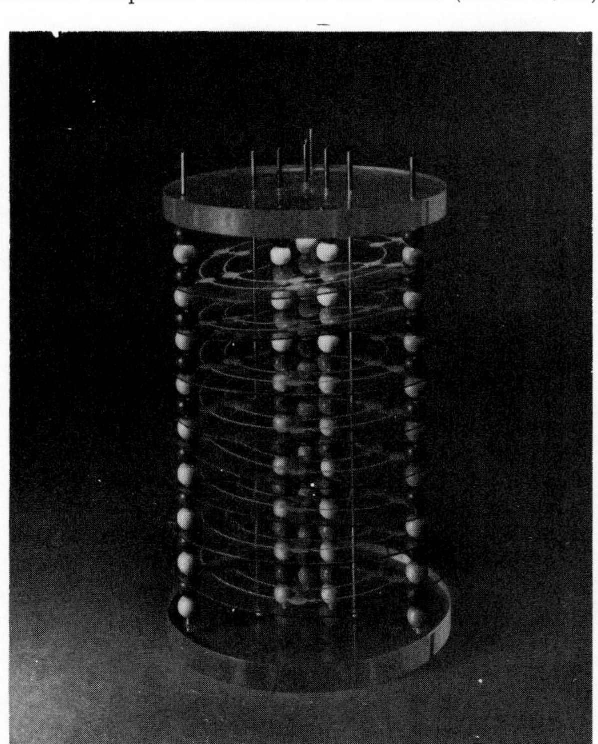

Fig. 2

This property is characteristic of any nondegenerate or efficient universal machine, i.e., one for which

$$C_{\text{macro}} = \sum^{n} C_{\text{micro}}$$

if for all j states of every microcomponent

$$P_{ij} = \frac{1}{N_i}$$

and the states of the microcomponents are independent random variables. Then the probability of every macrofunction (k) is equal to

$$P_k = \prod^n p_{ij} = \prod^n \frac{1}{N_i} = \frac{1}{N_{\text{macro}}}$$

The structure of PAL-I was motivated primarily to illustrate a macrosystem characterized by: (1) structurally and functionally uniform microcomponents; (2) relatively close-packed spatial distribution of microcomponents; and (3) simple, short-range connectivity. At the same time, universal macrofunction resulting from minimum possible microcapacity (and, hence, equiprobable macrofunction) was desired.

FAST CONVERGENCE OF MACROFUNCTION BY PERIPHERAL ACCESS CONDITIONING

In addition, this type of macromachine will converge very quickly on any desired or "satisfactory" response function by means of a "trial-and-error" conditioning program in which unsatisfactory responses are followed (within a limited time) by a general peripheral access indication of failure. This will occur if each switch (bistable microcomponent) is designed to be subject to a possible change of state if the "failure" stimulation occurs within a short period of time after a signal appears at its input. Since the conception of this machine, we have discovered that a group at the Melpar Corporation has devised an electronic model of a universal (2 : 1) unit which they call the "Generalized Artron" and which resembles PAL-I (a 3 : 3 machine) functionally, although not structurally. This same type of function and structure may be extended to a macromachine of any size.

EXISTENCE OF NONDEGENERATE UNIVERSAL MACHINES COMPOSED OF UNIVERSAL (2 : 1) MICROCOMPONENTS

By means of the logical expansion

$$X(a,b,c,d) = abf_{11}\ (c,d) + a\bar{b}f_{10}\ (c,d) + \bar{a}bf_{01}\ (c,d) + \bar{a}\bar{b}f_{00}\ (c,d)$$

it is clear that any binary function of four variables may be composed from four universal (2 : 1) functions (f's) and, furthermore,

$$C_{\text{macro}} = \Sigma\, C_{\text{micro}} = 16 \text{ bits}$$

Similar universal expressions may be immediately written down for any number of "inputs" (a, b, c, $d, \ldots$) and "outputs" ($X, \ldots$). However, direct mechanization of such expressions leads to structures which are asymmetrical with respect to their inputs.

Other universal structures may be derived by means of "reversible" or "one-to-one" transformations. There are just 24 such transformation pairs of two variables, involving only reverses, inverses, and "exclusive-OR" (or "Mod-2 addition") operations. For example, such a pair of transformations is

$$a' = a$$
$$b' = a \oplus b$$

This procedure may be applied successively ad infinitum, for example,

$$\begin{array}{lllll} a \longrightarrow & a & \longrightarrow & a \oplus c \oplus d & \\ b \longrightarrow & a \oplus b & \longrightarrow & a \oplus b & \\ c \longrightarrow & c & \longrightarrow & a \oplus b \oplus c & \text{etc.} \\ d \longrightarrow & c \oplus d & \longrightarrow & c \oplus d & \end{array}$$

LOSS OF CAPACITY BY REPLACING UNIVERSAL (2 : 1) UNITS BY SWITCHES

It may easily be seen from the preceding expressions that replacing all universal (2 : 1) units (4 bits each) by simple bistable switches (1 bit each) in such a nondegenerate universal machine is equivalent to the loss of just two inputs, regardless of the size of the machine. Thus, it appears that, in the case of complex machines with many inputs, little may be gained by going from simple bistable (1-bit) microcomponents to universal (2 : 1) units capable of producing all 16 possible Boolean functions. However, we continue to study such hypothetical structures (among others) for the sake of theoretical completeness and as a standard of comparison.

RELATION BETWEEN IMPOSSIBLE FUNCTIONS AND DEGENERACIES

In attempting to analyze the range of possible behavior of nets such as those to be described in the following section, a useful approach may sometimes be based on the direct relationship between impossible functions and degenerate functions (i.e., those which are produced by more than one combination of microstates). There are various alternate versions of this relationship but the following will serve to illustrate. All N's represent number of functions or number of states as indicated.

$$N_{\text{nondegenerate states}} = N_{\text{total states}} - N_{\text{degenerate states}}$$

and

$$N_{\text{possible functions}} = N_{\text{nondegenerate states}} + N_{\text{degenerate functions}}$$

Therefore,

$$N_{\text{possible functions}} = \left[N_{\text{total states}} - N_{\text{degenerate states}}\right] + N_{\text{degenerate functions}}$$

If, as is true of some of the lattices to be described,

$$\log_2 N_{\text{total states}} = 2^{N_i} N_o$$

where N_i and N_o are the number of macrosystem inputs and outputs, respectively, then

$$N_{\text{total states}} = N_{\text{possible functions}} + N_{\text{impossible functions}}$$

and, hence,

$$N_{\text{impossible functions}} = N_{\text{degenerate states}} - N_{\text{degenerate functions}}$$

Roughly speaking, the significance of this approach is that the maximum probability functions are related to the number of impossible functions.

BUILDING BLOCKS FOR BULK LOGIC

We have chosen to examine several lattice forms which will, in sufficient size, produce universal adaptable machines. The required size will, of course, depend on the assumed variability of microfunctions as well as the type of structure. We also plan to investigate the effects of slight structural irregularities and faults and have already done so to some extent, as in the case of the PAL-I model. The reasons for choosing certain lattice structures are too involved to discuss in detail here and are, in part, intuitive and suggested by personal speculations concerning advanced computer mechanizations. However, it is hoped that the following descriptions will give some insight into the types of structures being investigated.

Figure 3 shows a cluster of rhombic dodecahedrons, which are primarily of interest because of their relationship to a cluster of closest-packed spheres. Such polyhedral tessellations may be used to represent structurally homogeneous

Fig. 3

nets if we imagine that one "fiber" or "connection" of the net passes through the center of each face going either to or from one or more microcomponents contained within the polyhedron. Thus, we insure an infinitely extensible structure, uniformly filling all space, and with no loose ends. Decomposition of this particular structure leads to an interesting and unique property if we apply our basic rules [equations (4) and (5)] and the strictest form of the closure rule [equation (9)]

$$n_i \equiv n_o$$

for every component. We will successively decompose a single dodecahedron ($n_i = n_o = 6$) into six identical octahedrons ($n_i = n_o = 4$, see Fig. 4) and then into 48

Fig. 4

identical tetrahedrons ($n_i = n_o = 2$; the dark tetrahedron seen in Fig. 4 can be split into two identical tetrahedrons). Then, calculating the maximum structural capacity for each partitioning, we get a constant

$$
\begin{aligned}
&1 \text{ dodec} \longrightarrow 2^6 \cdot 6 = 384 \text{ bits} \\
&= 6 \text{ octas} \longrightarrow 6 \cdot 2^4 \cdot 4 = 384 \text{ bits} \\
&= 48 \text{ tetras} \longrightarrow 48 \cdot 2^2 \cdot 2 = 384 \text{ bits}
\end{aligned}
$$

The type of extensible structure shown in Fig. 5 is currently being studied and represents a "nondispersive" net (i.e., all path lengths and total delays from

Fig. 5

top to bottom are equal) which can be made universal and which, as shown, consists of identical (2 : 2) elements. A further partitioning of each (2 : 2) element as shown in Fig. 6 resolves the whole structure into simple (2 : 1) junctions [Boolean functions of two variables and (1 : 2) splits]. The macrosystem input stimuli are presumed to enter across a horizontal plane at the top and emerge as outputs across a similar horizontal plane at the bottom.

The (3 : 3) elementary net shown in Fig. 7 can likewise be stacked in a manner similar to the structure of a bee's honeycomb and be nondispersive. One such unit by itself, assuming all junctions and splits to be universal (4 bits apiece), has a total microcapacity of 24 bits, just equal to the minimum required for the entire unit to be universal ($2^3 \cdot 3 = 24$ bits). However, it obviously cannot be, since diametrically opposite outputs and inputs are unrelated (assuming unilateral signal flow from top to bottom). Figure 8 shows two such units cascaded, one on top of the other. If we now assume (perhaps more realistically) that the junctions are universal (4 bits or 16 functions apiece) but that the splits simply conduct a

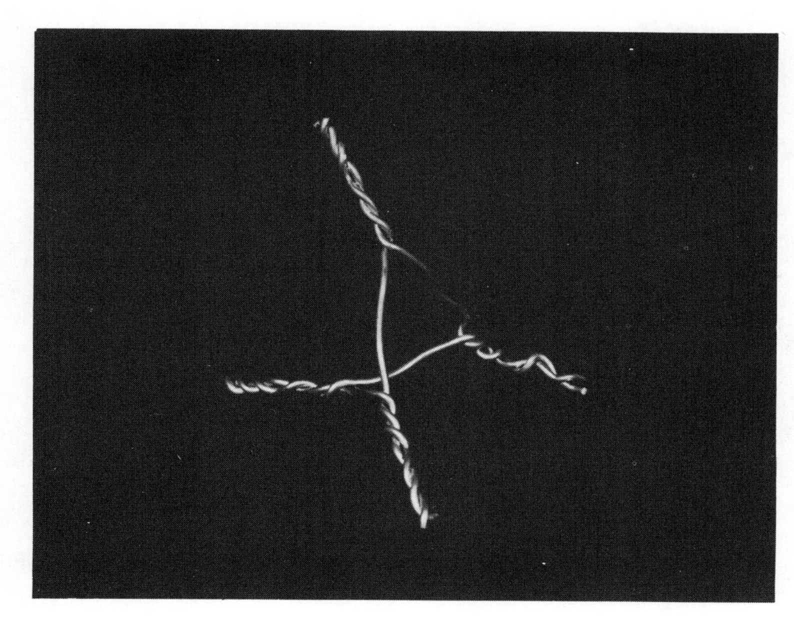

Fig. 6

signal identically in each direction, we again get 24 bits microcapacity. Although the previous argument no longer applies, it is also apparent that this structure is not universal, although the macrocapacity has certainly been increased. It cannot be universal since some macrofunctions are obviously highly degenerate (such as the zero-identity function, produced whenever the lower layer of junctions are all zero-identity functions, regardless of the 16^3 choice of states in the upper layer of the junctions). Since $2^{N_i} N_o = 24$ bits, universality would require that every possible combination of microstates produce a different macrofunction (see section on degeneracies). Analysis of a part of the structure as shown

IN

OUT

gives a total of 192 different possible functions (out of 256 to be universal). From this we can conclude that for the (3 : 3) "bird-cage" structure

$$N_{\text{macro}} \leq 192^3 = \left(\frac{27}{64}\right) \cdot 2^{24}$$

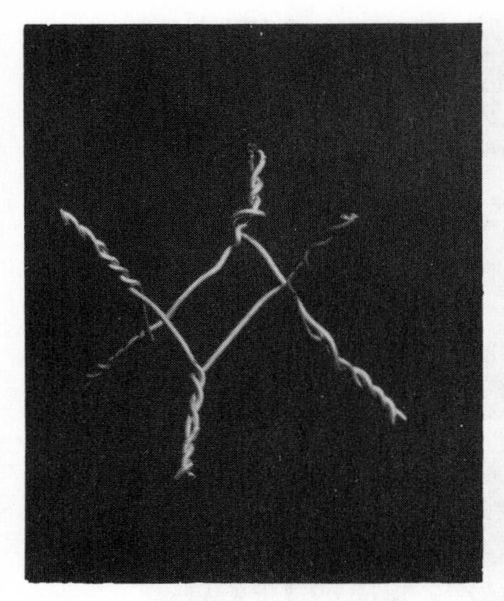

Fig. 7

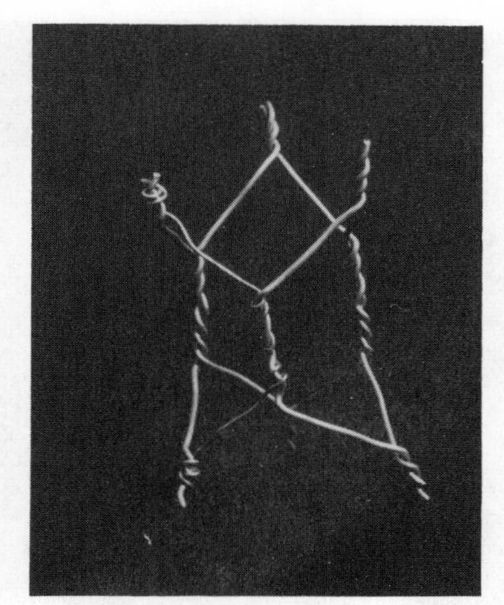

Fig. 8

or slightly less than 23 bits. We have not yet determined the exact maximum capacity of this structure.

RESTRICTED MICROLOGICS

Although much (but not all) of the preceding discussion has pertained to nets of universal elements, we hope eventually to document the results of similar analyses under more restrictive assumptions regarding elementary micrologic. This certainly does not imply that the theory of universal structures has no ultimate value, but rather that we will attempt to examine them with greater resolving power.

An interesting example of such a restricted but potentially complete micrologic is one consisting of 1-bit elements which may behave in either of the two ways: "OR" or "exclusive-OR." For completeness, this system requires one or more continuous sources of stimulation in addition to the "information-bearing" variable input stimuli ($x \oplus 1 = \bar{x}$). We have some inconclusive but promising experimental evidence that such a variation in behavior may be produced in an electrochemical system. The critical "exclusive-OR" response, $1 \oplus 1 = 0$, is believed to be brought about by a coincident wave-cancellation or annihilation phenomenon.

REFERENCES

Venn, J. 1880. Phil. Mag. July.
Wittgenstein, L. 1921. Logisch-philosophische Abhandlung. Ann. der Naturphil.

INDUCTION AND LOGICAL TYPES*

M. C. Goodall

Research Laboratory of Electronics
Massachusetts Institute of Technology, Cambridge, Massachusetts

INTRODUCTION

The theory of cognitive systems deals with an old subject, inductive inference, from a new point of view, that of constructibility. The latter has the merit of bringing to light almost immediately a basic paradox: a machine that can be defined cannot be intelligent. Suppose this machine has a basic strategy Q_0; then either this is fixed, in which case it cannot be intelligent, being incapable of self-improvement, or Q_0 must be the subject of another strategy Q_1 to which the same argument applies, and so on.

The above is analogous to the situation which developed in logic with the discovery of Russell's (1903) paradox (the class of all classes that are not members of themselves). To deal with this, Russell and Whitehead (1910) introduced a theory of logical types by means of which it is possible to recognize statements not admissible in two-valued logic. Subsequently, Gödel (1931) and others obtained the stronger result that no adequate logic can be both consistent and complete, which can be interpreted as saying that no adequate logic can be strictly two-valued, but must have in addition either one of the values, contradictory or undecidable.

Previously, Post (1921), in a very remarkable paper, had shown how it is possible to construct an arbitrary postulational system from two-valued logic which, in addition, could be interpreted as many-valued. However, I hope to show that the real significance of this does not appear until one tries to set up a logic of induction, that is, until one gives an interpretation of adequate logic which is considerably broader than "adequate for arithmetic."

THE FRAMEWORK OF INDUCTIVE LOGIC

First of all, let us consider induction in the narrow sense to be the converse of deduction. The latter will consist of a universe U of discourse (individuals, terms) and rules R_1 for the formation of sentences S, together with axioms A and transformation rules R_2 which generate a class $\{S_1\} \epsilon \{S\}$ of true sentences; that is

$$U \underset{R_1}{\longrightarrow} S \tag{1}$$

$$A \underset{R_2}{\longleftrightarrow} S_1 \tag{2}$$

Induction in the narrow sense will then consist of having data in the form $\{S_D\}$ and trying to find an (A, R_2) such that $\{S_D\} \epsilon \{S_1\}$ is subject to certain conditions of optimality which guarantee that (A, R_2) is a minimal description of the data. I call such a process a *resolving transformation* (RT).

Now, clearly, induction in the wide sense will involve another process, that of finding a (U, R_1) such that $\{S_D\}$ is an adequate description of the data. At this point,

*This work was supported in part by the U.S. Army Signal Corps, the Air Force (Aeronautical Systems Command), and the Office of Naval Research.

however, we have to face the fact that the data are unbounded; their appearance of not being so is simply an expression of a selection and punctuation process which should properly be included in induction. Thus, the formation of $\{S_D^\mu\}$ involves the selection of a neighborhood μ of the data and punctuating it into sentences S_D^μ; the latter, of course, is not independent of (U, R_1), so we shall call the whole process $(U^\mu, R_1^\mu, S_D^\mu)$ a selective punctuation (SP).

It is clear that induction in the wide sense consists of successive applications of the operations SP and RT and that these operations will not be independent, in the sense that conditions for the optimality of each will depend on what has gone before. Such conditions, whatever they may be, will be called an inductive strategy (IS). To discuss them we need a theory of types related to many-valued logic.

TYPES AND MANY-VALUED LOGIC

Types arise from iteration of the operation of class formation, as follows. Consider as a model of the external world an uncountable ordered collection U_∞ of binary symbols. The possible orderings in U_∞ is an impossible number, the highest ordinal (Burali-Forti paradox similar to Russell's). We are interested, however, in a constructive approach to finding some order in U_∞. Suppose then we look at strings $\{S_m^\mu\}$ of length $m_\mu \leq \overline{m}_\mu$ in some neighborhood μ of U_∞ and we find that among the universe $U(2^{\overline{m}}\mu)$ of $2^m\mu$ possible strings, some are more frequent; then by well-known principles of communication theory we could recode this into an optimal code which required less symbols. This would be an example of a primitive RT. However, and this is the essential difference from present communication theory, we can do better than this by going on to consider the $U(2^{2^{\overline{m}}\mu})$ of the approximately $2^{2^{\overline{m}\mu}}$ strings of strings which will be of higher logical type relative to $U(2^m\mu)$. This is not the same as just taking another $m' = 2^m$.

To see what is involved here, we can consider the case of ordinary language. One obtains a Shannon-Markov (1948) approximation by considering m-grams of letters; however, for $m > 6$ this is no longer effective and one has to go from letters to words. This is, of course, only possible because there is a punctuation symbol, the space, which is not statistically equivalent to a letter. That is, language is not a Markov process since if one counts the vocabulary $M(N)$ in a sample size N, this does not tend to a limit, but on the contrary

$$M \longrightarrow M_1 N^a \tag{3}$$

(Herdan, 1960) where M_1 is characteristic of the author and $a < 1$ of the language. This shows that language grows indefinitely and is, in fact, an example of what I shall call an evolutionary system. It is clear that this growth occurs because new words are defined in the text, and this is an example of sinking (conversely raising) the logical type for which punctuation is essential. In language there is also a qualitative hierarchy of punctuation types, going from spaces, periods, paragraphs, chapters, etc., and becoming more selective as one ascends.

Turning now to a neighborhood U_μ of U_∞, we have to insert an additional symbol, X, and our only criterion for doing so is the existence of some RT. The most primitive is the recognition that certain $\{S_D\}$ occur with more random frequency; correspondingly, the most primitive SP will consist of replacing each of those $S \notin \{S_D\}$ by an X to obtain an $U_{D\mu}$. The symbol X then has the meaning "don't care" or "undecidable." One can then iterate the process according to the scheme (1)-(2). In this case we can make the SP selective of the neighborhood μ by the convention that naming an $S_D \in U_{D\mu}$ identifies it within a certain probability measure.

INDUCTIVE STRATEGY

Conditions for the optimality of RT and SP consist in finding extrema for certain functionals whose interdependence can only be described in heuristic terms. We begin with RT.

Suppose we have an $y(t) \epsilon U_\mu$, where t is an ordering parameter (time if you like). Then

$$Sy = y(t+1) = F\ (y\ t), \ldots, y\ (t-m),\ x_1 \ldots x_2m) \tag{4}$$

will be an RT if

$$H(x) = -\sum_i^{2m} 2\ \rho_i \log \rho_i < 1 \tag{5}$$

where

$$\rho_i = \frac{1}{T} \sum^{T} x_i(t) \qquad T > 2^m$$

and F is a fixed minimal Boolean function such that the (x) represent the connections required to realize $F(y)$. If we now graph the ρ_i ordered by decreasing magnitude, we shall have three zones of significance

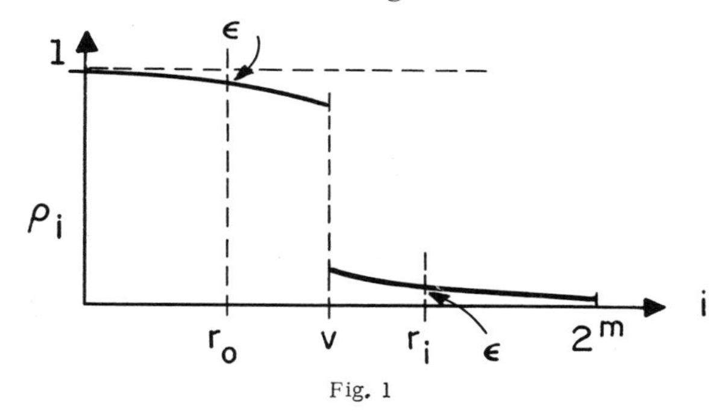

Fig. 1

namely, $\rho > 1-\epsilon, 1-\epsilon > \rho > \epsilon, \rho < \epsilon$, where $\epsilon < e^{-m}$. The first describes the structure extracted by the RT, the number r_0 being a measure of its complexity. The next $(r_1 - r_0)$ x's carry the contingent information (at this type level) corresponding to the "message" in communication theory. The remaining $(2^m - r_1)$ x's represent a kind of noise level of information which cannot be resolved at this type level.

Thus, the action of RT is to separate structural from contingent information, and this will be optimal when $H(x)$ of (5) is a minimum. However, we want to express another inductive principle, the principle of parsimony, which says that the extracted structure must be as simple as possible. We can include this condition if we minimize instead

$$H(x,\lambda) = \sum_i^{2m} \rho_i\ (\lambda - \log \rho_i) \tag{6}$$

incorporating the coefficient of parsimony λ.

We saw in the primitive case that an RT implicitly defines an SP; the same is true here. Because of (5), we can take $(x_{r_0} \ldots x_{r_1})$ and recode into a $z(\eta t)$ of smaller information rate $(\eta \ll 1)$ which can be the subject of a RT of higher type. Choice of neighborhood depends on that of $(x_1 \ldots x_{r_0})$. Obviously, a good heuristic principle here, which I am not discussing any further, is search for neighborhoods giving resolution of higher type.

PROBABILISTIC NETS

We are interested in realizability. From what has been said, inductive logic which recognizes "don't care" conditions explicitly cannot be realized by a completely deterministic machine (the principle of sufficient determination). Accordingly, we now introduce the probabilistic connection

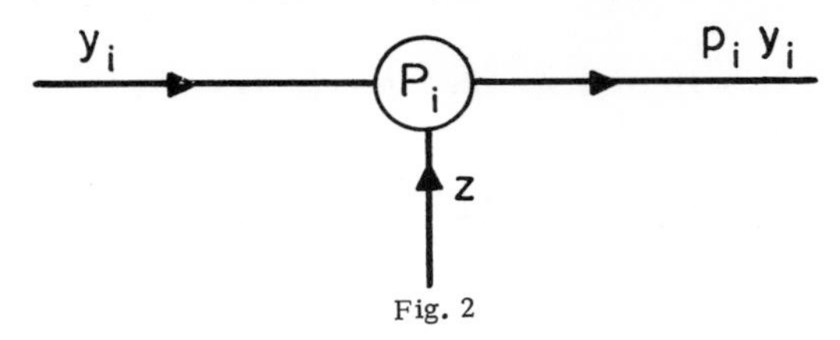

Fig. 2

such that

$$p_i = y_i(1 - Z)\,T \tag{7}$$

that is, the probability of connection is equal to the average over T of the product of the input and a parameter $x = 0, 1$. It should be noted that that is a generalization of McCulloch's (1956) interaction of afferents, which is essentially the case $T = 1$. We can realize an RT like (4) by iteration of networks with such connections, of the form

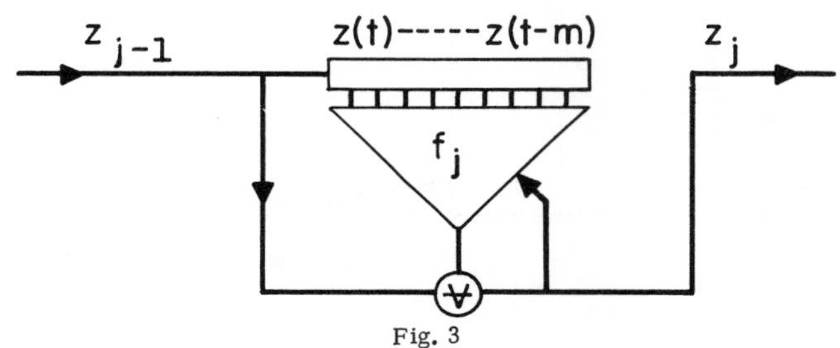

Fig. 3

which gives a representation

$$y(t) = z_0(t) = \bigvee_{r0}^{r1} x_j f_j$$

where z_j is a logical sum of x's, each coded distinctly and optimally as a result of the feedback. Thus, for some z_{r_1} we shall approach optimal coding for all x's. This $Z_{r_1}(t)$ can now be punctuated by the prescription that all sequences of 0's of length $> m$ be replaced by a neutral symbol; the resulting $Z_{r_1}(\eta t)$ is then ready for an RT of higher type.

The probability of a component representation j of multiplicity s requiring $r_0\,(j,s)$ connections is

$$p(j,s) = \prod_i^{r0} \langle y_i^s\,(1 - z_j)\rangle\, T \tag{8}$$

so that the probability of f_j is

$$p_j = \sum_s p(j,s) \tag{9}$$

for no redundancy of representation ($s = 1$) we have the majorization

$$p_j < (1 - \rho_j)\, r_0\,(j) \tag{10}$$

which is another expression of the principle of parsimony given by λ in (6), the effect of redundancy being to raise the bound for some j's.

However, the general significance of the latter is much more far-reaching as can be seen from the work of Cowan and Winograd (1961) on computation in the presence of noise (i.e., with probabilistic components). The basic idea is the decomposition

$$f_j = g_{j_1} \circ g_{j_2} \circ g_{j_3} \cdots \tag{11}$$

into iterated components such that the probability of error decreases with the iteration. However, what is important here is an associated notion—computation sharing. If we have a number of f's there will be a basic set of g's, some of them being used for more than one f.

We can use the above to reformulate our realization of an RT, as is shown in Fig. 4.

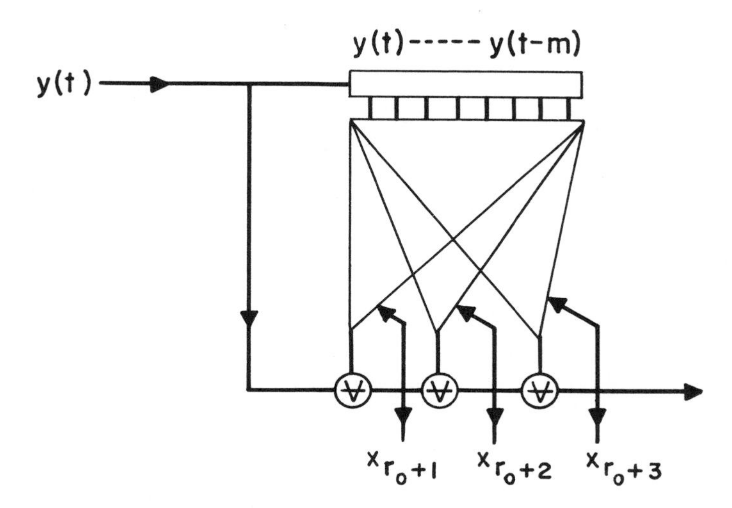

Fig. 4

The function net here first computes a g_i common to all f's, then further g's giving differentiation into individual f_j's.

To represent the control feedback in this net, we need a new convention in the form of antidromic signals x (which are independent of the forward signals) so that Fig. 2 is replaced by

y_i —→ (P_i) —→ $p_i y_i$; x

Fig. 5

together with the convention that all computing elements become intersections antidromically, the effect of the latter being to reinforce all connections contributing effectively to the computation.

The most likely mechanism of control of a higher type RT over a lower is that of increasing the redundancy since this, in general, leads to a sharpening of probability distributions. It is worth noting that questions of type enter into fairly mundane problems such as pattern recognition under a group of transformations. This already involves learning at type-level 2 since transformations are a relation of type 1 relative to the primary data (type 0). It is noteworthy that in the human cognitive system the separation between transformation and invariants is quite imperfect (try reading a book upside down).

REFERENCES

Note added in proof. Owing to a complementarity principle between SP and RT (Goodall, 1962), inductive strategy is best handled by methods similar to quantum statistical mechanics; only then is one able to make full use of the possibilities of Post (1921) logic.

Cowan, J. D. and Winograd, S. 1961. Phil. Trans. Roy. Soc. (in press).
Gödel, K. 1931. Monatshefte f. Math. u. Phys. 38, 173.
Goodall, M. C. 1962. A fundamental complementarity principle for inductive logic. Nature (to be published).
Herdan, G. 1960. Type-token mathematics. N. Holland.
McCulloch, W. S. 1956. Biological stability. Brookhaven Symposium.
Post, E. L. 1921. Am. J. Math. 43, 163.
Russell, B. 1903. Principles of mathematics.
Russell, B. and Whitehead, A. N. 1910. Principia mathematica.
Shannon, C. E. 1948. Bell Syst. Tech. J. 27, 379.

MICROWATT TRANSISTOR CIRCUITS—A SOLUTION TO THE HEAT PROBLEM IN ULTRALARGE COMPUTERS

C. Levy and M. J. Schuller

CBS Laboratories, Stamford, Connecticut

INTRODUCTION

It is evident that within the next few decades there will arise a need for computers of a size that is orders of magnitude larger than those in use today. These computers may be used in the field of bionics in many ways. One method is the programming of standard computers for the performance of experiments in the bionics field. Another may be the construction of special purpose machines based on theories arising out of bionic studies.

The manner in which these computers will be used in the field of bionics is not too important to us at present. What is significant at this date is the fact that techniques will have to be developed for the construction of extremely large computer systems. A few of the problems which must be encountered in the construction of such large systems will be discussed here.

There are three major problems to be encountered in the design of ultralarge computers. One of these is heat. Using present day circuitry techniques, a billion computer elements would consume such a large amount of power that the dissipation of heat would be next to impossible. Another problem is that of reliability. Again extrapolating present day techniques, a machine with a billion elements would be, to say the least, quite unreliable. The third factor which will be discussed is that of cost. Considering the cost of the slowest present day computers, an increase in size by orders of magnitude would be prohibitively expensive.

HEAT

Present day computer elements dissipate on the order of 1 to 10 mw (milliwatts) of power for each logical stage. If we extrapolate these figures to a billion-element computer, we see that 1 to 10 million watts would be dissipated by the computer elements alone, not including the air conditioning or the peripheral equipment. For this power consumption, it is obvious that the packing density of the elements would have to be very small, requiring an impractically large overall size for the computer.

One approach to this problem is the use of digital circuitry which requires less power per logical stage. It has been calculated that if each of a billion active circuits were to dissipate only 1 μw per stage, a computer of this size could be constructed in a volume of less than 10,000 ft^3, with a reasonable temperature rise within the system. On the other hand, if the circuits were to dissipate 1 mw each, the temperature rise within the system would be intolerable.

The main difficulty in designing circuitry utilizing such a small amount of power has been the fact that until recently transistors did not have adequate current gain at very low collector currents (in the order of 1 μa). It is now possible to construct a transistor with appreciable current gain at these levels. This permits operation at 1 v and 1 μa, for a total power dissipation of 1 μw per logical stage.

The transistor in question is a double-diffused planar silicon transistor with an extremely small base width. The progress in the fabrication of transistors which can be used in micropower circuitry is attributable to two factors. One of these is that new techniques have been developed with which the geometry of the device can be made extremely small, resulting in lower capacity and higher current gain at low currents. The other is that extremely pure silicon material is available for transistor fabrication, and that the purity of the basic material can be preserved throughout the complete fabrication process. This results in lower leakage currents and higher current gain at low currents.

Using photographic techniques for the control of the horizontal dimensions of the transistor, the active areas can be made as low as 15 square mils (10^{-4} cm^2). The transistor presently used in the micropower circuitry to be described is shown in Fig. 1. The scale is graduated in mils, and the collector junction area is therefore approximately 70 square mils. A reduction in the areas involved will, in the near future, result in reduced collector capacity and increased current gain at low currents.

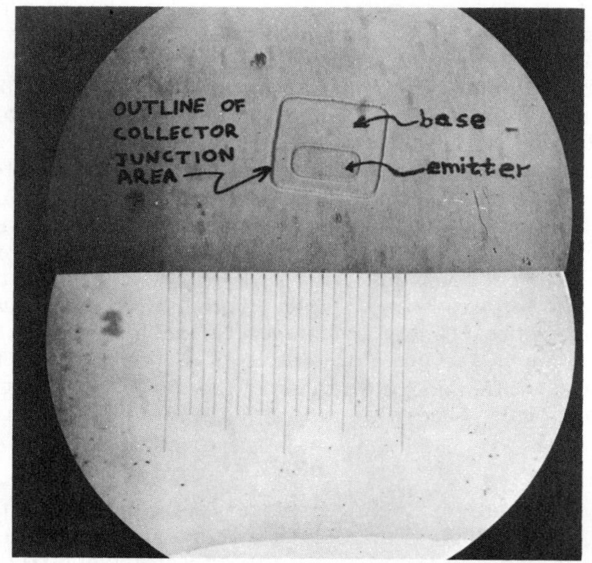

Fig. 1. View of transistor showing emitter and collector junction areas.

The vertical dimensions of the transistor can be tightly controlled by the precise timing of the diffusion of impurities into the silicon wafer, while maintaining good control of the temperature. Figure 2 is a microphotograph of the vertical dimensions of the transistor. From this figure, it can be seen that the base width is of the order of two half-wavelengths (fringes) of sodium light, or about 0.6 μ, which is extremely important for the achievement of higher current gain at low collector currents.

The recently developed technique of covering the p-n junctions of the transistor with a layer of silicon oxide serves the purpose of reducing the contamination of the junctions to an absolute minimum, both during and after the fabrication process. This serves to minimize carrier recombination effects, which previously resulted in high leakage currents and poor current gain at low currents.

The transistor characteristics which affect the design of micropower digital circuits are:

1. Beta. The common emitter current gain, h_{FE}, must be reasonably large at the particular current level of operation, since this dictates the fan-out properties

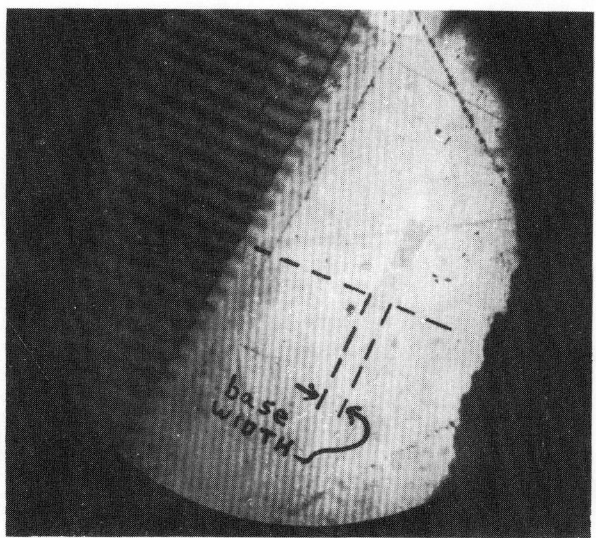

Fig. 2. Microphotograph showing base width of transistor.

of the system. A beta of 10 minimum is considered a reasonable figure to work with.

2. Leakage current. When operating at these low levels, the leakage current may be a problem; but in the transistors under consideration, the leakage currents have been so low as to never present a problem.

3. Saturation resistance. This is generally an important factor in series-connected direct coupled transistor circuits; but at these current levels, the collector to emitter voltage in the "on" stage is negligible.

4. Storage time. Although the transistors are generally driven heavily into saturation, storage time is not a problem since the circuit speed is limited by the collector capacity and the circuit capacity.

5. Collector capacity. This is the most important of the transistor characteristics affecting micropower circuitry, and, at present, leaves much room for improvement. The maximum speed of the circuitry at these current levels is a function of the circuit resistance and capacitance parameters, as opposed to the intrinsic frequency limitations of the transistor. At present, the collector capacity of the transistor in question is approximately 6 pf, but it is expected that this figure will be reduced by nearly an order of magnitude in the near future.

Some of the typical circuits to which these transistors have been applied are clock generators, delay elements, flip-flops, binary counters, shift registers, AND gates, and OR gates.

The circuit shown in Fig. 3 is a micropower astable multivibrator, operating at 1 kc. Using a 1-v supply, the complete circuit consumes approximately $2^1/_2$ μa of current, or $2^1/_2$ μw of total power dissipation in the circuit. The circuit was set to operate at 1 kc, and the upper frequency limit of operation for the present transistors is about 20 kc at the power levels shown in this circuit. This is because of the relatively high impedance levels necessary for operation at these currents, and the relatively high collector capacity of the present transistors. The output waveform of this multivibrator is shown in Fig. 4.

An example of one stage of a micropower shift register is shown in Fig. 5. This is simply a four-transistor flip-flop, which uses R-C integrating networks as temporary memory elements. The 220-pf capacitors "memorize" the state of

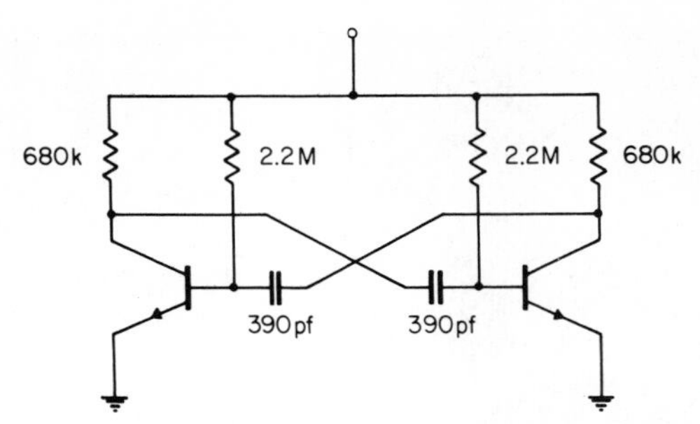

Fig. 3. Circuit diagram of a micropower astable multivibrator.

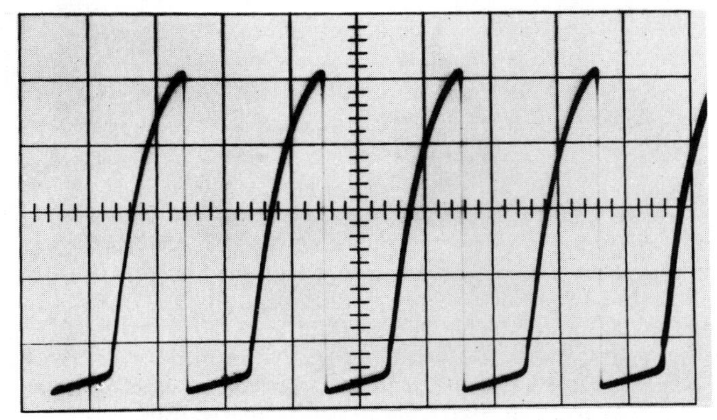

Fig. 4. Output waveform of the micropower astable multivibrator. Scale: 0.2 v/division, 500μsec/division.

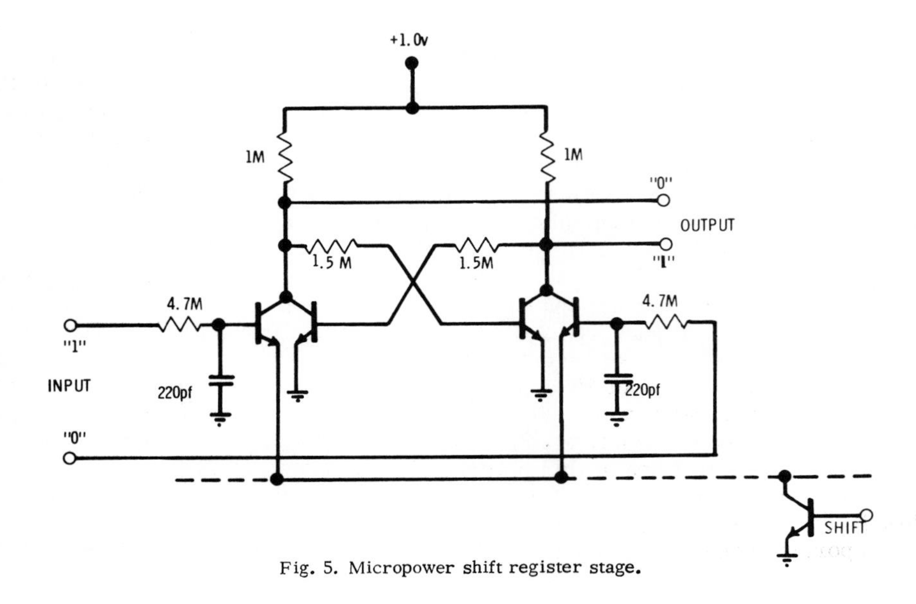

Fig. 5. Micropower shift register stage.

the previous stage, and this information is passed on to the flip-flop upon occurrence of a "ground" on the shift bus (dotted line). The total power consumption for this complete stage (four transistors) of the shift register is 1.25 μw, when operating from a 1.0-v supply. At this power level, the maximum speed of cascaded stages of this type is 1 kc, which is determined by the R-C integrating network.

An example of one stage of a binary counter is shown in Fig. 6. This is a straightforward diode-gated counter, with a driving transistor for each stage. The total power consumption for each stage (three transistors) of this counter is 3 μw, operating from a 1.5-v supply. The maximum operating frequency of this counter is approximately 15 kc, and is limited by the collector capacity of the transistor. Waveforms at the input, first-stage output, and second-stage output of a two-stage counter with a 5-kc input are shown in Fig. 7.

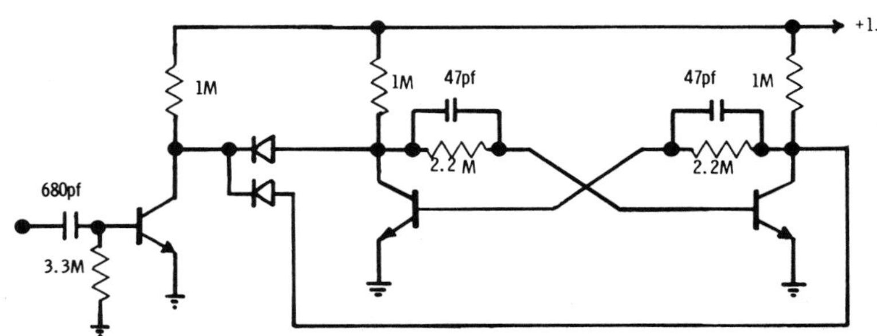

Fig. 6. Binary counter stage.

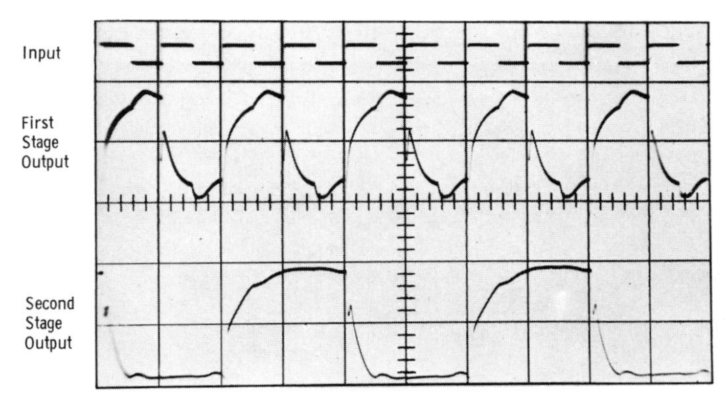

Fig. 7. Waveforms of two-stage binary counter. Scale: 0.5 v/division, 200 μsec/division.

RELIABILITY AND COST

The problems of reliability and cost of a billion-element system are intimately related, since both are functions of the number of components in the system, and the solution to one problem will probably provide the solution to the other.

It is obvious that the initial cost of such a system would be astronomical unless some method were found to produce large quantities of the active element (or, in fact, complete circuits) at a moderate cost. The first approach to this problem is to produce modular circuits on a completely solid-state basis, with one or more complete circuits within a single package. This would reduce another aspect of the initial cost of such a large system. This aspect is the cost of the testing of the elements to go into the system. The larger the number of complete circuits within a package, the lower will be the over-all testing cost.

At present, there are many approaches to the construction of modular packages. Until now, one of the major problems has been that the heat dissipation has limited the packing density of large numbers of these modules. With micropower circuitry, however, this is no longer a significant problem.

Within the next few decades, it will probably prove more economical to improve the reliability of large systems through the use of redundancy, rather than by making the basic components more reliable. One reason is that steps to increase the reliability of the component parts may limit the performance of these parts, and may increase the per-unit cost of these parts to an unreasonable point.

On the other hand, judicious use of circuit redundancy can lead to great improvements in the over-all reliability of a system. This method can reduce the maintenance cost of a system by permitting operation even after certain component failures have occurred. In fact, if redundancy is properly used, operation can proceed even if some of the system elements are defective from the time of manufacture. Thus redundancy can, to some extent, also reduce the cost of the initial testing of the component elements.

CONCLUSIONS

The advent of micropower transistors and their associated circuitry represents a small but significant step in the collection of the technology required for the construction of a billion-element computer. Before we can think in terms of ultralarge computers, however, much work must be done on the problems of packaging very large numbers of complete circuits into modular form economically and reliably. In addition, however, even greater strides must be made in the use of redundancy to increase the reliability of large systems.

THE IMITATION OF ONE FORM OF LIFE BY ANOTHER—BIOMIMESIS*

Warren S. McCulloch

Research Laboratory of Electronics
Massachusetts Institute of Technology
Cambridge, Massachusetts

I would like first to place bionics in a broader framework because there are several fields of interest which surround it on all sides. I therefore pick for my title "The Imitation of One Form of Life by Another—Biomimesis." There is nothing new in biomimesis. It is so important in avoiding enemies and catching prey that it is determined in the genes of many insects: the walking stick, the velvet ant, and so on. It has been of enormous importance; it has given us the images of our gods and the costumes of our witch doctors. It has given us, since the wings of Daedalus, all sorts of transportation. We have mimicked and mimicked. There are a few things of which we can boast, like the wheel and the seeking of power from indirect sources—first from the sun by eating each other, so to speak, and then from steam engines and what not—all one way or another from the sun until we got fission and now fusion. But aside from sources of power, and from the wheel, most of what we have done has been an imitation. The imitation used to be primarily for our muscular chores: to pump out a mine, to carry material from one place to another, and so forth. The first major deviation from that, curiously enough, was in the steam engine itself. It was not the replacement of the boy who used to push the slide valve by a stick; the boy still did that. That gave us the regenerative cycle. It was by replacement of the boy at the throttle, the boy who controlled the rate at which the steam was admitted to the slide valve, that the first major deviation from doing mere mechanical work came about. I would like to start from that point with what seems to me the major problem we have to face in bionics, as opposed to cybernetics.

Cybernetics, of course, really started with the first governor, the governor of the steam engine. Cybernetics came into its own when Julian Bigelow pointed out the fact that it was only information concerning the outcome of the previous act that had to return. Cybernetics, properly speaking, deals with that part of biomimesis. Of course we properly include the computer in the head, but there is only an inclusion in that part of the great big multiple closed-loop feedback system of this kind. Cybernetics has gone on from there to become a discipline now taught in universities, though it is just starting. It took from 1865 to the present day for it to become so established. It began, typically, in the solution of particular problems of regulation; the regulation of the steam engine being the first, then the regulation of the repeating stations in the Bell Telephone System. There was a marvelous paper by Black about 1930, but not until 1940 did it receive full synthesis, primarily due to Bigelow.

The full field of bionics opens up clearly within the general field of biomimesis, and it is not identical with cybernetics, nor a part of cybernetics. It is actually a broader field. It is concerned, I would say, primarily with an attempt to understand sufficiently well the tricks that nature actually uses to solve her problems, thus enabling us to turn them into hardware. The first hardware we

*This work was supported in part by the U.S. Army Signal Corps, the Air Force [ASD Contract AF 33(616)-7783], and the office of Naval Research; and in part by the National Institutes of Health [Grant B-1865-(C3)].

need is the natural numbers because we must have a logically decent theory to work with. I will come back to that later, for it is one of the main problems. I think I know exactly what Jack Steele meant when he coined the word "bionics." It is not a new word; it is a word which was used many years ago for what is now called histology. It meant then what it primarily means now: the attempt to know the living unit. That is the first task. From this living unit we can go on. The difficulty with every field like this is that it tends to require an increasing number of people who know two scientific disciplines. Engineering is, in this sense, a scientific discipline, though it differs from the physical sciences, being much more like biology. One has to have a reasonable knowledge of both engineering and biology in his own head, and there is no use in having in one room what should be in one head. This has been a standard failure. I've seen it happen and happen and happen. As a result, what you generally must have is close team play over the years between a youngster from biology and a youngster from engineering, until each knows both disciplines. This is about the only way it happens.

The solutions are going to come as particular solutions of this, that, or the other particular problem. We have now, for the first time, been able to record from the primary olfactory fibers in the frog. We owe that to Lettvin's development of microelectrodes, and to Pitt's theoretical investigations of olfactory receptors. This means that for the first time we are able to record from fibers about 0.2 μ in diameter. Until the last year or two, only about 1 or 2% of neurons were big enough for us to record them individually. Lettvin, Pitts, and Maturana are now in Naples working on the vision of the octopus. It will be a solution of one particular problem. When we get enough of these particular problems solved we are slowly going to see some of the more general aspects of our subjects unfold.

I think our greatest difficulty is at the level of logic itself; we are beginning to realize how great is our idiocy when we open our mouths concerning relations. This is not a new difficulty. In an argument between de Morgan and Jevons as to the utility of Aristotelian logic, one great logician said to the other that Aristotelian logic is no good because it does not follow from it that if a horse is an animal, then the head of a horse is the head of an animal, to which Bertrand Russell could only say, "Fortunate, Aristotle, for if a horse were a hydra, or a clam, the head of a horse would not be the head of an animal." The lack of logic of relations is, I think, the greatest problem at the present time in this field. We have looked vainly for either a foundation to back it up, or for governmental sources of funds. Most of our brilliant youngsters in logic have to spend half of their time in a department of philosophy and the other half in a department of mathematics, and usually fall between two stools. So, we are going to try to get together a little corporation and go out and beg money, to see if we can't get a few chronic fellowships set up. I think Albert Sperry probably will head up the group. He is very well aware of this problem.

It has become increasingly clear that our mathematics was made for the engineer, not for the biologist. An engineer or a physicist can make a sphere, a plane (or a pretty good imitation of a plane), a cylinder, or something else that he can handle mathematically, whereas we have to take things in the shape in which God gave them to us. The mathematics is going to be difficult. I worked for seven years trying to get a probabilistic logic for the biological problems that von Neuman had put to us. When I got it, it took three or four youngsters to put it in shape. We then realized it was inadequate. Cowan picked up multiple truth value logic and managed to make it work, so that we can now prove an information theoretic capacity in computation. He presented the beginnings of that work about a year ago to the meeting on Bionics at Wright Field and it is now being prepared for publication. I think those of us who are interested in the organizational aspects of living systems will be doing increasing work on a thermodynamics of open systems. I do not think it really exists yet, except for those that are barely open and those which are barely near equilibrium, and they are linear solutions to a highly nonlinear task.

May I point out that one of the things which haunts the engineer when he thinks about the large complicated systems is that he tends to think they must necessarily be relatively unstable, because his own are. That is to suppose that an elephant will be less stable than a germ. The elephant has an ability to survive a lot longer and in more diverse circumstances. We run into this problem in theories concerning nerve cells. It so happens that in order to get an increased information theoretic capacity, one wants more and more complicated and larger neurons, greater complexity of connections, greater size of the component, and greater structural complexity of the component. This is where it should arise, but the engineer looks at me and says "My goodness, do you think it could possibly behave properly if it has a thousand buttons on it ?" Well, on a Purkinji cell there are about a quarter of a million, and the Purkinji cell works very accurately. Engineers think this because in all of the devices that they are trying to build they have to hold the threshold to such a narrow limit, but that isn't the way the nervous system is built. Excitation and inhibition normally almost balance each other on a cell, so activity on one button more or less at the zero point produces a 100% shift in threshold. We have been wrong again and again in our thinking about order, regularity, and stability of structures. We compare our artifacts with natural objects and think that the large and complicated natural objects are as flimsy as our large and complicated artifacts, but this is not true.

The major advance is going to be, as it was in cybernetics, a way of thinking which properly belongs both to the engineer and the biologist. That way of thinking is going to require new mathematics, a crucial extension of thermodynamics, and, above all, a logic of relations. As we begin to grow, I think we will begin to see our problem in a much more unified sense. I would like to try to describe to you the thing that has always interested me most, the central nervous system. I am going to try to do it in words which an engineer or a biologist or the man on the street should be able to understand.

The nervous system only exists in animals which are made up of many cells, and it is made up primarily of cells called neurons. Neurons are identified by their affinity for certain dyestuffs. Anatomically, neurons constitute one system, for there is a path from any neuron to any other neuron within the mass of neurons. Electrically, neurons are identified by the impulses that they transmit. Physiologically, the neurons constitute one system, for the sequence of impulses in any neuron is affected by some other neurons and affects some other neurons. The net of these neurons is such that every neuron is ultimately connected to an effector, whether it is a muscle or a gland, and its behavior can be affected by any neuron that can be affected by any sensory transducer, be it a sensory cell or some other transducer, such as a free nerve ending. Every cell of the nervous system is traversed by at least one such path. Next is the locus of adjunction—the place of connection of two neurons, where the activity of one affects the other. The neuron transmits its effects primarily in one direction, so that a path composed of many in series transmits only in one direction. But there are numerous circuits—closed loops—within the nervous system. Closed loops also exist in the sense that every afferent peripheral neuron—that is, every neuron that picks up its impulses from a sensory output—has its generation or propagation impulses affected by other neurons. What is more, the muscles and glands which are under the control of the nervous system themselves alter the input of the transducers. Closed loops like these can be either regenerative in their activity, like the first cycle of the steam engine, or they can be inverse negative in their action, like the governor. Those circuits which are regenerative over our muscles and glands are effector circuits. They keep us alive. By these we breathe. Circuits which are regenerative within the central nervous system keep us lively. By these we attend. Circuits which are negative feedbacks—inverse feedbacks—over our muscles and glands, our reflexes, and similar closed circuits within the central nervous system, determine a state to which that part of the system shall return. They do it here as they do it in the engine. The output decreases the input. By the determination of the state of the system they give to behavior its purposive aspect. The notion of a purpose, which is truly alien to physics, but familiar enough in biology and engineering, is the tendency of a system to return when it is pushed away from that state which is determined by its inverse, or negative, feedbacks. And the system considered as a whole has purposes in this sense. It has its own ends. The engineer and the biologist both have to take this always into consideration. The system has a purpose, an end, built into it.

Now, since that is so, we will look at the receptive end of an organism and try to get this clearly stated. The receptive aspect of an organism is that part whence come the signals concerning the world around the organism. They may be touch, taste, smell, sight, hearing, or what you will. Here you deal with specialized structures, each exquisitely sensitive to changes in some form of energy or in the concentration of certain substances. Under normal conditions, it is these changes which are responsible for the pattern of impulses in afferent peripheral neurons, those which bring in impulses from the outside. Thus, under normal circumstances, when the stimulus is the one appropriate for that sense organ and that sense organ is in the state determined by that central nervous system at that time, impulses are signals. If those same impulses arose for any other reason, they would be noise. Signal and noise, necessarily distinguished by biologists and engineers, are both explained perfectly well physically, but they are not distinguished by the physicists. They differ, functionally, as they serve or fail to serve the ends of that organism. I think that this is the kernel of the way one has to think about the central nervous system. All the rest are special devices, special pleadings. It has taken me about thirty years to be able to say just that little so that it is understandable. I think as long as we can manage to get our problems that clearly stated we will have no trouble understanding each other, whether we are biologists or engineers. I want to make one crucial point about where I think we are going to have a major development coming. It is not an easy point to make. I have tried to make it again and again and I have seen Heinz von Foerster try to get it across too. It was not clear to me before the meeting on "biosimulation" (biomimesis—biosimulation is only a bad word for biomimesis) that it is this: if you looked at a natural process you would observe something that goes on in the face of ever-increasing entropy. The resultant natural object is incredibly tough; the structures which evolve are suited to the world in which they evolve, and they are stuck together with what Donald McKay calls "nature's glue." If you watch a bunch of little crystals going into solution and a big crystal forming, that big crystal, a very orderly large structure, is forming as a result of an entropic process. If you cut facets on that crystal and put it on your watch chain, entropy begins to take hold of your handiwork and it goes to pot. When we put order into things, we are taking material and torturing it, forcing an order upon it which is not at all something that came from the inside. It was something put upon it. Anything we do of this kind is slated for destruction. It does not evolve properly on its own. There are exceptions, such as Gordon Pask's evolving and growing threads, but in such cases we are making use of nature's glue.

Let me now set all this off from a third field of interest, which is concerned with artificial organisms that are to evolve and to learn. It is not that these are not problems within bionics—they are, and certainly within biomimesis. But the group of people whose major interest is in those problems will overlap much more nearly with the major group in cybernetics than with the straight bionical problems. What we are witnessing now is a very large popular swing among engineers and biologists to get their heads together. I would prefer to see little cells of bionics start growing. We have had a similar problem before us on at least four occasions in my short lifetime. When something gets noised abroad there rises up a large number of people and, possibly, sources of funds, and there are always those who want to get on the hay scales. There are always empire builders, there are always fourflushers, and they move in on a group like this just as fast as they can. We have had to break up and disband three whole societies which started that way, and start over again from scratch. I would hate to see such a thing as a large unit being organized now. Let it grow in small groups, and let the small groups have at least two fellows, each of whom knows the other one's business. I think, in a plain word of caution, that we ought not to let bionics get too "scopy." By that I mean don't let it try to cover the earth, either in topics or in numbers. It is going to be a hard job to understand any living process. I do not think we fully understand any one yet: not a nerve impulse, nor the contraction of a muscle, nor the multiplication of a virus. It will be some time before we do.